Student's Solutions Manual

to accompany

Calculus for Business, Economics, and the Social and Life Sciences

Brief Tenth Edition

Laurence Hoffmann
Smith Barney

Gerald Bradley
Claremont McKenna College

Prepared by
Devilyna Nichols
Purdue University

 **Higher Education**

Boston   Burr Ridge, IL   Dubuque, IA   New York   San Francisco   St. Louis
Bangkok   Bogotá   Caracas   Kuala Lumpur   Lisbon   London   Madrid   Mexico City
Milan   Montreal   New Delhi   Santiago   Seoul   Singapore   Sydney   Taipei   Toronto

The **McGraw·Hill** Companies

Student's Solutions Manual to accompany
CALCULUS FOR BUSINESS, ECONOMICS, AND THE SOCIAL AND LIFE SCIENCES,
BRIEF TENTH EDITION
LAURENCE HOFFMANN AND GERALD BRADLEY

Published by McGraw-Hill Higher Education, an imprint of The McGraw-Hill Companies, Inc., 1221 Avenue of the Americas,
New York, NY 10020. Copyright © 2010 by The McGraw-Hill Companies, Inc. All rights reserved.

This book is printed on recycled, acid-free paper containing 10% post consumer waste.

1 2 3 4 5 6 7 8 9 0 QPD/QPD 0 9

ISBN: 978-0-07-334902-2
MHID: 0-07-334902-X

www.mhhe.com

CONTENTS

Chapter 1

Functions, Graphs, and Limits

1.1 Functions

1. $f(x) = 3x + 5,$
$$f(0) = 3(0) + 5 = 5$$
$$f(-1) = 3(-1) + 5 = 2$$
$$f(2) = 3(2) + 5 = 11$$

3. $f(x) = 3x^2 + 5x - 2,$
$$f(0) = 3(0)^2 + 5(0) - 2 = -2,$$
$$f(-2) = 3(-2)^2 + 5(-2) - 2 = 0,$$
$$f(1) = 3(1)^2 + 5(1) - 2 = 6.$$

5. $g(x) = x + \dfrac{1}{x},$
$$g(-1) = -1 + \frac{1}{-1} = -2,$$
$$g(1) = 1 + \frac{1}{1} = 2,$$
$$g(2) = 2 + \frac{1}{2} = \frac{5}{2}.$$

7. $h(t) = \sqrt{t^2 + 2t + 4},$
$$h(2) = \sqrt{2^2 + 2(2) + 4} = 2\sqrt{3},$$
$$h(0) = \sqrt{0^2 + 2(0) + 4} = 2,$$
$$h(-4) = \sqrt{(-4)^2 + 2(-4) + 4} = 2\sqrt{3}$$

9. $f(t) = (2t - 1)^{-3/2} = \dfrac{1}{(\sqrt{2t-1})^3},$
$$f(1) = \frac{1}{[\sqrt{2(1)-1}]^3} = 1,$$
$$f(5) = \frac{1}{[\sqrt{2(5)-1}]^3} = \frac{1}{[\sqrt{9}]^3} = \frac{1}{27},$$
$$f(13) = \frac{1}{[\sqrt{2(13)-1}]^3} = \frac{1}{[\sqrt{25}]^3} = \frac{1}{125}.$$

11. $f(x) = x - |x - 2|,$
$$f(1) = 1 - |1 - 2| = 1 - |-1| = 1 - 1 = 0,$$
$$f(2) = 2 - |2 - 2| = 2 - |0| = 2,$$
$$f(3) = 3 - |3 - 2| = 3 - |1| = 3 - 1 = 2.$$

13. $h(x) = \begin{cases} -2x + 4 & \text{if } x \le 1 \\ x^2 + 1 & \text{if } x > 1 \end{cases}$
$$h(3) = (3)^2 + 1 = 10$$
$$h(1) = -2(1) + 4 = 2$$
$$h(0) = -2(0) + 4 = 4$$
$$h(-3) = -2(-3) + 4 = 10$$

15. $g(x) = \dfrac{x}{1 + x^2}.$

Since $1 + x^2 \ne 0$ for any real number, the domain is the set of all real numbers.

17. $f(t) = \sqrt{1 - t}.$

Since negative numbers do not have real square roots, the domain is all real numbers such that $1 - t \ge 0$, or $t \le 1$. Therefore, the domain is not the set of all real numbers.

19. $g(x) = \dfrac{x^2 + 5}{x + 2}.$

Since denominators cannot be 0, the domain consists of all real numbers such that $x \neq -2$.

21. $f(x) = \sqrt{2x + 6}$.

Since negative numbers do not have real square roots, the domain is all real numbers such that $2x + 6 \geq 0$, or $x \geq -3$.

23. $f(t) = \dfrac{t + 2}{\sqrt{9 - t^2}}$.

Since negative numbers do not have real square roots and denominators cannot be zero, the domain is the set of all real numbers such that $9 - t^2 > 0$, namely $-3 < t < 3$.

25. $f(u) = 3u^2 + 2u - 6$ and $g(x) = x + 2$, so

$$f(g(x)) = f(x + 2) = 3(x + 2)^2 + 2(x + 2) - 6$$
$$= 3x^2 + 14x + 10.$$

27. $f(u) = (u - 1)^3 + 2u^2$ and $g(x) = x + 1$, so

$$f(g(x)) = f(x + 1)$$
$$= [(x + 1) - 1]^3 + 2(x + 1)^2$$
$$= x^3 + 2x^2 + 4x + 2.$$

29. $f(u) = \dfrac{1}{u^2}$ and $g(x) = x - 1$, so

$$f(g(x)) = f(x - 1) = \frac{1}{(x - 1)^2}.$$

31. $f(u) = \sqrt{u + 1}$ and $g(x) = x^2 - 1$, so

$$f(g(x)) = f(x^2 - 1)$$
$$= \sqrt{(x^2 - 1) + 1}$$
$$= \sqrt{x^2} = |x|.$$

33. $f(x) = 4 - 5x$

$$\frac{f(x + h) - f(x)}{h} = \frac{4 - 5(x + h) - (4 - 5x)}{h}$$
$$\frac{4 - 5x - 5h - 4 + 5x}{h} = \frac{-5h}{h} = -5$$

35. $f(x) = 4x - x^2$

$$\frac{f(x + h) - f(x)}{h} = \frac{4(x + h) - (x + h)^2 - (4x - x^2)}{h}$$
$$= \frac{4x + 4h - (x^2 + 2xh + h^2) - 4x + x^2}{h}$$
$$= \frac{4x + 4h - x^2 - 2xh - h^2 - 4x + x^2}{h}$$
$$= \frac{4h - 2xh - h^2}{h} = \frac{h(4 - 2x - h)}{h}$$
$$= 4 - 2x - h$$

37. $f(x) = \dfrac{x}{x + 1}$

$$\frac{f(x + h) - f(x)}{h} = \frac{\frac{x+h}{(x+h)+1} - \frac{x}{x+1}}{h}$$
$$= \frac{\frac{x+h}{x+h+1} - \frac{x}{x+1}}{h} \cdot \frac{(x + h + 1)(x + 1)}{(x + h + 1)(x + 1)}$$
$$= \frac{(x + h)(x + 1) - x(x + h + 1)}{h(x + 1)(x + h + 1)}$$
$$= \frac{x^2 + hx + x + h - x^2 - xh - x}{h(x + 1)(x + h + 1)}$$
$$= \frac{h}{h(x + 1)(x + h + 1)} = \frac{1}{(x + 1)(x + h + 1)}$$

39. $f(g(x)) = f(1 - 3x) = \sqrt{1 - 3x}$
$g(f(x)) = g(\sqrt{x}) = 1 - 3\sqrt{x}$
To solve $\sqrt{1 - 3x} = 1 - 3\sqrt{x}$, square both sides, so

$$1 - 3x = 1 - 6\sqrt{x} + 9x$$
$$-3x = -6\sqrt{x} + 9x$$
$$6\sqrt{x} = 12x$$
$$\sqrt{x} = 2x$$

squaring both sides again,

$$x = 4x^2$$
$$0 = 4x^2 - x$$
$$0 = x(4x - 1)$$
$$x = 0, \quad x = \frac{1}{4}$$

Since squaring both sides can introduce extraneous solutions, need to check these values.

$$\sqrt{1-3(0)} \overset{?}{=} 1 - 3\sqrt{0}$$

$$1 = 1$$

$$\sqrt{1 - 3\left(\frac{1}{4}\right)} \overset{?}{=} 1 - 3\sqrt{\frac{1}{4}}$$

$$\frac{1}{2} \overset{?}{=} 1 - \frac{3}{2}$$

$$\frac{1}{2} \neq -\frac{1}{2}$$

Also check remaining value to see if is in domain of f and g functions. Since $f(0)$ and $g(0)$ are both defined, $f(g(x)) = g(f(x))$ when $x = 0$.

41.

$$f\left(g(x)\right) = f\left(\frac{x+3}{x-2}\right) = \frac{2\left(\frac{x+3}{x-2}\right)+3}{\frac{x+3}{x-2}-1} = x$$

$$g\left(f(x)\right) = g\left(\frac{2x+3}{x-1}\right) = \frac{\frac{2x+3}{x-1}+3}{\frac{2x+3}{x-1}-2} = x$$

Answer will be all real #'s for which f and g are defined. So, $f(g(x)) = g(f(x))$ for all real #'s except $x = 1$ and $x = 2$.

43.

$$f(x) = 2x^2 - 3x + 1,$$

$$f(x-2) = 2(x-2)^2 - 3(x-2) + 1$$

$$= 2x^2 - 11x + 15.$$

45.

$$f(x) = (x+1)^5 - 3x^2,$$

$$f(x-1) = [(x-1)+1]^5 - 3(x-1)^2$$

$$= x^5 - 3x^2 + 6x - 3.$$

47. $f(x) = \sqrt{x}$,

$$f(x^2 + 3x - 1) = \sqrt{x^2 + 3x - 1}.$$

49.

$$f(x) = \frac{x-1}{x},$$

$$f(x+1) = \frac{(x+1)-1}{x+1}$$

$$= \frac{x}{x+1}.$$

51. $f(x) = (x-1)^2 + 2(x-1) + 3$ can be rewritten as $g(h(x))$ with $g(u) = u^2 + 2u + 3$ and $h(x) = x - 1$.

53. $f(x) = \dfrac{1}{x^2 + 1}$

can be rewritten as $g(h(x))$

$$\text{with} \quad g(u) = \frac{1}{u}$$

$$\text{and} \quad h(x) = x^2 + 1.$$

55. $f(x) = \sqrt[3]{2-x} + \dfrac{4}{2-x}$

can be rewritten as $g(h(x))$ with

$$g(u) = \sqrt[3]{u} + \frac{4}{u}$$

$$\text{and} \quad h(x) = 2 - x.$$

57. $D(x) = -0.02x + 29$; $C(x) = 1.43x^2 + 18.3x + 15.6$

(a) $R(x) = xD(x) = x(-0.02x + 29)$

$$= -0.02x^2 + 29x$$

$$P(x) = R(x) - C(x)$$

$$= \left(-0.02x^2 + 29x\right) - \left(1.43x^2 + 18.3x + 15.6\right)$$

$$= -1.45x^2 + 10.7x - 15.6$$

(b) $P(x) > 0$ when

$-1.45x^2 + 10.7x - 15.6 > 0$

Using the quadratic formula, the zeros of P are

$$x = \frac{-10.7 \pm \sqrt{(10.7)^2 - (4)(-1.45)(-15.6)}}{2(-1.45)}$$

$$x = 2, 5.38$$

so, $P(x) > 0$ when $2 < x < 5.38$.

59. $D(x) = -0.5x + 39$; $C(x) = 1.5x^2 + 9.2x + 67$

(a) $R(x) = xD(x) = x(-0.5x + 39)$

$$= -0.5x^2 + 39x$$

$$P(x) = R(x) - C(x)$$

$$= \left(-0.5x^2 + 39x\right) - \left(1.5x^2 + 9.2x + 67\right)$$

$$= -2x^2 + 29.8x - 67$$

(b) $P(x) > 0$ when
$$-2x^2 + 29.8x - 67 > 0$$
Using the quadratic formula, the zeros of P are

$$x = \frac{-29.8 \pm \sqrt{(29.8)^2 - (4)(-2)(-67)}}{2(-2)}$$

$$x \approx 2.76, \ 12.14$$

so, $P(x) > 0$ when $2.76 < x < 12.14$.

61. $C(q) = 0.01q^2 + 0.9q + 2$

(a) $C(10) = 0.01(10)^2 + 0.9(10) + 2$
$$= \$12$$

(b) Cost of 10th unit

$$= \text{Cost of 10 units} - \text{Cost of 9 units}$$
$$= C(10) - C(9)$$

$$C(9) = 0.01(9)^2 + 0.9(9) + 2 = \$10.91$$

$$= \$12 - \$10.91 = \$1.09$$

63. $W(x) = \dfrac{600x}{300 - x}$

(a) $300 - x \neq 0$
$$x \neq 300$$
The domain is all real numbers except 300.

(b) Typically, the domain would be restricted to theh first quadrant. That is, $x \geq 0$. However, since x is a percentage, the restriction should be $0 \leq x \leq 100$.

(c) When $x = 50$,

$$W(50) = \frac{600(50)}{300 - 50}$$
$$= 120 \text{ worker-hours}$$

(d) To distribute to all of the households, $x = 100$ and

$$W(100) = \frac{600(100)}{300 - 100}$$
$$= 300 \text{ worker-hours}$$

(e) Need to find x when $W(x) = 150$.

$$150 = \frac{600x}{300 - x}$$
$$(150)(300 - x) = (1)(600x)$$
$$300 - x = 4x$$
$$x = 60$$

After 150 worker-hours, 60% of the households have received a new telephone book.

65. $C(x) = \dfrac{150x}{200 - x}$

(a) All real numbers except $x = 200$.

(b) All real numbers for which $0 \leq x \leq 100$. If $x < 0$ or $x > 200$ then $C(x) < 0$ but cost is non-negative. $x > 100$ means more than 100%.

(c) $C(50) = \dfrac{150(50)}{200 - 50} = 50$ million dollars.

(d) $C(100) = \dfrac{150(100)}{200 - 100} = 150$
$C(100) - C(50) = 100$ million dollars.

(e) $\dfrac{150x}{200 - x} = 37.5$

$$187.5x = 37.5(200),$$

$$x = \frac{7,500}{187.5} = 40\%.$$

67. $P(t) = 20 - \dfrac{6}{t + 1}$

(a) $P(9) = 20 - \dfrac{6}{9 + 1}$ or 19,400 people.

(b) $P(8) = 20 - \dfrac{6}{8 + 1}$

$$P(9) - P(8) = 20 - \frac{3}{5} - \left(20 - \frac{2}{3}\right) = \frac{1}{15}$$

This accounts for about $\frac{1}{15}$ of 1,000 people, or 67 people.

(c) $P(t)$ approaches 20, or 20,000 people. Writing exercise–Answers will vary.

69.
$$S(r) = C(R^2 - r^2)$$
$$= 1.76 \times 10^5 (1.2^2 \times 10^{-4} - r^2).$$

(a) $S(0) = (1.76 \times 10^5)(1.44 \times 10^{-4}) =$
25.344cm/sec.

(b) $S(0.6 \times 10^{-2})$

$$= 1.76 \times 10^5 (1.44 \times 10^4 - 0.6^2 \times 10^{-4})$$

$$= 1.76 \times 10^5 (1.08 \times 10^4)$$

$$= 19.008 \text{ cm/sec.}$$

71. $s(A) = 2.9\sqrt[3]{A}$

(a) $s(8) = 2.9\sqrt[3]{8} = 2.9 \times 2 = 5.8$
Since the number of species should be an integer, you would expect to find approximately 6 species.

(b) $s_1 = 2.9\sqrt[3]{A}$ and $s_2 = 2.9\sqrt[3]{2A}$
$s_2 = 2.9\sqrt[3]{2}\sqrt[3]{A} = \sqrt[3]{2}\left(2.9\sqrt[3]{A}\right) = \sqrt[3]{2}s_1$.

(c) $100 = 2.9\sqrt[3]{A}$

$$\frac{100}{2.9} = \sqrt[3]{A}$$

$$\left(\frac{100}{2.9}\right)^3 = \left(\sqrt[3]{A}\right)^3$$

$$\left(\frac{100}{2.9}\right)^3 = A$$

Need an area of approximately 41,002 square miles.

73. $Q(p) = \dfrac{4,374}{p^2}$ and
$p(t) = 0.04t^2 + 0.2t + 12$

(a) $Q(t) = \dfrac{4,374}{(0.04t^2 + 0.2t + 12)^2}$

(b)
$$Q(10) = \frac{4,374}{(4+2+12)^2} = \frac{4,374}{324}$$
$$= 13.5 \text{ kg/week.}$$

(c)
$$30.375 = \frac{4,374}{(0.04t^2 + 0.2t + 12)^2}$$

$$(0.04t^2 + 0.2t + 12)^2 = \frac{4,374}{30.375} = 144 = 12^2$$

So $0.04t^2 + 0.2t + 12 = \pm 12$.

The positive root leads to $t(0.04t + 0.2) = 0$ or $t = 0$. (Disregard $t < 0$.) The negative root produces imaginary numbers. $t = 0$ now.

75. (a) $c(p) = 0.4p + 1$ and $p(t) = 8 + 0.2t^2$
$c(t) = 0.4(8 + 0.2t^2) + 1 = 0.08t^2 + 4.2$ PPM.

(b) $c(2) = 0.08(2)^2 + 4.2 = 0.32 + 4.2 = 4.52$PPM.

(c) $6.2 = 0.08t^2 + 4.2, \quad t^2 = \dfrac{2}{0.08} = 25$, or $t = 5$ years.

77. To find the domain of $f(x) = \dfrac{4x^2 - 3}{2x^2 + x - 3}$, Press $\boxed{y=}$.
Enter $(4x \wedge 2 - 3) \div (2x \wedge 2 + x - 3)$ for $y_1 =$
Press $\boxed{\text{graph}}$.
For a better view of the vertical asymptotes, press $\boxed{\text{zoom}}$ and enter Zoom In. Use arrow buttons to move cross-hair to the left-most vertical asymptote. When it appears cross-hair is on the line, zoom in again for a more accurate reading. Move cross-hair again to be on the line. It appears that $x = -1.5$ is not in the domain of f. Zoom out once to move cross-hair to the rightmost vertical asymptote and repeat the procedure of zoom in to find that $x = 1$ is not the domain of f.
The domain consists of all values except $x = -1.5$ and $x = 1$.

79. For $f(x) = 2\sqrt{x-1}$ and $g(x) = x^3 - 1.2$, to find $f(g(2.3))$, we must find $g(2.3)$ first and then input that answer into f. Press $\boxed{y=}$.
Input $2\sqrt{(x-1)}$ for $y_1 =$ and press $\boxed{\text{enter}}$.
Input $x \wedge 3 - 1.2$ for $y_2 =$.
Use the window dimensions $[-15, 15]1$ by $[-10, 10]1$. Use the value function under the calc menu, input 2.3, and press $\boxed{\text{enter}}$.
Use $\uparrow$ and $\downarrow$ arrows to be sure that $y_2 = x \wedge 3 - 1.2$ is displayed in the upper left corner. The lower right corner display should read $y = 10.967$
Use the value function again and input 10.967.
Verify $y_1 = 2\sqrt{(x-1)}$ is displayed in the upper left corner.
The answer of $y = 6.31$ is displayed in lower right corner.

81. (a) VE1

Level of Education	Year 1991	1992
No H.S. diploma	$\dfrac{16,582}{16,582} = 1$	1
H.S. diploma	$\dfrac{24,007}{16,582} = 1.45$	$\dfrac{23,908}{16,344} = 1.46$
Some college	$\dfrac{27,017}{16,582} = 1.63$	$\dfrac{26,626}{16,344} = 1.63$
Bachelor's degree	$\dfrac{41,178}{16,582} = 2.48$	$\dfrac{41,634}{16,344} = 2.55$
Advanced degree	$\dfrac{60,525}{16,582} = 3.65$	$\dfrac{62,080}{16,344} = 3.80$

1993	1994	1995
1	1	1
$\dfrac{24,072}{15,889} = 1.52$	$\dfrac{24,458}{16,545} = 1.48$	$\dfrac{25,180}{16,465} = 1.53$
$\dfrac{26,696}{15,889} = 1.68$	$\dfrac{26,847}{16,545} = 1.62$	$\dfrac{28,037}{16,465} = 1.70$
$\dfrac{43,529}{15,889} = 2.74$	$\dfrac{44,963}{16,545} = 2.72$	$\dfrac{43,450}{16,465} = 2.64$
$\dfrac{69,145}{15,889} = 4.35$	$\dfrac{67,770}{16,545} = 4.10$	$\dfrac{66,581}{16,465} = 4.04$

1996	1997	1998
1	1	1
$\dfrac{25,289}{17,135} = 1.48$	$\dfrac{25,537}{17,985} = 1.42$	$\dfrac{25,937}{17,647} = 1.47$
$\dfrac{28,744}{17,135} = 1.68$	$\dfrac{29,263}{17,985} = 1.63$	$\dfrac{30,304}{17,647} = 1.72$
$\dfrac{43,505}{17,135} = 2.54$	$\dfrac{45,150}{17,985} = 2.51$	$\dfrac{48,131}{17,647} = 2.73$
$\dfrac{69,993}{17,135} = 4.08$	$\dfrac{70,527}{17,985} = 3.92$	$\dfrac{69,777}{17,647} = 3.95$

1999	2000
1	1
$\dfrac{26,439}{17,346} = 1.52$	$\dfrac{27,097}{18,727} = 1.45$
$\dfrac{30,561}{17,346} = 1.76$	$\dfrac{31,212}{18,727} = 1.67$
$\dfrac{49,149}{17,346} = 2.83$	$\dfrac{51,653}{18,727} = 2.76$
$\dfrac{72,841}{17,346} = 4.20$	$\dfrac{72,175}{18,727} = 3.85$

(b) 1.45, 1.67, 2.76, 3.85.
Writing exercise—Answers will vary.

1.2   The Graph of a Function

1. Since x-coordinate is positive and y-coordinate is positive, point is in quadrant I.

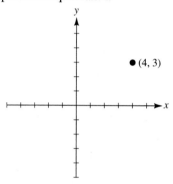

3. Since x-coordinate is positive and y-coordinate is negative, point is in quadrant IV.

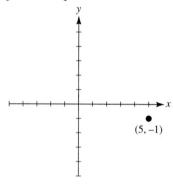

5. Since x-coordinate is zero and y-coordinate is negative, point is on y-axis, below the x-axis.

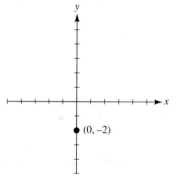

7. $P(3, -1)$, $Q(7, 1)$

$$D = \sqrt{(x_2 - x_1)^2 + (y_2 - y_1)^2}$$
$$= \sqrt{(1 - (-1))^2 + (7 - 3)^2}$$
$$= \sqrt{4 + 16} = \sqrt{20} = \sqrt{4 \cdot 5} = 2\sqrt{5}$$

9. $P(7, -3)$, $Q(5, 3)$

$$D = \sqrt{(x_2 - x_1)^2 + (y_2 - y_1)^2}$$
$$= \sqrt{(3 - (-3))^2 + (5 - 7)^2}$$
$$= \sqrt{36 + 4} = \sqrt{40} = \sqrt{4 \cdot 10} = 2\sqrt{10}$$

11. (a) Since of form x^n, where n is non-integer real number, is a power function.

(b) Since of form $a_n x^n + a_{n-1} x^{n-1} + \cdots + a_1 x + a_0$, where n is nonnegative integer, is polynomial function.

(c) Since can multiply out and simplify to form $a_{nx} x^n + a_{n-1} x^{n-1} + \cdots + a_1 x + a_0$, is polynomial function.

(d) Since is quotient of two polynomial functions is a rational function.

13. $f(x) = x$

A function of the form

$$y = f(x) = ax + b$$

is a linear function, and its graph is a line. Two points are sufficient to draw that line. The x-intercept is 0, as is the y-intercept, and $f(1) = 1$.

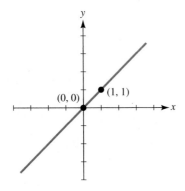

15. $f(x) = \sqrt{x}$

A function of the form $y = \sqrt{x}$ is the positive half of the function $y^2 = x$ (a parabola with vertex $(0, 0)$, a horizontal axis and opening to the right). The x-intercept and y-intercept are the same, namely $(0, 0)$. Choosing two more points on $y = \sqrt{x}$ (for example $P(1, 1)$ and $Q(2, 4)$), helps outline the shape of the half-parabola.

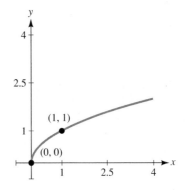

17. $f(x) = 2x - 1$

A function of the form $y = f(x) = ax + b$ is a linear function, and its graph is a line. Two points are sufficient to draw that line. The x-intercept is $\frac{1}{2}$ and the y-intercept is -1.

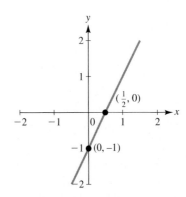

19. Since function is of form $y = Ax^2 + Bx + C$ (where $C = 0$), the graph is a parabola; its vertex is $\left(-\frac{5}{4}, -\frac{25}{8}\right)$, it opens up ($A$ is positive), and its intercepts are $(0,0)$ and $\left(-\frac{5}{2}, 0\right)$.

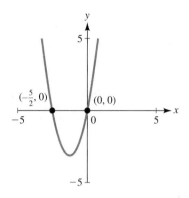

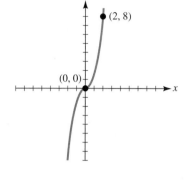

21. Since function is of form $y = Ax^2 + Bx + C$, the graph is a parabola which opens down (A is negative) and its vertex is $(-1, 16)$. Further,

$$f(x) = -x^2 - 2x + 15$$
$$= -(x^2 + 2x - 15)$$
$$= -(x + 5)(x - 3).$$

So the x-intercepts are $(-5, 0)$ and $(3, 0)$, and the y-intercept is $(0, 15)$.

25.
$$f(x) = \begin{cases} x - 1 & \text{if } x \le 0 \\ x + 1 & \text{if } x > 0 \end{cases}$$

Note that the graph consists of two half lines on either side of $x = 0$. There is no x-intercept for either half line. The half line $y = x - 1$ has a y-intercept of -1, while the half line $y = x + 1$ has no y-intercept.

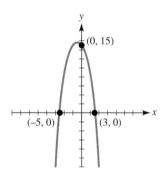

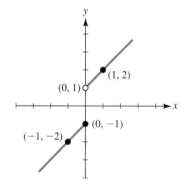

27. Graph consists of part of parabola $y = x^2 + x - 3$, namely portion corresponding to $x < 1$, and a half line for $x \ge 1$; for the parabola portion of the graph, the vertex is $\left(-\dfrac{1}{2}, -\dfrac{13}{4}\right)$, and the parabola opens up (A is positive); $\left(\dfrac{-1 - \sqrt{13}}{2}, 0\right)$ and $(0, -3)$ are its intercepts; the half line starts at $(1, -1)$ and includes the point $(2, -3)$.

23. $f(x) = x^3$

Note that if $x > 0$ then $f(x) > 0$ and if $x < 0$, then $f(x) < 0$. This means that the curve will only appear in the first and third quadrants. Since x^3 and $(-x)^3$ have the same absolute value, only their signs are opposites, the curve will be symmetric with respect to (wrt) the origin. The x-intercept is 0, as is the y-intercept.

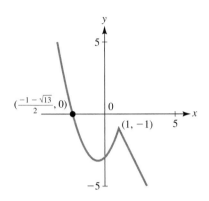

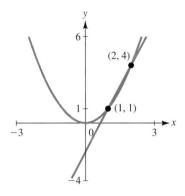

29. $y = 3x + 5$ and $y = -x + 3$

Add 3 times the second equation to the first. Then $4y = 14$ or $y = \dfrac{7}{2}$. Substitute in the first, then $x = 3 - y = -\dfrac{1}{2}$. The point of intersection is $P\left(-\dfrac{1}{2}, \dfrac{7}{2}\right)$.

33. $3y - 2x = 5$ and $y + 3x = 9$.

Multiply the second equation by -3 and add it to the first one. Then,

$$-2x - 9x = 5 - 27,$$
$$x = 2, \quad y = 9 - 3(2) = 3.$$

The point of intersection is $P(2, 3)$.

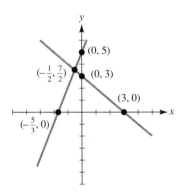

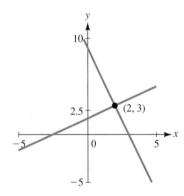

31. $y = x^2$ and $y = 3x - 2$

Setting the expressions equal to each other,

$$x^2 = 3x - 2$$
$$x^2 - 3x + 2 = 0$$
$$(x - 1)(x - 2) = 0$$
$$x = 1, 2$$

So points of intersection are $P_1(1, 1)$ and $P_2(2, 4)$.

35. **(a)** Crosses y-axis at $y = -1$, y-intercept is $(0, -1)$.
  (b) Crosses x-axis at $x = 1$, x-intercept is $(1, 0)$.
  (c) Largest value of f is 3 and occurs at $x = 4$ (highest point on graph).
  (d) Smallest value of f is -3 and occurs at $x = -2$ (lowest point on graph).

37. **(a)** Crosses y-axis at $y = 2$, y-intercept is $(0, 2)$.
  (b) Crosses x-axis at $x = -1$ and 3.5; x-intercepts are $(-1, 0)$ and $(3.5, 0)$.

(c) Largest value of f is 3 and occurs at $x = 2$ (highest point on graph).

(d) Smallest value of f is -3 and occurs at $x = 4$ (lowest point on graph).

39. The monthly profit is

$$P(p) = \text{(number of recorders sold)}$$
$$\text{(price} - \text{cost)}$$
$$= (120 - p)(p - 40)$$

So, the intercepts are $(40, 0)$, $(120, 0)$, and $(0, -4800)$. The graph suggests a maximum profit when $p \approx 80$, that is, when 80 recorders are sold.

$$P(80) = (120 - 80)(80 - 40) = 1600$$

So estimated max profit is $1600.

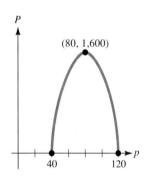

41. The weekly profit is

$$P(x) = \text{(number of sets sold)}$$
$$\cdot \text{(price-cost per set)}$$
$$= 5(27 - x)(x - 15)$$

So, the intercepts are $(27, 0)$, $(15, 0)$ and $(0, -2025)$. The graph suggest a maximum weekly profit when $x \approx 21$. That is, when the price per set is $21.

$$P(21) = 5(27 - 21)(21 - 15) = 180$$

So, estimated max profit is $180

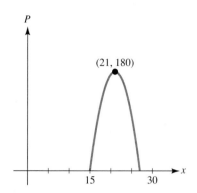

The number of sets corresponding to the max profit is

$$S(27 - 21) = 30 \text{ sets}$$

43. (a) $E(p) = \text{(price per unit)(demand)}$
$$= -200p(p - 60)$$

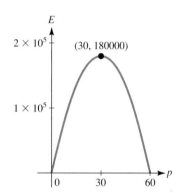

(b) The p intercepts represent prices at which consumers do not buy commodity.

(c) The graph suggests a maximum expenditure when $p \approx 30$.

$$E(30) = -200(30)(30 - 60) = 180,000$$

So estimated max expenditure is $180,000.

45. $H(t) = -16t^2 + 160t = -16t(t - 10)$

(a) The intercepts of the graph are $(0, 0)$ and $(10, 0)$. Due to symmetry, the vertex is when $t = 5$ and $y = H(5) = -16(5)^2 + 160(5) = 400.$

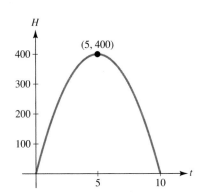

(b) Aside from when it is initially thrown, the height of the projectile is zero (ground level) when $t = 10$ seconds.

(c) The high point of the graph, which corresponds to the max height, is when y-coordinate is 400, or 400 feet.

47. (a) profit = revenue − cost

$$= (\text{#sold})(\text{sellingprice}) - \text{cost}$$

$$P(x) = x(-0.05x + 38) - (0.02x^2 + 3x + 574.77)$$

$$= -0.07x^2 + 35x - 574.77 \text{ hundred dollars}$$

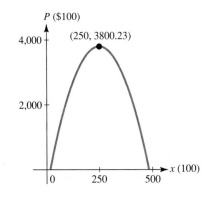

(b) The graph suggests a maximum profit when $x = 250$, that is, when 25,000 units are purchased. Note that the max profit is $P(250) = -0.07(250)^2 + 35(20) - 574.77 \approx 3800.23$ hundred, or \$380,023. For the unit price,

$$p = -0.05(250) + 38 = \$25.50$$

49. $D(v) = 0.065v^2 + 0.148v$

For practical domain, graph is part of parabola corresponding to $v \geq 0$.

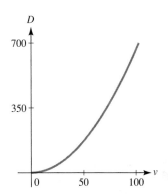

51. (a) revenue = (#apts) (rent per apt)

Since $\dfrac{p - 1200}{100}$ represents the number of \$100 increases,

$$150 - 5\left(\frac{p - 1200}{100}\right) = 210 - 0.05p$$

represents the number of apartments that will be leased. So,

$$R(p) = 210p - 0.05p^2$$

(b)

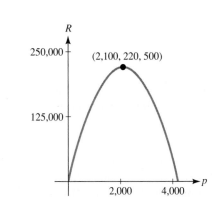

(c) The graph suggests a maximum profit when $p = 2100$; that is, when the rental price is \$2,100. The max profit is $R(2100) = 210(2100) - 0.05(2100)^2 \approx \$220,500$.

53. $N(t) = -35t^2 + 299t + 3{,}347$

(a)

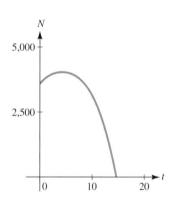

(b) Since the year 1995 is represented by $t = 5$, the amount predicted was $N(5) = -35(5)^2 + 299(5) + 3{,}347 = 3{,}967$ thousand tons.

(c) Based on the formula, the maximum lead emission would occur at the vertex, or when

$$t = -\frac{299}{2(-35)} \approx 4.27 \text{years}$$

This would be during March of the year 1994.

(d) No. From the graph, $N(t) < 0$ when $t \approx 15$, or during the year 2005.

55. The graph is a function because no vertical line intersects the graph more than once.

57. The graph is not a function because there are vertical lines intersecting the graph at more than one point; for example, the y-axis.

59. $f(x) = -9x^2 + 3600x - 358{,}200$
Answers will vary, but one viewing window has the following dimensions: [180, 200] 10 by [−500, 1850] 500.

61. **(a)** The graph of $y = x^2 + 3$ is graph of $y = x^2$ translated up 3 units.

(b)

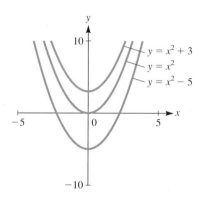

(c) When $c > 0$, the graph of g is the graph of f translated up c units. When $c < 0$, the graph is translated down $|c|$ units.

63. **(a)** The graph of $y = (x - 2)^2$ is the graph of $y = x^2$ translated two units to the right.

(b)

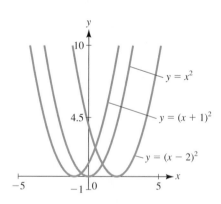

(c) When $c > 0$, the graph of g is the graph of f translated c units to the right. When $c < 0$, the graph is translated $|c|$ units to the left.

65. **(a)**

Days of Training	Mowers per Day
2	6
3	7.23
5	8.15
10	8.69
50	8.96

(b) The number of mowers per day approaches 9.

(c) To graph $N(t) = \dfrac{45t^2}{5t^2 + t + 8}$, press $\boxed{y=}$
Input $(45x \wedge 2) \div (5x \wedge 2 + x + 8)$ for $Y_1 =$.
Use window dimensions $[-10, 10]1$ by $[-10, 10]1$ (z standard).
Press $\boxed{\text{graph}}$.

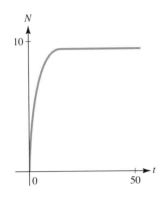

67. To graph $f(x) = \dfrac{-9x^2 - 3x - 4}{4x^2 + x - 1}$,

Press $\boxed{y=}$
Input $(-9x \wedge 2 - 3x - 4) \div (4x \wedge 2 + x - 1)$ for $y_1 =$
Press $\boxed{\text{graph}}$
Use the Zoom in function under the Zoom menu to find the vertical asymptotes to be $x_1 \approx -0.65$ and $x_2 \approx 0.39$. The function f is defined for all real x except $x_3 \approx -0.65$ and $x \approx 0.39$.

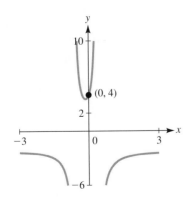

69. To graph $g(x) = -3x^3 + 7x + 4$ and find x-intercepts,
Press $\boxed{y=}$
Input $-3x \wedge 3 + 7x + 4$ for $y_1 =$

Press $\boxed{\text{graph}}$
Press $\boxed{\text{trace}}$
Use left arrow to move cursor to the left most x-intercept. When the cursor appears to be at the x-intercept, use the Zoom In feature under the Zoom menu twice. It can be seen that there are two x-intercepts in close proximity to each other. These x-intercepts appear to be $x_1 \approx -1$ and $x_2 \approx -0.76$. To estimate the third x-intercept, use the z-standard function under the Zoom menu to view the original graph. Use right arrow and zoom in to estimate the third x-intercept to be $x_3 \approx 1.8$.

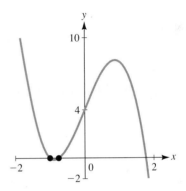

71. $(x - a)^2 + (y - b)^2 = R^2$

(a) Since the center of the circle is $(2, -3)$, $a = 2$ and $b = -3$. Since its radius is 4, $R = 4$.

$$(x - 2)^2 + (y - (-3))^2 = 4^2$$
$$(x - 2)^2 + (y + 3)^2 = 16$$

(b) $x^2 + y^2 - 4x + 6y = 11$
First, group the x terms together and the y terms together.

$$(x^2 - 4x) + (y^2 + 6y) = 11$$

Next, complete the square for each grouping

$$(x^2 - 4x + 4) - 4 + (y^2 + 6y + 9) - 9 = 11$$
$$(x - 2)^2 + (y + 3)^2 = 11 + 4 + 9$$
$$(x - 2)^2 + (y + 3)^2 = 24$$
$$(x - 2)^2 + (y - (-3))^2 = (\sqrt{24})^2$$

center: $(2, -3)$
radius: $\sqrt{24} = \sqrt{4 \cdot 6} = 2\sqrt{6}$

(c) Proceeding as in part (b),

$$(x^2 - 2x) + (y^2 + 4y) = -10$$
$$(x^2 - 2x + 1) - 1 + (y^2 + 4y + 4) - 4 = -10$$
$$(x - 1)^2 + (y + 2)^2 = -10 + 1 + 4$$
$$(x - 1)^2 + (y + 2)^2 = -5$$

Since the left-hand side is positive for all possible points (x, y) and the right-hand side is negative, the equality can never hold. That is, there are no points (x, y) that satisfy the equation.

1.3   Linear Functions

1. For $P_1(2, -3)$ and $P_2(0, 4)$ the slope is

$$m = \frac{4 - (-3)}{0 - 2} = -\frac{7}{2}$$

3. For $P_1(2, 0)$ and $P_2(0, 2)$ the slope is

$$m = \frac{2 - 0}{0 - 2} = -1$$

5. For $P_1(2, 6)$ and $P_2(2, -4)$ the slope is

$$m = \frac{6 - (-4)}{2 - 2},$$

which is undefined, since the denominator is 0. The line through the given points is vertical.

7. For $P_1\left(\frac{1}{7}, 5\right)$ and $P_2\left(-\frac{1}{11}, 5\right)$ the slope is

$$m = \frac{5 - 5}{-\frac{1}{11} - \frac{1}{7}} = \frac{0}{-\frac{18}{77}} = 0$$

9. The line has slope $= 2$ and an intercept of $(0, 0)$. So, the equation of line is $y = 2x + 0$, or $y = 2x$.

11. The slope of the line is $\frac{-5}{3}$. The x-intercept of the line is $(3, 0)$ and the y-intercept is $(0, 5)$. The equation of the line is $y = -\frac{5}{3}x + 5$.

13. The line $x = 3$ is a vertical line that includes all points of the form $(3, y)$. Therefore, the x-intercept is $(3, 0)$ and there is no y-intercept. The slope of the line is undefined, since $x_2 - x_1 = 3 - 3 = 0$.

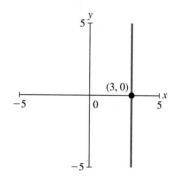

15. $y = 3x$
$m = 3$, y-intercept $b = 0$, and the x-intercept is 0.

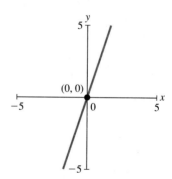

17. $3x + 2y = 6$ or $y = -\frac{3}{2}x + 3$

$$m = -\frac{3}{2},$$

y-intercept $b = 3$, and the x-intercept is 2.

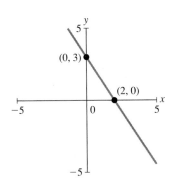

19. $\dfrac{x}{2} + \dfrac{y}{5} = 1$ or $y = -\dfrac{5}{2}x + 5$

$m = -\dfrac{5}{2}$, y-intercept $b = 5$, and the x-intercept is 2.

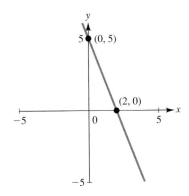

21. $m = 1$ and $P(2, 0)$, so

$$y - 0 = (1)(x - 2), \quad \text{or} \quad y = x - 2$$

23. $m = -\dfrac{1}{2}$ and $P(5, -2)$, so

$$y - (-2) = -\dfrac{1}{2}(x - 5), \quad \text{or} \quad y = -\dfrac{1}{2}x + \dfrac{1}{2}$$

25. Since the line is parallel to the x-axis, it is horizontal and its slope is 0. For $P(2, 5)$, the line is

$$y - 5 = 0(x - 2), \quad \text{or} \quad y = 5$$

27. $m = \dfrac{1 - 0}{0 - 1}$

and for $P(1, 0)$ the equation of the line is

$$y - 0 = -1(x - 1) \quad \text{or} \quad y = -x + 1$$

The equation would be the same if the point $(0, 1)$ had been used.

29.
$$m = \dfrac{1 - \left(\frac{1}{4}\right)}{-\left(\frac{1}{5}\right) - \left(\frac{2}{3}\right)} = -\dfrac{45}{52}$$

For $P\left(-\dfrac{1}{5}, 1\right)$, the line is $y - 1 = -\dfrac{45}{52}\left(x + \dfrac{1}{5}\right)$,

or $y = -\dfrac{45}{52}x + \dfrac{43}{52}$.

31. The slope is 0 because the y-values are identical. So, $y = 5$.

33. The given line $2x + y = 3$, or $y = -2x + 3$, has a slope of -2. Since parallel lines have the same slope, $m = -2$ for the desired line. Given that the point $(4, 1)$ is on the line, $y - 1 = -2(x - 4)$, or $y = -2x + 9$.

35. The given line $x + y = 4$, or $y = -x + 4$, has a slope of -1. A perpendicular line has slope $m = -\dfrac{1}{-1} = 1$. Given that the point $(3, 5)$ is on the line, $y - 5 = 1(x - 3)$, or $y = x + 2$.

37. Let x be the number of units manufactured. Then $60x$ is the cost of producing x units, to which the fixed cost must be added.

$$y = 60x + 5,000$$

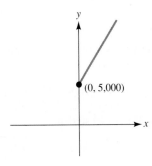

39. (a) Since $t = 0$ in the year 2000, $t = 5$ is the year 2005. The given information translates to the points (0, 7853) and (5, 9127). The slope of a line through these points is

$$m = \frac{9127 - 7853}{5 - 0} = \frac{1274}{5} = 254.8$$

So, the equation of the function is

$$D(t) = 254.8t + 7853$$

For practial purposes, the graph is limited to quadrant I.

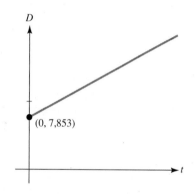

(b) In the year 2010, $t = 10$ and the predicted debt is

$$D(10) = 254.8(10) + 7853 = 10401$$

or $10,401.

(c) Need to find t where

$$D(t) = 2(7,853) = 15,706$$
$$254.8t + 7853 = 15706$$
$$254.8t = 7853$$
$$t \approx 30.8$$

Debt will be double the amount of 2000 during the year 2031.

41. (a) Let x be the number of hours spent registering students in person. During the first 4 hours $(4)(35) = 140$ students were registered. So,

$$360 - 140 = 220$$

students had pre-registered. Let y be the total number of students who register. Then,

$$y = 35x + 220$$

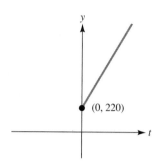

(b) $y = (3)(35) + 220 = 325$

(c) From part **(a)**, we see that 220 students had pre-registered.

43. The slope is

$$m = \frac{1,500 - 0}{0 - 10} = -150$$

Originally (when time $x = 0$), the value y of the books is 1500 (this is the y intercept.)

$$y = -150x + 1,500$$

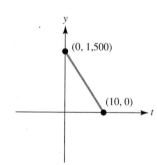

45. (a) Let x be the number of days. The slope is

$$m = \frac{200 - 164}{12 - 21} = -4$$

For $P(12, 200)$,
$$y - 200 = -4(x - 12), \text{ or } y = -4x + 248.$$

(b) $y = 248 - (4)(8) = 216$ million gallons.

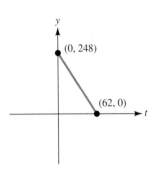

(c)

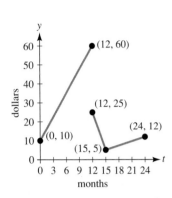

47. Let the *x*-axis represent time in months and the *y*-axis represent price per share.

(a)

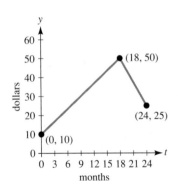

(b)

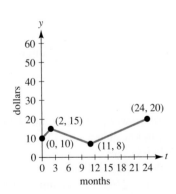

49. (a) $H(7) = 6.5(7) + 50 = 95.5$ cm tall.

(b) $150 = 6.5A + 50$, $A = 15.4$ years old

(c) $H(0) = 6.5(0) + 50 = 50$ cm tall. This height ≈ 19.7 inches) seems reasonable.

(d) $H(20) = 6.5(20) + 50 = 180$ cm tall. This height ≈ 5.9 feet) seems reasonable.

51. (a) Let *C* be the temperature in degrees Celsius and *F* the temperature in degrees Farenheit. The slope is

$$m = \frac{212 - 32}{100 - 0} = \frac{9}{5}$$

So, $\dfrac{F - 32}{C - 0} = \dfrac{9}{5}$,   or $F = \dfrac{9}{5}C + 32$

(b)
$$F = \frac{9}{5}(15) + 32$$
$$= 59 \text{ degrees}$$

(c)
$$68 = \frac{9}{5}C + 32,$$
$$36 = \frac{9}{5}C,$$
$$C = 20 \text{ degrees}$$

(d) Solving $C = \dfrac{9}{5}C + 32$, $C = -40$. So, the temperature $-40°$ C is also $-40°$ F.

53. (a) The original value of the book is $100 and the value doubles every 10 years. At the end of 30 years, in 1930, the book was worth $800. At the end of 90 years, in 1990, the book was worth

$51,200. At the end of 100 years, in 2000, the book will be worth $102,400.

(b) The value of the book is *not* a linear function.

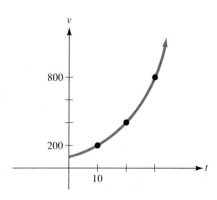

55. (a) Let t represent years after 1995. Using the points $(0, 575)$ and $(5, 545)$, the slope is $m = \dfrac{545 - 575}{5 - 0} = -6$. If S represents the average SAT score, $S(t) = -6t + 575$.

(b) $S(10) = -6(10) + 575 = 515$.

(c) $527 = -6t + 575$, $t = 8$, and the year would be 2003.

57. (a) Using the points $(0, V)$ and (N, S), the slope of the line is $\dfrac{S - V}{N}$. So, the value of an asset after t years is $B(t) = \dfrac{S - V}{N}t + V$.

(b) For this equipment, $B(t) = -6{,}400t + 50{,}000$. So, $B(3) = -6{,}400(3) + 50{,}000 = 30{,}800$. Value after three years is $30,800.

59. To graph $y = \dfrac{25}{7}x + \dfrac{13}{2}$ and $y = \dfrac{144}{45}x + \dfrac{630}{229}$ on the same set of axes, Press $\boxed{y=}$.

Input $\dfrac{(25x)}{7} + \dfrac{13}{2}$ for $y_1 =$ and press $\boxed{\text{enter}}$.

Input $\dfrac{(144x)}{45} + \dfrac{630}{229}$ for $y_2 =$.

Use the window dimensions $[0, 4]$ 0.5 by $[0, 14]$ 2 Press $\boxed{\text{graph}}$.

It does not appear that the lines are parallel. To verify this, press $\boxed{\text{2ND}}$ $\boxed{\text{quit}}$.

Input $\dfrac{25}{7} - \dfrac{144}{45}$ and $\boxed{\text{enter}}$.

If the lines were parallel the difference in their slopes would equal zero (the slopes would be the same). The difference of these slopes is 0.37 and therefore, the lines are not parallel.

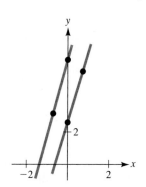

61. A rental company rents a piece of equipment for a $60.00 flat fee plus an hourly fee of $5.00 per hour.

(a) Let $y =$ cost of renting the equipment and $t =$ number of hours.

t	2	5	10	t
$y(t)$	70	85	110	$60 + 5t$

(b) $y(t) = 5t + 60$, $t \geq 0$

(c) Press $\boxed{y=}$.
Input $5x + 60$ for $y_1 =$.
Use dimensions $[-10, 10]$ 1 by $[-10, 100]$ 10
Press $\boxed{\text{graph}}$.

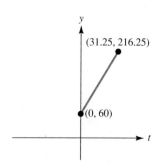

(d) To answer part (d), it may be easiest to use window dimensions $[30, 33]$ 5 by $[200, 230]$ 5. Press $\boxed{\text{graph}}$.
Press $\boxed{\text{trace}}$ and move cross-hairs to be as close to $y = 216.25$ as possible.

When $y = 216.2234$, the x-coordinate is 31.24. It takes approximately 31.24 hours for the rental charge to be \$216.25. Using algebra, we see it takes exactly 31.25 for the charge to be \$216.25.

63. The slope of -0.389 means the unemployment rate drops by approximately 0.389% from year to year. Writing exercise—Answers will vary.

65. The slope of L_1 is $m_1 = \dfrac{b}{a}$ and that of L_2 is $m_2 = \dfrac{c}{a}$. By hypothesis, $L_1 \perp L_2$.

$$OA = \sqrt{a^2 + b^2} \text{ and}$$

$$OB = \sqrt{a^2 + c^2}$$

Since $AB = b - c$ and by the Pythagorean theorem,

$$(a^2 + b^2) + (a^2 + c^2) = (b - c)^2$$
$$2a^2 + b^2 + c^2 = b^2 - 2bc + c^2$$

from which $2a^2 = -2bc$

$$-1 = \frac{bc}{a^2}$$

$$-1 = \left(\frac{b}{a}\right)\left(\frac{c}{a}\right) = m_1 m_2$$

or $\quad m_1 = -\dfrac{1}{m_2}$.

1.4 Functional Models

1. (a) Revenue = (number sold) · (selling price)
$\qquad R(x) = xp = x(-6x + 100)$ thousand dollars
or, $\quad R(x) = 1000x(-6x + 100)$ dollars

(b) $R(15) = 1000(15)(-6(15) + 100)$
$\qquad\quad = \$150,000$

3. (a) Let p be the selling price of the commodity. Then

Profit = Revenue − Costs
Revenue = (number sold) · (selling price)
$\qquad R(x) = xp$
Costs = (cost per unit) · (number units)
$\qquad\quad$ + fixed overhead
$\qquad C(x) = (p - 3)x + 17,000$
$\qquad C(x) = xp - 3x + 17,000$
$\qquad P(x) = xp - (xp - 3x + 17,000)$
$\qquad\quad = 3x - 17,000$

(b) $P(20,000) = 3(20,000) - 17,000 = 43,000$ or a profit of \$43,000
$P(5,000) = 3(5,000) - 17,000 = -2,000$ or a loss of \$2,000

5. Let x and y be the smaller and larger numbers, respectively. Then

$$xy = 318$$
$$y = \frac{318}{x}$$

The sum is $S = x + y = x + \dfrac{318}{x}$.

7. This problem has two possible forms of the solution. Assume the stream is along the length, say l. Then w is the width and

$$l + 2w = 1,000 \text{ or } l = 1,000 - 2w$$

The area is

$$A = lw = 2w(500 - w) \text{ squarefeet}$$

9. Let x be the length and y the width of the rectangle. Then

$$2x + 2y = 320 \quad \text{or} \quad y = 160 - x$$

The area is (length)(width) or

$$A(x) = x(160 - x)$$

The length is estimated to be 80 meters from the graph below, which also happens to be the width. So the maximum area seems to correspond to that of a square.

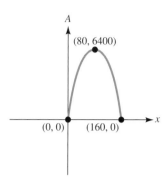

11. Let x be the length of the square base and y the height of the box. The surface area is $2x^2 + 4xy = 4{,}000$

So $y = \dfrac{2{,}000 - x^2}{2x}$ and the volume is

$$V = x^2 y = x\left(1{,}000 - \frac{x^2}{2}\right)$$

13. Let r be the radius and h the height of the cylinder. The surface area of the closed cylinder is

$$S = 120\pi = 2\pi r^2 + 2\pi rh \quad \text{or} \quad h = \frac{60 - r^2}{r}$$

So $V(r) = \pi r^2 h = \pi r(60 - r^2)$

15. Let r be the radius and h the height of the cylinder. Since the volume is

$$V = \pi r^2 h = 4\pi, \quad \text{or} \quad h = \frac{4}{r^2}$$

The cost of the top or bottom is

$$C_t = C_b = 2(0.02)\pi r^2,$$

while the cost of the side is

$$2\pi rh(0.02) = \frac{0.16\pi}{r}$$

The total cost is

$$C(x) = 0.08\pi r^2 + \frac{0.16\pi}{r}$$

17. Let R denote the rate of population growth and p the population size. Since R is directly proportional to p,

$$R(p) = kp,$$

where k is the constant of proportionality.

19. Let R denote the rate at which temperature changes, M the temperature of the medium, and T the temperature of the object. Then $T - M$ is the difference in the temperature between the object and the medium. Since the rate of change is directly proportional to the difference,

$$R(T) = k(T - M),$$

where k is the constant of proportionality.

21. Let R denote the rate at which people are implicated, x the number of people implicated, and n the total number of people involved. Then $n - x$ is the number of people involved but not implicated. Since the rate of change is jointly proportional to those implicated and those not implicated,

$$R(x) = kx(n - x),$$

where k is the constant of proportionality.

23. Let s be the speed of the truck.

The cost due to wages is $\dfrac{k_1}{s}$,

where k_1 is a constant of proportionality, and the cost due to gasoline is $k_2 s$, where k_2 is another constant of proportionality.
If $C(s)$ is the total cost,

$$C(s) = \frac{k_1}{s} + k_2 s$$

25.

$$C = \left(\frac{N+1}{24}\right)(300) = \left(\frac{N+1}{2}\right)(25)$$

$$C = \frac{2N \cdot 300}{25} = 24N$$

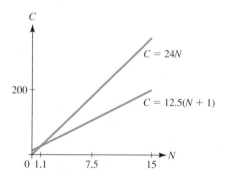

27. (a) The estimated surface area of the child is:

$$S = 0.0072(18)^{0.425}(91)^{0.725} \approx 0.6473$$

so, $C = \dfrac{(0.6473)(250)}{1.7} \approx 95.2\text{mg}$

(b) Using $2H$ and $2W$ for the larger child,

$$C = \frac{0.0072(2W)^{0.425}(2H)^{0.725}A}{1.7}$$

Comparing to drug dosage for the smaller child,

$$\frac{\frac{0.0072(2W)^{0.425}(2H)^{0.725}A}{1.7}}{\frac{0.0072W^{0.425}H^{0.725}A}{1.7}} = (2)^{0.425}(2)^{0.725} \approx 2.22$$

So, drug dosage for larger child is approx. 2.22 times the dosage for the smaller child.

29. Let x be the number of passengers. There will be $x - 40$ passengers between $40 < x \le 80$ (if the total number is below 80). The price for the second category is

$$60 - 0.5(x - 40) = 80 - 0.5x$$

The revenue generated in this category is

$$80x - 0.5x^2$$

$$R(x) = \begin{cases} 2,400 & \text{if } 0 < x \le 40 \\ 80x - 0.5x^2 & \text{if } 40 < x < 80 \\ 40x & \text{if } x \ge 80 \end{cases}$$

Only the points corresponding to the integers $x = 0, 1, 2, \cdots$ are meaningful in the practical context.

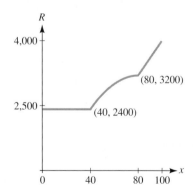

31. (a) For $0 < x \le 7,825$ the tax is

$$10\%x = 0.1x$$

For $7,825 < x \le 31,850$ the tax is

$$782.5 + 15\%(x - 7,825)$$
$$= 782.5 + 0.15(x - 7,825)$$
$$= 782.5 + 0.15x - 1,173.75$$
$$= 0.15x - 391.25$$

For $31,850 < x \le 64,250$ the tax is

$$4,386.25 + 25\%(x - 31,850)$$
$$= 4,386.25 + 0.25(x - 31,850)$$
$$= 4,386.25 + 0.25x - 7,962.5$$
$$= 0.25x - 3,576.25$$

For $64,250 < x \le 97,925$ the tax is

$$12,486.25 + 28\%(x - 64,250)$$
$$= 12,486.25 + 0.28(x - 64,250)$$
$$= 12,486.25 + 0.28x - 17,990$$
$$= 0.28x - 5,503.75$$

So,

$$T(x) = \begin{cases} 0.1x & \text{if } 0 < x \le 7,825 \\ 0.15x - 391.25 & \text{if } 7,825 < x \le 31,850 \\ 0.25x - 3,576.25 & \text{if } 31,850 < x \le 64,250 \\ 0.28x - 5,503.75 & \text{if } 64,250 < x \le 97,925 \end{cases}$$

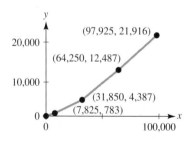

(b) The slopes of the segments are 0.1, 0.15, 0.25 and 0.28, respectively. As taxable income increases, the slopes of the segments increase. So, as you earn more, you pay more on your earnings.

33. (a) Volume = (length)(width)(height)
The height is given as 20 m and the perimeter is 320 m. So,

$$2(x + w) = 320$$
$$x + w = 160$$
$$w = 160 - x$$
$$V(x) = x(160 - x)(20)$$
$$= 20x(160 - x)$$

(b)

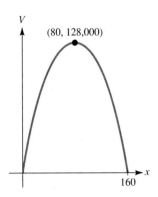

Since the high point of the graph occurs half-way between its intercepts, the max volume occurs when $x = 80$. The dimensions for the max volume are length $= 80$ m, width $= 160 - 80 = 80$ m and height $= 20$ m

(c)   Cost construction $=$ cost building
$\qquad\qquad\qquad\qquad + $ cost parking lot

Cost building $= 75(80)(80)(20)$
$\qquad\qquad\quad = \$9,600,000$

Cost parking lot $=$ cost top rectangle
$\qquad\qquad\qquad$ (across entire length)
$\qquad\qquad\qquad + $ cost right side rectangle
$\qquad\qquad\qquad$ (next to building)

Cost top rectangle
$\qquad\qquad = 50$ (area rectangle)
$\qquad\qquad = 50$ (length)(width)
$\qquad\qquad = 50$ (length)(100 $-$ width bldg)
$\qquad\qquad = 50(120)(100 - 80)$
$\qquad\qquad = \$120,000$

Cost right rectangle
$\qquad\qquad = 50$ (area rectangle)
$\qquad\qquad = 50$ (length)(width)
$\qquad\qquad = 50(120 - $ length bldg)(width)
$\qquad\qquad = 50(120 - 80)(80)$
$\qquad\qquad = \$160,000$

Cost construction
$\qquad\qquad = \$9,600,000 + \$120,000$
$\qquad\qquad\quad + \$160,000$
$\qquad\qquad = \$9,880,000$

35. Let x denote the width of the printed portion and y the length of the printed portion. Then $x + 4$ is the width of the poster and $y + 8$ is its length. The area A of the poster is
$$A = (x + 4)(y + 8)$$
which is a function of two variables. $A = 25$ leads to $xy = 25$ or $y = \dfrac{25}{x}$. So
$$A(x) = (x + 4)\left(\frac{25}{x} + 8\right) = 8x + 57 + \frac{100}{x}$$

37. Let x be the side of the square base and y the height of the open box. The area of the base is x^2 square meters and that of each side is xy square meters. The total cost is
$$4x^2 + 3(4xy) = 48$$
Solving for y in terms of x,
$$12xy = 48 - 4x^2$$
$$3xy = 12 - x^2$$
$$y = \frac{12 - x^2}{3x}$$
The volume of the box is
$$V = x^2 y = \frac{x(12 - x^2)}{3} = 4x - \frac{x^3}{3} \text{ cubic meters.}$$

39. Let x be the sales price per lamp. Then, $x - 30$ will be the number of \$1.00 increases over the base price of \$30, and $1,000(x - 30)$ is the number of unsold lamps. Therefore the number of lamps sold is $3,000 - 1,000(x - 30)$. The profit is

$$P = [3,000 - 1,000(x - 30)]x$$
$$- 18[3,000 - 1,000(x - 30)]$$
$$= [3,000 - 1,000(x - 30)](x - 18)$$
$$= (33,000 - 1,000x)(x - 18)$$

The optimal selling price is $25.50.

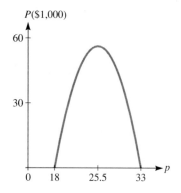

41. Let x be the number of machines used and t the number of hours of production. The number of kickboards produced per machine per hour is $30x$. It costs $20x$ to set up all the machines. The cost of supervision is $19.20t$. The number of kickboards produced by x machines in t hours is $30xt$ which must account for all 8,000 kickboards. Solving $30xt = 8,000$ for t leads to

$$t = \frac{800}{3x}$$

Cost of supervision: $19.20 \left(\dfrac{800}{3x} \right) = \dfrac{5,120}{x}$

Total cost: $C(x) = 20x + \dfrac{5,120}{x}$

The number of machines which minimize cost is approximately 16. Note that $C(16) = 20(16) + \dfrac{5,120}{16} = 640$. So, the estimated min cost is $640.

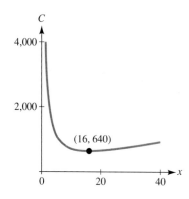

43. Let x denote the number of days after July 1 and $R(x)$ the corresponding revenue (in dollars). Then

$$R(x) = \text{(number of bushels sold)}$$
$$\text{(price per bushel)}$$

Since the crop increases at the rate of 1 bushel per day and 80 bushels were available on July 1, the number of bushels sold after x days is $140 + x$. Since the price per bushel decreases by 0.02 dollars per day and was $3 on July 1, the price per bushel after x days is $3 - 0.02x$ dollars. Putting it all together,

$$R(x) = (140 + x)(3 - 0.02x) = 0.02(150 - x)(140 + x)$$

The number of days to maximize revenue is approximately 5 days after July 1, or July 6. Note that $R(5) = 0.02(150 - 5)(140 + 5) = 420.50$. So, the estimated max revenue is $420.50.

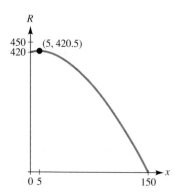

45. (a) Equilibrium occurs when $S(x)(D(x)$, or

$$3x + 150 = -2x + 275$$
$$5x = 125$$
$$x = 25$$

The corresponding equilibrium price is
$p = S(x) = D(x)$ or $p = 3(25) + 150 = \$225.$

(b)

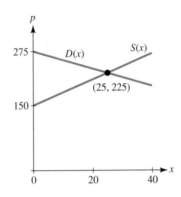

(c) There is a market shortage when demand exceeds supply. Here, a market shortage occurs when $0 < x < 25$. A market surplus occurs when supply exceeds demand. Here, a market surplus occurs when $x > 25$.

47. (a) Equilibrium occurs when $S(x) = D(x)$, or

$$2x + 7.43 = -0.21x^2 - 0.84x + 50$$
$$0.21x^2 + 2.84x - 42.57 = 0$$

Using the quadratic formula,

$$x = \frac{-2.84 \pm \sqrt{(2.84)^2 - 4(0.21)(-42.57)}}{2(0.21)}$$

so $x = 9$ (disregarding the negative root.) The corresponding equilibrium price is

$$p = S(x) = D(x), \text{ or } p = 2(9) + 7.43 = 25.43$$

(b)

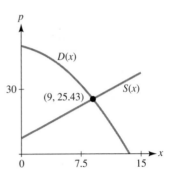

(c) There is a market shortage when demand exceeds supply. Here, a market shortage occurs when $0 < x < 9$. A market surplus occurs when supply exceeds demand. Here, a market surplus occurs when $x > 9$.

49. (a) Equilibrium occurs when $S(x) = D(x)$, or

$$2x + 15 = \frac{385}{x + 1}$$
$$(2x + 15)(x + 1) = 385$$
$$2x^2 + 17x + 15 = 385$$
$$2x^2 + 17x - 370 = 0$$

Using the quadratic formula,

$$x = \frac{-17 \pm \sqrt{(17)^2 - 4(2)(-370)}}{2(2)}$$

so $x = 10$ (disregard the negative root). The corresponding equilibrium price is
$p = S(x) = D(x)$, or $p = 2(10) + 15 = 35$

(b)

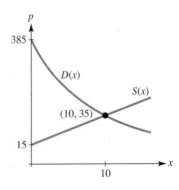

(c) The supply curve intersect the y-axis at $S(0) = 15$. Since this is the price at which producers are willing to supply zero units, it corresponds to their overhead at the start of production.

51. Let t be the number of hours the second plane has been flying. Since distance = (rate)(time), the equation for its distance is

$$d = 650t$$

The first plane has been flying for $t + \dfrac{1}{2}$ hours, so the equation for its distance is

$$d = 550 \left(t + \frac{1}{2} \right)$$

The planes will meet when

$$650t = 550 \left(t + \frac{1}{2} \right)$$
$$650t = 550t + 275$$
$$100t = 275$$
$$t = 2.75$$

Since three-quarters of an hour is 45 minutes, the second plane passes the first plane after it has been flying 2 hours and 45 minutes.

53. Royalties for publisher A are given by

$$R_A(N) = \begin{cases} 0.01(2)(N) & 0 < N \le 30,000 \\ 0.01(2)(30,000) & \\ +0.035(2)(N-30,000) & N > 30,000 \end{cases}$$

Royalties for publisher B are given by

$$R_B(N) = \begin{cases} 0 & N \le 4,000 \\ 0.02(3)(N-4,000) & N > 4,000 \end{cases}$$

Clearly, for $N \le 4,000$, publisher A offers the better deal. When $N = 30,000$, publisher A pays $600, but publisher B now pays more, paying $1,560. Therefore, the plans pay the same amount for some value of $N < 30,000$. To find the value,

$$0.01(2)(N) = 0.02(3)(N-4,000)$$
$$0.02N = 0.06N - 240$$
$$240 = 0.04N$$
$$6,000 = N$$

So, when $N < 6,000$, publisher A offers the better deal. When $N > 6,000$, publisher B initially offers the better deal. Then, the plans again pay the same amount when

$$0.01(2)(30,000) + 0.035(2)(N-30,000) = 0.02(3)(N-4,000)$$
$$0.07N - 1,500 = 0.06N - 240$$
$$0.01N = 1,260$$
$$N = 126,000$$

So, when more than 126,000 copies are sold, plan A becomes the better plan.

55. Since I is proportional to the area, A, of the pupil, $I = kA$, where k is a constant of proportionality. Since the pupil of the eye is circular and the area of a circle is $A = \pi r^2$, $I = k\pi r^2$.

57. (a) For a newborn child, the points $(0, 46)$ and $(100, 77)$ define the linear function. Its slope is

$$m = \frac{77 - 46}{100 - 0} = 0.31$$

and the function is

$$B(t) = 0.31t + 46$$

For a 65 year old, the points $(0, 76)$ and $(100, 83)$ define the linear function. Its slope is

$$m = \frac{83 - 76}{100 - 0} = 0.07$$

and the function is

$$E(t) = 0.07t + 76$$

(b)

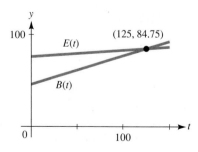

Need to find when $B(t) = E(t)$.

$$0.31t + 46 = 0.07t + 76$$
$$0.24t = 30$$
$$t = 125 \text{ years}$$

Note that this is where the graphs intersect.

(c) Writing exercise—Answers will vary.

59. $S(q) = aq + b$
$D(q) = cq + d$

(a) The graph of S is rising, while the graph of D is falling. So, $a > 0$ and $d < 0$. Further, since both y-intercepts are positive, $b > 0$ and $d > 0$.

(b)
$$aq + b = cq + d$$
$$(a - c)q = d - b$$
$$q_e = \frac{d - b}{a - c}$$
$$P_e = aq_e + b$$
$$= a\left(\frac{d - b}{a - c}\right) + b$$
$$= \frac{ad - ab}{a - c} + b$$
$$= \frac{ad - ab + b(a - c)}{a - c}$$
$$= \frac{ad - bc}{a - c}$$

(c) As a increases, the denominator in the expression for q_e increases. This results in a decrease in q_e. As d increases, the numerator in the expression for q_e increases. This results in an increase in q_e.

1.5   Limits

1. $\lim_{x \to a} f(x) = b$, even though $f(a)$ is not defined.

3. $\lim_{x \to a} f(x) = b$ even though $f(a) = c$.

5. $\lim_{x \to a} f(x)$ does not exist since as x approaches a from the left, the function becomes unbounded.

7. $\lim_{x \to 2} (3x^2 - 5x + 2)$
$$= 3 \lim_{x \to 2} x^2 - 5 \lim_{x \to 2} x + \lim_{x \to 2} 2$$
$$= 3(2)^2 - 5(2) + 2 = 4.$$

9. $\lim_{x \to 0} (x^5 - 6x^4 + 7)$
$$= \lim_{x \to 0} x^5 - 6 \lim_{x \to 0} x^4 + \lim_{x \to 0} 7 = 7.$$

11. $\lim_{x \to 3} (x - 1)^2 (x + 1)$
$$= \lim_{x \to 3} (x - 1)^2 \lim_{x \to 3} (x + 1)$$
$$= (3 - 1)^2 (3 + 1) = 16.$$

13. $\lim_{x \to 1/3} \dfrac{x + 1}{x + 2} = \dfrac{\lim_{x \to 1/3} x + 1}{\lim_{x \to 1/3} x + 2} = \dfrac{\frac{4}{3}}{\frac{7}{3}} = \dfrac{4}{7}$

15. $\lim_{x \to 5} \dfrac{x + 3}{5 - x}$ does not exist since the limit of the denominator is zero while the limit of the numerator is not zero.

17. $\lim_{x \to 1} \dfrac{x^2 - 1}{x - 1}$
$$= \lim_{x \to 1} \frac{(x + 1)(x - 1)}{x - 1}$$
$$= \lim_{x \to 1} (x + 1) = 2.$$

19. $\lim_{x \to 5} \dfrac{x^2 - 3x - 10}{x - 5}$
$$= \lim_{x \to 5} \frac{(x - 5)(x + 2)}{x - 5}$$
$$= \lim_{x \to 5} (x + 2) = 7.$$

21. $\lim_{x \to 4} \dfrac{(x + 1)(x - 4)}{(x - 1)(x - 4)}$
$$= \frac{\lim_{x \to 4} (x + 1)}{\lim_{x \to 4} (x - 1)} = \frac{5}{3}.$$

23.

$$\lim_{x \to -2} \frac{x^2 - x - 6}{x^2 + 3x + 2}$$

$$= \lim_{x \to -2} \frac{(x-3)(x+2)}{(x+1)(x+2)}$$

$$= \frac{\lim_{x \to -2}(x-3)}{\lim_{x \to -2}(x+1)} = \frac{-5}{-1} = 5.$$

25.

$$\lim_{x \to 4} \frac{\sqrt{x} - 2}{x - 4}$$

$$= \lim_{x \to 4} \frac{\sqrt{x} - 2}{x - 4} \frac{\sqrt{x} + 2}{\sqrt{x} + 2}$$

$$= \lim_{x \to 4} \frac{x - 4}{(x-4)(\sqrt{x} + 2)} = \frac{1}{4}.$$

27.

$$f(x) = x^3 - 4x^2 - 4,$$

$$\lim_{x \to +\infty} f(x) = \lim_{x \to +\infty} x^3 = +\infty$$

$$\lim_{x \to -\infty} f(x) = \lim_{x \to -\infty} x^3 = -\infty$$

29.

$$f(x) = (1 - 2x)(x + 5) = -2x^2 - 9x + 5$$

$$\lim_{x \to +\infty} f(x) = \lim_{x \to +\infty} -2x^2 = -\infty$$

$$\lim_{x \to -\infty} f(x) = \lim_{x \to -\infty} -2x^2 = -\infty$$

31.

$$f(x) = \frac{x^2 - 2x + 3}{2x^2 + 5x + 1}$$

$$\lim_{x \to +\infty} f(x) = \lim_{x \to +\infty} \frac{1 - \frac{2}{x} + \frac{3}{x^2}}{2 + \frac{5}{x} + \frac{1}{x^2}} = \frac{1}{2}$$

$$\lim_{x \to -\infty} f(x) = \lim_{x \to -\infty} \frac{1 - \frac{2}{x} + \frac{3}{x^2}}{2 + \frac{5}{x} + \frac{1}{x^2}} = \frac{1}{2}$$

33. $f(x) = \dfrac{2x + 1}{3x^2 + 2x - 7}$,

$$\lim_{x \to +\infty} f(x) = \lim_{x \to +\infty} \frac{\frac{2}{x} + \frac{1}{x^2}}{3 + \frac{2}{x} - \frac{7}{x^2}} = 0$$

$$\lim_{x \to -\infty} f(x) = \lim_{x \to -\infty} \frac{\frac{2}{x} + \frac{1}{x^2}}{3 + \frac{2}{x} - \frac{7}{x^2}} = 0$$

35. $f(x) = \dfrac{3x^2 - 6x + 2}{2x - 9}$,

$$\lim_{x \to +\infty} f(x) = \lim_{x \to +\infty} \frac{3x^2 - 6x + 2}{2x - 9}$$

$$= \lim_{x \to +\infty} \frac{3x - 6 + \frac{2}{x}}{2 - \frac{9}{x}}$$

$$\lim_{x \to +\infty} 3x - 6 + \frac{2}{x} = +\infty \quad \text{and}$$

$$\lim_{x \to +\infty} 2 - \frac{9}{x} = 2$$

$$\text{So, } \lim_{x \to +\infty} \frac{3x - 6 + \frac{2}{x}}{2 - \frac{9}{x}} = +\infty$$

$$\lim_{x \to -\infty} f(x) = \lim_{x \to -\infty} \frac{3x - 6 + \frac{2}{x}}{2 - \frac{9}{x}}$$

$$\lim_{x \to -\infty} 3x - 6 + \frac{2}{x} = -\infty \quad \text{and}$$

$$\lim_{x \to -\infty} 2 - \frac{9}{x} = 2$$

$$\text{So, } \lim_{x \to -\infty} \frac{3x - 6 + \frac{2}{x}}{2 - \frac{9}{x}} = -\infty$$

37. $\lim_{x \to +\infty} f(x) = 1$
and $\lim_{x \to -\infty} f(x) = -1$

39. The corresponding table values are:

$$f(1.9) = (1.9)^2 - 1.9 = 1.71$$

$$f(1.99) = (1.99)^2 - 1.99 = 1.9701$$

$$f(1.999) = (1.999)^2 - 1.999 = 1.997001$$

$$f(2.001) = (2.001)^2 - 2.001 = 2.003001$$

$$f(2.01) = (2.01)^2 - 2.01 = 2.0301$$

$$f(2.1) = (2.1)^2 - 2.1 = 2.31$$

$$\lim_{x \to 2} f(x) = 2$$

41. The corresponding table values are

$$f(0.9) = \frac{(0.9)^3 + 1}{0.9 - 1} = -17.29$$

$$f(0.99) = \frac{(0.99)^3 + 1}{0.99 - 1} = -197.0299$$

$$f(0.999) = \frac{(0.999)^3 + 1}{0.999 - 1} = -1,997.002999$$

$$f(1.001) = \frac{(1.001)^3 + 1}{1.001 - 1} = 2,003.003001$$

$$f(1.01) = \frac{(1.01)^3 + 1}{1.01 - 1} = 203.0301$$

$$f(1.1) = \frac{(1.1)^3 + 1}{1.1 - 1} = 23.31$$

$\lim\limits_{x \to 1} f(x)$ does not exist

43. $\lim\limits_{x \to c}[2f(x) - 3g(x)] = \lim\limits_{x \to c} 2f(x) - \lim\limits_{x \to c} 3g(x)$

$$= 2\lim\limits_{x \to c} f(x) - 3\lim\limits_{x \to c} g(x)$$

$$= 2(5) - 3(-2) = 16$$

45.

$$\lim\limits_{x \to c} \sqrt{f(x) + g(x)}$$

$$= \lim\limits_{x \to c}[f(x) + g(x)]^{1/2}$$

$$= \left[\lim\limits_{x \to c} f(x) + g(x))\right]^{1/2}$$

$$= \left[\lim\limits_{x \to c} f(x) + \lim\limits_{x \to c} g(x))\right]^{1/2}$$

$$= [5 + {}^-2]^{1/2} = \sqrt{3}$$

47.

$$\lim\limits_{x \to c} \frac{f(x)}{g(x)} = \frac{\lim\limits_{x \to c} f(x)}{\lim\limits_{x \to c} g(x)}$$

$$= \frac{5}{-2} = -\frac{5}{2}$$

49. $\lim\limits_{x \to \infty} \dfrac{2f(x) + g(x)}{x + f(x)}$

$$= \lim\limits_{x \to \infty} \frac{\frac{1}{x} \cdot 2f(x) + \frac{1}{x} \cdot g(x)}{1 + \frac{1}{x} \cdot f(x)}$$

$$= \frac{\lim\limits_{x \to \infty}\left[\frac{1}{x} \cdot 2f(x) + \frac{1}{x} \cdot g(x)\right]}{\lim\limits_{x \to \infty}\left[1 + \frac{1}{x} \cdot f(x)\right]}$$

$$= \frac{\lim\limits_{x \to \infty}\frac{1}{x} \cdot 2f(x) + \lim\limits_{x \to \infty}\frac{1}{x} \cdot g(x)}{\lim\limits_{x \to \infty} 1 + \lim\limits_{x \to \infty}\frac{1}{x} \cdot f(x)}$$

$$= \frac{\lim\limits_{x \to \infty}\frac{1}{x} \cdot 2\lim\limits_{x \to \infty} f(x) + \lim\limits_{x \to \infty}\frac{1}{x} \cdot \lim\limits_{x \to \infty} g(x)}{\lim\limits_{x \to \infty} 1 + \lim\limits_{x \to \infty}\frac{1}{x} \cdot \lim\limits_{x \to \infty} f(x)}$$

Since $\lim\limits_{x \to \infty} \dfrac{1}{x} = 0$ and $\lim\limits_{x \to \infty} 1 = 1$,

$$= \frac{0 + 0}{1 + 0} = 0$$

51. As the weight approaches 18 lbs., displacement approaches a limit of 1.8 inches.

53. $p = 0.2t + 1,500;\ E(t) = \sqrt{9t^2 + 0.5t + 179}$

(a) Since the units of p are thousands and the units of E are millions, the units of E/p will be thousands. $P(t) = \dfrac{\sqrt{9t^2 + 0.5t + 179}}{0.2t + 1500}$ thousand dollars per person

(b) Dividing each term by t (note that each term under the square root will be divided by t^2 since $\sqrt{t^2} = t$),

$$\lim\limits_{t \to \infty} P(t) = \lim\limits_{t \to \infty} \frac{\sqrt{9 + \frac{0.5}{t} + \frac{179}{t^2}}}{0.2 + \frac{1500}{t}}$$

$$= \frac{\sqrt{\lim\limits_{t \to \infty}\left(9 + \frac{0.5}{t} + \frac{179}{t^2}\right)}}{\lim\limits_{t \to \infty}\left(0.2 + \frac{1500}{t}\right)} = \frac{\sqrt{9}}{0.2} = 15$$

or, $15,000 per person.

55. (a) $\lim\limits_{S \to \infty} = \dfrac{aS}{S + c} = \lim\limits_{S \to \infty} \dfrac{a}{1 + \frac{c}{S}} = a$

As bite size increases indefinitely, intake approaches a limit of a. This signifies that the animal has a limit of how much it can consume, no matter how large its bites become.

(b) Writing exercise—Answers will vary.

57. $\lim\limits_{x \to +\infty} \dfrac{7.5x + 120{,}000}{x} = \lim\limits_{x \to +\infty} 7.5 + \dfrac{120{,}000}{x} =$
7.5 As the number of units produced increases indefinitely, the average cost per unit decreases, approaching a minimum of \$7.50. The average cost cannot decrease further, as the expense of materials cannot be eliminated completely.

59. $P(t) = \dfrac{30}{3+t}$, $Q(t) = \dfrac{64}{4-t}$

(a) $P(0) = \dfrac{30}{3} = 10$ thous, or $\quad 10{,}000$
$Q(0) = \dfrac{64}{4} = 16$ thous, or $\quad 16{,}000$

(b) Since the function P accepts all $t \geq 0$, the function values decrease as t increases. Further,

$$\lim\limits_{t \to +\infty} P(t) = \lim\limits_{t \to +\infty} \dfrac{30}{3+t} = 0$$

So, in the long run, P tends to zero. The Q function, however, only accepts values of t such that $0 \leq t \leq 4$. The function values increase as t increases. Further,

$$\lim\limits_{t \to 4^-} \dfrac{64}{4-t} = +\infty$$

(a t/Q table is an easy way to see this). So, Q increases without bound.

(c)

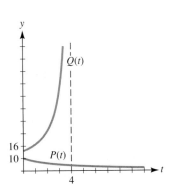

(d) Writing exercise—Answers will vary.

61. $C(t) = \dfrac{0.4}{t^{1.2}+1} + 0.013$

(a) $C(0) = \dfrac{0.4}{0^{1.2}+1} + 0.013$

$\qquad = 0.413$ mg/ml

(b) Need to find

$C(5) - C(4)$

$= \left[\dfrac{0.4}{5^{1.2}+1} + 0.013 \right] - \left[\dfrac{0.4}{4^{1.2}+1} + 0.013 \right]$

$= \dfrac{0.4}{5^{1.2}+1} - \dfrac{0.4}{4^{1.2}+1}$

$\approx 0.0506 - 0.0637$

$= -0.0131$

So, the concentration decreases approx. 0.013 mg/ml during this hour.

(c) $\lim\limits_{t \to +\infty} C(t) = \lim\limits_{t \to +\infty} \left[\dfrac{0.4}{t^{1.2}+1} + 0.013 \right]$

$\qquad = \lim\limits_{t \to +\infty} \dfrac{0.4}{t^{1.2}+1} + \lim\limits_{t \to +\infty} 0.013$

$\qquad = 0 + 0.013 = 0.013$ mg/ml

63. $\lim\limits_{x \to 0} f(x)$ does not exist because $f(x)$ oscillates infinitely many times between -1 and 1, regardless how close x gets to 0.

65. $\lim\limits_{x \to +\infty} = \dfrac{a_n x^n + a_{n-1} x^{n-1} + \cdots + a_1 x + a_0}{b_m x^m + b_{m-1} x^{m-1} + \cdots + b_1 x + b_0}$

(a) When $n < m$,

$= \lim\limits_{x \to +\infty} \dfrac{a_n + \frac{a_{n-1}}{x} + \cdots + \frac{a_1}{x^{n-1}} + \frac{a_0}{x^n}}{b_m \frac{x^m}{x^n} + b_{m-1} \frac{x^{m-1}}{x^n} + \cdots + b_1 \frac{x}{x^n} + b_0 \frac{1}{x^n}}$

Since

$$\lim\limits_{x \to +\infty} \dfrac{x^m}{x^n} = +\infty, \quad \lim\limits_{x \to +\infty} f(x) = 0$$

(b) When $n < m$,

$$\dfrac{x^m}{x^n} = 1 \text{ and } \lim\limits_{x \to +\infty} f(x) = \dfrac{a_n}{b_m}$$

(c) When $n > m$,

$$= \lim_{x \to +\infty} \frac{a_n \frac{x^n}{x^m} + a_{n-1}\frac{x^{n-1}}{x^m} + \cdots + a_1\frac{x}{x^m} + a_0\frac{1}{x^m}}{b_m + \frac{b_{m-1}}{x} + \cdots + \frac{b_1}{x^{m-1}} + \frac{b_0}{x^m}}$$

Now,

$$\lim_{x \to +\infty} a_n \frac{x^n}{x^m} + a_{n-1}\frac{x^{n-1}}{x^m} + \cdots + a_1\frac{x}{x^m} + a_0\frac{1}{x^m}$$
$$= \pm\infty,$$

depending on the sign of a_n. Also

$$\lim_{x \to +\infty} b_m + \frac{b_{m-1}}{x} + \cdots + \frac{b_1}{x^{m-1}} + \frac{b_0}{x^m} = b_m$$

So, $\lim_{x \to +\infty} \dfrac{a_n \frac{x^n}{x^m} + a_{n-1}\frac{x^{n-1}}{x^m} + \cdots}{b_m + \frac{b_{m-1}}{x} + \cdots} = \pm\infty$,

depending on the signs of a_n and b_m. When a_n and b_m have the same sign, the limit is $+\infty$; when they have opposite signs, the limit is $-\infty$.

1.6   One-Sided Limits and Continuity

1. $\lim_{x \to 2^-} f(x) = -2$; $\lim_{x \to 2^+} f(x) = 1$
Since $-2 \neq 1$, $\lim_{x \to 2} f(x)$ does not exist

3. $\lim_{x \to 2^-} f(x) = 2$; $\lim_{x \to 2^+} f(x) = 2$
Since limits are the same, $\lim_{x \to 2} f(x) = 2$.

5. $\lim_{x \to 4^+} (3x^2 - 9) = \lim_{x \to 4^+} 3x^2 - \lim_{x \to 4^+} 9$
$= 3(4)^2 - 9 = 39$

7. $\lim_{x \to 3^+} \sqrt{3x - 9} = \sqrt{3(3) - 9} = 0$

9.
$$\lim_{x \to 2^-} \frac{x+3}{x+2}$$
$$= \frac{\lim_{x \to 2^-}(x+3)}{\lim_{x \to 2^-}(x+2)} = \frac{2+3}{2+2}$$
$$= \frac{2+3}{2+2} = \frac{5}{4}$$

11. $\lim_{x \to 0^+} (x - \sqrt{x}) = 0 - 0 = 0$

13.
$$\lim_{x \to 3^+} \frac{\sqrt{x+1}-2}{x-3}$$
$$= \lim_{x \to 3^+} \frac{\sqrt{x+1}-2}{x-3} \cdot \frac{\sqrt{x+1}+2}{\sqrt{x+1}+2}$$
$$= \lim_{x \to 3^+} \frac{x+1-4}{(x-3)(\sqrt{x+1}+2)} = \frac{1}{4}.$$

15. $\lim_{x \to 3^-} f(x) = \lim_{x \to 3^-}(2x^2 - x) = 2(3)^2 - 3 = 15$
$\lim_{x \to 3^+} f(x) = \lim_{x \to 3^+}(3 - x) = 3 - 3 = 0.$

17. If $f(x) = 5x^2 - 6x + 1$, then $f(2) = 9$ and $\lim_{x \to 2} f(x) = 9$,
So, f is continuous at $x = 2$.

19. If $f(x) = \dfrac{x+2}{x+1}$,
then $f(1) = \dfrac{3}{2}$ and
$$\lim_{x \to 1} f(x) = \lim_{x \to 1} \frac{x+2}{x+1} = \frac{\lim_{x \to 1}(x+2)}{\lim_{x \to 1}(x+1)} = \frac{3}{2}$$
So, f is continuous at $x = 1$.

21. If $f(x) = \dfrac{x+1}{x-1}$,
$f(1)$ is undefined since the denominator is zero, and so f is not continuous at $x = 1$.

23. If $f(x) = \dfrac{\sqrt{x}-2}{x-4}$,
$f(4)$ is undefined since the denominator is zero, and so f is not continuous at $x = 4$.

25. If $f(x) = \begin{cases} x+1 & \text{if } x \leq 2 \\ 2 & \text{if } x > 2 \end{cases}$
then $f(2) = 3$ and $\lim_{x \to 2} f(x)$ must be determined.
As x approaches 2 from the left,
$$\lim_{x \to 2^-} f(x) = \lim_{x \to 2^-}(x+1) = 3$$
and as x approaches 2 from the right,
$$\lim_{x \to 2^+} f(x) = \lim_{x \to 2^+} 2 = 2$$

So the limit does not exist (since different limits are obtained from the left and the right), and f is not continuous at $x = 2$.

27. If $f(x) = \begin{cases} x^2 + 1 & \text{if } x \leq 3 \\ 2x + 4 & \text{if } x > 3 \end{cases}$

then $f(3) = (3)^2 + 1 = 10$ and $\lim\limits_{x \to 3} f(x)$ must be determined. As x approaches 3 from the left,

$$\lim\limits_{x \to 3^-} f(x) = \lim\limits_{x \to 3^-} (x^2 + 1) = (3)^2 + 1 = 10$$

and as x approaches 3 from the right,

$$\lim\limits_{x \to 3^+} f(x) = \lim\limits_{x \to 3^+} (2x + 4) = 2(3) + 4 = 10$$

So $\lim\limits_{x \to 3} f(x) = 10$. Since $f(x) = \lim\limits_{x \to 3} f(x)$, f is continuous at $x = 3$.

29. $f(a) = 3a^2 - 6a + 9$ so f is defined for all real numbers. $\lim\limits_{x \to a} f(a) = 3(a)^2 - 6a + 9$, so the limit of f exists for all real numbers. Since $f(a) = \lim\limits_{x \to a} f(a)$, there are no values for which f is not continous.

31. $f(x) = \dfrac{x + 1}{x - 2}$

is not defined at $x = 2$, so f is *not* continuous at $x = 2$.

33. $f(x) = \dfrac{3x + 3}{x + 1}$

is not defined at $x = -1$, so f is *not* continuous at $x = -1$.

35. $f(x) = \dfrac{3x - 2}{(x + 3)(x - 6)}$

is not defined at $x = -3$ and $x = 6$, so f is *not* continuous at $x = -3$ and $x = 6$.

37. $f(x) = \dfrac{x}{x^2 - x}$

is not defined at $x = 0$ and $x = 1$, so f is *not* continuous at $x = 0$ and $x = 1$.

39. f is defined for all real numbers. Further,

$$\lim\limits_{x \to 1^-} f(x) = 2 + 3 = 5$$
$$= \lim\limits_{x \to 1^+} f(x) = 6 - 1$$
$$= f(1),$$

so there are no values for which f is not continuous.

41. f is defined for all real numbers. However,

$$\lim\limits_{x \to 0^-} f(x) = \lim\limits_{x \to 0^-} 3x - 2 = 3(0) - 2 = -2$$
$$\lim\limits_{x \to 0^+} f(x) = \lim\limits_{x \to 0^+} x^2 + x = 0 + 0 = 0$$

So $\lim\limits_{x \to 0} f(x)$ does not exist and therefore f is *not* continuous at $x = 0$.

43. (a) When $v = 20$, the middle expression is used to find $W(v)$.

$$W(20) = 1.25(20) - 18.67\sqrt{20} + 62.3$$
$$\approx 3.75°\text{F}$$

For $v = 50$, the bottom expression is used to find $W(v)$, so $W(50) = -7°\text{F}$.

(b) If $0 \leq v \leq 4$, $W(v) = 30°\text{F}$, so v cannot be between 0 and 4 (inclusive). If $v \geq 45$, $W(v) = -7$, so v cannot be 45 or more. If $4 < v < 45$,

$$W(v) = 1.25v - 18.67\sqrt{v} + 62.3$$

If $W(v) = 0$, then

$$0 = 1.25v - 18.67\sqrt{v} + 62.3$$

Using the quadratic formula, $v = 25$ mph.

(c) When rounded to the nearest degree, for practical purposes,

$$\lim\limits_{v \to 4^-} W(v) = \lim\limits_{v \to 4^-} 30 = 30$$
$$\lim\limits_{v \to 4^+} W(v) = \lim\limits_{v \to 4^+} (1.25v - 18.67\sqrt{v} + 62.3)$$
$$= 1.25(4) - 18.67\sqrt{4} + 62.3 = 30$$

So, W is continuous at $v = 4$. Similarly for $v = 45$,

$$\lim\limits_{v \to 45^-} W(v) = \lim\limits_{v \to 45^-} (1.25v - 18.67\sqrt{v} + 62.3)$$
$$= 1.25(45) - 18.67\sqrt{45} + 62.3$$
$$\approx -7$$
$$= \lim\limits_{v \to 45^+} W(v) = \lim\limits_{v \to 45^+} -7 = -7$$

So, W is continuous at $v = 45$.

45. The graph of p will consist of line segments, with the left endpoints open and the right endpoints closed (from the inequalities).

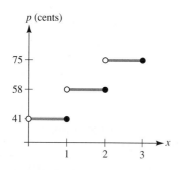

p (cents)

The function p is discontinuous at the segment endpoints, where the price jumps. That is, for $x = 1$ and 2.

47. The graph is discontinuous at $x = 10$ and $x = 25$. Sue is probably at the gas station replenishing fuel.

49. $C(x) = \dfrac{12x}{100 - x}$

(a) $C(25) = \dfrac{12(25)}{100 - 25} = 4$
   or, \$4,000
   $C(50) = \dfrac{12(50)}{100 - 50} = 12$
   or, \$12,000

(b)

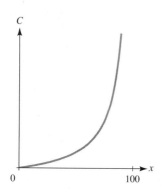

C

0   100

(c) From the graph,

$$\lim_{x \to 100^-} C(x) = \infty$$

So, it is not possible to remove all of the pollution.

51. $C(x) = \dfrac{8x^2 - 636x - 320}{x^2 - 68x - 960}$

(a) $C(0) = \dfrac{-320}{-960} = \dfrac{1}{3} \approx 0.333$

$C(100) = \dfrac{8(100)^2 - 636(100) - 320}{(100)^2 - 68(100) - 960} \approx 7.179$

(b) Since the denominator factors as $(x + 12)(x - 80)$, the function has a vertical asymptote when $x = 80$. This means that C is not continuous on the interval $0 \le x \le 100$, and the intermediate value theorem cannot be used.

53. $f(x) = \begin{cases} Ax - 3 & \text{if } x < 2 \\ 3 - x + 2x^2 & \text{if } 2 \le x \end{cases}$
f is continuous everywhere except possibly at $x = 2$, since $Ax - 3$ and $3 - x + 2x^2$ are polynomials. Since $f(2) = 3 - 2 + 2(2)^2 = 9$, in order that f be continuous at $x = 2$, A must be chosen so that $\lim\limits_{x \to 2} f(x) = 9$.
As x approaches 2 from the right,

$$\lim_{x \to 2^+} f(x) = \lim_{x \to 2^+} (3 - x + 2x^2)$$

$$= \lim_{x \to 2^+} 3 - \lim_{x \to 2^+} x + 2 \lim_{x \to 2^+} x^2$$

$$= 3 - 2 + 2(2)^2 = 9$$

and as x approaches from the left,

$$\lim_{x \to 2^-} f(x) = \lim_{x \to 2^-} (Ax - 3)$$

$$= A \lim_{x \to 2^-} x - \lim_{x \to 2^-} 3$$

$$= 2A - 3$$

For $\lim\limits_{x \to 2} f(x) = 9$, $2A - 3$ must equal 9, or $A = 6$. f is continuous at $x = 2$ only when $A = 6$.

55. On the open interval $0 < x < 1$, since $x \ne 0$,

$$f(x) = x \left(1 + \frac{1}{x}\right) = x + 1$$

So, $f(x)$, a polynomial on $0 < x < 1$, is continuous. On the closed interval $0 \le x \le 1$, the endpoints must now be considered.

$$f(x) = x\left(x + \frac{1}{x}\right)$$

is not continuous at $x = 0$ since $f(0)$ is not defined. However, f is continuous at $x = 1$ since

$$f(1) = 1\left(1 + \frac{1}{1}\right) = 2$$ and as x approaches 1 from the left,

$$\lim_{x \to 1^-} x\left(x + \frac{1}{x}\right) = \lim_{x \to 1^-} x \cdot \lim_{x \to 1^-}\left(x + \frac{1}{x}\right)$$

$$= 1\left(1 + \frac{1}{1}\right) = 2$$

57. Rewrite as $\sqrt[3]{x - 8} + 9x^{2/3} - 29$ and notice that at $x = 0$ this expression is negative and at $x = 8$ it is positive. Therefore, by the intermediate value property, there must be a value of x between 0 and 8 such that this expression is 0 or

$$\sqrt[3]{x - 8} + 9x^{2/3} = 29$$

59. To investigate the behavior of

$$f(x) = \frac{2x^2 - 5x + 2}{x^2 - 4},$$

Press $\boxed{y=}$.
Input $(2x \wedge 2 - 5x + 2)/(x \wedge 2 - 4)$ for $y_1 =$
Press $\boxed{\text{graph}}$.

(a) Press $\boxed{\text{trace}}$. Use arrows to move cursor to be near $x = 2$ we see that (1.9, 0.72) and (2.1, 0.79) are two points on the graph. By zooming in, we find (1.97, 0.74) and (2.02, 0.76) to be two points on the graph. The $\lim_{x \to 2} f(x) = \frac{3}{4}$, however, the function is not continuous at $x = 2$ since $f(2)$ is undefined. To show this, use the value function under the calc menu and enter $x = 2$. There is no y-value displayed, which indicates the function is undefined for $x = 2$.

(b) Use the z standard function under the Zoom menu to return to the original graph. We see from the graph that there is a vertical asymptote at $x = -2$. The $\lim_{x \to -2^-} f(x) = \infty$ and $\lim_{x \to -2^+} f(x) = -\infty$

and therefore $\lim_{x \to -2} f(x)$ does not exist. So f is not continuous at $x = -2$.

61. Let's assume the hands of a clock move in a continuous fashion. During each hour the minute hand moves from being behind the hour to being ahead of the hour. Therefore, at some time, the hands must be in the same place.

Checkup for Chapter 1

1. Since negative numbers do not have square roots and denominators cannot be zero, the domain of the function $f(x) = \frac{2x - 1}{\sqrt{4 - x^2}}$ is all real numbers such that $4 - x^2 > 0$ or $(2 + x)(2 - x) > 0$, namely $-2 < x < 2$.

2. $g(h(x)) = g\left(\frac{x + 2}{2x + 1}\right) = \frac{1}{2\left(\frac{x+2}{2x+1}\right) + 1} = \frac{1}{\frac{2x+4}{2x+1} + 1}$

$$= \frac{1}{\frac{2x+4+2x+1}{2x+1}} = \frac{2x + 1}{4x + 5}, \quad x \neq -\frac{1}{2}$$

3. **(a)** Since $m = -\frac{1}{2}$ and the point $((1,2)$ is on the line, the equation of the line is

$$y - 2 = -\frac{1}{2}(x - (-1))$$

$$y - 2 = -\frac{1}{2}(x + 1)$$

$$y - 2 = -\frac{1}{2}x - \frac{1}{2}$$

$$y = -\frac{1}{2}x - \frac{1}{2} + 2$$

$$y = -\frac{1}{2}x + \frac{3}{2}$$

(b) Since $m = 2$ and $b = -3$, the equation of the line is $y = 2x - 3$.

4. **(a)** The graph is a line with x-intercept $\frac{5}{3}$ and y-intercept -5.

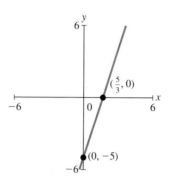

(b) The graph is a parabola which opens down (since $A < 0$). The vertex is

$$\left(-\frac{b}{2a},\ f\left(-\frac{b}{2a}\right)\right),\ \text{or}\ \left(\frac{3}{2},\frac{25}{4}\right).$$

The x-intercepts are

$$0 = -x^2 + 3x + 4$$
$$0 = x^2 - 3x - 4$$
$$0 = (x-4)(x+1)$$
$$x = 4, -1$$

The y-intercept is 4.

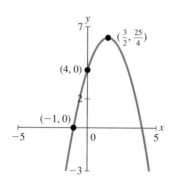

5. (a)
$$\lim_{x\to -1}\frac{x^2 + 2x - 3}{x - 1} = \frac{(-1)^2 + 2(-1) - 3}{-1 - 1}$$
$$= \frac{1 - 2 - 3}{-2} = 2$$

(b)
$$\lim_{x\to 1}\frac{x^2 + 2x - 3}{x - 1} = \lim_{x\to 1}\frac{(x + 3)(x - 1)}{1 - 2}$$
$$= \lim_{x\to 1} x + 3 = 4$$

(c) $\displaystyle \lim_{x\to 1}\frac{x^2 - x - 1}{x - 2} = \frac{(1)^2 - 1 - 1}{x - 1} = \frac{-1}{-1} = 1$

(d) $\displaystyle \lim_{x\to +\infty}\frac{2x^3 + 3x - 5}{-x^2 + 2x + 7} = \lim_{x\to +\infty}\frac{2x + 3 - \dfrac{5}{x^2}}{-1 + \dfrac{2}{x} + \dfrac{7}{x^2}}$

Since $\displaystyle \lim_{x\to +\infty} 2x + 3 - \frac{5}{x^2} = +\infty$ and

$$\lim_{x\to +\infty} -1 + \frac{2}{x} + \frac{7}{x^2} = -1,$$
$$\lim_{x\to +\infty}\frac{2x^3 + 3x - 5}{-x^2 + 2x + 7} = -\infty.$$

6. The function is defined at $x = 1$, and $f(1) = 2(1) + 1 = 3$. If $\displaystyle \lim_{x\to 1} f(x) = 3$, the function will be continuous at $x = 1$. From the left of $x = 1$,

$$\lim_{x\to 1^-} f(x) = \lim_{x\to 1^-} 2x + 1 = 2(1) + 1 = 3.$$

From the right of $x = 1$,

$$\lim_{x\to 1^+} f(x) = \lim_{x\to 1^+}\frac{x^2 + 2x - 3}{x - 1}$$
$$= \lim_{x\to 1^+}\frac{(x + 3)(x - 1)}{x - 1} = \lim_{x\to 1^+} (x + 3)$$
$$= 1 + 3 = 4.$$

Since $\displaystyle \lim_{x\to 1^-} f(x) \neq \lim_{x\to 1^+} f(x)$, the limit does not exist and the function is not continuous at $x = 1$.

7. (a) Let t denote the time in months since the beginning of the year and $P(t)$ the corresponding price (in cents) of gasoline. Since the price increases at a constant rate of 2 cents per gallon per month, P is a linear function of t with slope $m = 2$. Since the price on June first (when $t = 5$) is 380 cents, the graph passes through $(5, 380)$. The equation is therefore

$$P - 380 = 2(t - 5)$$

or $P(t) = 2t + 370$ cents,
$P(t) = 0.02t + 3.70$ dollars.

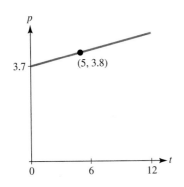

(b) When $t = 0$, $P(0) = 0.02(0) + 3.70 = 3.70$
The price was \$3.70.

(c) On October 1st, $t = 9$ and $P(9) = 0.02(9) +$
$3.70 = 3.88$
The price will be \$3.88

8. Let t be the time, in hours, that has passed since
the truck was 300 miles due east of the car. The
distance the truck is from the car's original location
is $300 - 30t$. The car's distance from its original
location is $60t$ (due north). These two distances
form theh legs of a right triangle, where the distance
between the car and the truck is its hypotenuse. So,

$$D(t) = \sqrt{(60t)^2 + (300 - 30t)^2}$$
$$= 30\sqrt{5t^2 - 20t + 100}$$

9. $S(x) = x^2 + A$; $D(x) = Bx + 59$

(a) Since no units are supplied until the selling price
is greater than \$3 (assuming continuity),

$$3 = 0 + A, \text{ or } A = 3.$$

Equilibrium occurs when

$$S(7) = D(7)$$
$$(7)^2 + 3 = B(7) + 59$$
$$-1 = B$$

The equilibrium price is

$$S(7) = (7)^2 + 3 = \$52$$

(b)

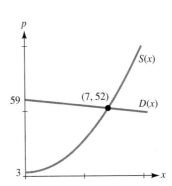

(c) When 5 units are produced the supply price
is $S(5) = (5)^2 + 3 = \$28$ and the demand
price is $D(5) = -(5) + 59 = \$54$. When
10 units are produced, the supply price is
$S(10) = (10)^2 + 3 = \$103$, and the demand
price is $D(10) = -(10) + 59 = \$49$. The
difference is $\$103 - \$49 = \$54$. (Note that for 5
units, the demand price is higher than the supply
price. However, for 10 units, the opposite is
true.)

10. **(a)** The population is positive and increasing for
$0 \le t < 5$. However, for $t \ge 5$, the population
decreases. Therefore, the colony dies out when

$$-8t + 72 = 0, \quad \text{or } t = 9$$

(b) $f(1) = 8$ and $f(7) = -56 + 72 = 16$. Since

$$f(5) = \lim_{x \to 5} f(x) = 32,$$

f is continuous. Since $8 < 10 < 16$, by the
intermediate value property there exists a value
$1 < c < 7$ such that $f(c) = 10$.

11. Since M is a linear function of D, $M = aD + b$,
for some constants a and b. Using $M = 7.7$ when
$D = 3$, and $M = 12.7$ when $D = 5$, solve the system

$$a \cdot 3 + b = 7.7$$
$$a \cdot 5 + b = 12.7$$

So, $a = 2.5$ and $b = 0.2$. Thus, $M = 2.5D + 0.2$
When $D = 0$, $M = 0.2$, so 0.2% will mutate when
no radiation is used.

Review Problems

1. **(a)** The domain of the quadratic function

$$f(x) = x^2 - 2x + 6$$

is all real numbers x.

(b) Since denominators cannot be zero, the domain of the rational function

$$f(x) = \frac{x-3}{x^2 + x - 2} = \frac{x-3}{(x+2)(x-1)}$$

is all real numbers x except $x = -2$ and $x = 1$.

(c) Since negative numbers do not have square roots, the domain of the function

$$f(x) = \sqrt{x^2 - 9} = \sqrt{(x+3)(x-3)}$$

is all real numbers x such that $(x+3)(x-3) \geq 0$, that is for $x \leq -3$, or $x \geq 3$, or $|x| \geq 3$.

3. **(a)** If $g(u) = u^2 + 2u + 1$ and $h(x) = 1 - x$

then $g(h(x)) = g(1 - x)$

$$= (1-x)^2 + 2(1-x) + 1$$
$$= x^2 - 4x + 4.$$

(b) If $g(u) = \dfrac{1}{2u+1}$ and $h(x) = x + 2$,

then $g(h(u)) = g(x + 2)$

$$= \frac{1}{2(x+2)+1} = \frac{1}{2x+5}.$$

5. **(a)** $f(3-x) = 4 - (3-x) - (3-x)^2$

$$= 4 - 3 + x - (9 - 6x + x^2)$$
$$= 1 + x - 9 + 6x - x^2$$
$$= -x^2 + 7x - 8$$

(b) $f(x^2 - 3) = (x^2 - 3) - 1$

$$= x^2 - 4$$

(c) $f(x+1) - f(x)$

$$= \frac{1}{(x+1)-1} - \frac{1}{x-1}$$

$$= \frac{1}{x} - \frac{1}{x-1}$$

$$= \frac{1}{x} \cdot \frac{x-1}{x-1} - \frac{1}{x-1} \cdot \frac{x}{x}$$

$$= \frac{x-1}{x(x-1)} - \frac{x}{x(x-1)}$$

$$= \frac{x-1-x}{x(x-1)} = -\frac{1}{x(x-1)}$$

7. **(a)** One of many possible solutions is

$$g(u) = u^5 \quad \text{and} \quad h(x) = x^2 + 3x + 4.$$

Then,

$$g(h(x)) = g(x^2 + 3x + 4)$$
$$= (x^2 + 3x + 4)^5 = f(x).$$

(b) One of many possible solutions is

$$g(u) = u^2 + \frac{5}{2(u+1)^3} \text{ and } h(x) = 3x + 1.$$

Then,

$$g(h(x)) = g(3x + 1) = (3x + 1)^2 + \frac{5}{2((3x+1)+1)^3}$$

$$= (3x + 1)^2 + \frac{5}{2(3x+2)^3} = f(x).$$

9. $f(x) = x^2 + 2x - 8 = (x+4)(x-2)$

The intercepts of the function are $(-4, 0)$, $(2, 0)$ and $(0, -8)$. Further, the vertex of the parabola is

$$x = -\frac{B}{2A}, \quad y = f\left(-\frac{B}{2A}\right)$$

$$x = -\frac{2}{2(1)} = -1$$

$$y = f(-1) = (-1)^2 + 2(-1) - 8$$
$$= 1 - 2 - 8 = -9$$

So, the vertex is $(-1, -9)$.

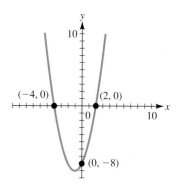

11. (a) If $y = 3x + 2$, $m = 3$ and $b = 2$.

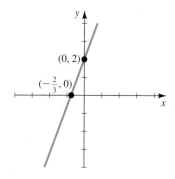

(b) If $5x - 4y = 20$ then

$$y = \frac{5}{4}x - 5$$

and $m = \frac{5}{4}$, $b = -5$.

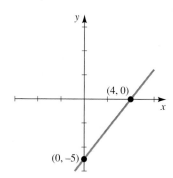

13. (a) $m = 5$ and y-intercept $b = -4$, so $y = 5x - 4$

(b) $m = -2$ and $P(1, 3)$, so
$y - 3 = -2(x - 1)$, or

$y = -2x + 5$

(c) $2x + y = 3 \rightarrow y = -2x + 3$,
so $m = -2$ and $P(5, 4)$
$y - 4 = -2(x - 5)$, or
$y = -2x + 14 \rightarrow 2x + y = 14$

15. (a) The graphs of

$$y = -3x + 5 \quad \text{and} \quad y = 2x - 10$$

intersect when

$$-3x + 5 = 2x - 10, \quad \text{or} \quad x = 3.$$

When $x = 3$, $y = -3(3) + 5 = -4$. So the point of intersection is $(3, -4)$.

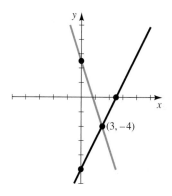

(b) The graphs of

$$y = x + 7 \quad \text{and} \quad y = -2 + x$$

are lines having the same slope, so they are parallel lines and there are no points of intersection.

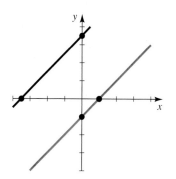

17. If the graph of

$$y = 3x^2 - 2x + c$$

passes through the point (2, 4),

$$4 = 3(2)^2 - 2(2) + c \quad \text{or} \quad c = -4$$

19.
$$\lim_{x \to 1} \frac{x^2 + x - 2}{x^2 - 1}$$

$$= \lim_{x \to 1} \frac{(x + 2)(x - 1)}{(x + 1)(x - 1)} = \lim_{x \to 1} \frac{x + 2}{x + 1}$$

$$= \frac{\lim_{x \to 1}(x + 2)}{\lim_{x \to 1}(x + 1)} = \frac{1 + 2}{1 + 1} = \frac{3}{2}$$

21. $\lim_{x \to 2} \dfrac{x^3 - 8}{2 - x} = \lim_{x \to 2} \dfrac{(x - 2)(x^2 + 2x + 4)}{-(x - 2)}$

$$= \lim_{x \to 2} -(x^2 + 2x + 4) = -(2^2 + 2(2) + 4) = -12.$$

23.
$$\lim_{x \to 0} \left(2 - \frac{1}{x^3}\right) = \lim_{x \to 0} 2 - \lim_{x \to 0} \frac{1}{x^3}$$

Now, $\lim_{x \to 0} 2 = 2$; but $\lim_{x \to 0^+} \dfrac{1}{x^3} = +\infty$ and $\lim_{x \to 0^-} \dfrac{1}{x^3} = -\infty$. Since $\lim_{x \to 0} \dfrac{1}{x^3}$ does not exist, $\lim_{x \to 0} \left(x^3 - \dfrac{1}{x^3}\right)$ does not exist.

25.
$$\lim_{x \to -\infty} \frac{x}{x^2 + 5} = \lim_{x \to -\infty} \frac{\frac{1}{x}}{1 + \frac{5}{x^2}} = 0$$

27.
$$\lim_{x \to -\infty} \frac{x^4 + 3x^2 - 2x + 7}{x^3 + x + 1} = \lim_{x \to -\infty} \frac{x + \frac{3}{x} - \frac{2}{x^2} + \frac{7}{x^3}}{1 + \frac{1}{x^2} + \frac{1}{x^3}}$$

Since

$$\lim_{x \to -\infty} \left(x + \frac{3}{x} - \frac{2}{x^2} + \frac{7}{x^3}\right) = -\infty$$

and

$$\lim_{x \to -\infty} \left(1 + \frac{1}{x^2} + \frac{1}{x^3}\right) = 1,$$

then

$$\lim_{x \to -\infty} \frac{x^4 + 3x^2 - 2x + 7}{x^3 + x + 1} = -\infty$$

29. Since $\lim_{x \to -\infty} \left(1 + \dfrac{1}{x} + \dfrac{1}{x^2}\right) = 1$ and

$$\lim_{x \to -\infty} (x^3 + x + 1) = -\infty,$$

$$\lim_{x \to -\infty} \frac{1 + \frac{1}{x} + \frac{1}{x^2}}{x^3 + x + 1} = 0$$

31.
$$\lim_{x \to 0^-} x\sqrt{1 - \frac{1}{x}} = \left(\lim_{x \to 0^-} x\right)\left(\lim_{x \to 0^-} \sqrt{1 - \frac{1}{x}}\right)$$

Since $\lim_{x \to 0^-} x = 0$, and $\lim_{x \to 0^-} \left(1 - \dfrac{1}{x}\right) = \infty$ implies

$$\lim_{x \to 0^-} \sqrt{1 - \frac{1}{x}} = \infty, \quad \text{then } \lim_{x \to 0^-} x\sqrt{1 - \frac{1}{x}} = 0.$$

33. $f(x) = \dfrac{x^2 - 1}{x + 3}$

is not continuous at $x = -3$

since $f(-3) = \dfrac{10}{0}$ and division by 0 is undefined.

35.
$$h(x) = \begin{cases} x^3 + 2x - 33 & \text{if } x \le 3 \\ \dfrac{x^2 - 6x + 9}{x - 3} & \text{if } x > 3 \end{cases}$$

The denominator in $\dfrac{x^2 - 6x + 9}{x - 3}$ will never be zero, since $x = 3$ is not included in its domain. However, in checking the break point (the only point in question),

$$h(3) = (3)^3 + 2(3) - 33 = 0$$

Further, $\lim_{x \to 3^-} h(x) = \lim_{x \to 3^-} (x^3 + 2x - 33) = 0$ and

$$\lim_{x \to 3^+} h(x) = \lim_{x \to 3^+} \frac{x^2 - 6x + 9}{x - 3} = \lim_{x \to 3^+} \frac{(x - 3)(x - 3)}{x - 3}$$

$$= \lim_{x \to 3^+} (x - 3) = 3 - 3 = 0.$$

Since $h(3) = \lim_{x \to 3} h(x)$, h is continuous for all x.

37. $P(x) = 40 + \dfrac{30}{x+1}$

(a) $P(5) = 40 + \dfrac{30}{5+1}$
$$= 40 + 5 = \$45$$

(b) need $P(5) - P(4)$

$$P(4) = 40 + \frac{30}{4+1}$$
$$= 40 + 6 = \$46$$
$$P(5) - P(4) = 45 - 46 = -1$$

Price drops one dollar during the 5th month.

(c) Find x so that $P(x) = 43$

$$40 + \frac{30}{x+1} = 43$$
$$\frac{30}{x+1} = \frac{3}{1}$$
$$3(x+1) = 30$$
$$3x + 3 = 30$$
$$3x = 27$$
$$x = 9$$

The price will be \$43 nine months from now.

(d)
$$\lim_{x \to +\infty} P(x) = \lim_{x \to +\infty} 40 + \frac{30}{x+1}$$
$$= \lim_{x \to +\infty} 40 + \lim_{x \to +\infty} \frac{30}{x+1}$$
$$= 40 + 0 = 40$$

In the long run, the price will approach \$40.

39. The number of weeks needed to reach x percent of the fund raising goal is given by

$$f(x) = \frac{10x}{150 - x}$$

(a) Since x denotes a percentage, the function has a practical interpretation for

$$0 \le x \le 100$$

The corresponding portion of the graph is sketched.

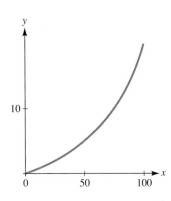

(b) The number of weeks needed to reach 50% of the goal is

$$f(50) = \frac{10(50)}{150 - 50} = 5 \text{weeks}$$

(c) The number of weeks needed to reach 100% of the goal is

$$f(100) = \frac{10(100)}{150 - 100} = 20 \text{weeks}$$

41.
$$S = 4\pi r^2, \text{ or } r = \sqrt{\frac{S}{4\pi}} = \left(\frac{S}{4\pi}\right)^{1/2}$$

$$V(S) = \frac{4}{3}\pi\left(\left(\frac{S}{4\pi}\right)^{1/2}\right)^3 = \frac{4}{3}\pi\left(\frac{S}{4\pi}\right)^{3/2}$$

$$V(S) = \frac{4}{3}\pi\frac{S^{3/2}}{4^{3/2}\pi^{3/2}} = \frac{4}{3}\pi\frac{S^{3/2}}{8\pi^{3/2}} = \frac{S^{3/2}}{6\pi^{1/2}} = \frac{S^{3/2}}{6\sqrt{\pi}}$$

$$V(2S) = \frac{(2S)^{3/2}}{6\sqrt{\pi}} = \frac{2^{3/2}S^{3/2}}{6\sqrt{\pi}},$$

so volume increased by a factor of $2^{3/2}$, or $2\sqrt{2}$, when S is doubled.

43. Let x denote the number of machines used and $C(x)$ the corresponding cost function. Then,

$$C(x) = (\text{set up cost}) + (\text{operating cost})$$
$$= 80(\text{number of machines})$$
$$+ 5.76(\text{ number of hours}).$$

Since 400,000 medals are to be produced and each of the x machines can produce 200 medals per hour,

$$\text{number of hours} = \frac{400{,}000}{200x} = \frac{2{,}000}{x}$$

So,

$$C(x) = 80x + 5.76 \left(\frac{2{,}000}{x} \right)$$

$$= 80x + \frac{11{,}520}{x}.$$

The graph suggests that the cost will be smallest when x is approximately 12.
Note: In chapter 3 you will learn how to use calculus to find the optimal number of machines exactly.

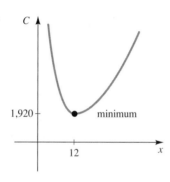

45. If p represents the selling price, the monthly profit is
$P(p) =$(number of cameras sold) (price $-$ cost)
Since $\dfrac{340 - P}{5}$ represents the number of \$5 decreases,

$$40 + 10 \left(\frac{340 - p}{5} \right) =$$

represents the number of cameras that will sell. So,

$$P(p) = (720 - 2p)(p - 150)$$

$$= 2(360 - p)(p - 150)$$

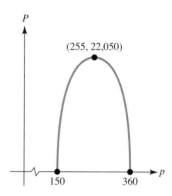

The graph suggests a maximum profit when $p = 255$, that is when the selling price is \$255.

47. Taxes under Proposition A are $100 + .08a$, where a is the assessed value of the home. Taxes under Proposition B are $1{,}900 + .02a$. Taxes are the same when

$$100 + .08a = 1{,}900 + .02a$$

$$.06a = 1{,}800$$

$$a = 30{,}000$$

or for an assessed value of \$30,000.
Since both tax functions are linear, it is only necessary to test one additional assessed value to determine which proposition is best for all assessed values. For $a = 20{,}000$

$$100 + .08(20{,}000) = \$1{,}700$$

$$1{,}900 + .02(20{,}000) = \$2{,}300$$

So, for $0 < a < 30{,}000$, Proposition A is preferable while for $a > 30{,}000$, Proposition B is preferable.

49. (a) Let x denote the number of units manufactured and sold. $C(x)$ and $R(x)$ are the corresponding cost and revenue functions, respectively.

$$C(x) = 4{,}500 + 50x$$

$$R(x) = 80x$$

For the manufacturer to break even, since profit $=$ revenue $-$ cost, $0 =$ revenue $-$ cost, or revenue $=$ cost. That is.

$$4{,}500 + 50x = 80x \quad \text{or} \quad x = 150 \text{ units}$$

(b) Let $P(x)$ denote the profit from the manufacture and sale of x units. Then,

$$P(x) = R(x) - C(x)$$
$$= 80x - (4{,}500 + 50x)$$
$$= 30x - 4{,}500.$$

When 200 units are sold, the profit is

$$P(200) = 30(200) - 4{,}500 = \$1{,}500$$

(c) The profit will be $900 when

$$900 = 30x - 4{,}500 \quad \text{or} \quad x = 180$$

that is, when 180 units are manufactured and sold.

51. Let x denote the number of relevant facts recalled, n the total number of relevant facts in the person's memory, and $R(x)$ the rate of recall.
Then $n - x$ is the number of relevant facts not recalled.
So, $R(x) = k(n - x)$
where k is a constant of proportionality.

53. The cost for the clear glass is
(area) (cost per sq ft) $= (2xy)(3)$, and similarly, the cost for the stained glass is

$$\left(\frac{1}{2}\pi x^2\right)(10)$$

So, $C = 6xy + 5\pi x^2$.
Now, the perimeter is $\dfrac{1}{2}(2\pi x) + 2x + 2y = 20$
so, $\quad \pi x + 2x + 2y = 20,$
or $\quad y = \dfrac{20 - \pi x - 2x}{2}$
Cost as a function of x is

$$C(x) = 6x\left(\frac{20 - \pi x - 2x}{2}\right) + 5\pi x^2$$
$$= 3x(20 - \pi x - 2x) + 5\pi x^2$$
$$= 60x - 3\pi x^2 - 6x^2 + 5\pi x^2$$
$$= 60x - 6x^2 + 2\pi x^2$$

55. The fixed cost is $1,500 and the cost per unit is $2, so the cost is $C(x) = 1{,}500 + 2x$, for $0 \le x \le 5{,}000$. As to the question of continuity, the answer is both

yes and no. Yes, if (as we normally do) x is any real number. No, if x is discrete ($x = 0, 1, 2, \ldots, 5{,}000$).

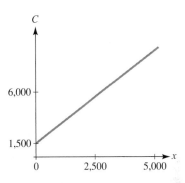

57.
$$w(x) = \begin{cases} Ax & \text{if} \quad x \le 4{,}000 \\ \dfrac{B}{x^2} & \text{if} \quad x > 4{,}000 \end{cases}$$

For continuity,

$$4{,}000A = \frac{B}{(4{,}000)^2}$$

or $\quad B = A(4{,}000)^3$

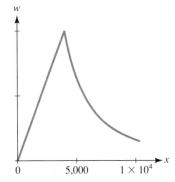

59. This limit does exist. The curve is bounded by the lines $y = mx$ and $y = -mx$. Since $-m|x| \le g(x) \le m|x|$, as x approaches 0, the bounding values on the right and the left of the inequality also approach 0. The function in the middle $g(x)$, is squeezed or sandwiched between 0 and 0. Its limit has to be 0.
Note: $\lim\limits_{x \to 0^-} |x|\sin(1/x) = \lim\limits_{x \to 0^+} |x|\sin(1/x) = 0$ since $-1 \le \sin x \le 1$.

61. To graph $y = \dfrac{21}{9}x - \dfrac{84}{35}$ and $y = \dfrac{654}{279}x - \dfrac{54}{10}$, press
$\boxed{y=}$.
Input $(21x)/9 - 84/35$ for $y_1 =$ and press $\boxed{\text{enter}}$.
Input $(654x)/279 - 54/10$ for $y_2 =$.
Use the z-standard function under the zoom menu to
use the window dimensions given.
Press $\boxed{\text{graph}}$.
It appears from the graph that the two lines are
parallel. However, the difference in the slopes is
$\dfrac{21}{9} - \dfrac{654}{279} = -.01$ which shows that, in fact, the
lines are not parallel since they have different slopes.

63. Press $\boxed{y=}$.
Input $(x \wedge 2 + 1)/(x \leq 1)$ for $y_1 =$ and press $\boxed{\text{enter}}$.
(You can obtain the $\leq$ from $\boxed{\text{2ND}}$ $\boxed{\text{test}}$ and enter 6:
$\leq$).
Input $(x \wedge 2 - 1)/(x > 1)$ for $y_2 =$ and press $\boxed{\text{enter}}$.
(You can obtain the $>$ from $\boxed{\text{2ND}}$ $\boxed{\text{test}}$ and enter 3:
$>$). Press $\boxed{\text{graph}}$.
The graph of y is discontinuous $x = 1$.

Chapter 2

Differentiation: Basic Concepts

2.1 The Derivative

1. If $f(x) = 4$, then

$$f(x + h) = 4$$

The difference quotient (DQ) is

$$\frac{f(x + h) - f(x)}{h}$$

$$= \frac{4 - 4}{h} = 0$$

$$f'(x) = \lim_{h \to 0} \frac{f(x + h) - f(x)}{h} = 0$$

The slope is $m = f'(0) = 0$.

3. If $f(x) = 5x - 3$, then

$$f(x + h) = 5(x + h) - 3$$

The difference quotient (DQ) is

$$\frac{f(x + h) - f(x)}{h}$$

$$= \frac{[5(x + h) - 3] - [5x - 3]}{h} = \frac{5h}{h} = 5$$

$$f'(x) = \lim_{h \to 0} \frac{f(x + h) - f(x)}{h} = 5$$

The slope is $m = f'(2) = 5$.

5. If $f(x) = 2x^2 - 3x + 5$, then

$$f(x + h) = 2(x + h)^2 - 3(x + h) + 5$$

The difference quotient (DQ) is

$$\frac{f(x + h) - f(x)}{h}$$

$$\frac{[2(x + h)^2 - 3(x + h) + 5]}{h} - \frac{[2x^2 - 3x + 5]}{h}$$

$$= \frac{4xh + 2(h)^2 - 3h}{h} = 4x + 2h - 3$$

$$f'(x) = \lim_{h \to 0} \frac{f(x + h) - f(x)}{h} = 4x - 3$$

The slope is

$$m = f'(0) = -3$$

7. If $f(x) = x^3 - 1$, then

$$f(x + h) = (x + h)^3 - 1$$

$$= (x^2 + 2xh + h^2)(x + h) - 1$$

$$= x^3 + 3x^2h + 3xh^2 + h^3 - 1$$

The difference quotient (DQ) is

$$\frac{f(x + h) - f(x)}{h}$$

$$= \frac{x^3 + 3x^2h + 3xh^2 + h^3 - 1 - (x^3 - 1)}{h}$$

$$= \frac{3x^2h + 3xh^2 + h^3}{h} = \frac{h(3x^2 + 3xh + h^2)}{h}$$

$$= 3x^2 + 3xh + h^2$$

$$f'(x) = \lim_{h \to 0} \frac{f(x + h) - f(x)}{h}$$

$$= \lim_{h \to 0} 3x^2 + 3xh + h^2 = 3x^2$$

The slope is $m = f'(2) = 3(2)^2 = 12$.

43

9. If $g(t) = \dfrac{2}{t}$, then

$$g(t + h) = \frac{2}{t + h}$$

The difference quotient (DQ) is

$$\frac{g(t + h) - g(t)}{h}$$

$$= \frac{\dfrac{2}{t+h} - \dfrac{2}{t}}{h}$$

$$= \frac{\dfrac{2}{t+h}}{h} \cdot \frac{t(t+h)}{t(t+h)}$$

$$= \frac{2t - 2(t+h)}{h(t)(t+h)} = \frac{-2}{t(t+h)}$$

$$g'(t) = \lim_{h \to 0} \frac{g(t+h) - g(t)}{h} = -\frac{2}{t^2}$$

The slope is $m = g'\left(\dfrac{1}{2}\right) = -8$.

11. If $H(u) = \dfrac{1}{\sqrt{u}}$, then

$$H(u + h) = \frac{1}{\sqrt{u + h}}$$

The difference quotient is

$$\frac{f(x + h) - f(x)}{h}$$

$$= \frac{\dfrac{1}{\sqrt{u+h}} - \dfrac{1}{\sqrt{u}}}{h} \cdot \frac{\sqrt{u}\sqrt{u+h}}{\sqrt{u}\sqrt{u+h}}$$

$$= \frac{\sqrt{u} - \sqrt{u+h}}{h\sqrt{u}\sqrt{u+h}} \cdot \frac{(\sqrt{u} + \sqrt{u+h})}{(\sqrt{u} + \sqrt{u+h})}$$

$$= \frac{u - (u + h)}{h\sqrt{u}\sqrt{u+h}(\sqrt{u} + \sqrt{u+h})}$$

$$= \frac{-h}{h\sqrt{u}\sqrt{u+h}(\sqrt{u} + \sqrt{u+h})}$$

$$= \frac{-1}{\sqrt{u}\sqrt{u+h}(\sqrt{u} + \sqrt{u+h})}$$

$$H'(u) = \lim_{h \to 0} \frac{f(x + h) - f(x)}{h}$$

$$= \lim_{h \to 0} \frac{-1}{\sqrt{u}\sqrt{u+h}(\sqrt{u} + \sqrt{u+h})}$$

$$= \frac{-1}{\sqrt{u} \cdot \sqrt{u}(\sqrt{u} + \sqrt{u})}$$

$$= \frac{-1}{u(2\sqrt{u})} = -\frac{1}{2u\sqrt{u}}$$

The slope is $m = H'(4)$

$$= -\frac{1}{2(4)\sqrt{4}} = -\frac{1}{16}$$

13. If $f(x) = 2$, then

$$f(x + h) = 2$$

The difference quotient (DQ) is

$$\frac{f(x + h) - f(x)}{h}$$

$$= \frac{2 - 2}{h} = 0$$

$$f'(x) = \lim_{h \to 0} \frac{f(x + h) - f(x)}{h}$$

$$= \lim_{h \to 0} 0 = 0$$

The slope of the tangent is zero for all values of x. Since $f(13) = 2$,

$$y - 2 = 0(x - 13),$$

$$\text{or} \quad y = 2$$

15. If $f(x) = 7 - 2x$, then

$$f(x + h) = 7 - 2(x + h)$$

The difference quotient (DQ) is

$$\frac{f(x + h) - f(x)}{h}$$

$$= \frac{[7 - 2(x + h)] - [7 - 2x]}{h}$$

$$= -2$$

$$f'(x) = \lim_{h \to 0} \frac{f(x + h) - f(x)}{h} = -2$$

The slope of the line is $m = f'(5) = -2$.
Since $f(5) = -3$, $(5, -3)$ is a point on the curve and the equation of the tangent line is

$$y - (-3) = -2(x - 5)$$

$$\text{or} \quad y = -2x + 7$$

17. If $f(x) = x^2$, then

$$f(x + h) = (x + h)^2$$

The difference quotient (DQ) is

$$\frac{f(x + h) - f(x)}{h}$$

$$= \frac{(x + h)^2 - x^2}{h}$$

$$= \frac{2xh + h^2}{h}$$

$$= 2x + h$$

$$f'(x) = \lim_{h \to 0} \frac{f(x + h) - f(x)}{h} = 2x$$

The slope of the line is $m = f'(1) = 2$.
Since $f(1) = 1$, $(1, 1)$ is a point on the curve and the equation of the tangent line is

$$y - 1 = 2(x - 1)$$

$$\text{or} \quad y = 2x - 1$$

19. If $f(x) = -\dfrac{2}{x}$, then

$$f(x + h) = \frac{-2}{x + h}$$

The difference quotient (DQ) is

$$\frac{f(x + h) - f(x)}{h}$$

$$= \frac{\dfrac{-2}{x + h} - \dfrac{-2}{x}}{h}$$

$$= \frac{\dfrac{-2}{x + h} + \dfrac{2}{x}}{h} \cdot \frac{x(x + h)}{x(x + h)}$$

$$= \frac{-2x + 2(x + h)}{h(x)(x + h)} = \frac{2}{x(x + h)}$$

$$f'(x) = \lim_{h \to 0} \frac{f(x + h) - f(x)}{h} = \frac{2}{x^2}$$

The slope of the line is $m = f'(-1) = 2$.
Since $f(-1) = 2$, $(-1, 2)$ is a point on the curve and the equation of the tangent line is

$$y - 2 = 2(x - (-1))$$

$$y = 2x + 4$$

21. Since $\dfrac{d}{dx} k \cdot f(x) = k \cdot \dfrac{d}{dx} f(x)$, from problem 7,

$$f'(x) = 2\left(\frac{1}{2\sqrt{x}}\right) = \frac{1}{\sqrt{x}}$$

The slope is $m = f'(4) = \dfrac{1}{2}$, $f(4) = 4$, the equation of the tangent line is

$$y - 4 = \frac{1}{2}(x - 4), \text{ or}$$

$$y = \frac{1}{2}x + 2$$

23. If $f(x) = \frac{1}{x^3}$, then

$$f(x + h) = \frac{1}{(x + h)^3}$$

The difference quotient (DQ) is

$$\frac{f(x + h) - f(x)}{h}$$

$$= \frac{\dfrac{1}{(x+h)^3} - \dfrac{1}{x^3}}{h} \cdot \frac{x^3(x + h)^3}{x^3(x + h)^3}$$

$$= \frac{x^3 - (x + h)^3}{hx^3(x + h)^3}$$

$$= \frac{x^3 - (x^3 + 3x^2h + 3xh^2 + h^3)}{hx^3(x + h)^3}$$

$$= \frac{-3x^2h - 3xh^2 - h^3}{hx^3(x + h)^3}$$

$$= \frac{h(-3x^2 - 3xh - h^2)}{hx^3(x + h)^3}$$

$$= \frac{-3x^2 - 3xh - h^2}{x^3(x + h)^3}$$

$$f'(x) = \lim_{h \to 0} \frac{f(x+h) - f(x)}{h}$$

$$= \lim_{h \to 0} \frac{-3x^2 - 3xh - h^2}{x^3(x+h)^3}$$

$$= \frac{-3x^2}{x^3(x)^3} = -\frac{3}{x^4}$$

The slope is $m = f'(1)$

$$= -\frac{3}{(1)^4} = -3$$

Further, $f(1) = 1$ so the equation of the line is

$$y - 1 = -3(x - 1), \text{ or}$$
$$y = -3x + 4$$

25. If $y = f(x) = 3$, then

$$f(x+h) = 3$$

The difference quotient (DQ) is

$$\frac{f(x+h) - f(x)}{h}$$

$$= \frac{3 - 3}{h} = 0$$

$$\frac{dy}{dx} = \lim_{h \to 0} \frac{f(x+h) - f(x)}{h} = 0$$

$$\frac{dy}{dx} = 0 \text{ when } x = 2.$$

27. If $y = f(x) = 3x + 5$, then

$$f(x+h) = 3(x+h) + 5$$
$$= 3x + 3h + 5$$

The difference quotient (DQ) is

$$\frac{f(x+h) - f(x)}{h}$$

$$= \frac{3x + 3h + 5 - (3x + 5)}{h}$$

$$= \frac{3h}{h} = 3$$

$$\frac{dy}{dx} = \lim_{h \to 0} \frac{f(x+h) - f(x)}{h}$$

$$= \lim_{h \to 0} 3 = 3$$

$$\frac{dy}{dx} = 3 \text{ when } x = 1$$

29. If $y = f(x) = x(1 - x)$, or $f(x) = x - x^2$, then

$$f(x+h) = (x+h) - (x+h)^2$$

The difference quotient (DQ) is

$$\frac{f(x+h) - f(x)}{h}$$

$$= \frac{\left[(x+h) - (x+h)^2\right] - \left[x - x^2\right]}{h}$$

$$= \frac{h - 2xh - h^2}{h} = 1 - 2x - h$$

$$\frac{dy}{dx} = \lim_{h \to 0} \frac{f(x+h) - f(x)}{h} = 1 - 2x$$

$$\frac{dy}{dx} = 3 \text{ when } x = -1.$$

31. If $y = f(x) = x - \frac{1}{x}$, then

$$f(x+h) = x + h - \frac{1}{x+h}$$

The difference quotient (DQ) is

$$\frac{f(x+h) - f(x)}{h}$$

$$= \frac{x + h - \frac{1}{x+h} - \left(x - \frac{1}{x}\right)}{h}$$

$$= \frac{h - \frac{1}{x+h} + \frac{1}{x}}{h} \cdot \frac{x(x+h)}{x(x+h)}$$

$$= \frac{hx(x+h) - x + x + h}{h}$$

$$= \frac{hx^2 + h^2x + h}{h}$$

$$= \frac{h(x^2 + hx + 1)}{h} = x^2 + hx + 1$$

$$\frac{dy}{dx} = \lim_{h \to 0} \frac{f(x+h) - f(x)}{h}$$

$$= \lim_{h \to 0} x^2 + hx + 1 = x^2 + 1$$

When $x = 1$,

$$\frac{dy}{dx} = (1)^2 + 1 = 2$$

33. (a) If $f(x) = x^2$, then $f(-2) = (-2)^2 = 4$ and $f(-1.9) = (-1.9)^2 = 3.61$. The slope of the secant line joining the points $(-2, 4)$ and $(-1.9, 3.61)$ on the graph of f is

$$m_{\text{sec}} = \frac{y_2 - y_1}{x_2 - x_1} = \frac{3.61 - 4}{-1.9 - (-2)} = -3.9$$

(b) If $f(x) = x^2$, then

$$f(x+h) = (x+h)^2 = x^2 + 2xh + h^2$$

The difference quotient (DQ) is

$$\frac{f(x+h) - f(x)}{h}$$

$$= \frac{x^2 + 2xh + h^2 - x^2}{h}$$

$$= \frac{2xh + h^2}{h} = \frac{h(2x + h)}{h} = 2x + h$$

$$f'(x) = \lim_{h \to 0} \frac{f(x+h) - f(x)}{h}$$

$$= \lim_{h \to 0} 2x + h = 2x$$

The slope of the tangent line at the point $(-2, 4)$ on the graph of f is

$$m_{\text{tan}} = f'(-2) = 2(-2) = -4$$

35. (a) If $f(x) = x^3$, then $f(1) = 1$, $f(1.1) = (1.1)^3 = 1.331$.

The slope of the secant line joining the points $(1,1)$ and $(1.1, 1.331)$ on the graph of f is

$$m_{\text{sec}} = \frac{y_2 - y_1}{x_2 - x_1} = \frac{1.331 - 1}{1.1 - 1} = 3.31$$

(b) If $f(x) = x^3$, then

$$f(x+h) = (x+h)^3$$

The difference quotient (DQ) is

$$\frac{f(x+h) - f(x)}{h}$$

$$= \frac{(x+h)^3 - x^3}{h}$$

$$= \frac{3x^2h + 3xh^2 + h^3}{h}$$

$$= 3x^2 + 3xh + h^2$$

$$f'(x) = \lim_{h \to 0} \frac{f(x+h) - f(x)}{h} = 3x^2$$

The slope is $m_{\text{tan}} = f'(1) = 3$
Notice that this slope was approximated by the slope of the secant in part **(a)**.

37. (a) If $f(x) = 3x^2 - x$, the average rate of change of f is

$$\frac{f(x_2) - f(x_1)}{x_2 - x_1}$$

Since $f(0) = 0$ and $f\left(\frac{1}{16}\right) = 3\left(\frac{1}{16}\right)^2 - \frac{1}{16} = -\frac{13}{256}$,

$$\frac{f(x_2) - f(x_1)}{x_2 - x_1} = \frac{-\frac{13}{256} - 0}{\frac{1}{16} - 0} = -\frac{13}{16} = -0.8125$$

(b) If $f(x) = 3x^2 - x$, then

$$f(x+h) = 3(x+h)^2 - (x+h)$$

The difference quotient (DQ) is

$$\frac{f(x+h) - f(x)}{h}$$

$$= \frac{3(x+h)^2 - (x+h) - (3x^2 - x)}{h}$$

$$= \frac{3x^2 + 6xh + 3h^2 - x - h - 3x^2 + x}{h}$$

$$= \frac{6xh + 3h^2 - h}{h} = 6x + 3h - 1$$

$$f'(x) = \lim_{h \to 0}(6x + 3h - 1) = 6x - 1$$

The instantaneous rate of change at $x = 0$ is $f'(0) = -1$. Notice that this rate is estimated by the average rate in part **(a)**.

39. **(a)** If $s(t) = \dfrac{t-1}{t+1}$, the average rate of change of s is
$$\frac{s(t_2) - s(t_1)}{t_2 - t_1}$$
Since $s\left(-\dfrac{1}{2}\right) = \dfrac{\frac{1}{2} - 1}{-\frac{1}{2} + 1} = -3$ and $s(0) = \dfrac{0-1}{0+1} = -1, = \dfrac{-3+1}{-\frac{1}{2} - 0} = 4$

(b) If $s(t) = \dfrac{t-1}{t+1}$, then

$$s(t+h) = \frac{(t+h) - 1}{(t+h) + 1}$$

The difference quotient (DQ) is

$$\frac{s(t+h) - s(t)}{h}$$

$$= \frac{\dfrac{t+h-1}{t+h+1} - \dfrac{t-1}{t+1}}{h}$$

Multiplying numerator and denominator by $(t+h+1)(t+1)$,

$$= \frac{(t+h-1)(t+1) - (t-1)(t+h+1)}{h(t+h+1)(t+1)}$$

$$= \frac{t^2 + th - t + t + h - 1 - t^2 - th - t + t + h + 1}{h(t+h+1)(t+1)}$$

$$= \frac{2h}{h(t+h+1)(t+1)} = \frac{2}{(t+h+1)(t+1)}$$

$$s'(t) = \lim_{h \to 0}\frac{2}{(t+h+1)(t+1)} = \frac{2}{(t+1)^2}$$

The instantaneous rate of change when $t = -\dfrac{1}{2}$ is

$$s'\left(-\frac{1}{2}\right) = \frac{2}{\left(-\frac{1}{2} + 1\right)^2} = 8$$

Notice that the estimate given by the average rate in part **(a)** differs significantly.

41. **(a)** The average rate of temperature change between t_0 and $t_0 + h$ hours after midnight. The instanteous rate of temperature change t_0 hours after midnight.

(b) The average rate of change in blood alcohol level between t_0 and $t_0 + h$ hours after consumption. The instantaneous rate of change in blood alcohol level t_0 hours after consumption.

(c) The average rate of change of the 30-year fixed mortgage rate between t_0 and $t_0 + h$ years after 2000. The instantaneous rate of change of 30-year fixed mortgage rate t_0 years after 2000.

43. When $t = 30$, $\dfrac{dV}{dt} \approx \dfrac{65 - 50}{50 - 30} = \dfrac{3}{4}$.
In the "long run", the rate at which V is changing with respect to time is getting smaller and smaller, decreasing to zero.

45. When $h = 1,000$ meters,

$$\frac{dT}{dh} \approx \frac{-6 - 0}{2,000 - 1,000} = \frac{-6}{1,000} = -0.006 \,°\text{C/meter}$$

When $h = 2,000$ meters,

$$\frac{dT}{dh} = 0 \,°\text{C/meter}$$

Since the line tangent to the graph at $h = 2,000$ is horizontal, its slope is zero.

47. $P(x) = 4,000(15 - x)(x - 2)$

(a) The difference quotient (DQ) is

$$\frac{P(x + h) - P(x)}{h}$$

$$= \frac{[4,000\,(15 - (x + h))\,((x + h) - 2)]}{h}$$

$$- \frac{[4,000(15 - x)(x - 2)]}{h}$$

$$= \frac{4,000\,[(15 - x - h)(x + h - 2) - (15 - x)(x - 2)]}{h}$$

$$= \frac{4,000(17h - 2xh - h^2)}{h} = 4,000(17 - 2x - h)$$

$$P'(x) = \lim_{h \to 0} \frac{P(x + h) - P(x)}{h} = 4,000(17 - 2x)$$

(b) $P'(x) = 0$ when

$$4,000(17 - 2x) = 0$$

$$x = \frac{17}{2} = 8.5, \text{ or } 850 \text{ units.}$$

When $P'(x) = 0$, the line tangent to the graph of P is horizontal. Since the graph of P is a parabola which opens down, this horizontal tangent indicates a maximum profit.

49. $C(x) = 0.04x^2 + 5.1x + 40$

(a) The average rate of change is

$$\frac{C(x_2) - C(x_1)}{x_2 - x_1}$$

Since $C(10) = 0.04(10)^2 + 5.1(10) + 40 = 95$ and $C(11) = 0.04(11)^2 + 5.1(11) + 40 = 100.94$,

$$\frac{C(x_2) - C(x_1)}{x_2 - x_1} = \frac{100.94 - 95}{11 - 10} = \$5.94 \text{ per unit}$$

(b) $C(x + h) = 0.04(x + h)^2 + 5.1(x + h) + 40$

So, the difference quotient (DQ) is
$$\frac{C(x + h) - C(x)}{h}$$

$$= \frac{0.04(x + h)^2 + 5.1(x + h) + 40 - (0.04x^2 + 5.1x + 40)}{h}$$

$$= \left[0.04x^2 + 0.08xh + 0.04h^2 + 5.1x + 5.1h + 40\right.$$

$$\left. -0.04x^2 - 5.1x - 40\right] \Big/ h$$

$$= \frac{0.08xh + 0.04h^2 + 5.1h}{h}$$

$$= 0.08x + 0.04h + 5.1$$

$$C'(x) = \lim_{h \to 0} (0.08x + 0.04h + 5.1) = 0.08x + 5.1$$

The instantaneous rate of change when $x = 10$ is $C'(10) = 0.08(10) + 5.1 = \$5.90$ per unit. Since $C'(10)$ is positive, the cost is increasing when 10 units are being produced.

51. Writing Exercise—Answers will vary.

53. $H(t) = 4.4t - 4.9t^2$

(a) $H(t + h) = 4.4(t + h) - 4.9(t + h)^2$

$$= 4.4t + 4.4h - 4.9(t^2 + 2th + h^2)$$

$$= 4.4t + 4.4h - 4.9t^2 - 9.8th - 4.9h^2$$

The difference quotient (DQ) is

$$\frac{H(t + h) - H(t)}{h}$$

$$= \frac{4.4t + 4.4h - 4.9t^2 - 9.8th - 4.9h^2 - (4.4t - 4.9t^2)}{h}$$

$$= \frac{4.4h - 9.8th - 4.9h^2}{h}$$

$$= \frac{h(4.4 - 9.8t - 4.9h)}{h}$$

$$= 4.4 - 9.8t - 4.9h$$

$$H'(t) = \lim_{h \to 0} \frac{H(t+h) - H(t)}{h}$$

$$= \lim_{h \to 0} 4.4 - 9.8t - 4.9h$$

$$= 4.4 - 9.8t$$

After 1 second, H is changing at a rate of $H'(1) = 4.4 - 9.8(1) = -5.4$ m/sec, where the negative represents that H is decreasing.

(b) $H'(t) = 0$ when

$$4.4 - 9.8t = 0, \text{ or}$$
$$t \approx 0.449 \text{ seconds}$$

This represents the time when the height is not changing (neither increasing nor decreasing). That is, this represents the highest point in the jump.

(c) When the flea lands, the height $H(t)$ will be zero (as it was when $t = 0$).

$$4.4t - 4.9t^2 = 0$$
$$(4.4 - 4.9t)t = 0$$
$$4.4 - 4.9t = 0$$
$$t = \frac{44}{49} \approx 0.898 \text{ seconds}$$

At this time, the rate of change is

$$H'\left(\frac{44}{49}\right) = 4.4 - 9.8\left(\frac{44}{49}\right)$$
$$= -4.4 \text{ m/sec}$$

Again, the negative represents that H is decreasing.

55. $D(p) = -0.0009p^2 + 0.13p + 17.81$

(a) The average rate of change is

$$\frac{D(p_2) - D(p_1)}{p_2 - p_1}$$

Since $D(60) = -0.0009(60)^2 + 0.13(60) + 17.81 = 22.37$
and $D(61) = -0.0009(61)^2 + 0.13(61) + 17.81 = 22.3911,$

$$= \frac{22.3911 - 22.37}{61 - 60}$$
$$= 0.0211 \text{ mm per mm of mercury}$$

(b) $D(p + h) = -0.0009(p + h)^2 + 0.13(p + h) + 17.81$
So, the difference quotient (DQ) is
$$\frac{D(p + h) - D(p)}{h}$$

$$= \left[-0.0009(p + h)^2 + 0.13(p + h) + 17.81\right.$$
$$\left. -(-0/0009p^2 + 0.13p + 17.81)\right]\Big/h$$
$$= \left[-0.0009p^2 - 0.0018ph - 0.0009h^2 + 0.13p\right.$$
$$\left. +0.13h + 17.81 + 0.0009p^2 - 0.13p - 17.81\right]\Big/h$$
$$= \frac{-0.0018ph - 0.0009h^2 + 0.13h}{h}$$
$$= -0.0018p - 0.0009h + 0.13$$
$$D'(x) = \lim_{h \to 0}(-0.0018p - 0.0009h + 0.13)$$
$$= -0.0018p + 0.13$$

The instantaneous rate of change when $p = 60$ is $D'(60) = -0.0018(60) + 0.13 = 0.022$ mm per mm of mercury. Since $D'(60)$ is positive, the pressure is increasing when $p = 60$.

(c) $-0.0018p + 0.13 = 0$
$$p \approx 72.22 \text{ mm of mercury}$$
At this pressure, the diameter is neither increasing nor decreasing.

57. (a) For $y = f(x) = x^2$,
$f(x + h) = (x + h)^2$
The difference quotient (DQ) is

$$\frac{f(x + h) - f(x)}{h} = \frac{(x + h)^2 - x^2}{h}$$
$$= \frac{2xh + h^2}{h} = 2x + h$$
$$\frac{dy}{dx} = f'(x) = \lim_{h \to 0}\frac{f(x + h) - f(x)}{h} = 2x$$

For $y = f(x) = x^2 - 3$,
$f(x + h) = (x + h)^2 - 3$
The difference quotient (DQ) is

$$\frac{\left[(x + h)^2 - 3\right] - (x^2 - 3)}{h}$$
$$= \frac{2xh + h^2}{h} = 2x + h$$
$$\frac{dy}{dx} = f'(x) = \lim_{h \to 0}\frac{f(x + h) - f(x)}{h} = 2x$$

The graph of $y = x^2 - 3$ is the graph of $y = x^2$ shifted down 3 units. So the graphs are parallel and their tangent lines have the same slopes for any value of x. This accounts geometrically for the fact that their derivatives are identical.

(b) Since $y = x^2 + 5$ is the parabola $y = x^2$ shifted up 5 units and the constant appears to have no effect on the derivative, the derivative of the function $y = x^2 + 5$ is also $2x$.

59. (a) For $y = f(x) = x^2$,
$f(x + h) = (x + h)^2$
The difference quotient (DQ) is

$$\frac{f(x + h) - f(x)}{h} = \frac{(x + h)^2 - x^2}{h}$$

$$= \frac{2xh + h^2}{h} = 2x + h$$

$$\frac{dy}{dx} = f'(x) = \lim_{h \to 0} \frac{f(x + h) - f(x)}{h} = 2x$$

For $y = f(x) = x^3$,
$f(x + h) = (x + h)^3$
The difference quotient (DQ) is

$$\frac{(x + h)^3 - x^3}{h}$$

$$= \frac{3x^2h + 3xh^2 + h^3}{h} = 3x^2 + 3xh + h^2$$

$$\frac{dy}{dx} = f'(x) = \lim_{h \to 0} \frac{f(x + h) - f(x)}{h} = 3x^2$$

(b) The pattern seems to be that the derivative of x raised to a power (x^n) is that power times x raised to the power decreased by one (nx^{n-1}). So, the derivative of the function $y = x^4$ is $4x^3$ and the derivative of the function $y = x^{27}$ is $27x^{26}$.

61. When $x < 0$, the difference quotient (DQ) is

$$\frac{f(x + h) - f(x)}{h} = \frac{-(x + h) - (-x)}{h} = \frac{-h}{h} = -1$$

So, $f'(x) = \lim_{h \to 0} -1 = -1$.
When $x > 0$, the difference quotient (DQ) is

$$\frac{f(x + h) - f(x)}{h} = \frac{(x + h) - x}{h} = 1$$

So, $f'(x) = \lim_{h \to 0} 1 = 1$.
Since there is a sharp corner at $x = 0$ (graph changes from $y = -x$ to $y = x$), the graph makes an abrupt change in direction at $x = 0$. So, f is not differentiable at $x = 0$.

63. To show that $f(x) = \dfrac{|x^2 - 1|}{x - 1}$ is not differentiable at $x = 1$,
Press $\boxed{y=}$ and input $(abs(x^2 - 1))/(x - 1)$ for $y_1 =$

The abs is under the NUM menu in the math application.
Use window dimensions $[-4, 4]1$ by $[-4, 4]1$
Press $\boxed{\text{Graph}}$

We see that f is not defined at $x = 1$. There can be no point of tangency.

$$\lim_{x \to 1^+} \frac{|x^2 - 1|}{x - 1} = \lim_{x \to 1^+} \frac{|(x - 1)(x + 1)|}{x - 1} = 2$$

$$\lim_{x \to 1^-} \frac{|x^2 - 1|}{x - 1} = \lim_{x \to 1^-} \frac{|(x - 1)(x + 1)|}{x - 1} = -2$$

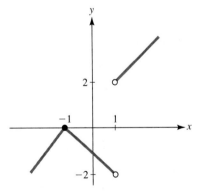

65. To find the slope of line tangent to the graph of $f(x) = \sqrt{x^2 + 2x} - \sqrt{3x}$ at $x = 3.85$, fill in the table below.
The $x + h$ row can be filled in manually.
For $f(x)$, press $\boxed{y=}$ and input
$\sqrt{\left(x \wedge 2 + 2x - \sqrt{(3x)}\right)}$ for $y_1 =$
Use window dimensions $[-1, 10]1$ by $[-1, 10]1$

Use the value function under the calc menu and enter $x = 3.85$ to find $f(x) = 4.37310$.

For $f(x + h)$, use the value function under the calc menu and enter $x = 3.83$ To find $f(x + h) = 4.35192$. Repeat this process for $x = 3.84, 3.849, 3.85, 3.851, 3.86,$ and 3.87.

The $\dfrac{f(x + h) - f(x)}{h}$ can be filled in manually given that the rest of the table is now complete. So, slope $= f'(3.85) \approx 1.059$.

h	-0.02	-0.01	-0.001
$x + h$	3.83	3.84	3.849
$f(x)$	4.37310	4.37310	4.37310
$f(x + h)$	4.35192	4.36251	4.37204
$\dfrac{f(x + h) - f(x)}{h}$	1.059	1.059	1.059

0	0.001	0.01	0.02
3.85	3.851	3.86	3.87
4.37310	4.37310	4.37310	4.37310
4.37310	4.37415	4.38368	4.39426
undefined	1.05	1.058	1.058

2.2   Techniques of Differentiation

1.   Since the derivative of any constant is zero,

$$y = -2$$

$$\frac{dy}{dx} = 0$$

(Note: $y = -2$ is a horizontal line and all horizontal lines have a slope of zero, so $\dfrac{dy}{dx}$ must be zero.)

3.
$$y = 5x - 3$$
$$\frac{dy}{dx} = \frac{d}{dx}(5x) - \frac{d}{dx}(3)$$
$$\frac{dy}{dx} = 5 - 0 = 5$$

5. $y = x^{-4}$

$$\frac{dy}{dx} = -4x^{-4-1} = -4x^{-5} = -\frac{4}{x^5}$$

7. $y = x^{3.7}$

$$\frac{dy}{dx} = 3.7x^{3.7-1} = 3.7x^{2.7}$$

9. $y = \pi r^2$

$$\frac{dy}{dx} = \pi \left(2r^{2-1}\right) = 2\pi r$$

11. $y = \sqrt{2x} = \sqrt{2} \cdot x^{1/2}$

$$\frac{dy}{dx} = \sqrt{2} \left(\frac{1}{2}x^{1/2-1}\right) = \sqrt{2}\left(\frac{1}{2}x^{-1/2}\right)$$

$$= \sqrt{2} \cdot \frac{1}{2x^{1/2}} = \frac{1}{\sqrt{2}x^{1/2}} \text{ or } \frac{1}{\sqrt{2x}}$$

13. $y = \dfrac{9}{\sqrt{t}} = 9t^{-1/2}$

$$\frac{dy}{dx} = 9\left(-\frac{1}{2}t^{-1/2-1}\right) = 9\left(-\frac{1}{2}t^{-3/2}\right)$$

$$= -\frac{9}{2t^{3/2}} \text{ or } -\frac{9}{2\sqrt{t^3}}$$

15.
$$y = x^2 + 2x + 3$$
$$\frac{dy}{dx} = \frac{d}{dx}(x^2) + \frac{d}{dx}(2x) + \frac{d}{dx}(3)$$
$$\frac{dy}{dx} = 2x + 2$$

17.
$$y = x^9 - 5x^8 + x + 12$$
$$\frac{dy}{dx} = \frac{d}{dx}(x^9) - \frac{d}{dx}(5x^8) + \frac{d}{dx}(x) + \frac{d}{dx}(12)$$
$$\frac{dy}{dx} = 9x^8 - 40x^7 + 1$$

19.
$$f(x) = -0.02x^3 + 0.3x$$
$$f'(x) = \frac{d}{dx}(-0.02x^3) + (0.3x)$$
$$f'(x) = -0.02(3x^2) + 0.3 = -0.06x^2 + 0.3$$

21.
$$y = \frac{1}{t} + \frac{1}{t^2} - \frac{1}{\sqrt{t}}$$

$$= t^{-1} + t^{-2} - t^{-1/2}$$

$$\frac{dy}{dt} = \frac{d}{dt}(t^{-1}) + \frac{d}{dt}(t^{-2}) - \frac{d}{dt}\left(t^{-1/2}\right)$$

$$= -1t^{-1-1} + -2t^{-2-1} - \left(-\frac{1}{2}t^{-1/2-1}\right)$$

$$= -1t^{-2} - 2t^{-3} + \frac{1}{2}t^{-3/2}$$

$$= -\frac{1}{t^2} - \frac{2}{t^3} + \frac{1}{2t^{3/2}}, \text{ or } -\frac{1}{t^2} - \frac{2}{t^3} + \frac{1}{2\sqrt{t^3}}$$

23. $f(x) = \sqrt{x^3} + \dfrac{1}{\sqrt{x^3}} = x^{3/2} + x^{-3/2}$,

$$f'(x) = \frac{d}{dx}(x^{3/2}) + \frac{d}{dx}(x^{-3/2})$$

$$= \frac{3}{2}x^{3/2-1} + \frac{-3}{2}x^{-3/2-1}$$

$$= \frac{3}{2}x^{1/2} - \frac{3}{2}x^{-5/2}$$

$$= \frac{3}{2}x^{1/2} - \frac{3}{2x^{5/2}}, \text{ or } \frac{3}{2}\sqrt{x} - \frac{3}{2\sqrt{x^5}}$$

25.
$$y = -\frac{x^2}{16} + \frac{2}{x} - x^{3/2} + \frac{1}{3x^2} + \frac{x}{3}$$

$$= -\frac{1}{16}x^2 + 2x^{-1} - x^{3/2} + \frac{1}{3}x^{-2} + \frac{1}{3}x,$$

$$\frac{dy}{dx} = \frac{d}{dx}\left(-\frac{1}{16}x^2\right) + \frac{d}{dx}\left(2x^{-1}\right)$$

$$\quad - \frac{d}{dx}\left(x^{3/2}\right) + \frac{d}{dx}\left(\frac{1}{3}x^{-2}\right) + \frac{d}{dx}\left(\frac{1}{3}x\right)$$

$$= -\frac{1}{16}(2x) + 2(-1x^{-1-1}) - \frac{3}{2}x^{3/2-1}$$

$$\quad + \frac{1}{3}(-2x^{-2-1}) + \frac{1}{3}$$

$$= -\frac{1}{8}x - 2x^{-2} - \frac{3}{2}x^{1/2} - \frac{2}{3}x^{-3} + \frac{1}{3}$$

$$= -\frac{1}{8}x - \frac{2}{x^2} - \frac{3}{2}x^{1/2} - \frac{2}{3x^3} + \frac{1}{3},$$

$$\text{or } -\frac{1}{8}x - \frac{2}{x^2} + \frac{3}{2}\sqrt{x} - \frac{2}{3x^3} + \frac{1}{3}$$

27.
$$y = \frac{x^5 - 4x^2}{x^3} = \frac{x^5}{x^3} - \frac{4x^2}{x^3} = x^2 - \frac{4}{x} = x^2 - 4x^{-1}$$

$$\frac{dy}{dx} = \frac{d}{dx}(x^2) - \frac{d}{dx}(4x^{-1}) = 2x - 4(-1x^{-1-1})$$

$$= 2x + 4x^{-2} = 2x + \frac{4}{x^2}$$

29.
$$y = -x^3 - 5x^2 + 3x - 1$$

$$\frac{dy}{dx} = -3x^2 - 10x + 3$$

At $x = -1$, $\dfrac{dy}{dx} = 10$. The equation of the tangent line at $(-1, -8)$ is

$$y + 8 = 10(x + 1),$$

$$\text{or } y = 10x + 2$$

31.
$$y = 1 - \frac{1}{x} + \frac{2}{\sqrt{x}}$$

$$= 1 - x^{-1} + 2x^{-1/2}$$

$$\frac{dy}{dx} = x^{-2} - x^{-3/2} = \frac{1}{x^2} - \frac{1}{x^{3/2}}$$

At $\left(4, \dfrac{7}{4}\right)$, $\dfrac{dy}{dx} = -\dfrac{1}{16}$. The equation of the tangent line is

$$y - \frac{7}{4} = -\frac{1}{16}(x - 4), \text{ or }$$

$$y = -\frac{1}{16}x + 2$$

33.
$$y = (x^2 - x)(3 + 2x) = 2x^3 + x^2 - 3x$$

$$\frac{dy}{dx} = 6x^2 + 2x - 3$$

At $x = -1$, $\dfrac{dy}{dx} = 1$. The equation of the tangent line at $(-1, 2)$ is

$$y - 2 = 1(x + 1), \text{ or } y = x + 3$$

35.
$$f(x) = -2x^3 + \frac{1}{x^2} = -2x^3 + x^{-2}$$

$$f'(x) = -6x^2 - \frac{2}{x^3}$$

At $x = -1$, $f'(-1) = -4$. Further, $y = f(-1) = 3$. The equation of the tangent line at $(-1, 3)$ is

$$y - 3 = -4(x + 1), \text{ or } y = -4x - 1$$

37.
$$f(x) = x - \frac{1}{x^2} = x - x^{-2}$$

$$f'(x) = 1 + \frac{2}{x^3}$$

At $x = 1$, $f'(1) = 3$. Further, $y = f(1) = 0$. The equation of the tangent line at $(1,0)$ is

$$y - 0 = 3(x - 1), \text{ or } y = 3x - 3$$

39.
$$f(x) = -\frac{1}{3}x^3 + \sqrt{8x} = -\frac{1}{3}x^3 + \sqrt{8} \cdot x^{1/2}$$

$$f'(x) = -x^2 + \frac{\sqrt{8}}{2x^{1/2}}$$

At $x = 2$, $f'(2) = -4 + \frac{\sqrt{8}}{2\sqrt{2}} = -4 + \frac{1}{2}\sqrt{\frac{8}{2}}$

$= -4 + \frac{1}{2} \cdot 2 = -3$.

Further, $y = f(2) = -\frac{8}{3} + 4 = \frac{4}{3}$. The equation of the tangent line at $\left(2, \frac{4}{3}\right)$ is

$$y - \frac{4}{3} = -3(x - 2), \text{ or } y = -3x + \frac{22}{3}$$

41.
$$f(x) = 2x^4 + 3x + 1$$
$$f'(x) = 8x^3 + 3$$

The rate of change of f at $x = -1$ is $f'(-1) = -5$.

43.
$$f(x) = x - \sqrt{x} + \frac{1}{x^2} = x - x^{1/2} + x^{-2}$$

$$f'(x) = 1 - \frac{1}{2x^{1/2}} - \frac{2}{x^3}$$

The rate of change of f at $x = 1$ is $f'(1) = -\frac{3}{2}$.

45.
$$f(x) = \frac{x + \sqrt{x}}{\sqrt{x}} = \frac{x}{\sqrt{x}} + \frac{\sqrt{x}}{\sqrt{x}} = \sqrt{x} + 1 = x^{1/2} + 1$$

$$f'(x) = \frac{1}{2x^{1/2}}$$

The rate of change of f at $x = 1$ is $f'(1) = \frac{1}{2}$.

47.
$$f(x) = 2x^3 - 5x^2 + 4$$
$$f'(x) = 6x^2 - 10x$$

The relative rate of change is

$$\frac{f'(x)}{f(x)} = \frac{6x^2 - 10x}{2x^3 - 5x^2 + 4}$$

When $x = 1$,

$$\frac{f'(1)}{f(1)} = \frac{6 - 10}{2 - 5 + 4} = -4$$

49.
$$f(x) = x\sqrt{x} + x^2 = x \cdot x^{1/2} + x^2 = x^{3/2} + x^2$$

$$f'(x) = \frac{3}{2}x^{1/2} + 2x = \frac{3}{2}\sqrt{x} + 2x$$

The relative rate of change is

$$\frac{f'(x)}{f(x)} = \frac{\frac{3}{2}\sqrt{x} + 2x}{x\sqrt{x} + x^2} \cdot \frac{2}{2}$$

$$= \frac{3\sqrt{x} + 4x}{2(x\sqrt{x} + x^2)}$$

When $x = 4$,

$$\frac{f'(4)}{f(4)} = \frac{3\sqrt{4} + 4(4)}{2(4\sqrt{4} + 4^2)} = \frac{11}{24}$$

51. (a)
$$A(t) = 0.1t^2 + 10t + 20$$
$$A'(t) = 0.2t + 10$$

In the year 2004, the rate of change is

$$A'(4) = 0.8 + 10 \text{ or } \$10,800 \text{ per year}$$

(b) $A(4) = (0.1)(16) + 40 + 20 = 61.6$, so the percentage rate of change is

$$\frac{(100)(10.8)}{61.6} = 17.53\%$$

53. (a) $f(x) = -6x + 582$
The rate of change of SAT scores is $f'(x) = -6$.

(b) The rate of change is constant, so the drop will not vary from year to year. The rate of change is negative, so the scores are declining.

55. (a) $T(x) = 20x^2 + 40x + 600$ dollars
The rate of change of property tax is

$$T'(x) = 40x + 40 \text{ dollars/year}$$

In the year 2005, $x = 0$, $T'(0) = 40$ dollars/year.

(b) In the year 2009, $x = 4$ and $T(4) = \$1,080$.
In the year 2005, $x = 0$ and $T(0) = \$600$.
The change in property tax is
$T(4) - T(0) = \$480$.

57. (a) $P(x) = 2x + 4x^{3/2} + 5,000$ is the population x months from now. The rate of population growth is

$$P'(x) = 2 + 4\left(\frac{3x^{1/2}}{2}\right) = 2 + 6x^{1/2}$$

people per month. Nine months from now, the population will be changing at the rate of

$$P'(9) = 2 + 6(9^{1/2}) = 20 \text{ people per month.}$$

(b) The percentage rate at which the population will be changing 9 months from now is

$$100\frac{P'(9)}{P(9)} = \frac{100(20)}{2(9) + 4(9^{3/2}) + 5,000}$$

$$= \frac{2,000}{5,126} = 0.39\%$$

59. $N(t) = 10t^3 + 5t + \sqrt{t} = 10t^3 + 5t + t^{1/2}$
The rate of change of the infected population is

$$N'(t) = 30t^2 + 5 + \frac{1}{2t^{1/2}} \text{ people/day}$$

On the 9th day, $N'(9) = 2,435$ people/day.

61. (a) $$Q(t) = 0.05t^2 + 0.1t + 3.4 \text{ PPM}$$
$$Q'(t) = 0.1t + 0.1 \text{ PPM/year}$$

The rate of change of Q is at $t = 1$ is
$Q'(1) = 0.2$ PPM/year.

(b) $Q(1) = 3.55$ PPM, $Q(0) = 3.40$, and
$Q(1) - Q(0) = 0.15$ PPM.

(c) $Q(2) = 0.2 + 0.2 + 3.4 = 3.8$, $Q(0) = 3.4$, and
$Q(2) - Q(0) = 0.4$ PPM.

63. (a) Since your starting salary is $45,000 and you get a raise of $2,000 per year, your salary t years from now will be

$$S(t) = 45,000 + 2,000t \text{ dollars.}$$

The percentage rate of change of this salary t years from now is

$$100\left[\frac{S'(t)}{S(t)}\right] = 100\left(\frac{2,000}{45,000 + 2,000t}\right)$$

$$= \frac{200}{45 + 2t} \text{ percent per year.}$$

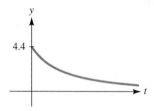

(b) The percentage rate of change after 1 year is

$$\frac{200}{47} \approx 4.26\%$$

(c) In the long run, $\dfrac{200}{45 + 2t}$ approaches 0.
That is, the percentage rate of your salary will approach 0 (even though your salary will continue to increase at a constant rate).

65. (a) $T(t) = -68.07t^3 + 30.98t^2 + 12.52t + 37.1$

$$T'(t) = -204.21t^2 + 61.96t + 12.52$$

$T'(t)$ represents the rate at which the bird's temperature is changing after t days, measured in °C per day.

(b) $T'(0) = 12.52$ °C/day
since $T'(0)$ is positive, the bird's temperature is increasing.

$$T'(0.713) \approx -47.12 \text{ °C/day}$$

Since $T'(0.713)$ is negative, the bird's temperature is decreasing.

(c) Find t so that $T'(t) = 0$.

$$0 = -204.21t^2 + 61.96t + 12.52$$

$$t = \frac{-61.96 \pm \sqrt{(61.96)^2 - 4(-204.21)(12.52)}}{2(-204.21)}$$

$t \approx 0.442$ days.
The bird's temperature when $t = 0.442$ is
$T(0.442) \approx 42.8°C$.
The bird's temperature starts at $T(0) = 37.1°C$,
increases to $T(0.442) = 42.8°C$, and then
begins to decrease.

67. (a) Costs = cost driver + cost gasoline

$$\text{cost driver} = 20(\#hrs) = 20\left(\frac{250mi}{x}\right) = \frac{5,000}{x}$$

$$\text{cost gasoline} = 4.0(\#gals)$$

$$= 4.0(250)\left[\frac{1}{250}\left(\frac{1,200}{x} + x\right)\right]$$

$$= \frac{4,800}{x} + 4.0x \text{ dollars}$$

So, the cost function is $C(x) = \dfrac{9,800}{x} + 4x$.

(b) The rate of change of the cost is $C'(x)$.

$$C(x) = 9,800x^{-1} + 4x$$

$$C'(x) = -\frac{9,800}{x^2} + 4 \text{ dollars/miles per hr.}$$

When $x = 40$, $C'(40) = -2.125$ dollars/miles
per hour. Since $C'(40)$ is negative, the cost is
decreasing.

69. (a) $s(t) = 3t^2 + 2t - 5$ for $0 \le t \le 1$
$v(t) = 6t + 2$ and $a(t) = 6$

(b) $6t + 2 = 0$ at $t = -3$. The particle is not
stationary between $t = 0$ and $t = 1$.

71. (a) $s(t) = t^4 - 4t^3 + 8t$ for $0 \le t \le 4$
$v(t) = 4t^3 - 12t^2 + 8$ and $a(t) = 12t^2 - 24t$

(b) To find all time in given interval when stationary,

$$4t^3 - 12t^2 + 8 = 0$$
$$4(t^3 - 3t^2 + 2) = 0$$
$$t^3 - 3t^2 + 2 = 0$$

Press $\boxed{y=}$ Input $x \wedge 3 - 3x^2 + 2$ for $y_1 =$
Use window dimensions $[-4, 4]1$ by $[-4, 4]1$
Use trace and zoom-in to find the x-intercepts
or use the zero function under the calc menu.
To use the zero function (for the left-most x-
intercept), enter a value to the left of (but close
to) the x-intercept for the left bound. Enter a
value close to but to the right of the x-intercept
for the right bound. Enter $x = -0.7$ for the
guess. We see that the left most x-intercept is
$x \approx -0.732$.
Repeat this process for the other two x-intercepts
to find $x = 1$ and $x \approx 2.73$.
In the interval $0 \le t \le 4$, the particle is stationary
when $t = 1$ and $t \approx 2.73$.

73. (a) If after 2 seconds the ball passes you on the way
down, then

$$H(2) = H_0$$

where $H(t) = -16t^2 + V_0t + H_0$.
So, $-16(2^2) + (V_0)(2) + H_0 = H_0$,
$$-64 + 2V_0 = 0, \text{ or } V_0 = 32\frac{ft}{sec}.$$

(b) The height of the building is H_0 feet. From part
(a) you know that

$$H(t) = -16t^2 + 32t + H_0$$

Moreover, $H(4) = 0$ since the ball hits the
ground after 4 seconds.
So, $-16(4^2) + 32(4) + H_0 = 0$, or
$H_0 = 128$ feet.

(c) From parts (a) and (b) you know that

$$H(t) = -16t^2 + 32t + 128$$

and so the speed of the ball is

$$H'(t) = -32t + 32\frac{ft}{sec}$$

After 2 seconds, the speed will be $H'(2) = -32$ feet per second, where the minus sign indicates that the direction of motion is down.

(d) The speed at which the ball hits the ground is

$$H'(4) = -96 \frac{\text{ft}}{\text{sec}}$$

75. $f(x) = ax^2 + bx + c$

Since $f(0) = 0$, $c = 0$ and $f(x) = ax^2 + bx$.

Since $f(5) = 0$, $0 = 25a + 5b$.

Further, since the slope of the tangent is 1 when $x = 2$, $f'(2) = 1$.

$$f'(x) = 2ax + b$$
$$1 = 2a(2) + b = 4a + b$$

Now, solve the system: $0 = 25a + 5b$ and $1 = 4a + b$. Since $1 - 4a = b$, using substitution

$$0 = 25a + 5(1 - 4a)$$
$$0 = 25a + 5 - 20a$$
$$0 = 5a + 5$$

or $a = -1$ and
$$b = 1 - 4(-1) = 5$$

So, $f(x) = -x^2 + 5x$.

77. $(f + g)'(x)$

$$= \lim_{h \to 0} \frac{(f + g)(x + h) - (f + g)(x)}{h}$$

$$= \lim_{h \to 0} \frac{f(x + h) + g(x + h) - [f(x) + g(x)]}{h}$$

$$= \lim_{h \to 0} \frac{f(x + h) - f(x) + g(x + h) - g(x)}{h}$$

$$= \lim_{h \to 0} \frac{f(x + h) - f(x)}{h} + \lim_{h \to 0} \frac{g(x + h) - g(x)}{h}$$

$$= f'(x) + g'(x).$$

79. (a) Using the graph, the x-value (tax rate) that appears to correspond to a y-value (percentage reduction) of 50 is 150, or a tax rate of 150 dollars per ton carbon.

(b) Using the points (200,60) and (300,80), from the graph, the rate of change is approximately

$$\frac{dP}{dT} \approx \frac{80 - 60}{300 - 200} = \frac{20}{100} = 0.2\%$$

or increasing at approximately 0.2% per dollar. (Answers will vary depending on the choice of h.)

(c) Writing Exercise—Answers will vary.

2.3 Product and Quotient Rules; Higher-Order Derivatives

1. $f(x) = (2x + 1)(3x - 2)$,

$$f'(x) = (2x + 1)\frac{d}{dx}(3x - 2) + (3x - 2)\frac{d}{dx}(2x + 1)$$
$$= (2x + 1)(3) + (3x - 2)(2)$$
$$= 12x - 1.$$

3. $y = 10(3u + 1)(1 - 5u)$,

$$\frac{dy}{du} = 10\frac{d}{du}(3u + 1)(1 - 5u)$$

$$= 10\left[(3u + 1)\frac{d}{du}(1 - 5u) + (1 - 5u)\frac{d}{du}(3u + 1)\right]$$

$$= 10[(3u + 1)(-5) + (1 - 5u)(3)]$$

$$= -300u - 20.$$

5.
$$f'(x) = \frac{1}{3}\left[(x^5 - 2x^3 + 1)\frac{d}{dx}\left(x - \frac{1}{x}\right)\right.$$
$$\left. + \left(x - \frac{1}{x}\right)\frac{d}{dx}\left(x^5 - 2x^3 + 1\right)\right]$$

$$= \frac{1}{3}\left[\left(x^5 - 2x^3 + 1\right)\left(1 + \frac{1}{x^2}\right)\right.$$
$$\left. + \left(x - \frac{1}{x}\right)\left(5x^4 - 6x^2\right)\right]$$

$$= 2x^5 - 4x^3 + \frac{4}{3}x + \frac{1}{3x^2} + \frac{1}{3}$$

7. $y = \dfrac{x+1}{x-2}$,

$$\frac{dy}{dx} = \frac{(x-2)\frac{d}{dx}(x+1) - (x+1)\frac{d}{dx}(x-2)}{(x-2)^2}$$

$$= \frac{(x-2)(1) - (x+1)(1)}{(x-2)^2}$$

$$= -\frac{3}{(x-2)^2}.$$

9. $f(t) = \dfrac{t}{t^2-2}$,

$$f'(t) = \frac{(t^2-2)\frac{d}{dt}(t) - t\frac{d}{dt}(t^2-2)}{(t^2-2)^2}$$

$$= \frac{(t^2-2)(1) - (t)(2t)}{(t^2-2)^2}$$

$$= \frac{-t^2-2}{(t^2-2)^2}.$$

11. $y = \dfrac{3}{x+5}$,

$$\frac{dy}{dx} = \frac{(x+5)\frac{d}{dx}(3) - 3\frac{d}{dx}(x+5)}{(x+5)^2}$$

$$= \frac{(x+5)(0) - 3(1)}{(x+5)^2}$$

$$= -\frac{3}{(x+5)^2}.$$

13. $f(x) = \dfrac{x^2-3x+2}{2x^2+5x-1}$,

$$f'(x) = \frac{(2x^2+5x-1)\frac{d}{dx}(x^2-3x+2)}{(2x^2+5x-1)^2}$$

$$- \frac{(x^2-3x+2)\frac{d}{dx}(2x^2+5x-1)}{(2x^2+5x-1)^2}$$

$$= \frac{(2x^2+5x-1)(2x-3)}{(2x^2+5x-1)^2}$$

$$- \frac{(x^2-3x+2)(4x+5)}{(2x^2+5x-1)^2}$$

$$= \frac{11x^2-10x-7}{(2x^2+5x-1)^2}.$$

15. $f(x) = \dfrac{(2x-1)(x+3)}{x+1} = \dfrac{2x^2+5x-3}{x+1}$

$$f'(x) = \frac{(x+1)\frac{d}{dx}(2x^2+5x-3)}{(x+1)^2}$$

$$- \frac{(2x^2+5x-3)\frac{d}{dx}(x+1)}{(x+1)^2}$$

$$= \frac{(x+1)(4x+5) - (2x^2+5x-3)(1)}{(x+1)^2}$$

$$= \frac{2x^2+4x+8}{(x+1)^2} = \frac{2(x^2+2x+4)}{(x+1)^2}$$

17. $f(x) = (2+5x)^2 = (2+5x)(2+5x)$

$$f'(x) = (2+5x)\frac{d}{dx}(2+5x) + (2+5x)\frac{d}{dx}(2+5x)$$

$$= 2(2+5x)\frac{d}{dx}(2+5x)$$

$$= 2(2+5x)(5)$$

$$= 20 + 50x = 10(2+5x)$$

19. $g(t) = \dfrac{t^2+\sqrt{t}}{2t+5} = \dfrac{t^2+t^{1/2}}{2t+5}$

$$g'(t) = \frac{(2t+5)\frac{d}{dt}(t^2+t^{1/2}) - (t^2+t^{1/2})\frac{d}{dt}(2t+5)}{(2t+5)^2}$$

$$= \frac{(2t+5)\left(2t+\dfrac{1}{2t^{1/2}}\right) - (t^2+t^{1/2})(2)}{(2t+5)^2}$$

$$= \frac{2t^2 + 10t - t^{1/2} + \dfrac{5}{2t^{1/2}}}{(2t+5)^2} \cdot \frac{2t^{1/2}}{2t^{1/2}}$$

$$= \frac{4t^{5/2} + 20t^{3/2} - 2t + 5}{2t^{1/2}(2t+5)^2}$$

$$= \frac{4\sqrt{t^5} + 20\sqrt{t^3} - 2t + 5}{2\sqrt{t}(2t+5)^2}$$

21.
$$y = (5x - 1)(4 + 3x)$$

$$\frac{dy}{dx} = 30x + 17$$

When $x = 0$, $y = -4$ and $\dfrac{dy}{dx} = 17$. The equation of the tangent line at $(0, -4)$ is

$$y + 4 = 17(x - 0), \text{ or } y = 17x - 4$$

23.
$$y = \frac{x}{2x + 3}$$

$$\frac{dy}{dx} = \frac{3}{(2x + 3)^2}$$

When $x = -1$, $y = -1$ and $\dfrac{dy}{dx} = 3$. The equation of the tangent line at $(-1, -1)$ is

$$y + 1 = 3(x + 1), \text{ or } y = 3x + 2$$

25. $y = \left(3\sqrt{x} + x\right)\left(2 - x^2\right) = \left(3x^{1/2} + x\right)\left(2 - x^2\right)$

$$\frac{dy}{dx} = -3x^2 - \frac{15}{2}x^{3/2} + \frac{3}{x^{1/2}} + 2$$

When $x = 1$, $y = 4$ and $\dfrac{dy}{dx} = -\dfrac{11}{2}$
The equation of the tangent line at $(1,4)$ is

$$y - 4 = -\frac{11}{2}(x - 1), \text{ or } y = -\frac{11}{2}x + \frac{19}{2}$$

27. $f(x) = (x + 1)(x^2 - x - 2)$

$$f'(x) = (x + 1)(2x - 1) + (x^2 - x - 2)(1)$$

$$= 3x^2 - 3$$

Since $f'(x)$ represents the slope of the tangent line and the slope of a horizontal line is zero, need to solve

$$0 = 3x^2 - 3 = 3(x + 1)(x - 1)$$
or $x = -1, 1$.
When $x = -1$, $f(-1) = 0$ and when $x = 1$,
$f(1) = -4$. So, the tangent line is horizontal at the points $(-1, 0)$ and $(1, -4)$.

29.
$$f(x) = \frac{x + 1}{x^2 + x + 1}$$

$$f'(x) = \frac{-x^2 - 2x}{(x^2 + x + 1)^2}$$

Since $f'(x)$ represents the slope of the tangent line and the slope of a horizontal line is zero, need to solve

$$0 = \frac{-x^2 - 2x}{(x^2 + x + 1)^2}$$

$$0 = -x^2 - 2x = -x(x + 2)$$

or $x = 0, -2$.

When $x = 0$, $f(0) = 1$ and when $x = -2$,
$f(-2) = -\dfrac{1}{3}$. So, the tangent line is horizontal at the points $(0,1)$ and $\left(-2, -\dfrac{1}{3}\right)$.

31.
$$f(x) = x^3(x - 5)^2$$

$$f'(x) = x^3 \cdot 2(x - 5)(1) + (x - 5)^2(3x^2)$$

$$= x^2(x - 5)\left[2x + 3(x - 5)\right]$$

$$= x^2(x - 5)(5x - 15)$$

$$= 5x^2(x - 5)(x - 3)$$

Since $f'(x)$ represents the slope of the tangent line and the slope of a horizontal line is zero, need to solve
$0 = 5x^2(x - 5)(x - 3)$
or $x = 0, 3, 5$.
When $x = 0$, $f(0) = 0$; when $x = 3$, $f(3) = 108$;
and when $x = 5$, $f(5) = 0$. So, the tangent line is horizontal at the points $(0, 0)$, $(3, 108)$ and $(5, 0)$.

33.
$$y = (x^2 + 3)(5 - 2x^3)$$

$$\frac{dy}{dx} = (x^2 + 3)(-6x^2) + (5 - 2x^3)(2x)$$

When $x = 1$,

$$\frac{dy}{dx} = (1+3)(-6) + (5-2)(2) = -18$$

35. $y = x + \dfrac{3}{2 - 4x}$

$$\frac{dy}{dx} = 1 + \frac{(2-4x)(0) - 3(-4)}{(2-4x)^2}$$

When $x = 0$,

$$\frac{dy}{dx} = 1 + \frac{12}{(2)^2} = 4$$

37.

$$y = \frac{2}{x} - \sqrt{x} = 2x^{-1} - x^{1/2}$$

$$\frac{dy}{dx} = \frac{-2}{x^2} - \frac{1}{2x^{1/2}}$$

When $x = 1$,

$$\frac{dy}{dx} = -2 - \frac{1}{2} = -\frac{5}{2}$$

The slope of a line perpendicular to the tangent line at $x = 1$ is $\dfrac{2}{5}$. The equation of the normal line at $(1,1)$ is

$$y - 1 = \frac{2}{5}(x - 1), \text{ or } y = \frac{2}{5}x + \frac{3}{5}$$

39. $y = \dfrac{5x + 7}{2 - 3x}$

$$\frac{dy}{dx} = \frac{(2-3x)(5) - (5x+7)(-3)}{(2-3x)^2}$$

When $x = 1$,

$$\frac{dy}{dx} = \frac{(2-3)(5) - (5+7)(-3)}{(2-3)^2} = 31$$

The slope of a line perpendicular to the tangent line at $x = 1$ is $-\dfrac{1}{31}$.
The equation of the normal line at $(1, -12)$ is

$$y + 12 = -\frac{1}{31}(x - 1), \text{ or } y = -\frac{1}{31}x - \frac{371}{31}$$

41. (a) $y = \dfrac{2x - 3}{x^3}$

$$\frac{dy}{dx} = \frac{(x^3)(2) - (2x-3)(3x^2)}{x^6} = \frac{-4x^3 + 9x^2}{x^6}$$

$$= \frac{-4x + 9}{x^4}$$

(b) $y = (2x - 3)(x^{-3})$

$$\frac{dy}{dx} = (2x - 3)(-3x^{-4}) + (x^{-3})(2)$$

$$= \frac{-3(2x - 3) + 2x}{x^4}$$

$$= \frac{-4x + 9}{x^4}$$

(c) $y = 2x^{-2} - 3x^{-3}$

$$\frac{dy}{dx} = -4x^{-3} + 9x^{-4} = \frac{-4}{x^3} + \frac{9}{x^4} = \frac{-4x + 9}{x^4}$$

43.

$$f(x) = \frac{2}{5}x^5 - 4x^3 + 9x^2 - 6x - 2$$

$$f'(x) = 2x^4 - 12x^2 + 18x - 6$$

$$f''(x) = 8x^3 - 24x + 18$$

45. $y = \dfrac{2}{3}x^{-1} - \sqrt{2}x^{1/2} + \sqrt{2}x - \dfrac{1}{6}x^{-1/2}$

$$\frac{dy}{dx} = y' = -\frac{2}{3}x^{-2} - \frac{\sqrt{2}}{2}x^{-1/2} + \sqrt{2} + \frac{1}{12}x^{-3/2}$$

$$\frac{d^2y}{dx^2} = y'' = \frac{4}{3}x^{-3} + \frac{\sqrt{2}}{4}x^{-3/2} - \frac{1}{8}x^{-5/2}$$

$$= \frac{4}{3x^3} + \frac{\sqrt{2}}{4x^{3/2}} - \frac{1}{8x^{5/2}}$$

47.

$$y = (x^3 + 2x - 1)(3x + 5)$$

$$\frac{dy}{dx} = y' = (x^3 + 2x - 1)(3) + (3x + 5)(3x^2 + 2)$$

$$= 12x^3 + 15x^2 + 12x + 7$$

$$\frac{d^2y}{dx^2} = y'' = 36x^2 + 30x + 12$$

49. $S(t) = \dfrac{2000t}{4 + 0.3t}$

So,

$f'(y) =$

$$\dfrac{3(1-4y)^{1/2} - (3y+1) \cdot \dfrac{-2}{(1-4y)^{1/2}}}{1-4y} \cdot \dfrac{(1-4y)^{1/2}}{(1-4y)^{1/2}}$$

$$= \dfrac{3(1-4y) + 2(3y+1)}{(1-4y)^{3/2}}$$

$$= \dfrac{5-6y}{(1-4y)^{3/2}}$$

43. $f(x) = \sqrt{3x+4} = (3x+4)^{1/2}$

$$f'(x) = \dfrac{1}{2}(3x+4)^{-1/2} \cdot 3 = \dfrac{3}{2\sqrt{3x+4}}$$

$m = f'(0) = \dfrac{3}{2\sqrt{3(0)+4}} = \dfrac{3}{4}$ and $f(0) = 2$

So, the equation of the tangent line at $(0, 2)$ is

$$y = \dfrac{3}{4}x + 2$$

45. $f(x) = (3x^2+1)^2$

$$f'(x) = 2(3x^2+1)(6x)$$

$m = f'(-1) = -48$ and $f(-1) = 16$, so the equation of the tangent line at $(-1, 16)$ is

$$y - 16 = -48(x+1), \text{ or } y = -48x - 32$$

47. $f(x) = \dfrac{1}{(2x-1)^6} = (2x-1)^{-6}$

$$f'(x) = -6(2x-1)^{-5}(2) = -\dfrac{12}{(2x-1)^5}$$

$m = f'(1) = -12$ and $f(1) = 1$, so the equation of the tangent line at $(1, 1)$ is

$$y - 1 = -12(x-1), \text{ or } y = -12x + 13$$

49. $f(x) = \sqrt[3]{\dfrac{x}{x+2}} = \left(\dfrac{x}{x+2}\right)^{1/3}$

$$f'(x) = \dfrac{1}{3}\left(\dfrac{x}{x+2}\right)^{-2/3} \cdot \dfrac{(x+2)(1) - (x)(1)}{(x+2)^2}$$

$$= \dfrac{(x+2)^{2/3}}{3x^{2/3}} \cdot \dfrac{2}{(x+2)^2}$$

$$= \dfrac{2}{3x^{2/3}(x+2)^{4/3}}$$

$m = f'(-1) = \dfrac{2}{3}$ and $f(-1) = -1$, so the equation of the tangent line at $(-1, -1)$ is

$y + 1 = \dfrac{2}{3}(x+1)$, or $y = \dfrac{2}{3}x - \dfrac{1}{3}$

51. $f(x) = (x^2+x)^2$

$$f'(x) = 2(x^2+x)(2x+1) = 2x(x+1)(2x+1) = 0$$

when $x = -1$, $x = 0$, and $x = -\dfrac{1}{2}$.

53. $f(x) = \dfrac{x}{(3x-2)^2}$

$$f'(x) = \dfrac{(3x-2)^2(1) - (x)\left[2(3x-2)(3)\right]^2}{\left[(3x-2)^2\right]^2}$$

$$= \dfrac{(3x-2)\left[(3x-2) - 6x\right]}{(3x-2)^4}$$

$$= \dfrac{-3x-2}{(3x-2)^3}$$

$0 = \dfrac{-3x-2}{(3x-2)^3}$ when $-3x-2 = 0$, or $x = -\dfrac{2}{3}$.

55. $f(x) = \sqrt{x^2-4x+5} = (x^2-4x+5)^{1/2}$

$$f'(x) = \dfrac{1}{2}(x^2-4x+5)^{-1/2}(2x-4)$$

$$= \dfrac{2x-4}{2(x^2-4x+5)^{1/2}}$$

$$= \dfrac{x-2}{(x^2-4x+5)^{1/2}}$$

$0 = \dfrac{x-2}{(x^2-4x+5)^{1/2}}$ when $x-2 = 0$, or $x = 2$.

57. $f(x) = (3x + 5)^2$

    (a) $f'(x) = 2(3x + 5)(3) = 6(3x + 5)$

    (b) $f(x) = (3x + 5)(3x + 5)$

        $f'(x) = (3x + 5)(3) + (3x + 5)(3) = 6(3x + 5)$

59. $f(x) = (3x + 1)^5$

$$f'(x) = 5(3x + 1)^4(3) = 15(3x + 1)^4,$$

$$f''(x) = 60(3x + 1)(3)^3 = 180(3x + 1)^3$$

61. $h = (t^2 + 5)^8$

$$\frac{dh}{dt} = 8(t^2 + 5)^7(2t) = 16t(t^2 + 5)^7,$$

$$\frac{d^2h}{dt^2} = 16t[7(t^2 + 5)^6(2t)] + (t^2 + 5)^7(16)$$

$$= 16(t^2 + 5)^6[14t^2 + (t^2 + 5)]$$

$$= 16(t^2 + 5)^6(15t^2 + 5)$$

$$= 80(t^2 + 5)^6(3t^2 + 1)$$

63.

$$f(x) = \sqrt{1 + x^2} = (1 + x^2)^{1/2}$$

$$f'(x) = \frac{1}{2}(1 + x^2)^{-1/2}(2x)$$

$$= \frac{x}{(1 + x^2)^{1/2}}$$

$$f''(x) = \frac{(1 + x^2)^{1/2}(1) - (x)\left[\frac{1}{2}(1 + x^2)^{-1/2}(2x)\right]}{1 + x^2}$$

$$= \frac{(1 + x^2)^{1/2} - \dfrac{x^2}{(1 + x^2)^{1/2}}}{1 + x^2} \cdot \frac{(1 + x^2)^{1/2}}{(1 + x^2)^{1/2}}$$

$$= \frac{1 + x^2 - x^2}{(1 + x^2)^{3/2}} = \frac{1}{(1 + x^2)^{3/2}}$$

65. (a)

$$f(t) = \sqrt{10t^2 + t + 236}$$

$$= (10t^2 + t + 236)^{1/2}$$

The rate at which the earnings are growing is

$$f'(t) = \frac{1}{2}(10t^2 + t + 236)^{-1/2}(20t + 1)$$

$$= \frac{20t + 1}{2(10t^2 + t + 236)^{1/2}}$$

thousand dollars per year.
The rate of growth in 2003 ($t = 5$) is

$$f'(5) = \frac{20(5) + 1}{2(10(5)^2 + 5 + 236)^{1/2}} = 2.279$$

or \$2,279 per year.

(b) The percentage rate of the earnings increases in 2003 was

$$100\frac{f'(5)}{f(5)}$$

$$= \frac{100(2.279)}{\sqrt{10(5^2) + 5 + 236}} = 10.285\% \text{ per year.}$$

67. $D(p) = \dfrac{4{,}374}{p^2} = 4{,}374p^{-2}$

    (a) $\dfrac{dD}{dp} = -8{,}748p^{-3} = \dfrac{-8{,}784}{p^3}$ When the price is \$9,

$$\frac{dD}{dp} = \frac{-8{,}748}{(9)^3} = -12 \text{ pounds per dollar}$$

    (b) $\dfrac{dD}{dt} = \dfrac{dD}{dp} \cdot \dfrac{dp}{dt}$

    Now, $p(t) = 0.02t^2 + 0.1t + 6$

$$\frac{dp}{dt} = 0.04t + 0.1 \text{ dollars per week}$$

$$\frac{dD}{dt} = \frac{-8{,}748}{p^3}(0.04t + 0.1) \text{ pounds per week}$$

When $t = 10$,
$p(10) = 0.02(10)^2 + 0.1(10) + 6 = 9$

$$\text{so,} \quad \frac{dD}{dt} = \frac{-8{,}748}{9^3}[0.04(10) + 0.1]$$

$$= -6 \text{ pounds per week}$$

Since the rate is negative, demand will be decreasing.

69. $p(t) = 20 - \dfrac{6}{t + 1} = 20 - 6(t + 1)^{-1}$

$$c(p) = 0.5\sqrt{p^2 + p + 58} = 0.5(p^2 + p + 58)^{1/2}$$

(a)
$$\frac{dc}{dp} = \frac{1}{4}(p^2 + p + 58)^{-1/2}(2p + 1)$$

$$= \frac{2p + 1}{4\sqrt{p^2 + p + 58}}$$

When $p = 18$,

$$\frac{dc}{dp} = \frac{2(18) + 1}{4\sqrt{18^2 + 18 + 58}}$$

$$= \frac{37}{80} = 0.4625 \text{ ppm/thous people}$$

(b)
$$\frac{dc}{dt} = \frac{dc}{dp} \cdot \frac{dp}{dt}$$

$$\frac{dp}{dt} = 0 + 6(t + 1)^{-2} \cdot 1 = \frac{6}{(t + 1)^2}$$

$$\frac{dc}{dt} = \frac{2p + 1}{4\sqrt{p^2 + p + 58}} \cdot \frac{6}{(t + 1)^2}$$

When $t = 2$, $p(2) = 20 - \frac{6}{2+1} = 18$ and

$$\frac{dc}{dt} = (0.4625) \cdot \frac{6}{(2 + 1)^2}$$

$$\approx 0.308 \text{ ppm/year}$$

Since $\frac{dc}{dt}$ is positive, the level is increasing.

71. $L = 0.25w^{2.6}$; $w = 3 + 0.21A$

(a) $\frac{dL}{dw} = 0.65w^{1.6}$ mm per kg

When $w = 60$,

$$\frac{dL}{dw} = 0.65(60)^{1.6} \approx 455 \text{ mm per kg}$$

(b) When $A = 100$, $w = 3 + 0.21(100) = 24$ and
$L(24) = 0.25(24)^{2.6} \approx 969$ mm long.

$$\frac{dL}{dA} = \frac{dL}{dw} \cdot \frac{dw}{dA}$$

Since $\frac{dw}{dA} = 0.21$,

$$\frac{dL}{dA} = (0.65w^{1.6})(0.21)$$

When $A = 100$, since $w = 24$,

$$\frac{dL}{dA} = 0.65(24)^{1.6}(0.21) \approx 22.1$$

The tiger's length is increasing at the rate of about 22.1 mm per day

73. $P(t) = 1 - \frac{12}{t+12} + \frac{144}{(t+12)^2}$

(a) $P(t) = 1 - 12(t + 12)^{-1} + 144(t + 12)^{-2}$

$P'(t) = 0 + 12(t + 12)^{-2} \cdot 1 - 288(t + 12)^{-3} \cdot 1$

$$= \frac{12}{(t + 12)^2} - \frac{288}{(t + 12)^3}$$

When $t = 10$,

$$P'(10) = \frac{12}{(10 + 12)^2} - \frac{288}{(10 + 12)^3}$$

$$\approx -0.002254 = -0.2254\% \text{ per day}$$

where the negative sign indicates that the proportion is decreasing.

(b)
$$P'(15) = \frac{12}{(15 + 12)^2} - \frac{288}{(15 + 12)^3}$$

$$\approx 0.001829$$

Since this value is positive, the proportion is increasing.

(c)
$$\lim_{t \to +\infty} P(t) = \lim_{t \to +\infty} 1 - \frac{12}{t + 12} + \frac{144}{(t + 12)^2}$$

$$= 1 - 0 + 0 = 1$$

Since $P(0) = 1$, this is the normal level in the lake.

75.
$$Q(K) = 500K^{2/3}$$

$$K(t) = \frac{2t^4 + 3t + 149}{t + 2}$$

(a) $K(3) = \frac{2(3)^4 + 3(3) + 149}{3 + 2} = 64$ or \$64,000.

$Q(64) = 500(64)^{2/3} = 8,000$ units

(b) $\frac{dQ}{dt} = \frac{dQ}{dK} \cdot \frac{dK}{dt}$

$$\frac{dQ}{dK} = 500\left(\frac{2}{3}K^{-1/3}\right) = \frac{1000}{3K^{1/3}}$$

$$\frac{dK}{dt} = \frac{(t + 2)(8t^3 + 3) - (2t^4 + 3t + 149)(1)}{(t + 2)^2}$$

$$= \frac{6t^4 + 16t^3 - 143}{(t + 2)^2}$$

When $t = 5$, $K(5) = \dfrac{2(5)^4 + 3(5) + 149}{5 + 2} =$ 202. So,

$$\frac{dQ}{dt} = \frac{1000}{3(202)^{1/3}} \cdot \frac{6(5)^4 + 16(5)^3 - 143}{(5 + 2)^2}$$

$$\approx 6,501 \text{ units per month}$$

Since $\dfrac{dQ}{dt}$ is positive when $t = 5$, production will be increasing.

77. $V(T) = 0.41(-0.01T^2 + 0.4T + 3.52)$

$$m(V) = \frac{0.39V}{1 + 0.09V}$$

(a) $\dfrac{dV}{dt} = 0.41(-0.02T + 0.4)\text{cm}^3$ per °C

(b)

$$\frac{dm}{dV} = \frac{(1 + 0.09V)(0.39) - (0.39V)(0.09)}{(1 + 0.09V)^2}$$

$$= \frac{0.39}{(1 + 0.09V)^2} \text{ gm per cm}^3$$

(c) When $T = 10$,

$$V(10) = 0.41[-0.01(10)^2 + 0.4(10) + 3.52] = 2.6732\text{cm}^3$$

$$\frac{dm}{dT} = \frac{dm}{dV} \cdot \frac{dV}{dt}$$

$$= \frac{0.39}{(1 + 0.09V)^2} \cdot 0.41(-0.02T + 0.4)$$

When $T = 10$,

$$\frac{dm}{dT} = \frac{0.39}{[1 + 0.09(2.6732)]^2} \cdot 0.41[-0.02(10) + 0.4]$$

$$= 0.02078 \text{ gm per °C}$$

79. $T = aL\sqrt{L - b} = aL(L - b)^{1/2}$

(a) $\dfrac{dT}{dL} = aL \cdot \dfrac{1}{2}(L - b)^{-1/2}(1) + (L - b)^{1/2}(a)$

$$= \frac{aL}{2(L - b)^{1/2}} + a(L - b)^{1/2}\frac{2(L - b)^{1/2}}{2(L - b)^{1/2}}$$

$$= \frac{aL + 2a(L - b)}{2(L - b)^{1/2}} = \frac{3aL - 2ab}{2\sqrt{L - b}} = \frac{a(3L - 2b)}{2\sqrt{L - b}}$$

$\dfrac{dT}{dL}$ is the rate of change in the time required with respect to the number of items in the list.

(b) Writing Exercise—Answers will vary.

81. $s(t) = (3 + t - t^2)^{3/2}$, $0 \le t \le 2$

(a) $v(t) = s'(t) = \dfrac{3}{2}(3 + t - t^2)^{1/2}(1 - 2t)$

$a(t) = v'(t)$

$$= \frac{3}{2}\Big[(3 + t - t^2)^{1/2}(-2)$$

$$+ (1 - 2t)\frac{1}{2}(3 + t - t^2)^{-1/2}(1 - 2t)\Big]$$

$$= \frac{3}{2}\Big[-2(3 + t - t^2)^{1/2}\frac{2(3 + t - t^2)^{1/2}}{2(3 + t - t^2)^{1/2}}$$

$$+ \frac{(1 - 2t)^2}{2(3 + t - t^2)^{1/2}}\Big]$$

$$= \frac{3}{2}\Big[\frac{-4(3 + t - t^2) + (1 - 2t)^2}{2(3 + t - t^2)^{1/2}}\Big]$$

$$= \frac{3}{2}\Big[\frac{-12 - 4t + 4t^2 + 1 - 4t + 4t^2}{2(3 + t - t^2)^{1/2}}\Big]$$

$$= \frac{24t^2 - 24t - 33}{4\sqrt{3 + t - t^2}}$$

(b) To find when object is stationary for $0 \le t \le 2$,

$$\frac{3}{2}\sqrt{3 + t - t^2}(1 - 2t) = 0$$

Press $\boxed{y=}$ and input $1.5\sqrt{(3 + x - x^2)} * (1 - 2x)$ for $y_1 =$
Use window dimensions $[-5, 5]1$ by $[-5, 5]1$
Use the zero function under calc menu to find the only x-intercept occurs at $x = 1/2$.
(Note: algebraically, $\sqrt{3 + t - t^2} = 0$ when $t = \dfrac{1 + \sqrt{13}}{2}$, but this value is not in the domain.)

Object is stationary when $t = 1/2$.

$$s\left(\frac{1}{2}\right) = \left[3 + \frac{1}{2} - \left(\frac{1}{2}\right)^2\right]^{3/2} = \frac{\sqrt{2197}}{8} \approx 5.859$$

$$a\left(\frac{1}{2}\right) = \frac{24\left(\frac{1}{2}\right)^2 - 24\left(\frac{1}{2}\right) - 33}{4\sqrt{3 + \frac{1}{2} - \left(\frac{1}{2}\right)^2}}$$

$$= \frac{-39}{2\sqrt{13}} = \frac{-3\sqrt{13}}{2} \approx -5.4083$$

For $a(1/2)$ you can use the dy/dx function under the calc menu and enter $x = .5$ to find $v'(1/2) = a(1/2) \approx -5.4083$.

(c) To find when the acceleration is zero for $0 \le t \le 2$,

$$\frac{24t^2 - 24t - 33}{4\sqrt{3 + t - t^2}} = 0$$

Press $\boxed{y=}$ and input $(24x^2 - 24x - 33)/$
$(4\sqrt{(3 + x - x^2)})$ for $y_2 =$
Press $\boxed{\text{Graph}}$
You may wish to deactivate y_1 so only the graph of y_2 is shown.
Use the zero function under the calc menu to find the x-intercepts are $x \approx -0.775$ and $x \approx 1.77$. (disregard $x = -0.775$.)
The acceleration is zero for $t = 1.77$,
$s(1.77) = (3 + 1.77 - (1.77)^2)^{3/2} \approx 2.09$
Reactivate y_1 and use the value function under the calc menu. Make sure that y_1 is displayed in the upper left corner and enter $x = 1.77$ to find $v(1.77) \approx -4.87$.

(d) We already have $v(t)$ inputted for $y_1 =$ and $a(t)$ inputted for $y_2 =$
Press $\boxed{y=}$ and input $(3 + x - x^2) \wedge (3/2)$ for $y_3 =$
Use window dimensions $[0, 2]1$ by $[-5, 5]1$
Press $\boxed{\text{Graph}}$

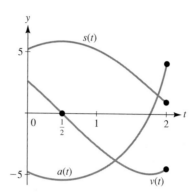

(e) To determine when $v(t)$ and $a(t)$ have opposite signs, press $\boxed{y=}$ and deativate $y_3 =$ so only $v(t)$ and $a(t)$ are shown. Press $\boxed{\text{graph}}$. We see from the graph, $v(t)$ and $a(t)$ have opposite signs in two intervals. We know the t-intercept of $v(t)$ is $t = 1/2$ and the t-intercept of $a(t)$ is $t = 1.77$. The object is slowing down for $0 \le t < 0.5$ and $1.77 < t \le 2$.

83. To prove that

$$\frac{d}{dx}[h(x)]^2 = 2h(x)h'(x),$$

use the product rule to get

$$\frac{d}{dx}[h(x)]^2 = \frac{d}{dx}[h(x)h(x)]$$
$$= h(x)h'(x) + h'(x)h(x)$$
$$= 2h(x)h'(x).$$

85. To use numeric differentiation to calculate $f'(1)$ and $f'(-3)$, press $\boxed{y=}$ and input $(3.1x^2 + 19.4) \wedge (1/3)$ for $y_1 =$
Use the window dimensions $[-5, 5]1$ by $[-3, 8]1$
Press $\boxed{\text{Graph}}$
Use the dy/dx function under the calc menu and enter $x = 1$ to find $f'(1) \approx 0.2593$
Repeat this for $x = -3$ to find $f'(-3) \approx -0.474$
Since there is only one minimum, we can conclude the graph has only one horizontal tangent.

2.5 Marginal Analysis; Approximations Using Increments

1. $C(x) = \frac{1}{5}x^2 + 4x + 57$;

$p(x) = \frac{1}{4}(36 - x) = 9 - \frac{1}{4}x$

(a) Marginal cost $= C'(x) = \frac{2}{5}x + 4$

Revenue $=$ (# sold)(selling price)

$$R(x) = x\left(9 - \frac{1}{4}x\right) = 9x - \frac{x^2}{4}$$

Marginal revenue $= R'(x) = 9 - \frac{x}{2}$

(b) Estimated cost of 4th unit $= C'(3) = \frac{2}{5}(3) + 4 =$ 5.20

(c) Actual cost of 4th unit $= C(4) - C(3)$

$$= \left[\frac{1}{5}(4)^2 + 4(4) + 57\right] - \left[\frac{1}{5}(3)^2 + 4(3) + 57\right]$$

$$= \$5.40$$

(d) Estimated revenue from sale of 4th unit
$= R'(3) = 9 - \frac{3}{2} = \$7.50$

(e) Actual revenue from sale of 4th unit

$$= R(4) - R(3)$$

$$= \left[9(4) - \frac{(4)^2}{4}\right] - \left[9(3) - \frac{(3)^2}{4}\right] = \$7.25$$

3. $C(x) = \frac{1}{3}x^2 + 2x + 39$; $p(x) = -x^2 - 4x + 80$

(a) $C'(x) = \frac{2}{3}x + 2$

$R(x) = x(-x^2 - 4x + 80) = -x^3 - 4x^2 + 80x$, so

$R'(x) = -3x^2 - 8x + 80$

(b) $C'(3) = \frac{2}{3}(3) + 2 = \$4.00$

(c) $C(4) - C(3) = \left[\frac{1}{3}(4)^2 + 2(4) + 39\right]$

$$- \left[\frac{1}{3}(3)^2 + 2(3) + 39\right]$$

$$\approx \$4.33$$

(d) $R'(3) = -3(3)^2 - 8(3) + 80 = \$29$

(e) $R(4) - R(3) = \left[-(4)^3 - 4(4)^2 + 80(4)\right]$

$$- \left[-(3)^3 - 4(3)^2 + 80(3)\right]$$

$$= \$15$$

5. $C(x) = \frac{1}{4}x^2 + 43$; $p(x) = \frac{3 + 2x}{1 + x}$

(a) $C'(x) = \frac{1}{2}x$

$$R(x) = x\left(\frac{3 + 2x}{1 + x}\right) = \frac{3x + 2x^2}{1 + x}, \text{ so}$$

$$R'(x) = \frac{(1 + x)(3 + 4x) - (3x + 2x^2)(1)}{(1 + x)^2}$$

$$= \frac{2x^2 + 4x + 3}{(1 + x)^2}$$

(b) $C'(3) = \frac{1}{2}(3) = \$1.50$

(c) $C(4) - C(3) = \left[\frac{1}{4}(4)^2 + 43\right] - \left[\frac{1}{4}(3)^2 + 43\right]$

$$= 47 - 45.25 = \$1.75$$

(d) $R'(3) = \frac{2(3)^2 + 4(3) + 3}{(1 + 3)^2} = \frac{33}{16} \approx \$2.06$

(e) $R(4) - R(3)$

$$= \frac{3(4) + 2(4)^2}{1 + 4} - \frac{3(3) + 2(3)^2}{1 + 3}$$

$$= \frac{44}{5} - \frac{27}{4} = \$2.05$$

7. $f(x) = x^2 - 3x + 5$; x increases from 5 to 5.3

$$\Delta f \approx f'(x)\Delta x$$

$$f'(x) = 2x - 3$$

$$\Delta x = 5.3 - 5 = 0.3$$

$$\Delta f \approx [2(5) - 3](0.3) = 2.1$$

9. $f(x) = x^2 + 2x - 9$; x increases from 4 to 4.3.
Estimated percentage change is

$$100\frac{\Delta f}{f} \text{ where } \Delta f \approx f'(x)\Delta x$$

$$f'(x) = 2x + 2, \ \Delta x = 4.3 - 4 = 0.3$$

$$\Delta f \approx [2(4) + 2](0.3) = 3$$

$$f(4) = (4)^2 + 2(4) - 9 = 15$$

$$100\frac{\Delta f}{f} = 100\frac{3}{15} = 20\%$$

11. $C(q) = 0.1q^3 - 0.5q^2 + 500q + 200$

(a) $\qquad C'(q) = 0.3q^2 - q + 500$

$$C'(3) = 0.3(3)^2 - 3 + 500$$

$$= \$499.70$$

(b) $C(4) - C(3)$

$$= [0.1(4)^3 - 0.5(4)^2 + 500(4) + 200]$$

$$- [0.1(3)^3 - 0.5(3)^2 500(3) + 200]$$

$$= \$2198.40 - \$1698.20 = \$500.20$$

13. $C(q) = 3q^2 + q + 500$

(a) $\qquad C'(q) = 6q + 1$

$$C'(40) = 6(40) + 1 = \$241$$

(b) $C(41) - C(40)$

$$= [3(41)^2 + 41 + 500] - [3(40)^2 + 40 + 500]$$

$$= \$244$$

15. $C(t) = 100t^2 + 400t + 5,000$

$$\Delta C \approx C'(t)\Delta t$$

$$C'(t) = 200t + 400$$

Since t is measured in years, the next six months
$= \frac{1}{2}$ year $= \Delta t$

$$\Delta C \approx C'(0)\left(\frac{1}{2}\right) = [200(0) + 400]\left(\frac{1}{2}\right) = 200,$$

or an increase of approximately 200 newspapers.

17. $\qquad R(q) = 240q - 0.05q^2$

$$\Delta R \approx R'(q)\Delta q$$

$$R'(q) = 240 - 0.1q$$

Since will decrease by 0.65 unit,

$$\Delta q = -0.65$$

$$\Delta R \approx R'(80)(-0.65) = [240 - 0.1(80)](-0.65)$$

$$= -150.8, \text{ or a decrease of approximately } \$150.80.$$

19. $Q(K) = 600K^{1/2}$

$$\Delta Q \approx Q'(K)\Delta K$$

$$Q'(K) = 300K^{-1/2} = \frac{300}{\sqrt{K}}$$

Since K is measured in thousands of dollars, the current value of K is 900 and

$$\Delta K = \frac{800}{1000} = 0.8$$

$$\Delta Q \approx Q'(900)(0.8) = \left(\frac{300}{\sqrt{900}}\right)(0.8)$$

$$= 8,$$

or an increase of approximately 8 units.

21. $T(x) = 60x^{3/2} + 40x + 1,200$
Estimated percentage change is

$$100\frac{\Delta T}{T} \text{ where } \Delta T \approx T'(x)\Delta x$$

$$T'(x) = 90x^{1/2} + 40 = 90\sqrt{x} + 40$$

The beginning of the year 2010 is 8 years after the beginning of 2002, so the beginning value of t is 8. Measured in years, 6 months $= \frac{1}{2}$ year $= \Delta t$.

$$\Delta T \approx T'(8)\left(\frac{1}{2}\right) = \left(90\sqrt{8} + 40\right)\left(\frac{1}{2}\right) = 147.279$$

$$T(8) = 60(8)^{3/2} + 40(8) + 1,200 = 2,877.645$$

$$100\frac{\Delta T}{T} = 100\frac{147.279}{2877.645} \approx 5.12\%$$

23. $Q = 3,000K^{1/2}L^{1/3}$
Since labor force is to remain unchanged, write Q as

$$Q = 3,000\sqrt[3]{1331}K^{1/2}$$

Since increase in $K = 1$ (noting that K is measured in thousands of dollars)

$$\Delta Q \approx Q'(K)$$

$$Q'(K) = 1{,}500\sqrt[3]{1{,}331}K^{-1/2} = \frac{1{,}500\sqrt[3]{1{,}331}}{\sqrt{K}}$$

In thousands of dollars, the current value of $K = 400$, so

$$\Delta Q \approx Q'(400) = \frac{1{,}500\sqrt[3]{1{,}331}}{\sqrt{400}} = 825,$$

or an increase of approximately 825 units.

25. $C(q) = \dfrac{1}{6}q^3 + 642q + 400$

$$\Delta C \approx C'(q)\Delta q$$

We want to approximate Δq, so

$$\Delta q \approx \frac{\Delta C}{C'(q)}$$

$$C'(q) = \frac{1}{2}q^2 + 642, \quad C'(4) = \frac{1}{2}(4)^2 + 642 = 650,$$

and $\Delta C = -130$. So, $\Delta q \approx \frac{-130}{650} = -0.2$, or increase production by 0.2 units.

27. The maximum percentage error in C is

$$100\frac{\Delta C}{C} \quad \text{where } \Delta C \approx C'(x)\Delta x$$

$$C'(x) = -a(x-b)^{-2}(1) = \frac{-a}{(x-b)^2}$$

$$\Delta C \approx C'(c)(\pm 0.03c) = \frac{-a}{(c-b)^2}(\pm 0.03c)$$

$$= \frac{\pm.03ac}{(c-b)^2}$$

$$C(c) = \frac{a}{c-b}$$

$$\text{So,} \quad 100\frac{\Delta C}{C} = 100\frac{\dfrac{\pm.03ac}{(c-b)^2}}{\dfrac{a}{(c-b)}}$$

$$= \frac{\pm 3c}{|c-b|}\%$$

29. $V = \pi R^2 L$, where L is constant for a given artery. The percentage error in V is

$$100\frac{\Delta V}{V} \quad \text{where } \Delta V \approx V'(R)\Delta R$$

$V'(R) = 2\pi RL$ so, noting that the radius is decreased by the plaque,

$$\Delta V \approx V'(0.3)(-0.07) = 2\pi(0.3)L(-0.07)$$
$$= -0.042\pi L$$

$$V(0.3) = \pi(0.3)^2 L = 0.09\pi L, \text{ so}$$

$$100\frac{\Delta V}{V} = 100\frac{-0.042\pi L}{0.09\pi L} = -46.67\%,$$

or a blockage in the volume of 46.67%.

31. $\Delta L \approx L'(T)\Delta T$

Since $\sigma = \dfrac{L'(T)}{L(T)}, \quad L'(T) = \sigma L(T)$.

Also, $\Delta T = 35 - (-20) = 55$.

$$\text{So, } \Delta L \approx \sigma L(T)\Delta T$$

$$\approx (1.4 \times 10^{-5})(50)(55)$$

$$\approx 3{,}850 \times 10^{-5}$$

or an increase in length of approximately 0.0385 feet.

33. First application of Newton's method:
The equation of the tangent line at $(x_0, f(x_0))$ is

$$y - f(x_0) = f'(x_0)(x - x_0)$$

The x-intercept is when $y = 0$, or when

$$-f(x_0) = f'(x_0)(x - x_0)$$

Solving for $x = x_1$

$$x_1 = x_0 - \frac{f(x_0)}{f'(x_0)}$$

Second application of Newton's method:
Using the point $(x, f(x_1))$,

$$y - f(x_1) = f'(x_1)(x - x_1)$$
$$-f(x_1) = f'(x_1)(x - x_1)$$

Solving for $x = x_2$

$$x_2 = x_1 - \frac{f(x_1)}{f'(x_1)}$$

In general, using the point $(x_{n-1}, f(x_{n-1}))$,

$$y - f(x_{n-1}) = f'(x_{n-1})(x - x_{n-1})$$

$$- f(x_{n-1}) = f'(x_{n-1})(x - x_{n-1})$$

Solving for $x = x_n$,

$$x_n = x_{n-1} - \frac{f(x_{n-1})}{f'(x_{n-1})}$$

35. To use graphing utility to graph f and to estimate each root,
Press y= and input $x \wedge 4 - 4x \wedge 3 + 10$ for $y_1 =$
Use window dimensions $[-10, 10]1$ by $[-20, 20]2$
Press Graph
Use the zero function under the calc menu to find the zeros (x-intercepts) of f to be $x \approx 1.6$ and $x \approx 3.8$
To use Newton's method, $f(x) = x^4 - 4x^3 + 10$
and $f'(x) = 4x^3 - 12x^2$

$$x - \frac{f(x)}{f'(x)} = x - \frac{x^4 - 4x^3 + 10}{4x^3 - 12x^2} = \frac{3x^4 - 8x^3 - 10}{4x^3 - 12x^2}$$

For $n = 1, 2, 3, \ldots$

$$x_n = \frac{3x_{n-1}^4 - 8x_{n-1}^3 - 10}{4x_{n-1}^3 - 12x_{n-1}^2}$$

Using the graph shown on the calculator, we see one x-intercept is between 1 and 2.
Let $x_0 = 1$, then

$$x_1 = \frac{3x_0^4 - 8x_0^3 - 10}{4x_0^3 - 12x_0^2} = \frac{-15}{-8} = 1.875 \text{ using } x_0 = 1$$

$$x_2 = \frac{3x_1^4 - 8x_1^3 - 10}{4x_1^3 - 12x_1^2} = 1.621 \text{ using } x_1 = 1.875$$

Thus, one x-intercept is $x = 1.6$
The second x-intercept is between 3 and 4.
Let $x_0 = 4$, then

$$x_1 = \frac{3x_0^4 - 8x_0^3 - 10}{4x_0^3 - 12x_0^2} = 3.844 \text{ using } x_0 = 4$$

$$x_2 = \frac{3x_1^4 - 8x_1^3 - 10}{4x_1^3 - 12x_1^2} = 3.821 \text{ using } x_1 = 3.844$$

Thus, the second x-intercept is $x = 3.8$.
Note: Enter $(3x \wedge 4 - 8x \wedge 3 - 10)/(4x \wedge 3 - 12x \wedge 2)$ for $y_2 =$ and use the value function under

the calc menu to do all the calculations for Newton's method.

37. $f(x) = \sqrt[3]{x} = x^{1/3}; \ f'(x) = \frac{1}{3}x^{-2/3} = \frac{1}{3x^{2/3}}$

(a)
$$x_{n+1} = x_n - \frac{(x_n)^{1/3}}{\frac{1}{3(x_n)^{2/3}}}$$

$$x_{n+1} = x_n - 3x_n, \text{ or } x_{n+1} = -2x_n$$

So, if x_0 is first guess,

$$x_1 = -2x_0,$$
$$x_2 = -2x_1 = -2(-2x_0) = 4x_0$$
$$x_3 = -2x_2 = -2(4x_0) = -8x_0,$$

etc.

(b) To use the graphing utility to graph f and to draw the tangent lines,
Press y= and input $x \wedge (1/3)$ for $y_1 =$
Use window dimensions $[-5, 5]1$ by $[-5, 5]1$

Arbitrarily, let's use $x_0 = 1$. Then we will draw tangent lines to the graph of f for $x = 1, -2, 4 \ldots$
Press 2nd Draw and use the tangent function.
Enter $x = 1$ and the tangent line is drawn.
Repeat for $x = -2$ and $x = 4$.
>From the graph, can see that $x = 0$ is the root of $\sqrt[3]{x}$. Any choice besides zero for the first estimate leads to successive approximations on opposite sides of the root, getting farther and farther from the root.

2.6 Implicit Differentiation and Related Rates

1. $2x + 3y = 7$

(a) $2 + 3\dfrac{dy}{dx} = 0$

$$\frac{dy}{dx} = -\frac{2}{3}$$

(b) Solving for y,

$$y = -\frac{2}{3}x + \frac{7}{3}$$

$$\frac{dy}{dx} = -\frac{2}{3}$$

3. $x^3 - y^2 = 5$

(a) $3x^2 - 2y\frac{dy}{dx} = 0$

$$\frac{dy}{dx} = \frac{3x^2}{2y}$$

(b) Solving for y,

$$y = \sqrt{x^3 - 5} = (x^3 - 5)^{1/2}$$

$$\frac{dy}{dx} = \frac{1}{2}(x^3 - 5)^{-1/2} \cdot 3x^2$$

$$= \frac{3x^2}{2\sqrt{x^3 - 5}} = \frac{3x^2}{2y}$$

5. $xy = 4$

(a) $x \cdot \frac{dy}{dx} + y \cdot 1 = 0$

$$\frac{dy}{dx} = -\frac{y}{x}$$

(b) Solving for y,

$$y = \frac{4}{x} = 4x^{-1}$$

$$\frac{dy}{dx} = -4x^{-2} = -\frac{4}{x^2}$$

$$= -\frac{\frac{4}{x}}{x} = -\frac{y}{x}$$

7. $xy + 2y = 3$

(a) $x\frac{dy}{dx} + y \cdot 1 + 2\frac{dy}{dx} = 0$

$$(x + 2)\frac{dy}{dx} = -y$$

$$\frac{dy}{dx} = \frac{-y}{x + 2}$$

(b) Solving for y,

$$y = \frac{3}{x + 2} = 3(x + 2)^{-1}$$

$$\frac{dy}{dx} = -3(x + 2)^{-2}(1) = \frac{-3}{(x + 2)^2}$$

$$= \frac{3}{x + 2} \cdot \frac{-1}{x + 2}$$

$$= y \cdot \frac{-1}{x + 2} = \frac{-y}{x + 2}$$

9.
$$x^2 + y^2 = 25$$

$$2x + 2y\frac{dy}{dx} = 0$$

$$\frac{dy}{dx} = -\frac{x}{y}$$

11.
$$x^3 + y^3 = xy,$$

$$3x^2 + 3y^2\frac{dy}{dx} = x\frac{dy}{dx} + y \cdot 1$$

$$(3y^2 - x)\frac{dy}{dx} = y - 3x^2,$$

$$\frac{dy}{dx} = \frac{y - 3x^2}{3y^2 - x}$$

13. $y^2 + (2x)(y^2) - 3x + 1 = 0$

$$2y\frac{dy}{dx} + (2x)\left(2y\frac{dy}{dx}\right) + (y^2)(2) - 3 + 0 = 0$$

$$(2y + 4xy)\frac{dy}{dx} = 3 - 2y^2$$

$$\frac{dy}{dx} = \frac{3 - 2y^2}{2y(1 + 2x)}$$

15. $\sqrt{x} + \sqrt{y} = 1$, or $x^{1/2} + y^{1/2} = 1$

$$\frac{1}{2}x^{-1/2} + \frac{1}{2}y^{-1/2}\frac{dy}{dx} = 0$$

$$x^{-1/2} + y^{-1/2}\frac{dy}{dx} = 0$$

$$\frac{dy}{dx} = \frac{-x^{-1/2}}{y^{-1/2}} = \frac{-\sqrt{y}}{\sqrt{x}}$$

$$f'(x) = \frac{(1-5x)(1) - (x+1)(-5)}{(1-5x)^2}$$

$$f'(x) = \frac{1 - 5x + 5x + 5}{(1-5x)^2} = \frac{6}{(1-5x)^2}$$

$$f'(1) = \frac{6}{(1-5)^2} = \frac{3}{8}$$

5. $T(x) = 3x^2 + 40x + 1800$

(a) $T'(x) = 6x + 40$
In 2003, $x = 3$ and $T'(3) = 6(3) + 40 = \$58$ per year.

(b) Need $100 \dfrac{T'(3)}{T(3)}$

$$T(3) = 3(3)^2 + 40(3) + 1800 = 1947$$

$$100\frac{T'(3)}{T(3)} = 100\frac{58}{1947} \approx 2.98\%$$

6. $s(t) = 2t^3 - 3t^2 + 2, \ t \geq 0$

(a) $v(t) = s'(t) = 6t^2 - 6t$
$a(t) = s''(t) = 12t - 6$

(b) When stationary, $v(t) = 0$

$$6t^2 - 6t = 0$$

$$6t(t-1) = 0, \text{ or } t = 0, 1$$

When $0 < t < 1$, $v(t) < 0$, so retreating
$t > 1$, $v(t) > 0$, so advancing.

(c) $|s(1) - s(0)| + |s(2) - s(1)|$
$= 1 + 5 = 6$

7. $C(x) = 0.04x^2 + 5x + 73$

(a) $C'(x) = 0.08x + 5$

$$C'(5) = 0.08(5) + 5 = 5.4, \text{ or } \$540 \text{ per unit}$$

(b) $C(6) - C(5) = 104.44 - 99 = 5.44, \text{ or } \$544$

8. $Q = 500L^{3/4}$

$$\Delta Q \approx Q'(L)\Delta L$$

$$Q'(L) = 375L^{-1/4} = \frac{375}{L^{1/4}}$$

$$Q'(2401) = \frac{375}{(2401)^{1/4}} = \frac{375}{7}$$

Since $\Delta L = 200$,

$$\Delta Q \approx \frac{375}{7}(200) = \frac{75{,}000}{7},$$

or an increase of approximately 10,714.29 units.

9. $S = 0.2029w^{0.425}$

$$\frac{dS}{dt} = (0.2029)(0.425)w^{-0.575}\frac{dw}{dt}$$

$$= \frac{(0.2029)(0.425)}{(30)^{0.575}}(0.13) \approx 0.001586,$$

or increasing at a rate of 0.001586 m^2 per week.

10. (a)
$$V(r) = \frac{4}{3}\pi r^3$$

$$V'(r) = 4\pi r^2$$

$$V'(0.75) = 4\pi(0.75)^2$$

$$= 2.25\pi$$

$$\approx 7.069 \text{ cm}^3 \text{ per cm}$$

(b) $V = \dfrac{4}{3}\pi r^3$
Want $100 \frac{\Delta V}{V} \leq 8$, where $\Delta V \approx V'(r)\Delta r$,
$V'(r) = 4\pi r^2$ and $\Delta r = a \cdot r$, where a
represents the % error in the measure of r
(as a decimal).

$$100\frac{\Delta V}{V} \leq 8$$

$$100\frac{4\pi r^2 \cdot ar}{\frac{4}{3}\pi r^3} \leq 8$$

$$100a \leq \frac{8}{3}$$

or $\dfrac{8}{3}\%$ error in the measurement of r.

Review Problems

1. $f(x) = x^2 - 3x + 1$

$$\frac{f(x+h) - f(x)}{h} =$$

$$\frac{\left[(x+h)^2 - 3(x+h) + 1\right] - (x^2 - 3x + 1)}{h}$$

$$= \frac{x^2 + 2xh + h^2 - 3x - 3h + 1 - x^2 + 3x + 1}{h}$$

$$= \frac{2xh + h^2 - 3h}{h} = 2x + h - 3$$

$$f'(x) = \lim_{h \to 0} 2x + h - 3 = 2x - 3$$

3. $f(x) = 6x^4 - 7x^3 + 2x + \sqrt{2}$

$$f'(x) = 24x^3 - 21x^2 + 2$$

5.

$$y = \frac{2 - x^2}{3x^2 + 1}.$$

$$\frac{dy}{dx} = \frac{(3x^2 + 1)(-2x) - (2 - x^2)(6x)}{(3x^2 + 1)^2}$$

$$= \frac{-14x}{(3x^2 + 1)^2}$$

7. $f(x) = (5x^4 - 3x^2 + 2x + 1)^{10}$

$$f'(x) = 10(5x^4 - 3x^2 + 2x + 1)^9(20x^3 - 6x + 2)$$

9.

$$y = \left(x + \frac{1}{x}\right)^2 - \frac{5}{\sqrt{3x}}$$

$$= (x + x^{-1})^2 - \frac{5}{\sqrt{3}}x^{-1/2}$$

$$\frac{dy}{dx} = 2(x + x^{-1})(1 - x^{-2}) + \frac{5}{2\sqrt{3}}x^{-3/2}$$

$$= 2\left(x + \frac{1}{x}\right)\left(1 - \frac{1}{x^2}\right) + \frac{5}{2\sqrt{3}x^{3/2}}$$

11.

$$f(x) = (3x + 1)\sqrt{6x + 5}$$

$$= (3x + 1)(6x + 5)^{1/2}.$$

$$f'(x) = (3x + 1)\left(\frac{1}{2}\right)(6x + 5)^{-1/2}(6)$$

$$+ (6x + 5)^{1/2}(3)$$

$$= \frac{3(3x + 1)}{(6x + 5)^{1/2}} + 3(6x + 5)^{1/2}$$

$$= \frac{3(3x + 1) + 3(6x + 5)}{(6x + 5)^{1/2}}$$

$$= \frac{27x + 18}{(6x + 5)^{1/2}}$$

$$= \frac{9(3x + 2)}{\sqrt{6x + 5}}$$

13. $y = \sqrt{\dfrac{1 - 2x}{3x + 2}} = \left(\dfrac{1 - 2x}{3x + 2}\right)^{1/2}$

$$\frac{dy}{dx} = \frac{1}{2}\left(\frac{1 - 2x}{3x + 2}\right)^{-1/2} \cdot$$

$$\frac{(3x + 2)(-2) - (1 - 2x)(3)}{(3x + 2)^2}$$

$$= \frac{1}{2}\frac{(3x + 2)^{1/2}}{(1 - 2x)^{1/2}} \cdot \frac{-7}{(3x + 2)^2}$$

$$= \frac{-7}{2(1 - 2x)^{1/2}(3x + 2)^{3/2}}$$

15.

$$f(x) = \frac{4}{x - 3}$$

$$f'(x) = \frac{-4}{(x - 3)^2}$$

$f(1) = -2.$
The slope of the tangent line at $(1, -2)$ is $f'(1) = -1$.
The equation of the tangent line is

$$y + 2 = -(x - 1), \text{ or } y = -x - 1$$

17. $f(x) = \sqrt{x^2 + 5} = (x^2 + 5)^{1/2}$

$$f'(x) = \frac{1}{2}(x^2 + 5)^{-1/2}(2x) = \frac{x}{\sqrt{x^2 + 5}}$$

$f(-2) = 3.$ The slope of the tangent line at $(-2, 3)$
is $f'(-2) = -2/3$.

The equation of the tangent line is

$$y - 3 = -\frac{2}{3}(x + 2), \text{ or } y = -\frac{2}{3}x + \frac{5}{3}$$

19. (a) $f(t) = t^3(t^2 - 1), \ t = 0$

The rate of change of f is

$$f'(t) = (t^3)(2t) + (t^2 - 1)(3t^2)$$

When $t = 0$, the rate is

$$f'(0) = (0^3)(2 \cdot 0) + (0^2 - 1)(3 \cdot 0^2) = 0$$

(b) $f(t) = (t^2 - 3t + 6)^{1/2}, \ t = 1$

The rate of change of f is

$$f'(t) = \frac{1}{2}(t^2 - 3t + 6)^{-1/2}(2t - 3)$$

$$= \frac{2t - 3}{2(t^2 - 3t + 6)^{1/2}}$$

When $t = 1$, the rate is

$$f'(1) = \frac{2(1) - 3}{2\sqrt{1^2 - 3(1) + 6}} = -\frac{1}{4}$$

21. (a) $f(t) = t^2(3 - 2t)^3$

$$f'(t) = t^2 \cdot 3(3 - 2t)^2(-2) + (3 - 2t)^3(2t)$$

$$f'(1) = 1 \cdot 3(3 - 2)^2(-2) + (3 - 2)^3(2) = -4$$

$$f(1) = 1(3 - 2)^3 = 1$$

$$100\frac{f'(1)}{f(1)} = 100\frac{-4}{1} = -400\%$$

(b)

$$f(t) = \frac{1}{t + 1} = (t + 1)^{-1}$$

$$f'(t) = -(t + 1)^{-2} = \frac{-1}{(t + 1)^2}$$

$$f'(0) = \frac{-1}{(0 + 1)^2} = -1$$

$$f(0) = \frac{1}{0 + 1} = 1$$

$$100\frac{f'(0)}{f(0)} = 100\frac{-1}{1} = -100\%$$

23. (a) $y = (u + 1)^2, \ u = 1 - x$

$$\frac{dy}{du} = 2(u + 1)(1), \ \frac{du}{dx} = -1$$

$$\frac{dy}{dx} = \frac{dy}{du} \cdot \frac{dy}{dx}$$

$$= 2(u + 1) \cdot -1 = -2(u + 1)$$

Since $u = 1 - x$,

$$\frac{dy}{dx} = -2[(1 - x) + 1]$$

$$= -2(2 - x)$$

(b) $y = \frac{1}{\sqrt{u}} = u^{-1/2}, \ u = 2x + 1$

$$\frac{dy}{du} = -\frac{1}{2}u^{-3/2}, \ \frac{du}{dx} = 2$$

$$\frac{dy}{dx} = \frac{dy}{du} \cdot \frac{du}{dx}$$

$$= -\frac{1}{2u^{3/2}} \cdot 2 = -\frac{1}{u^{3/2}}$$

25. (a) $y = u^3 - 4u^2 + 5u + 2, \ u = x^2 + 1.$

$$\frac{dy}{du} = 3u^2 - 8u + 5, \ \frac{du}{dx} = 2x,$$

$$\frac{dy}{dx} = \frac{dy}{du}\frac{du}{dx}$$

When $x = 1$, $u = 2$, and so

$$\frac{dy}{dx} = [3(2^2) - 8(2) + 5][2(1)] = 2$$

(b)

$$y = \sqrt{u} = u^{1/2},$$

$$u = x^2 + 2x - 4,$$

$$\frac{dy}{du} = \frac{1}{2u^{1/2}},$$

$$\frac{du}{dx} = 2x + 2,$$

$$\frac{dy}{dx} = \frac{dy}{du} \cdot \frac{du}{dx}$$

When $x = 2$, $u = 4$, and so

$$\frac{dy}{dx} = \frac{1}{2(4)^{1/2}} \cdot [2(2) + 2] = \frac{3}{2}$$

(c)
$$y = \left(\frac{u-1}{u+1}\right)^{1/2}, \ u = \sqrt{x-1} = (x-1)^{1/2}$$

$$\frac{dy}{du} = \frac{1}{2}\left(\frac{u-1}{u+1}\right)^{-1/2} \cdot \frac{(u+1)(1)-(u-1)(1)}{(u+1)^2}$$

$$= \frac{(u+1)^{1/2}}{2(u-1)^{1/2}} \cdot \frac{2}{(u+1)^2}$$

$$= \frac{1}{(u-1)^{1/2}(u+1)^{3/2}}$$

$$\frac{du}{dx} = \frac{1}{2}(x-1)^{-1/2}(1) = \frac{1}{2(x-1)^{1/2}}$$

$$\frac{dy}{dx} = \frac{dy}{du} \cdot \frac{du}{dx}$$

When $x = \dfrac{34}{9}$, $u = \sqrt{\dfrac{34}{9} - 1} = \dfrac{5}{3}$, and so

$$\frac{dy}{dx} = \frac{1}{\left(\frac{5}{3}-1\right)^{1/2}\left(\frac{5}{3}+1\right)^{3/2}} \cdot \frac{1}{2\left(\frac{34}{9}-1\right)^{1/2}}$$

$$= \frac{1}{\left(\frac{2}{3}\right)^{1/2}\left(\frac{8}{3}\right)^{3/2}} \cdot \frac{1}{2\left(\frac{5}{3}\right)}$$

$$= \frac{1}{\left(\frac{2}{3}\right)^{1/2}\left(\frac{512}{27}\right)^{1/2}} \cdot \frac{3}{10}$$

$$= \frac{1}{\left(\frac{1024}{81}\right)^{1/2}} \cdot \frac{3}{10}$$

$$= \frac{9}{32} \cdot \frac{3}{10} = \frac{27}{310}$$

27. (a)
$$f(x) = 4x^3 - 3x$$
$$f'(x) = 12x^2 - 3$$
$$f''(x) = 24x$$

(b)
$$f(x) = 2x(x+4)^3$$
$$f'(x) = (2x) \cdot 3(x+4)^2(1) + (x+4)^3(2)$$
$$= 2(x+4)^2[3x + (x+4)]$$

$$= 2(x+4)^2(4x+4)$$
$$= 8(x+4)^2(x+1)$$
$$f''(x) = 8[(x+4)^2(1) + (x+1) \cdot 2(x+4)(1)]$$
$$= 8(x+4)[(x+4) + 2(x+1)]$$
$$= 8(x+4)(3x+6)$$
$$= 24(x+4)(x+2)$$

(c)
$$f(x) = \frac{x-1}{(x+1)^2}$$

$$f'(x) = \frac{(x+1)^2(1) - (x-1) \cdot 2(x+1)(1)}{[(x+1)^2]^2}$$

$$= \frac{(x+1)[(x+1) - 2(x-1)]}{(x+1)^4}$$

$$= \frac{3-x}{(x+1)^3}$$

$$f''(x) = \frac{(x+1)^3(-1) - (3-x) \cdot 3(x+1)^2(1)}{[(x+1)^3]^2}$$

$$= \frac{(x+1)^2[-(x+1) - 3(3-x)]}{(x+1)^6}$$

$$= \frac{2x-10}{(x+1)^4} = \frac{2(x-5)}{(x+1)^4}$$

29. (a) $x^2 y = 1$,

$$x^2 \frac{dy}{dx} + y(2x) = 0$$

$$\frac{dy}{dx} = -\frac{2xy}{x^2} = -\frac{2y}{x}$$

(b) $(1-2xy^3)^5 = x + 4y$

$$5(1-2xy^3)^4\left(-2x \cdot 3y^2\frac{dy}{dx} + y^3 \cdot -2\right)$$

$$= 1 + 4\frac{dy}{dx}$$

$$-30xy^2(1-2xy^3)^4\frac{dy}{dx} - 10y^3(1-2xy^3)^4$$

$$= 1 + 4\frac{dy}{dx}$$

$$\frac{dy}{dx} = \frac{1 + 10y^3(1-2xy^3)^4}{-30xy^2(1-2xy^3)^4 - 4}$$

31. (a)
$$x^2 + 2y^3 = \frac{3}{xy}, \quad (1, 1)$$

$$x^2 + 2y^3 = 3(xy)^{-1}$$

$$2x + 6y^2 \cdot \frac{dy}{dx} = -3(xy)^{-2}\left(x \cdot \frac{dy}{dx} + y \cdot 1\right)$$

$$2x + 6y^2 \cdot \frac{dy}{dx} = \frac{-3\left(x \cdot \frac{dy}{dx} + y\right)}{(xy)^2}$$

When $x = 1$ and $y = 1$

$$2(1) + 6(1)^2 \cdot \frac{dy}{dx} = \frac{-3\left(1 \cdot \frac{dy}{dx} + 1\right)}{(1 \cdot 1)^2}$$

$$2 + 6 \cdot \frac{dy}{dx} = -3 \cdot \frac{dy}{dx} - 3$$

$$9 \cdot \frac{dy}{dx} = -5$$

$$\frac{dy}{dx} = -\frac{5}{9}$$

The slope of the tangent to the curve at (1, 1) is $-\frac{5}{9}$.

(b) $y = \frac{x+y}{x-y}, \quad (6, 2)$

$$\frac{dy}{dx} = \frac{(x-y)\left(1 + \frac{dy}{dx}\right) - (x+y)\left(1 - \frac{dy}{dx}\right)}{(x-y)^2}$$

$$\frac{dy}{dx} = \frac{x + x\frac{dy}{dx} - y - y\frac{dy}{dx} - \left(x - x\frac{dy}{dx} + y - y\frac{dy}{dx}\right)}{(x-y)^2}$$

$$\frac{dy}{dx} = \frac{2x\frac{dy}{dx} - 2y}{(x-y)^2}$$

When $x = 6$ and $y = 2$,

$$\frac{dy}{dx} = \frac{2(6)\frac{dy}{dx} - 2(2)}{(6-2)^2} = \frac{12\frac{dy}{dx} - 4}{16}$$

$$16\frac{dy}{dx} = 12\frac{dy}{dx} - 4$$

$$4\frac{dy}{dx} = -4$$

$$\frac{dy}{dx} = -1$$

The slope of the tangent to the curve at (6, 2) is -1.

33. $3x^2 - 2y^2 = 6,$

$$6x - 4y\frac{dy}{dx} = 0, \text{ or } \frac{dy}{dx} = \frac{3x}{2y}$$

$$\frac{d^2y}{dx^2} = \frac{2y(3) - 3x\left(2\frac{dy}{dx}\right)}{(2y)^2} = \frac{3y - 3x\frac{dy}{dx}}{2y^2}$$

Since $\dfrac{dy}{dx} = \dfrac{3x}{2y}$

$$\frac{d^2y}{dx^2} = \frac{3y - 3x\left(\frac{3x}{2y}\right)}{2y^2} = \frac{6y^2 - 9x^2}{4y^3}$$

From the original equation

$$6y^2 - 9x^2 = 3(2y^2 - 3x^2)$$
$$= -3(3x^2 - 2y^2) = -3(6) = -18$$

and so $\dfrac{d^2y}{dx^2} = -\dfrac{18}{4y^3} = -\dfrac{9}{2y^3}$

35. $P(t) = -t^3 + 9t^2 + 48t + 200$

(a)
$$P'(t) = -3t^2 + 18t + 48$$
$$P'(3) = -3(3)^2 + 18(3) + 48 = 75,$$

or increasing at a rate of 75,000 people per year.

(b)
$$P''(t) = -6t + 18$$
$$P''(3) = -6(3) + 18 = 0 \text{ people per year}$$

37. $s(t) = \dfrac{2t+1}{t^2+12}$ for $0 \le t \le 4$

(a)
$$v(t) = \frac{(t^2+12)(2) - (2t+1)(2t)}{(t^2+12)^2}$$

$$= \frac{-2t^2 - 2t + 24}{(t^2+12)^2}$$

$$= \frac{-2(t+4)(t-3)}{(t^2+12)^2}$$

$$a(t) = \frac{(t^2 + 12)^2(-4t - 2)}{(t^2 + 12)^4}$$

$$- \frac{(-2t^2 - 2t + 24)2(t^2 + 12)(2t)}{(t^2 + 12)^4}$$

$$= -2(t^2 + 12)\left[\frac{(t^2 + 12)(2t + 1)}{(t^2 + 12)^4}\right.$$

$$\left. + \frac{(-2t^2 - 2t + 24)(2t)}{(t^2 + 12)^4}\right]$$

$$= \frac{2(2t^3 + 3t^2 - 72t - 12)}{(t^2 + 12)^3}$$

Now, for $0 \leq t \leq 4$,
$v(t) = 0$ when $t = 3$ and $a(t) \neq 0$.
When $0 \leq t < 3$, $v(t) > 0$ and $a(t) < 0$, so the object is advancing and decelerating.
When $3 < t \leq 4$, $v(t) < 0$ and $a(t) < 0$, so the object is retreating and decelerating.

(b) The distance for $0 < t < 3$ is

$$|s(3) - s(0)| = \left|\frac{1}{3} - \frac{1}{12}\right| = \frac{1}{4}$$

The distance for $3 < t < 4$ is

$$|s(4) - s(3)| = \left|\frac{9}{28} - \frac{1}{3}\right| = \frac{1}{84}$$

So, the total distance travelled is

$$\frac{1}{4} + \frac{1}{84} = \frac{22}{84} = \frac{11}{42}$$

39. (a) $Q(x) = 50x^2 + 9,000x$

$$\Delta Q \approx Q'(x) = 100x + 9,000$$

$Q'(30) = 12,000$, or an increase 12,000 units.

(b) The actual increase in output is
$Q(31) - Q(30) = 12,050$ units.

41.
$$Q(L) = 20,000L^{1/2}$$

$$\Delta Q \approx Q'(L)\Delta L$$

$$Q'(L) = 10,000L^{-1/2} = \frac{10,000}{\sqrt{L}}$$

$$Q'(900) = \frac{10,000}{\sqrt{900}} = \frac{1,000}{3}$$

Since L will decrease to 885,

$$\Delta L = 885 - 900 = -15$$

$$\Delta Q \approx \left(\frac{1,000}{3}\right)(-15) = -5,000,$$

or a decrease in output of 5,000 units.

43. Let A be the level of air pollution and p be the population.
$A = kp^2$, where k is a constant of proportionality

$$\Delta A \approx A'(p)\Delta p$$

$$A'(p) = 2kp \text{ and } \Delta p = .05p, \text{ so}$$

$$\Delta A \approx (2kp)(0.05p)$$

$$= 0.1kp^2 = 0.1A,$$

or a 10% increase in air pollution.

45. $D = 36m^{-1.14}$

(a) $D = 36(70)^{-1.14} \approx 0.2837$ individuals per square kilometer.

(b) $(0.2837 \text{ individuals/km}^2)(9.2 \times 10^6)\text{km}^2$
≈ 2.61 million people.

(c) The ideal population density would be

$$36(30)^{-1.14} \approx 0.7454 \text{ animals/km}^2$$

Since the area of the island is 3,000 km^2, the number of animals on the island for the ideal population density would be
$(0.7454 \text{ animals/km}^2)(3,000 \text{ km}^2) \approx$
2,235 animals.
Since the animal population is given by

$$P(t) = 0.43t^2 + 13.37t + 200,$$

this population is reached when

$$2236 = 0.43t^2 + 13.37t + 200$$

$$0 = 0.43t^2 + 13.37t - 2036$$

or, using the quadratic formula, when $t \approx 55$ years. The rate the population is changing at this time is $P'(55)$, where $P'(t) = 0.86t + 13.37$, or
$0.86(55) + 13.37 = 60.67$ animals per year.

47. Need $100\dfrac{\Delta L}{L}$, given that $100\dfrac{\Delta Q}{Q} = 1\%$, where $\Delta Q \approx Q'(L)\Delta L$. Since,

$$100\frac{Q/(L)\Delta L}{Q(L)} = 1,$$

solving for ΔL yields

$$\Delta L = \frac{Q(L)}{100Q'(L)} \text{ and}$$

$$100\frac{\Delta L}{L} = 100\frac{\frac{Q(L)}{100Q'(L)}}{L}$$

$$= \frac{Q(L)}{Q'(L)\cdot L}$$

Since $Q(L) = 600L^{2/3}$,

$$Q'(L) = 400L^{-1/3} = \frac{400}{L^{1/3}}$$

$$100\frac{\Delta L}{L} = \frac{600L^{2/3}}{\left(\frac{400}{L^{1/3}}\right)(L)} = \frac{3}{2}, \text{ or } 1.5\%$$

Increase labor by approximately 1.5%.

49. $F = kD^2\sqrt{A-C} = kD^2(A-C)^{1/2}$

(a) Treating A and D as constants,

$$\frac{dF}{dC} = \frac{1}{2}kD^2(A-C)^{-1/2}(-1)$$

$$= \frac{-kD^2}{2\sqrt{A-C}}$$

As C increases, the denominator increases, so F decreases.

(b) We need $100\dfrac{dF/dA}{F}$

Treating C and D as constants,

$$\frac{dF}{dA} = \frac{1}{2}kD^2(A-C)^{-1/2}(1)$$

$$= \frac{kD^2}{2\sqrt{A-C}}$$

$$100\frac{\frac{dF}{dA}}{F} = 100\frac{\frac{kD^2}{2\sqrt{A-C}}}{kD^2\sqrt{A-C}}$$

$$= \frac{50}{(A-C)}\%$$

51. Need $\Delta A \approx A'(r)\Delta r$

Since $A = \pi r^2$,

$$A'(r) = 2\pi r$$

When $r = 12$, $A'(12) = 2\pi(12) = 24\pi$

Since $\Delta r = \pm 0.03r$, $\Delta r = \pm 0.03(12) = \pm 0.36$ and

$$\Delta A \approx (24\pi)(\pm 0.36)$$

$$\approx \pm 27.14\text{cm}^2$$

When $r = 12$, $A = \pi(12)^2 = 144\pi \approx 452.39$ square centimeters. The calculation of area is off by ± 27.14 at most, so

$$425.25 \le A \le 479.53$$

53. $Q = 600K^{1/2}L^{1/3}$

Need $100\dfrac{\Delta Q}{Q}$, where $\Delta Q \approx Q'(L)\Delta L$

Treating K as a constant

$$Q'(L) = 200K^{1/2}L^{-2/3} = \frac{200K^{1/2}}{L^{2/3}}$$

with $\Delta L = 0.02L$

$$100\frac{\Delta Q}{Q} = 100\frac{\left(\frac{200K^{1/2}}{L^{2/3}}\right)(0.02L)}{600K^{1/2}L^{1/3}}$$

$$\approx 0.67\%$$

55. The error in the calculation of the tumor's surface area, due to the error in measuring its radius is

$$\Delta S \approx S'(r)\Delta r$$

$$= 8\pi r(\Delta r)$$

Since $3\%r = 0.03r = 0.03(1.2) = 0.036$,

$$= 8\pi(1.2)(\pm 0.036)$$

$$= \pm 0.3456\pi$$

The calculated surface area is

$$S = 4\pi(1.2)^2 = 5.76\pi$$

The true surface area is between

$$S + \Delta S = 5.76\pi \pm 0.3456\pi, \text{ or}$$

$$17.01 \le S \le 19.18$$

The measurement is accurate within

$$\frac{0.3456\pi}{5.76\pi} = 0.06, \text{ or } 6\%$$

57. $\quad D(p) = \dfrac{32{,}670}{2p+1} = 32{,}670(2p+1)^{-1}$

$$p(t) = 0.04t^{3/2} + 44$$

Need $\dfrac{dD}{dt}$ when $t = 25$.

$$\frac{dD}{dt} = \frac{dD}{dp} \cdot \frac{dp}{dt}$$

Now,

$$\frac{dD}{dp} = -32{,}670(2p+1)^{-2}(2) = -\frac{65{,}340}{(2p+1)^2}$$

$$\frac{dp}{dt} = 0.06t^{1/2}$$

When $t = 25$, $p = 0.04(25)^{3/2} + 44 = 49$, so

$$\frac{dD}{dt} = -\frac{65{,}340}{[2(49)+1]^2} \cdot 0.06(25)^{1/2}$$
$$= -2,$$

or the demand will be decreasing at a rate of 2 toasters per month.

59. $\quad P(t) = 20 - \dfrac{6}{t+1} = 20 - 6(t+1)^{-1}$

Need $100\dfrac{\Delta P}{P}$, where $\Delta P \approx P'(t)\Delta t$

$$P'(t) = 6(t+1)^{-2}(1) = \frac{6}{(t+1)^2}$$

The next quarter year is from $t = 0$ to $t = \dfrac{1}{4}$, so

$P(0) = 14$, $P'(0) = 6$ and $\Delta t = \dfrac{1}{4}$.

$$100\frac{\Delta P}{P} = 100\frac{(6)\left(\frac{1}{4}\right)}{14} \approx 10.7\%$$

61. $\qquad\qquad s(t) = 88t - 8t^2$

$$v(t) = s'(t) = 88 - 16t$$

The car is stopped when $v(t) = 0$, so

$$0 = 88 - 16t, \text{ or } t = 5.5 \text{ seconds.}$$

The distance travelled until it stops is

$$s(5.5) = 88(5.5) - 8(5.5)^2 = 242 \text{ feet}$$

63. $\ P(t) = -t^3 + 7t^2 + 200t + 300$

(a) $\qquad P'(t) = -3t^2 + 14t + 200$
$$P'(5) = -3(5)^2 + 14(5) + 200 = 195,$$

or increasing at a rate of $195 per unit per month.

(b) $\qquad\quad P''(t) = -6t + 14$
$$P''(5) = -6(5) + 14 = -16,$$

or decreasing at a rate of $16 per unit per month per month.

(c) Need $\Delta P' \approx P''(t)\Delta t$

Now, $P''(5) = -16$ and the first six months of the sixth year corresponds to $\Delta t = \dfrac{1}{2}$.

$$\Delta P' \approx (-16)\left(\frac{1}{2}\right) = -8,$$

or a decrease of $8 per unit per month.

(d) Need $P'(5.5) - P'(5)$

$$P'(5.5) = -3(5.5)^2 + 14(5.5) + 200 = 186.25$$

The actual change in the rate of price increase is $186.25 - 195 = -8.75$, or decreasing at a rate of $8.75 per unit per month.

65. $\ C(x) = 0.06x + 3x^{1/2} + 20$ hundred

$$\frac{dx}{dt} = -11 \text{ when } x = 2{,}500$$

$$\frac{dC}{dt} = \frac{dC}{dx} \cdot \frac{dx}{dt}$$

$$\frac{dC}{dx} = 0.06 + 1.5x^{-1/2} = 0.06 + \frac{1.5}{\sqrt{x}}$$

$$\frac{dC}{dt} = \left(0.06 + \frac{1.5}{\sqrt{2{,}500}}\right)(-11)$$

$$= -0.99 \text{ hundred,}$$

or decreasing at a rate of $99 per month.

67. Consider the volume of the shell as a change in volume, where $r = \dfrac{8.5}{2}$ and $\Delta r = \dfrac{1}{8} = 0.125$.

$$\Delta V \approx V'(r)\Delta r$$

$$V(r) = \frac{4}{3}\pi r^3$$

$$V'(r) = 4\pi r^2$$

$$V'(4.25) = 4\pi(4.25)^2 = 72.25\pi$$

$$\Delta V = (72.25\pi)(0.125) \approx 28.37 \text{ in}^3$$

69. Let the length of string be the hypotenuse of the right triangle formed by the horizontal and vertical distance of the kite from the child's hand. Then,

$$s^2 = x^2 + (80)^2$$

$$2s\frac{ds}{dt} = 2x\frac{dx}{dt}$$

$$\frac{ds}{dt} = \frac{2x\dfrac{dx}{dt}}{2s} = \frac{x\dfrac{dx}{dt}}{s}$$

When $s = 100$, $(100)^2 = x^2 + (80)^2$, or $x = 60$

$$\frac{ds}{dt} = \frac{(60)(5)}{100} = 3, \text{ or increasing at a rate of 3 feet}$$

per second.

71. Need $\dfrac{dx}{dt}$.

$$x^2 + y = (10)^2$$

$$2x\frac{dx}{dt} + 2y\frac{dy}{dt} = 0$$

$$\frac{dx}{dt} = \frac{-2y\dfrac{dy}{dt}}{2x} = \frac{-y\dfrac{dy}{dt}}{x}$$

When $y = 6$, $x^2 + 36 = 100$, or $x = 8$.

Since $\dfrac{dy}{dt} = -3$,

$$\frac{dx}{dt} = \frac{(-6)(-3)}{8} = 2.25,$$

or increasing at a rate of 2.25 feet per second.

73. Let x be the distance from the player to third base. Then,

$$s^2 = x^2 + (90)^2$$

$$2s\frac{ds}{dt} = 2x\frac{dx}{dt}$$

$$\frac{ds}{dt} = \frac{2x\dfrac{dx}{dt}}{2s} = \frac{x\dfrac{dx}{dt}}{s}$$

When $x = 15$, $s^2 = (15)^2 + (90)^2$, or $s = \sqrt{8325}$.

$$\frac{ds}{dt} = \frac{(15)(-20)}{\sqrt{8325}} \approx -3.29,$$

or decreasing at a rate of 3.29 feet per second.

75. Let x be the distance from point P to the object.

$$V = ktx$$

When $t = 5$ and $x = 20$, $V = 4$, so

$$4 = k(5)(20), \text{ or } k = \frac{1}{25}$$

Since $a = V'$,

$$a = k\left(t\frac{dx}{dt} + x \cdot 1\right)$$

$$a = \frac{1}{25}(5 \cdot 4 + 20) = \frac{8}{5}\text{ft/sec}^2$$

77. Need $100\dfrac{y'}{y}$ as $x \to \infty$.

$$y = mx + b$$

$$y' = m$$

$$100\frac{y'}{y} = 100\frac{m}{mx + b}$$

As x approaches ∞, this value approaches zero.

79. To use a graphing utility to graph f and f', Press $\boxed{y=}$ and input $(3x + 5)(2x \wedge 3 - 5x + 4)$ for $y_1 =$

$$f'(x) = (3x + 5)(6x^2 - 5) + (3)(2x^3 - 5x + 4)$$

Input $f'(x)$ for $y_2 =$
Use window dimensions $[-3, 2]1$ by $[-20, 30]10$
Use trace and zoom-in to find the x-intercepts of
$f'(x)$ or use the zero function under the calc menu.
In either case, make sure that y_2 is displayed in the
upper left corner. The three zeros are $x \approx -1.78$,
$x \approx -0.35$, and $x \approx 0.88$.

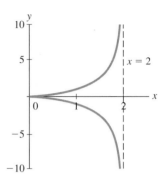

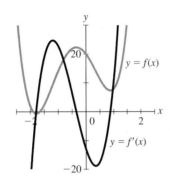

81. (a) To graph $y^2(2 - x) = x^3$,

$$y^2 = \frac{x^3}{2 - x}$$

$$y = \pm\sqrt{\frac{x^3}{2 - x}}$$

Press $\boxed{y=}$ and input $\sqrt{((x) \div (2 - x))}$ for $y_1 =$
and input $-y_1$ for $y_2 =$ (you can find y_1 by
pressing $\boxed{\text{vars}}$ and selecting function under the
y-vars menu). Use window dimensions $[-2, 5]1$
by $[-10, 10]5$ and press $\boxed{\text{graph}}$.

(b) With the graph shown, press $\boxed{\text{2nd}}$ $\boxed{\text{Draw}}$ and select
the tangent function. Enter $x = 1$ to obtain the
equation of the tangent line to be approximately
$y = x - 5$.

(c) It can be seen as x approaches 2 from the
left the portion of the graph above the x-axis
approaches ∞ and the portion below the x-axis
approaches $-\infty$.

(d) From the graph, the portion above the graph
has a horizontal tangent of $x = 0$, as does the
portion below the graph.

Chapter 3

Additional Applications of the Derivative

3.1 Increasing and Decreasing Functions; Relative Extrema

1. $f'(x) > 0$ when f is increasing, or $-2 < x < 2$
$f'(x) < 0$ when f is decreasing, or $x < -2$ and $x > 2$

3. $f'(x) > 0$ when f is increasing, or $x < -4$ and $0 < x < 2$
$f'(x) < 0$ when f is decreasing, or $-4 < x < -2$, $-2 < x < 0$, and $x > 2$

5. Function is decreasing, so $f'(x) < 0$ and graph of f' is below the x-axis. Function then levels, so $f'(x) = 0$ and graph of f crosses the x-axis. Function next increases for a period of time, so $f'(x) > 0$ and graph of f' is above the x-axis. Function then levels again, so $f'(x) = 0$ and graph of f' crosses the x-axis. Lastly, function decreases, so $f'(x) < 0$ and graph of f' is below the x-axis. Therefore, graph of f' is B.

7. Function is decreasing, so $f'(x) < 0$ and graph of f' is below the x-axis. Function then levels, so $f'(x) = 0$ and graph of f' crosses the x-axis. Function next increases, so $f'(x) > 0$ and graph of f' is above the x-axis. Therefore, graph of f' is D.

9.
$$f(x) = x^2 - 4x + 5$$
$$f'(x) = 2x - 4$$
f is increasing when $f'(x) > 0$
$$2x - 4 > 0, \text{ or } x > 2$$

f is decreasing when $f'(x) < 0$
$$2x - 4 < 0, \text{ or } x < 2$$

11.
$$f(x) = x^3 - 3x - 4$$
$$f'(x) = 3x^2 - 3 = 3(x+1)(x-1)$$
$f'(x) = 0$ when $x = -1, 1$

When $x < -1, \quad f'(x) > 0$
$-1 < x < 1, \quad f'(x) < 0$
$x > 1, \quad f'(x) > 0.$

So, f is increasing when $x < -1$ and $x > 1$; f is decreasing when $-1 < x < 1$.

13.
$$g(t) = t^5 - 5t^4 + 100$$
$$g'(t) = 5t^4 - 20t^3 = 5t^3(t-4)$$
$g'(t) = 0$ when $t = 0, 4$

When $t > 0, \quad g'(t) > 0$
$0 < t < 4, \quad g'(t) < 0$
$t > 4, \quad g'(t) > 0.$

So, g is increasing when $t < 0$ and $t > 4$; g is decreasing when $0 < t < 4$.

15. $f(t) = \dfrac{1}{4 - t^2} = (4 - t^2)^1$, defined for $t \neq -2, 2$
$$f'(t) = -(4 - t^2)^{-2}(-2t)$$
$$= \frac{2t}{(4 - t^2)^2} = \frac{2t}{[(2+t)(2-t)]^2}$$
$f'(t) = 0$ when $t = 0$

When $t < -2,\ f'(t) < 0$

$\quad\quad -2 < t < 0,\ f'(t) < 0$

$\quad\quad\ \ 0 < t < 2,\ f'(t) > 0$

$\quad\quad\quad\ \ t > 2,\ f'(t) > 0.$

So, f is increasing when $0 < t < 2$ and $t > 2$; f is decreasing when $t < -2$ and $-2 < t < 0$.

17. $h(u) = \sqrt{9 - u^2} = (9 - u^2)^{1/2}$

$\quad\quad = [(3 + u)(3 - u)]^{1/2},\ \text{defined for } -3 \le u \le 3$

$h'(u) = \dfrac{1}{2}(9 - u^2)^{-1/2}(-2u) = \dfrac{-u}{\sqrt{9 - u^2}}$

$h'(u) = 0$ when $u = 0$

$\quad\quad$ When $-3 < u < 0,\ h'(u) > 0$

$\quad\quad\quad\quad\quad 0,\ u < 3,\ h'(u) < 0.$

So, h is increasing when $-3 < u < 0$; h is decreasing when $0 < u < 3$.

19.

$\quad\quad F(x) = x + \dfrac{9}{x} = x + 9x^{-1} = \dfrac{x^2 + 9}{x},$

$\quad\quad\quad\quad \text{defined when } x \ne 0$

$\quad\quad F'(x) = 1 - 9x^{-2} = 1 - \dfrac{9}{x^2} = \dfrac{x^2 - 9}{x^2}$

$\quad\quad\quad\quad = \dfrac{(x + 3)(x - 3)}{x^2}$

$F'(x) = 0$ when $x = -3, 3$

$\quad\quad$ When $\quad x < -3,\ F'(x) > 0$

$\quad\quad\quad\quad -3 < x < 0,\ F'(x) < 0$

$\quad\quad\quad\quad\ \ 0 < x < 3,\ F'(x) < 0$

$\quad\quad\quad\quad\quad\ \ x > 3,\ F'(x) > 0.$

So, F is increasing when $x < -3$ and $x > 3$; F is decreasing when $-3 < x < 0$ and $0 < x < 3$.

21. $f(x) = \sqrt{x} + \dfrac{1}{\sqrt{x}} = x^{1/2} + x^{-1/2} = \dfrac{x + 1}{\sqrt{x}},$

$\quad\quad\quad\quad \text{defined for } x > 0$

$f'(x) = \dfrac{1}{2}x^{-1/2} - \dfrac{1}{2}x^{-3/2} = \dfrac{1}{2x^{1/2}} - \dfrac{1}{2x^{3/2}},$

$\quad\quad = \dfrac{x - 1}{2x^{3/2}}$

$f'(x) = 0$ when $x = 1$

$\quad\quad$ When $\quad 0 < x < 1,\ f'(x) < 0$

$\quad\quad\quad\quad\quad\quad\ \ x > 1,\ f'(x) > 0.$

So, f is increasing when $x > 1$; f is decreasing when $0 < x < 1$.

23. $\quad\quad f(x) = 3x^4 - 8x^3 + 6x^2 + 2$

$\quad\quad f'(x) = 12x^3 - 24x^2 + 12x = 12x(x - 1)^2$

$\quad\quad f'(x) = 0$ when $x = 0, 1$

$\quad\quad$ When $\quad x < 0,\ f'(x) < 0$ so f decreasing

$\quad\quad\quad\quad 0 < x < 1,\ f'(x) > 0$ so f increasing

$\quad\quad\quad\quad\quad\ \ x > 1,\ f'(x) > 0$ so f increasing.

When $x = 0,\ f(0) = 2$ and the point $(0,2)$ is a relative minimum. When $x = 1,\ f(1) = 3$, but there is no relative extremum at $(1,3)$.

25. $\quad\quad f(t) = 2t^3 + 6t^2 + 6t + 5$

$\quad\quad f'(t) = 6t^2 + 12t + 6 = 6(t + 1)^2$

$\quad\quad f'(t) = 0$ when $t = -1$

$\quad\quad$ When $\quad t < -1,\ f'(t) > 0$ so f increasing

$\quad\quad\quad\quad\quad\ \ t > -1,\ f'(t) > 0$ so f increasing.

When $t = -1,\ f(-1) = 3$, but there is no relative extremum at $(-1, 3)$.

27. $\quad\quad\quad g(x) = (x - 1)^5$

$\quad\quad\quad g'(x) = 5(x - 1)^4(1)$

$\quad\quad\quad g'(x) = 0$ when $x = 1$

$\quad\quad$ When $\quad x < 1, g'(x) > 0$ so g increasing

$\quad\quad\quad\quad\quad\ \ x > 1, g'(x) > 0$ so g increasing.

When $x = 1,\ g(1) = 0$, but there is no relative extremum at $(1,0)$.

29.
$$f(t) = \frac{t}{t^2 + 3}$$

$$f'(t) = \frac{(t^2 + 3)(1) - (t)(2t)}{(t^2 + 3)^2} = \frac{3 - t^2}{(t^2 + 3)^2}$$

$f'(t) = 0$ when $t = \pm\sqrt{3}$

When $t < -\sqrt{3}, \ f'(t) < 0$ so f decreasing

$\quad\quad -\sqrt{3} < t < \sqrt{3}, \ f'(t) > 0$ so f increasing

$\quad\quad\quad\quad t > \sqrt{3}. \ f'(t) < 0$ so f decreasing.

When $x = -\sqrt{3}, \ f\left(-\sqrt{3}\right) = -\dfrac{\sqrt{3}}{6}$ and the point

$\left(-\sqrt{3}, -\dfrac{\sqrt{3}}{6}\right)$ is a relative minimum.

When $x = \sqrt{3}, \ f(\sqrt{3}) = \dfrac{\sqrt{3}}{6}$ and the point

$\left(\sqrt{3}, \dfrac{\sqrt{3}}{6}\right)$ is a relative maximum.

31.
$$h(t) = \frac{t^2}{t^2 + t - 2} = \frac{t^2}{(t + 2)(t - 1)}$$

defined for $t \neq -2, 1$

$$h'(t) = \frac{(t^2 + t - 2)(2t) - (t^2)(2t + 1)}{(t^2 + t - 2)^2}$$

$$= \frac{t(t - 4)}{(t^2 + t - 2)^2}$$

$h'(t) = 0$ when $t = 0, 4$

When $-2 < t < 0, \ h'(t) > 0$ so h increasing

$\quad\quad 0 < t < 1, \ h'(t) < 0$ so h decreasing

$\quad\quad 1 < t < 4, \ h'(t) < 0$ so h decreasing

$\quad\quad\quad\quad t > 4, \ h'(t) > 0$ so h increasing.

When $t = 0, \ h(0) = 0$ and the point $(0, 0)$ is a relative maximum.

When $t = 4, \ h(4) = \dfrac{8}{9}$ and the point $\left(4, \dfrac{8}{9}\right)$ is a relative minimum.

33.
$$s(t) = (t^2 - 1)^4$$

$$s'(t) = 4(t^2 - 1)^3(2t) = 8t \left[(t + 1)(t - 1)\right]^3$$

$s'(t) = 0$ when $t = -1, 0, 1$

When $t < -1, \ s'(t) < 0$ so s decreasing

$\quad\quad -1 < t < 0, \ s'(t) > 0$ so s increasing

$\quad\quad 0 < t < 1, \ s'(t) < 0$ so s decreasing

$\quad\quad\quad\quad t > 1, \ s'(t) > 0$ so s increasing.

When $t = -1, \ s(-1) = 0$ and the point $(-1, 0)$ is a relative minimum. When $t = 0, \ s(0) = 1$ and the point $(0, 1)$ is a relative maximum. When $t = 1,$ $s(1) = 0$ and the point $(1, 0)$ is a relative minimum.

35. $f(x) = x^3 - 3x^2 = x^2(x - 3),$
intercepts: $(0, 0) \ (3, 0)$
$f'(x) = 3x^2 - 6x = 3x(x - 2)$
$f'(x) = 0$ when $x = 0, 2$

When $x < 0, \ f'(x) > 0$ so f increasing

$\quad\quad\quad\quad x = 0, \ f'(x) = 0$ so f levels

$\quad\quad 0 < x < 2, \ f'(x) < 0$ so f decreasing

$\quad\quad\quad\quad x = 2, \ f'(x) = 0$ so f levels

$\quad\quad\quad\quad x > 0, \ f'(x) > 0$ so f increasing.

The point $(0, 0)$ is a relative maximum and the point $(2, -4)$ is a relative minimum.

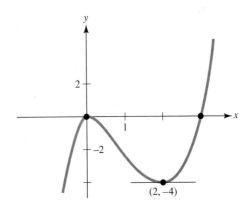

37. $f(x) = 3x^4 - 8x^3 + 6x^2 + 2$

When $x = 0, \ f(0) = 2$ so $(0, 2)$ is an intercept.

$\quad\quad f(x) = 0$ is too difficult to solve.

$f'(x) = 12x^3 - 24x^2 + 12x$
$\quad\quad = 12x(x - 1)(x - 1)$
$f'(x) = 0$ when $x = 0, 1$

When $x < 0$, $f'(x) < 0$ so f decreasing

$x = 0$, $f'(x) = 0$ so f levels

$0 < x < 1$, $f'(x) > 0$ so f increasing

$x = 1$, $f'(x) = 0$ so f levels

$x > 1$, $f'(x) > 0$ so f increasing.

The point $(0, 2)$ is a relative minimum, but the point $(1, 3)$ is not a relative extremum.

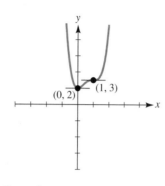

39. $f(t) = 2t^3 + 6t^2 + 6t + 5$
$f'(t) = 6t^2 + 12t + 6 = 6(t + 1)^2$
$f'(t) = 0$ when $t = -1$

When $t < -1$, $f'(t) > 0$ so f increasing

$t = -1$, $f'(t) = 0$ so f levels

$t > -1$, $f'(t) > 0$ so f increasing.

The point $(-1, 3)$ is not a relative extremum.

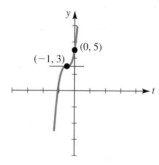

41. $g(t) = \dfrac{t}{t^2 + 3}$

$g'(t) = \dfrac{(t^2 + 3)(1) - (t)(2t)}{t^2 + 3} = \dfrac{3 - t^2}{(t^2 + 3)^2}$

$g'(t) = 0$ when $t = -\sqrt{3}, \sqrt{3}$

When $t < -\sqrt{3}$, $f'(t) < 0$ so f decreasing

$t = -\sqrt{3}$, $f'(t) = 0$ so f levels

$-\sqrt{3} < t < \sqrt{3}$, $f'(t) > 0$ so f increasing

$t = \sqrt{3}$, $f'(t) = 0$ so f levels

$t > \sqrt{3}$, $f'(t) < 0$ so f decreasing.

The point $\left(-\sqrt{3}, \dfrac{-\sqrt{3}}{6}\right)$ is a relative minimum and the point $\left(\sqrt{3}, \dfrac{\sqrt{3}}{6}\right)$ is a relative maximum.

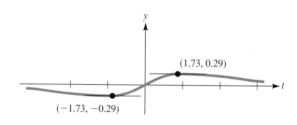

43. $f(x) = 3x^5 - 5x^3 + 4$
$f'(x) = 15x^4 - 15x^2 = 15x^2(x + 1)(x - 1)$
$f'(x) = 0$ when $x = -1, 0, 1$

When $x < -1$, $f'(x) > 0$ so f increasing

$x = -1$, $f'(x) = 0$ so f levels

$-1 < x < 0$, $f'(x) < 0$ so f decreasing

$x = 0$, $f'(x) = 0$ so f levels

$0 < x < 1$, $f'(x) < 0$ so f decreasing

$x = 1$, $f'(x) = 0$ so f levels

$x > 1$, $f'(x) > 0$ so f increasing.

The point $(-1, 6)$ is a relative maximum, the point $(0, 4)$ is not a relative extremum, and the point $(1, 2)$ is a relative minimum.

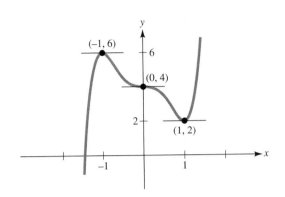

45. $f'(x) = x^2(4 - x^2) = x^2(2 + x)(2 - x)$
$f'(x) = 0$ when $x = -2, 0, 2$

$$\text{When} \quad x < -2, \quad f'(x) < 0 \text{ so } f \text{ decreasing}$$
$$-2 < x < 0, \quad f'(x) > 0 \text{ so } f \text{ increasing}$$
$$0 < x < 2, \quad f'(x) > 0 \text{ so } f \text{ increasing}$$
$$x > 2, \quad f'(x) < 0 \text{ so } f \text{ decreasing.}$$

When $x = -2$, f has a relative minimum, when $x = 0$, f does not have a relative extremum, and when $x = 2$, f has a relative maximum.

47. $f'(x) = \dfrac{(x + 1)^2(4 - 3x)^3}{(x^2 + 1)^2}$

$f'(x) = 0$ when $x = -1, \dfrac{4}{3}$

$$\text{When} \quad x < -1, \quad f'(x) > 0 \text{ so } f \text{ increasing}$$
$$-1 < x < \frac{4}{3}, \quad f'(x) > 0 \text{ so } f \text{ increasing}$$
$$x > \frac{4}{3}, \quad f'(x) < 0 \text{ so } f \text{ decreasing.}$$

When $x = -1$, f does not have a relative extremum, and when $x = \dfrac{4}{3}$, f has a relative maximum.

49. When
   $x < 1$, f is decreasing and graph of f' is below
      x-axis
   $x = 1$, f levels and graph of f' crosses the x-axis
   $1 < x < 3$, f is increasing and graph of f' is above
      x-axis
   $x = 3$, f levels and graph of f' crosses the x-axis

$x > 3$, f is decreasing and graph of f' is below
   x-axis.

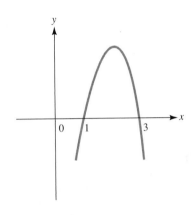

51. When
   $x < 2$, f is decreasing and graph of f' is below
      x-axis
   $x = 2$, f levels and graph of f' crosses the x-axis
   $2 < x < 5$, f is increasing and graph of f' is above
      x-axis
   $x = 5$, f levels and graph of f' touches x-axis
   $x > 5$, f is increasing and graph of f' is above
      x-axis.

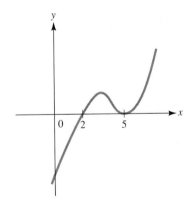

53. $C(x) = x^3 - 20x^2 + 179x + 242$

(a) $A(x) = \dfrac{C(x)}{x} = \dfrac{x^3 - 20x^2 + 179x + 242}{x}$

$= x^2 - 20x + 179 + \dfrac{242}{x}$

$= x^2 - 20x + 179 + 242x^{-1}$

$A'(x) = 2x - 20 - \dfrac{242}{x^2}$

(b) $A'(x) = 0$ when

$0 = 2x - 20 - \dfrac{242}{x^2}$

$0 = 2x^3 - 20x^2 - 242$

$x^3 - 10x^2 - 121 = 0$

Press $\boxed{\text{y=}}$ and enter $x^3 - 10x^2 - 121$ for $y_1 =$.
Use window dimensions $[-10, 100]10$ by
$[-500, 500]100$.
Press $\boxed{\text{graph}}$.
To find the zero (x-intercept), enter the zero
function under the calc menu. Enter a left bound
close to the x-intercept, a right bound close to
the x-intercept and a guess. The x-intercept or
zero is $x = 11$.

When $0 \le x < 11$, $A'(x) < 0$ so A decreasing

$x > 11$, $A'(x) > 0$ so A increasing.

(c)   When $x = 11$, A has a relative minimum which
is actually an absolute minimum. So the average
cost is minimized when 11 units are produced.
The corresponding minimum average cost is

$A(11) = (11)^2 - 20(11) + 179 + \dfrac{242}{11} = 102$

or \$102,000 per unit.

55. $R(x) = xp(x) = x(10 - 3x)^2, \; 0 \le x \le 3$

$R'(x) = x \cdot 2(10 - 3x)(-3) + (10 - 3x)^2(1)$

$= (10 - 3x)(-6x + 10 - 3x)$

$= (10 - 3x)(10 - 9x)$

$R'(x) = 0$ when $x = \dfrac{10}{9}, \dfrac{10}{3}$

When $0 \le x < \dfrac{10}{9}$, $R'(x) > 0$ so R increasing

$x = \dfrac{10}{9}$, $R'(x) = 0$ so R levels

$\dfrac{10}{9} < x \le 3$, $R'(x) < 0$ so R decreasing.

The point (1.11, 49.38) is a relative maximum, so
revenue is maximized when approximately 1.11
hundred, or 111 units are produced.

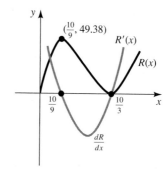

57. $C(t) = \dfrac{0.15t}{t^2 + 0.81}$
Note that, since degree numerator < degree of
denominator, $y = 0$ is a horizontal asymptote.

$C'(t) = \dfrac{(t^2 + 0.81)(0.15) - (0.15t)(2t)}{(t^2 + 0.81)^2}$

$\dfrac{-0.15t^2 + 0.1215}{(t^2 + 0.81)^2}$

$C'(t) = 0$ when $t = 0.9$

When $0 < t < 0.9$, $C'(t) > 0$ so C increasing

$t = 0.9$, $C'(t) = 0$ and C levels

$t > 0.9$, $C'(t) < 0$ and C decreasing.

The point (0.9, 0.083) is a relative maximum, so the
maximum concentration occurs when $t = 0.9$ hours.

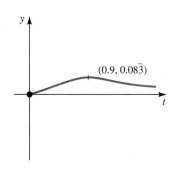

(0.9, 0.08$\overline{3}$)

59. $S(x) = -2x^3 + 27x^2 + 132x + 207, \ 0 \leq x \leq 17$

(a) $\qquad S'(x) = -6x^2 + 54x + 132$
$\qquad\qquad\quad = -6(x - 11)(x + 2)$
$\qquad S'(x) = 0$ when $x = -2, 11$

When $0 \leq x < 11, \ S'(x) > 0$ and S is increasing
$\qquad\quad x = 11, \ S'(x) = 0$ and S is levels
$\quad 11 < x \leq 17, \ S'(x) < 0$ and S is decreasing.

The point $(11, 2264)$ is a relative maximum.

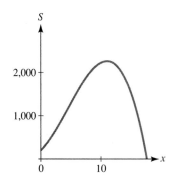

(b) $S(0) = 207$, or 207 units will sell.
(c) Since $(11, 2264)$ is a relative maximum, sales are maximized when 11 thousand, or \$11,000 are spent on advertising. The maximum number of units sold is 2,264.

61. $M(r) = \dfrac{1 + 0.05r}{1 + 0.004r^2}$

(a) $M'(r) = \dfrac{(1 + 0.004r^2)(0.005) - (1 + 0.05r)(0.008r)}{(1 + 0.004r^2)^2}$

$\qquad\quad = \dfrac{0.05 - 0.008r - 0.0002r^2}{(1 + 0.004r^2)^2}$

$\qquad\quad = \dfrac{500 - 80r - 2r^2}{10,000(1 + 0.004r^2)^2}$

Using the quadratic formula, $M'(r) = 0$ When

$$r = \frac{80 \pm \sqrt{(-80)^2 - (4)(-2)(500)}}{2(-2)}$$

$r \approx 5.495$ (rejecting the negative answer)
When $0 \leq r < 5.495, \ M'(r) > 0$ so M is increasing
$\qquad\quad r > 5.495, \ M'(r) < 0$ so M is decreasing.

(b) When $r \approx 5.495$, M has a relative maximum which is actually an absolute maximum. So, the number of mortages is maximized when the rate is 5.495%. The corresponding maximum number of mortages is

$$M(5.495) = \frac{1 + 0.05(5.495)}{1 + 0.004(5.495)^2} \approx 1.137$$

or 1,137 refinanced mortgages.

63. **(a)** Approximately 1971, 1976, 1980, 1983, 1988, 1994.
(b) Approximately 1973, 1979, 1981, 1985, 1989.
(c) Approximately $\dfrac{1}{2}$% per year.
(d) Approximately $\dfrac{1}{2}$% per year.

65. **(a)** Yield $= \left(\begin{smallmatrix}\text{orig}\\ \text{\#fish}\end{smallmatrix}\right) \left(\begin{smallmatrix}\text{proportion}\\ \text{still living}\end{smallmatrix}\right) \left(\begin{smallmatrix}\text{weight}\\ \text{per fish}\end{smallmatrix}\right)$

$$Y(t) = 300\left(\frac{31}{31+t}\right)(3+t-0.05t^2)$$

$$= 9,300(31+t)^{-1}(3+t-0.05t^2)$$

$$Y'(t) = 9,300\left[(31+t)^{-1}(1-0.1t)\right.$$

$$\left. +(3+t-0.05t^2)\cdot -(31+t)^{-2}(1)\right]$$

$$= 9,300\left(\frac{1-0.1t}{31+t} - \frac{3+t-0.05t^2}{(31+t)^2}\right)$$

$$= 9,300\frac{29-3.1t-0.05t^2}{(31+t)^2}$$

$Y'(t) = 0$ when $t \approx 8.3$

When

$0 \le t < 8.3$, $Y'(t) > 0$ and Y is increasing

$t = 8.3$, $Y'(t) = 0$ and Y levels

$8.3 < t \le 10$, $Y'(t) < 0$ and Y is decreasing.

The point $(8.3, 1859)$ is a relative maximum.

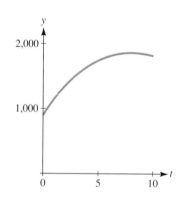

(b) Since $(8.3, 1859)$ is a relative maximum, the yield is maximized after 8.3 weeks and the maximum yield is 1,859 pounds.

67. $H(t) = -053T^2 + 25T - 209,\ 15 \le T \le 30$

$H'(t) = -1.06T + 25$

When $H'(0) = 0$ when $t \approx 23.58$
When $15 \le T < 23.58$, $H'(T) > 0$ so H is
    increasing
$T = 23.58$, $H'(T) = 0$ so H levels
$23.58 < T \le 30$, $H'(t) < 0$ so H is decreasing.
The point $(23.58, 85.81)$ is a relative maximum.

So, the maximum percentage is 85.81% and it occurs at 23.58°C.

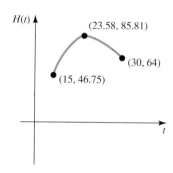

69. (a) Graph levels when $x = 0,\ 1,\ 2$.

  (b) Graph is decreasing when $0 < x < 1$.

  (c) Graph is increasing when $x < 0,\ 1 < x < 2$, and
        $x > 2$.

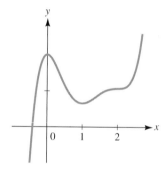

71. (a) Graph is decreasing when $x < -1$.

  (b) Graph is increasing when $-1 < x < 3$ and
        $x > 3$.

  (c) Graph levels when $x = -1,\ 3$.

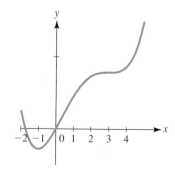

73.
$$f(x) = ax^3 + bx^2 + cx + d$$
$$f'(x) = 3ax^2 + 2bx + c$$
$$f'(x) = 0 \text{ when } x = -2, \text{ so}$$
$$0 = 3a(-2)^2 + 2b(-2) + c$$
$$0 = 12a - 4b + c$$
$$f'(x) = 0 \text{ when } x = 1, \text{ so}$$
$$0 = 3a(1)^2 + 2b(1) + c$$
$$0 = 3a + 2b + c$$

So, $12a - 4b + c = 3a + 2b + c$, or $b = \dfrac{3}{2}a$.

Now, $f(-2) = 8$ so

$$8 = a(-2)^3 + \frac{3}{2}a(-2)^2 + c(-2) + d$$
$$8 = -8a + 6a - 2c + d$$
$$8 = -2a - 2c + d$$
or, $d = 8 + 2a + 2c$

Now, $f(1) = -19$ so

$$-19 = a(1)^3 + \frac{3}{2}a(1)^2 + c(1) + d$$
$$-19 = \frac{5}{2}a + c + (8 + 2a + 2c)$$
$$-27 = \frac{9}{2}a + 3c, \text{ or}$$
$$c = \frac{1}{3}\left(-27 - \frac{9}{2}a\right) = -9 - \frac{3}{2}a$$

Using

$$0 = 3a + 2b + c$$
$$0 = 3a + 2\left(\frac{3}{2}a\right) + \left(-9 - \frac{3}{2}a\right)$$
$$0 = \frac{9}{2}a - 9, \text{ or}$$
$$a = 2, \ b = \frac{3}{2}(2) = 3,$$
$$c = -9 - \frac{3}{2}(2) = -12,$$
$$d = 8 + 2(2) + 2(-12) = -12$$

75. $f(x) = 1 - x^{3/5}$

When $x = 0$, $f(0) = 1$ so $(0,1)$ is an intercept.
$f(x) = 0$, $x = 1$ so $(1,0)$ is an intercept.

$$f'(x) = -\frac{3}{5}x^{-2/5}$$
$$= \frac{-3}{5x^{2/5}}$$

When $x < 0$, $f'(x) < 0$ so f is decreasing
$x > 0$, $f'(x) < 0$ so f is decreasing.

f' is undefined when $x = 0$, but f is defined, so this corresponds to a vertical tangent at $x = 0$.

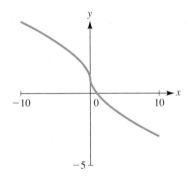

77. $y = (x - p)(x - q)$
$$y' = (x - p)(1) + (x - q)(1)$$
$$= 2x - p - q$$

So, $y' = 0$ when $0 = 2x - p - q$ or, $x = \dfrac{p+q}{2}$, which is the midpoint of the segment PQ. So any relative extremum occurs midway between its intercepts.

79. $f(x) = (x^2 + x - 1)^3(x + 3)^2$
Press $\boxed{y=}$ and input f for $y_1 =$
Use the window dimensions $[-4, 2]1$ by $[-20, 25]5$
Press $\boxed{\text{Graph}}$

$$f'(x) = 3(x^2 + x - 1)^2(2x + 1)(x + 3)^2$$
$$+ (x^2 + x - 1)^3(2)(x + 3)$$
$$= (x^2 + x - 1)^2(x + 3)[3(2x + 1)(x + 3)$$
$$+ (x^2 + x - 1)(2)]$$
$$= (x^2 + x - 1)^2(x + 3)(8x^2 + 23x + 7)$$

Press $\boxed{y=}$ and input $f'(x)$ for $y_2 =$
Press $\boxed{\text{Graph}}$
To find the values of x for which $f'(x) = 0$,
it may be easiest to deactivate y_1 so only the
graph of $y_2 = f'$ is shown. Use $\boxed{\text{Trace}}$ and verify
$y_2 = (x^2 + x - 1)^2(x + 3)(8x^2 + 23x + 7)$ is
shown in the upper left corner. Trace along
the graph to move near an x-intercept. Use
Zoom in function for more accurate readings.
The values of x for which $f'(x) = 0$ are
$x_1 \approx -3$, $x_2 \approx -2.5$, $x_3 \approx -1.6$, $x_4 \approx -0.35$,
$x_5 \approx 0.62$.

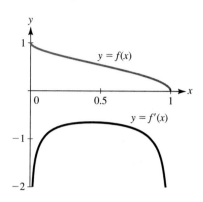

83. Let $f(x) = 4 + \sqrt{9 - 2x - x^2}$. Before graphing, f
appears to be the upper half of a circle.

$$y = 4 + \sqrt{9 - 2x - x^2}$$

$$y - 4 = \sqrt{9 - 2x - x^2}$$

By squaring both sides and completing the square
we obtain the equation of the whole circle with
center $(-1, 4)$ and radius $\sqrt{10}$.

$$(y - 4)^2 = 9 - 2x - x^2$$

$$x^2 + 2x + 1 + (y - 4)^2 = 9 + 1$$

$$(x + 1)^2 + (y - 4)^2 = 10$$

Therefore, $f(x) = 4 + \sqrt{9 - 2x - x^2}$ should be the
upper half of this circle.
Press $\boxed{y=}$ and input f for $y_1 =$
Use window dimensions $[-5, 5]$ by $[-10, 10]$
Press $\boxed{\text{Graph}}$
Initially, the graph appears to be the upper half of an
ellipse but by using the Zsquare function, we see the
graph is, in fact, the upper half of the circle.

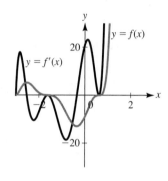

81. $f(x) = (1 - x^{1/2})^{1/2}$
Press $\boxed{y=}$ and input f for $y_1 =$
Use the window dimensions $[0, 1]0.5$ by $[-2, 1]1$
(the domain of f is $0 < x < 1$)
Press $\boxed{\text{Graph}}$

$$f'(x) = \frac{1}{2}(1 - x^{1/2})^{-1/2}\left(-1/2x^{-1/2}\right)$$

$$f'(x) = \frac{-1}{4x^{1/2}(1 - x^{1/2})^{1/2}}$$

Press $\boxed{y=}$ and input f' for $y_2 =$
Press $\boxed{\text{Graph}}$
We see from the graph that there are no values of x
for which $f'(x) = 0$.

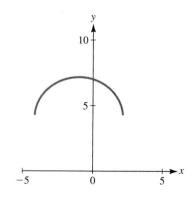

3.2 Concavity and Points of Inflection

1. The graph is:
   concave downward ($f''(x) < 0$) for $x < 2$,
   and concave upward ($f''(x) > 0$) for $x > 2$.

3. The graph is:
   concave downward ($f''(x) < 0$) for $-1 < x < 1$,
   and concave upward ($f''(x) > 0$) for $x < -1$ and
   $x > 1$.

5.
$$f(x) = x^3 + 3x^2 + x + 1$$
$$f'(x) = 3x^2 + 6x + 1$$
$$f''(x) = 6x + 6 = 6(x + 1)$$
$$f''(x) = 0 \text{ when } x = -1$$

   When $x < -1$, $f''(x) < 0$ so f is concave down
   $$x > -1, \ f''(x) > 0 \text{ so } f \text{ is concave up.}$$

   Since the concavity changes at the critical value
   $x = -1$, the point $(-1, 2)$ is an inflection point.

7. $f(x) = x(2x + 1)^2 = x(4x^2 + 4x + 1) = 4x^3 + 4x^2 + x$
$$f'(x) = 12x^2 + 8x + 1$$
$$f''(x) = 24x + 8 = 8(3x + 1)$$
$$f''(x) = 0 \text{ when } x = -\frac{1}{3}$$

   When $x < -\frac{1}{3}$, $f''(x) < 0$ so f is concave down
   $$x > -\frac{1}{3}, \ f''(x) > 0 \text{ so } f \text{ is concave up.}$$

   Since the concavity changes at the critical value
   $x = -\frac{1}{3}$, the point $\left(-\frac{1}{3}, -\frac{1}{27}\right)$ is an inflection
   point.

9.
$$g(t) = t^2 - \frac{1}{t} = t^2 - t^{-1}$$
$$g'(t) = 2t + t^{-2}$$
$$g''(t) = 2 - 2t^{-3} = 2 - \frac{2}{t^3} = \frac{2t^3 - 2}{t^3} = \frac{2(t^3 - 1)}{t^3}$$
$$g''(t) = 0 \text{ when } t = 1$$

(Note that $g''(t)$ and $g(t)$ are undefined for $t = 0$.)

   When $t < 0$, $g''(t) > 0$ so g is concave up
   $$0 < t < 1, \ g''(t) < 0 \text{ so } g \text{ is concave down}$$
   $$t > 1, \ g''(t) > 0 \text{ so } g \text{ is concave up.}$$

Since the concavity changes at the critical value
$t = 1$, the point $(1, 0)$ is an inflection point.

11.
$$f(x) = x^4 - 6x^3 + 7x - 5$$
$$f'(x) = 4x^3 - 18x^2 + 7$$
$$f''(x) = 12x^2 - 36x = 12x(x - 3)$$
$$f''(x) = 0 \text{ when } x = 0, 3$$

   When $x < 0$, $f''(x) > 0$ so f is concave up
   $$0 < x < 3, \ f''(x) < 0 \text{ so } f \text{ is concave down}$$
   $$x > 3, \ f''(x) > 0 \text{ so } f \text{ is concave up.}$$

Since the concavity changes at both critical values
$x = 0$ and $x = 3$, the points $(0, -5)$ and $(3, -65)$ are
inflection points.

13.
$$f(x) = \frac{1}{3}x^3 - 9x + 2$$
$$f'(x) = x^2 - 9 = (x + 3)(x - 3)$$
$$f'(x) = 0 \text{ when } x = -3, 3$$
$$f''(x) = 2x$$
$$f''(x) = 0 \text{ when } x = 0$$

   When $x < -3$, $f'(x) > 0$ so f is increasing
   $$f''(x) < 0 \text{ so } f \text{ is concave down}$$
   $$-3 < x < 0, \ f'(x) < 0 \text{ so } f \text{ is decreasing}$$
   $$f''(x) < 0 \text{ so } f \text{ is concave down}$$
   $$0 < x < 3, \ f'(x) < 0 \text{ so } f \text{ is decreasing}$$
   $$f''(x) > 0 \text{ so } f \text{ is concave up}$$
   $$x > 3, \ f'(x) > 0 \text{ so } f \text{ is increasing}$$
   $$f''(x) > 0 \text{ so } f \text{ is concave up.}$$

Overall, f is increasing for $x < -3$ and $x > 3$;
decreasing for $-3 < x < 3$; concave up for $x > 0$;
and concave down for $x < 0$.
The critical value $x = -3$ corresponds to the point
$(-3, 20)$, which is a relative maximum.

The critical value $x = 3$ corresponds to the point $(3, -16)$, which is a relative minimum. Since the concavity changes at $x = 0$, the point $(0, 2)$ is an inflection point.

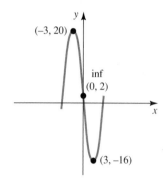

15.

$$f(x) = x^4 - 4x^3 + 10$$
$$f'(x) = 4x^3 - 12x^2 = 4x^2(x - 3)$$
$$f'(x) = 0 \text{ when } x = 0, 3$$
$$f''(x) = 12x^2 - 24x = 12x(x - 2)$$
$$f''(x) = 0 \text{ when } x = 0, 2$$

When $x < 0$, $f'(x) < 0$ so f is decreasing
$\qquad\qquad f''(x) > 0$ so f is concave up
$0 < x < 2$, $f'(x) < 0$ so f is decreasing
$\qquad\qquad f''(x) < 0$ so f is concave down
$2 < x < 3$, $f'(x) < 0$ so f is decreasing
$\qquad\qquad f''(x) > 0$ so f is concave up
$x > 3$, $f'(x) > 0$ so f is increasing
$\qquad\qquad f''(x) > 0$ so f is concave up.

Overall, f is increasing for $x > 3$; decreasing $x < 3$; concave up for $x < 0$ and $x > 2$; and concave down for $0 < x < 2$.
The critical value $x = 0$ corresponds to the point $(0, 10)$, which is not a relative extremum. However, the concavity charges at $x = 0$, so $(0, 10)$ is an inflection point. The concavity changes again at $x = 2$, so the point $(2, -6)$ is also an inflection point. The critical value $x = 3$ corresponds to the point $(3, -17)$, which is a relative minimum.

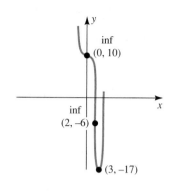

17.

$$f(x) = (x - 2)^3$$
$$f'(x) = 3(x - 2)^2(1)$$
$$f'(x) = 0 \text{ when } x = 2$$
$$f''(x) = 6(x - 2)$$
$$f''(x) = 0 \text{ when } x = 2$$

When $x < 2$, $f'(x) > 0$ so f is increasing
$\qquad\qquad f''(x) < 0$ so f is concave down
$x > 2$, $f'(x) > 0$ so f is increasing
$\qquad\qquad f''(x) > 0$ so f is concave up.

Overall, f is increasing for all values of x; concave up for $x > 2$; and concave down for $x < 2$.
The critical value $x = 2$ corresponds to the point $(2, 0)$ which is not a relative extremum. However, the concavity changes at $x = 2$, so $(2, 0)$ is an inflection point.

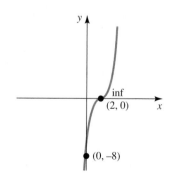

19. $f(x) = (x^2 - 5)^3$

$f'(x) = 3(x^2 - 5)^2(2x) = 6x(x^2 - 5)^2$

$f'(x) = 0$ when $x = -\sqrt{5}, 0, \sqrt{5}$

$f''(x) = (6x)\left[2(x^2 - 5)(2x)\right] + (x^2 - 5)^2(6)$

$\quad = 6(x^2 - 5)\left[4x^2 + x^2 - 5\right]$

$\quad = 6(x^2 - 5)(5x^2 - 5)$

$\quad = 30(x^2 - 5)(x + 1)(x - 1)$

$f''(x) = 0$ when $x = -\sqrt{5}, -1, 1, \sqrt{5}$

When $x < -\sqrt{5}$, $f'(x) < 0$ so f is decreasing

$\qquad\qquad\quad f''(x) > 0$ so f is concave up

$-\sqrt{5} < x < -1$, $f'(x) < 0$ so f is decreasing

$\qquad\qquad\quad f''(x) < 0$ so f is concave down

$-1 < x < 0$, $f'(x) < 0$ so f is decreasing

$\qquad\qquad\quad f''(x) > 0$ so f is concave up

$0 < x < 1$, $f'(x) > 0$ so f is increasing

$\qquad\qquad\quad f''(x) > 0$ so f is concave up

$1 < x < \sqrt{5}$, $f'(x) > 0$ so f is increasing

$\qquad\qquad\quad f''(x) < 0$ so f is concave down

$x > \sqrt{5}$, $f'(x) > 0$ so f is increasing

$\qquad\qquad\quad f''(x) > 0$ so f is concave up.

Overall, f is increasing for $x > 0$; decreasing for $x < 0$; concave up for $x < -\sqrt{5}$, $-1 < x < 1$, and $x > \sqrt{5}$; and concave down for $-\sqrt{5} < x < -1$ and $1 < x < \sqrt{5}$.
The critical value $x = -\sqrt{5}$ corresponds to the point $(-\sqrt{5}, 0)$, which is not a relative extremum. However, the concavity changes at $x = -\sqrt{5}$, so $(-\sqrt{5}, 0)$ is an inflection point. The concavity changes again at $x = -1$, so the point $(-1, -64)$ is also an inflection point. The critical value $x = 0$ corresponds to the point $(0, -125)$, which is a relative minimum. The concavity next changes at $x = 1$, so the point $(1, -64)$ is an inflection point. The critical value $x = \sqrt{5}$ corresponds to the point $(\sqrt{5}, 0)$, which is not a relative extremum. However,

the concavity changes at $x = \sqrt{5}$, so $(\sqrt{5}, 0)$ is an inflection point.

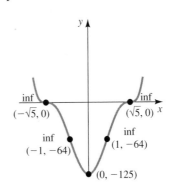

21. $f(s) = 2s(s + 4)^3$

$f'(s) = (2s)\left[3(s + 4)^2(1)\right] + (s + 4)^3(2)$

$\quad = 2(s + 4)^2[3s + s + 4]$

$\quad = 8(s + 4)^2(s + 1)$

$f'(s) = 0$ when $s = -4, -1$

$f''(s) = 8\left[(s + 4)^2(1) + (s + 1)\left(2(s + 4)(1)\right)\right]$

$\quad = 8(s + 4)\left[s + 4 + 2(s + 1)\right]$

$\quad = 24(s + 4)(s + 2)$

$f''(s) = 0$ when $s = -4, -2$

When $s < -4$, $f'(s) < 0$ so f is decreasing

$\qquad\qquad\quad f''(s) > 0$ so f is concave up

$-4 < s < -2$, $f'(s) < 0$ so f is decreasing

$\qquad\qquad\quad f''(s) < 0$ so f is concave down

$-2 < s < -1$, $f'(s) < 0$ so f is decreasing

$\qquad\qquad\quad f''(s) > 0$ so f is concave up

$s > -1$, $f'(s) > 0$ so f is increasing

$\qquad\qquad\quad f''(s) > 0$ so f is concave up.

Overall, f is increasing for $s > -1$; decreasing for $s < -1$; concave up for $s < -4$ and $s > -2$; and concave down for $-4 < s < -2$.
The critical value $s = -4$ corresponds to the point $(-4, 0)$, which is not a relative extremum. However, the concavity changes at $s = -4$, so $(-4, 0)$ is an inflection point. The concavity changes again at

$s = -2$, so the point $(-2, -32)$ is also an inflection point. The critical value $s = -1$ corresponds to the point $(-1, -54)$, which is a relative minimum.

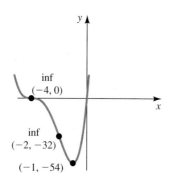

23. $g(x) = \sqrt{x^2 + 1} = (x^2 + 1)^{1/2}$

$g'(x) = \frac{1}{2}(x^2 + 1)^{-1/2}(2x) = \frac{x}{\sqrt{x^2 + 1}}$

$g'(x) = 0$ when $x = 0$

$g''(x) = \dfrac{(x^2 + 1)^{1/2}(1) - (x)\left[\frac{1}{2}(x^2 + 1)^{-1/2}(2x)\right]}{\left(\sqrt{x^2 + 1}\right)^2}$

$g''(x) = \dfrac{(x^2 + 1)^{1/2} - \dfrac{x^2}{(x^2 + 1)^{1/2}}}{x^2 + 1} \cdot \dfrac{(x^2 + 1)^{1/2}}{(x^2 + 1)^{1/2}}$

$\quad = \dfrac{x^2 + 1 - x^2}{(x^2 + 1)^{3/2}} = \dfrac{1}{(x^2 + 1)^{3/2}}$

When $x < 0$, $g'(x) < 0$ so g is decreasing

$\qquad\qquad g''(x) > 0$ so g is concave up

$\quad x > 0$, $g'(x) > 0$ so g is increasing

$\qquad\qquad g''(x) > 0$ so g is concave up.

Overall, g is increasing for $x > 0$; decreasing for $x < 0$; and concave up for all values of x.
The critical value $x = 0$ corresponds to the point $(0, 1)$, which is a relative minimum.

25. $f(x) = \dfrac{1}{x^2 + x + 1} = (x^2 + x + 1)^{-1}$

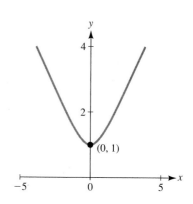

$f'(x) = -(x^2 + x + 1)^{-2}(2x + 1) = \dfrac{-(2x + 1)}{(x^2 + x + 1)^2}$

$f'(x) = 0$ when $x = -\dfrac{1}{2}$

$f''(x) = \dfrac{1}{\left[(x^2 + x + 1)^2\right]^2}\left[(x^2 + x + 1)^2(-2)\right.$

$\qquad\qquad \left. + (2x + 1)(2)(x^2 + x + 1)(2x + 1)\right]$

$\quad = \dfrac{2(x^2 + x + 1)\left[-(x^2 + x + 1) + (2x + 1)^2\right]}{(x^2 + x + 1)^4}$

$\quad = \dfrac{6x(x + 1)}{(x^2 + x + 1)^3}$

$f''(x) = 0$ when $x = -1, 0$

When $x < -1$, $f'(x) > 0$ so f is increasing

$\qquad\qquad f''(x) > 0$ so f is concave up

$-1 < x < -\dfrac{1}{2}$, $f'(x) > 0$ so f is increasing

$\qquad\qquad f''(x) < 0$ so f is concave down

$-\dfrac{1}{2} < x < 0$, $f'(x) < 0$ so f is decreasing

$\qquad\qquad f''(x) < 0$ so f is concave down

$\quad x > 0$, $f'(x) < 0$ so f is decreasing

$\qquad\qquad f''(x) > 0$ so f is concave up.

Overall, f is increasing for $x < -\dfrac{1}{2}$; decreasing for $x > -\dfrac{1}{2}$; concave up for $x < -1$ and $x > 0$; and concave down for $-1 < x < 0$.

At $x = -1$, the concavity changes, so the point $(-1, 1)$ is an inflection point. The critical value $x = -\dfrac{1}{2}$ corresponds to the point $\left(-\dfrac{1}{2}, \dfrac{4}{3}\right)$, which is relative maximum. The concavity changes again at $x = 0$, so the point $(0, 1)$ is an inflection point.

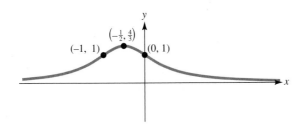

27.
$$f(x) = x^3 + 3x^2 + 1$$
$$f'(x) = 3x^2 + 6x = 3x(x + 2)$$
$$f'(x) = 0 \text{ when } x = -2, 0$$
$$f''(x) = 6(x + 1)$$
$$f''(0) = 6 > 0 \text{ and } f''(-2) = -6 < 0,$$
$$\text{and } f(-2) = 5 \text{ and } f(0) = 1.$$

So $(0, 1)$ is a relative minimum, and $(-2, 5)$ is a relative maximum.

29.
$$f(x) = (x^2 - 9)^2$$
$$f'(x) = 2(x^2 - 9)(2x) = 4x(x - 3)(x + 3)$$
$$f'(x) = 0 \text{ when } x = -3, 0, 3$$
$$f''(x) = 12(x^2 - 3)$$

$f''(-3) = 72 > 0$, $f''(0) = -36 < 0$, and $f''(3) = 72 > 0$; $f(\pm 3) = 0$ and $f(0) = 81$.
So $(0, 81)$ is a relative maximum, and $(-3, 0)$, $(3, 0)$ are relative minima.

31.
$$f(x) = 2x + 1 + \frac{18}{x}$$
$$f'(x) = 2 - \frac{18}{x^2}$$
$$= \frac{2(x - 3)(x + 3)}{x^2}$$
$$f'(x) = 0 \text{ when } x = -3, 3$$
$$f''(x) = \frac{36}{x^3}$$

$f''(-3) = -\dfrac{4}{3} < 0$ and $f''(3) = \dfrac{4}{3} > 0$;
$f(-3) = -11$, $f(3) = 13$.
So $(-3, -11)$ is a relative maximum,
$(3, 13)$ is a relative minimum.

33.
$$f(x) = x^2(x - 5)^2 = x^4 - 10x^3 + 25x^2$$
$$f'(x) = 4x^3 - 30x^2 + 50x = 2x(x - 5)(2x - 5)$$
$$f'(x) = 0 \text{ when } x = 0, 2.5, 5$$
$$f''(x) = 12x^2 - 60x + 50$$

$f''(0) = 50 > 0$, $f''(2.5) = -25 < 0$, and
$f''(5) = 50 > 0$; $f(0) = 0$, $f(2.5) = 39.0625$ and
$f(5) = 0$. So $(0, 0)$ and $(5, 0)$ are relative minima
and $(2.5, 39.065)$ is a relative maximum.

35.
$$h(t) = \frac{2}{1 + t^2} = 2(1 + t^2)^{-1}$$
$$h'(t) = -2(1 + t^2)^{-2}(2t)$$
$$= \frac{-4t}{(1 + t^2)^2}$$
$$h'(t) = 0 \text{ when } t = 0$$
$$h''(t) = \frac{-4(1 + t^2)^2 - (-4t)(2)(1 + t^2)(2t)}{(1 + t^2)^4}$$
$$= \frac{4(1 + t)\left[-(1 + t^2) + 4t^2\right]}{(1 + t^2)^4}$$
$$= \frac{4(3t^2 - 1)}{(1 + t^2)^3}$$

$h''(0) = -4 < 0$ and $h(0) = 2$. So, $(0, 2)$ is a relative maximum.

37.

$$f(x) = \frac{(x-2)^3}{x^2}$$

$$f'(x) = \frac{x^2\left[3(x-2)^2(1)\right] - (x-2)^3(2x)}{x^4}$$

$$= \frac{x(x-2)^2\left[3x - 2(x-2)\right]}{x^4}$$

$$= \frac{(x-2)^2(x+4)}{x^3}$$

$f'(x) = 0$ when $x = -4, 2$

$$f''(x) = \frac{1}{x^6}\left(x^3\left[(x-2)^2(1) + (x+4)(2)(x-2)\right]\right.$$

$$\left. - \left[(x-2)^2(x+4)(3x^2)\right]\right)$$

$$= \frac{x^2(x-2)\left(x\left[(x-2) + 2(x+4)\right] - 3(x-2)(x+4)\right)}{x^6}$$

$$= \frac{24(x-2)}{x^4}$$

$f''(-4) = -\dfrac{9}{16} < 0$ and $f(-4) = -13.5$. So, $(-4, -13.5)$ is a relative maximum. $f''(2) = 0$, so the test fails.

39. $f''(x) = x^2(x-3)(x-1)$
$f''(x) = 0$ when $x = 0, 1, 3$

When $x < 0$, $f''(x) > 0$ so f is concave up

$0 < x < 1$, $f''(x) > 0$ so f is concave up

$1 < x < 3$, $f''(x) < 0$ so f is concave down

$x > 3$, $f''(x) > 0$ so f is concave up.

Overall, f is concave up for $x < 0$, $0 < x < 1$, and $x > 3$; concave down for $1 < x < 3$. There are inflection points at $x = 1$ and $x = 3$, as the concavity changes at those values.

41. $f''(x) = (x-1)^{1/3}$
$f''(x) = 0$ when $x = 1$

When $x < 1$, $f''(x) < 0$ so f is concave down

$x > 1$, $f''(x) > 0$ so f is concave up.

There is an inflection point at $x = 1$, as the concavity changes at that value.

43. $f'(x) = x^2 - 4x$

(a) $f'(x) = x(x-4)$
$f'(x) = 0$ when $x = 0, 4$

When $x < 0$, $f'(x) > 0$ so f is increasing

$0 < x < 4$, $f'(x) < 0$ so f is decreasing

$x > 4$, $f'(x) > 0$ so f is increasing.

(b) $f''(x) = 2x - 4 = 2(x-2)$
$f''(x) = 0$ when $x = 2$

When $x < 2$, $f''(x) < 0$ so f is concave down

$x > 2$, $f''(x) > 0$ so f is concave up.

(c) at $x = 0$, there is a relative maximum;
at $x = 4$, there is a relative minimum;
at $x = 2$, there is an inflection point.

(d)

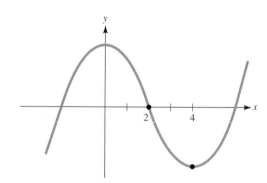

45. $f'(x) = 5 - x^2$
$f'(x) = 0$ when $-\sqrt{5}, \sqrt{5}$

(a) When $x < -\sqrt{5}$, $f'(x) < 0$ so f is decreasing

$-\sqrt{5} < x < \sqrt{5}$, $f'(x) > 0$ so f is increasing

$x > \sqrt{5}$, $f'(x) < 0$ so f is decreasing.

(b) $f''(x) = -2x$
$f''(x) = 0$ when $x = 0$

When $x < 0$, $f''(x) > 0$ so f is concave up

$x > 0$, $f''(x) < 0$ so f is concave down.

(c) at $x = -\sqrt{5}$, there is a relative minimum;
at $x = \sqrt{5}$, there is a relative maximum;

at $x = 0$, there is an inflection point.

(d)

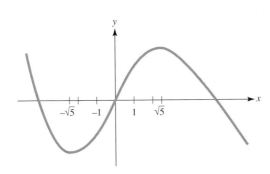

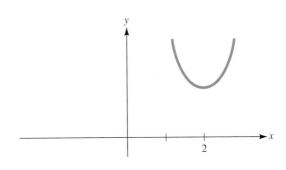

47. (a) The curve rises for $x < -1$ and $x > 3$.
   (b) It falls when $-1 < x < 3$.
   (c) The curve is concave down for $x < 2$.
   (d) The curve is concave up for $x > 2$.
        Here is a possible graph.

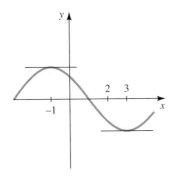

49.   When $x < 2$, $f'(x) < 0$ so f is decreasing
          $x = 2$, $f'(x) = 0$
             and there is a relative minimum
          $x > 2$, $f'(x) > 0$ so f is increasing.

Since f' is increasing for all values of x, its rate of change $f''(x) > 0$ for all x, and f is concave up for all x.

51. When $x < -3$, $f'(x) < 0$ so f is decreasing
          $x = -3$, $f'(x) = 0$ so f levels

but there is not a relative extremum

          $-3 < x < 2$, $f'(x) < 0$ so f is decreasing
          $x = 2$, $f'(x) = 0$
             and there is a relative minimum
          $x > 2$, $f'(x) > 0$ so f is increasing

Since $f'(x)$ is increasing for $x < -3$ and for $x > -1$, $f''(x) > 0$ on these intervals and f is concave up. Since $f'(x)$ is decreasing for $-3 < x < -1$, $f''(x) < 0$ on that interval and f is concave down. Since the concavity changes at $x = -3$ and $x = -1$, there are inflection points at these values.

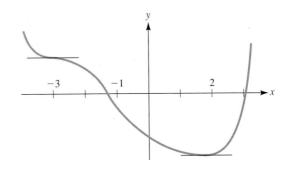

53. (a) $C(x) = 0.3x^3 - 5x^2 + 28x + 200$
          $M(x) = C'(x) = 0.9x^2 - 10x + 28$

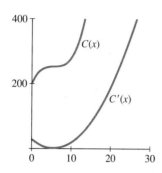

(b) $M'(x) = C''(x) = 1.8x - 10$

$C''(x) = 0$ when $x \approx 5.56$

Critical values of C'' are x values of possible extrema of C', which is the marginal cost function. $x = 5.56$ corresponds to a minimum on the graph of C'.

55. $S(x) = -x^3 + 33x^2 + 60x + 1{,}000$

(a) When $x = 0$,

$$S(0) = -(0)^3 + 33(0)^2 + 60(0) + 1{,}000$$
$$= 1{,}000$$

One thousand units will be sold.

(b) $S'(x) = -3x^2 + 66x + 60 = -3(x^2 - 22x - 20)$

$S'(x) = 0$ when

$$x = \frac{22 \pm \sqrt{(-22)^2 - 4(1)(-20)}}{2(1)}$$

$$\approx 22.9 \text{ (deleting negative root)}$$

$S''(x) = -6x + 66 = -6(x - 11)$

$S''(x) = 0$ when $x = 11$

When $0 \le x < 11$, $S'(x) > 0$ so S is increasing

$S''(x) > 0$ so S is concave up

$11 < x < 22.9$, $S'(x) > 0$ so S is increasing

$S''(x) < 0$ so S is concave down

$x > 22.9$, $S'(x) < 0$ so S is decreasing

$S''(x) < 0$ so S is concave down

Overall, S is increasing for $0 \le x < 22.9$; decreasing for $x > 22.9$; concave up for $0 \le x < 11$; concave down for $x > 22.9$. The critical value $x = 22.9$ corresponds to

the point $(22.9, 7671)$, which is a relative maximum. When $x = 11$, the corresponding point is $(11, 4322)$, which is an inflection point.

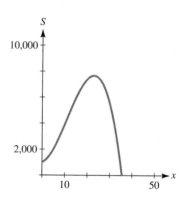

The inflection point corresponds to the amount spent on marketing ($11,000) related to when sales are increasing most rapidly (since it is the critical value for S').

57. Need to maximize the rate of output on the interval $0 \le t \le 4$. Since the output is

$$Q(t) = -t^3 + \frac{9}{2}t^2 + 15t$$

the rate of change of the output is

$$R(t) = Q'(t) = -3t^2 + 9t + 15$$
$$R'(t) = Q''(t) = -3(2t - 3)$$
$$R'(t) = 0 \text{ when } t = 1.5$$

Using the interval endpoints and this critical value, $R(0) = 15$, $R(1.5) = 21.75$, and $R(4) = 3$. So, an absolute maximum occurs at $t = 1.5$ and an absolute minimum when $t = 4$.

(a) The worker is performing most efficiently when $t = 1.5$, at 9:30 a.m.

(b) and least efficiently when $t = 4$, at 12:00 noon.

59. Need to optimize the rate of population growth on the interval $0 \le t \le 5$. Since the population is

$$P(t) = -t^3 + 9t^2 + 48t + 50$$

the rate of growth is

$$R(t) = P'(t) = -3t^2 + 18t + 48$$

$$R'(t) = P''(t) = -6t + 18$$

$$R'(t) = 0 \text{ when } t = 3$$

Using the interval endpoints and this critical value, $R(0) = 48$, $R(3) = 75$, and $R(5) = 63$.

(a) The rate of growth is greatest when $t = 3$, or 3 years from now.

(b) It is smallest when $t = 0$, or now.

(c) The rate the population growth changes most rapidly is when $R'(t)$ is a maximum. Since $R'(t) = -6t + 18$, is most rapid when $t = 0$, or now.

61. $M(r) \dfrac{1 + 0.02r}{1 + 0.009r^2}$

(a) $M'r = \dfrac{(1 + 0.009r^2)(0.02) - (1 + 0.02r)(0.018r)}{(1 + 0.009r^2)^2}$

$$= \dfrac{0.02 - 0.018r - 0.00018r^2}{(1 + 0.009r^2)^2}$$

$$M''(r) = \Big[(1 + 0.009r^2)^2(-0.018 - 0.00036r)$$

$$-(0.02 - 0.018r - 0.00018r^2) \cdot 2(1 + 0.09r^2)(0.018r)\Big] \Big/$$

$$(1 + 0.009r^2)^4$$

$$= \Big[0.018(1 + 0.009r^2)\Big[(1 + 0.009r^2)(-1 - 0.02r)$$

$$-2r(0.02 - 0.018r - 0.00018r^2)\Big]\Big] \Big/$$

$$(1 + 0.009r^2)^4$$

$$= 0.018\Big[-1 - 0.06r + 0.0027r^2 + 0.00018r^3\Big] \Big/$$

$$(1 + 0.009r^2)^3$$

(b) Press $\boxed{y=}$ and input $(1 + 0.02x) \div (1 + 0.009x^2)$ for $y_1 =$.
Use window dimensions [0, 20]0.05 by [0, 2]0.25.
Press $\boxed{\text{graph}}$.

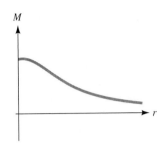

(c) To find the rate of interest at which the rate of construction of new houses is minimized, we must find r for which $M''(r) = 0$. $M'(r)$ gives us the rate of construction and thus to minimize this, we take $M''(r)$ and set it equal to zero. Press $\boxed{y=}$ and input M'' for $y_1 =$.
Use window dimensions [−10, 10]1 by[−0.005, 0.005]0.001.
Press $\boxed{\text{graph}}$. Since we are only concerned with the positve zero, use the zero function under the calc menu with a close value to the positive x-intercept for the left bound, right bound and guess. We find the interest rate to be $r = 7.10\%$.

63. $N(t) = \dfrac{St}{12 + t^2}$

(a) $N'(t) = \dfrac{(12 + t^2)(5) - (5t)(2t)}{(12 + t^2)^2}$

$$= \dfrac{60 - 5t^2}{(12 + t^2)^2}$$

$$N''(t) = \dfrac{(12 + t^2)^2(-10t) - (60 - 5t^2) \cdot 2(12 + t^2)(2t)}{(12 + t^2)^4}$$

$$= \dfrac{2t(12 + t^2)\Big[-5(12 + t^2) - 2(60 - 5t^2)\Big]}{(12 + t^2)^4}$$

$$= \dfrac{2t(5t^2 - 180)}{(12 + t^2)^4} = \dfrac{10t(t^2 - 36)}{(12 + t^2)^4}$$

(b) $N'(t) = 0$ when $t = \sqrt{12} \approx 3.46$. Since $N''(3.46) < 0$, the maximum number of reported cases occurs after 3.46 weeks. The corresponding maximum number of new cases is

$$N(3.46) = \dfrac{5\sqrt{12}}{12 + 12} \approx 0.7217$$

or 722 new cases.

(c) $N''(t) = 0$ when $t = 0, 6$

When $0 < t < 6$, $N''(t) < 0$ so N' is decreasing

$t > 0$, $N''(t) > 0$ so N' is increasing

So, the rate of reported cases N' is minimized after 6 weeks. The corresponding minimum number of new cases is

$$N(6) = \frac{5(6)}{12 + 36} = 0.625$$

or approximately 63 new cases.

65. Let R represent the rate at which a rumor spreads. Since it is jointly proportional to N and $P - N$,

$$R(N) = kN(P - N)$$

where k is a constant of proportionality

$$R'(N) = k[N(-1) + (P - N)(1)]$$
$$= k(P - 2N)$$

$R'(N) = 0$ when

$$P - 2N = 0, \text{ or}$$

$$N = \frac{P}{2}$$

$R''(N) = k(-2)$, which is always negative.

So, when $N = \frac{P}{2}$ (or when half the population has heard the rumor), the rate is a maximum.

67. $\dfrac{dA}{dt} = k\sqrt{A(t)}\,[M - A(t)], \; k > 0$

(a) $R(t) = \dfrac{dA}{dt} = k\,[A(t)]^{1/2}\,[M - A(t)]$

$$R'(t) = k\left[[A(t)]^{1/2} \left(-\frac{dA}{dt} \right) \right.$$

$$\left. + (M - A(t)) \left(\frac{1}{2}\,[A(t)]^{-1/2}\,\frac{dA}{dt} \right) \right]$$

$$= k\frac{dA}{dt}\left[-[A(t)]^{1/2} \cdot \frac{2\,[A(t)]^{1/2}}{2\,[A(t)]^{1/2}} + \frac{M - A(t)}{2\,[A(t)]^{1/2}} \right]$$

$$= k\frac{dA}{dt}\left[\frac{-2A(t) + M - A(t)}{2\,[A(t)]^{1/2}} \right]$$

$$= k\frac{dA}{dt}\left[\frac{M - 3A(t)}{2[A(t)]^{1/2}} \right]$$

$R'(t) = 0$ when $M - 3A(t) = 0$, or $A(t) = \dfrac{M}{3}$.

(b) When $A(t) < \dfrac{M}{3}$, $M - 3A(t) > 0$ and $R'(t) > 0$, so R is increasing.

When $A(t) > \dfrac{M}{3}$, $M - 3A(t) < 0$ and $R'(t) < 0$, so R is decreasing.

So, when $A(t) = \dfrac{M}{3}$, the rate is the greatest.

(c) $R'(t) = A''(t)$, so graph of A has an inflection point when $A(t) = \dfrac{M}{3}$.

69.
$$f(x) = x^4 + x$$
$$f'(x) = 4x^3 + 1$$
$$f'(x) = 0 \text{ when } x = \sqrt[3]{-\frac{1}{4}} \approx -0.63$$
$$f''(x) = 12x^2$$
$$f''(x) = 0 \text{ when } x = 0$$

When $x < -0.63$, $f'(x) < 0$ so f is decreasing

$f''(x) > 0$ so f is concave up

$-0.63 < x < 0$, $f'(x) > 0$ so f is increasing

$f''(x) > 0$ so f is concave up

$x > 0$, $f'(x) > 0$ so f is increasing

$f''(x) > 0$ so f is concave up.

When $x = -0.63$, f has a relative minimum. When $x = 0$, f does not have a relative extremum, nor does f have an inflection point, as the concavity does not switch.

$f(-0.63) \approx -0.47$; $f(0) = 0$

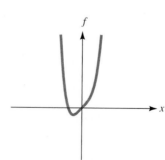

71. As shown by the following counterexample, the sum h needn't also have an inflection point at $x = c$.

$$f(x) = \frac{1}{6}x^3 - x^2$$

$$g(x) = -\frac{1}{6}x^3 + x^2$$

Then,

$$f'(x) = \frac{1}{2}x^2 - 2x$$

$$f''(x) = x - 2,$$

so f has an inflection point when $x = 2$

$$g'(x) = -\frac{1}{2}x^2 + 2x$$

$$g''(x) = -x + 2,$$

so g also has an inflection point when $x = 2$. However,

$$h(x) = f(x) + g(x) = 0,$$

so h does *not* have an inflection point when $x = 2$.

73. $f(x) = 2x^3 + 3x^2 - 12x - 7$

(a) To graph,
Press $\boxed{y=}$ and input f for $y_1 =$
Use *z*standard function of zoom for viewing window.
Press $\boxed{\text{Graph}}$
Change window dimensions to $[-10, 10]1$ by $[-20, 20]2$
Press $\boxed{\text{Graph}}$

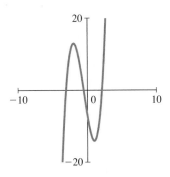

(b)
$$f'(x) = 6x^2 + 6x - 12$$
$$f''(x) = 12x + 6$$

To use the TI-84 to find these values, input f for $y_1 =$, f' for $y_2 =$, and f'' for $y_3 =$. De-select $y_2 =$ and $y_3 =$ so only $y_1 =$ is activated.
Use the value function in the calc menu. For $f(-4)$, input $x = -4$ and press $\boxed{\text{enter}}$. The display shows $y = -39$. Repeat process for $x = -2, -1, 0, 1,$ and 2. For the $f'(x)$ values, de-select $y_1 =$ and activate $y_2 =$ and repeat process.
For the $f''(x)$ values, de-select $y_2 =$ and activate $y_3 =$ and repeat process.

x	-4	-2	-1	0	1	2
$f(x)$	-39	13	6	-7	-14	-3
$f'(x)$	60	0	-12	-12	0	24
$f''(x)$	-42	-18	-6	6	18	30

(c) To approximate the x-intercepts and y-intercept, Use *z*standard function, activate $y_1 =$ and press $\boxed{\text{graph}}$.
You may use $\boxed{\text{trace}}$ and zoom-in to estimate x-intercepts to be $x_1 \approx -3.08$, $x_2 \approx -0.54$, and $x_3 \approx 2.11$.
An alternative is to use the zero function under the calc menu. Press $\boxed{\text{2nd}}$ $\boxed{\text{calc}}$ and enter zero function. The graph is displayed with left bound? For the left-most x-intercept, trace the graph to a value close to the intercept, but to the left of it and press $\boxed{\text{enter}}$. For the right bound? enter a value close to the x-intercept but to the right of it.

To guess a value, enter an x-value in between the bounds and press [enter].

The display shows the zero value of $x_1 \approx -3.08$. Repeat this process for the other two x-intercepts.

For the y-intercept, use zstandard and read the y-intercept as $y = -7$ (also given from the table in part (b)).

(d) To find the relative maximum and relative minimum points,

Use zstandard function with $y_1 =$ activated. Press [graph]. Trace graph left until off the screen (near the relative maximum) and press [enter]. This will move the viewing window to the relative maximum. Use trace and zoom functions to estimate the maximum point to be $(-2, 13)$.

As an alternative, use the maximum function under the calc menu. Enter a left bound, right bound, and guess. For the relative minimum, use z-standard to view the original graph and move cross-hair so relative minimum is in window. Use the minimum function under the calc menu to find the relative minimum to be $(1, -14)$.

(e) Using the graph and the information from part (d), f is increasing on $x < -2$ and $x > 1$.

(f) Using the graph and the information from part (d), f is decreasing on $-2 < x < 1$.

(g) There is an inflection value on $-2 < x < 1$, since the concavity changes from downward to upward.

On the TI-84, de-select $y_1 =$ and activate y_3. Press [graph]. Use the zero function under the calc menu to find the zero of f'' to be $x = -0.5$. Activate $y_1 =$ and use the value function under the calc menu to find $f(-0.5) = -0.5$. The inflection point is $(-0.5, -0.5)$

(h) Using the graph of f and the information from the previous parts, f is concave upward on $x > -\frac{1}{2}$.

(i) Using the graph of f and the information from the previous parts, f is concave downward on $x < -\frac{1}{2}$.

(j) To verify f changes from concave downward to concave upward, use the value function under the calc menu to show

$$f''(-0.6) = -1.2$$
$$f''(-0.4) = 1.2$$

(Make sure that you have $y_3 = 12x + 6$ activated.)

(k) Relative minimum point: $(1, -14)$
Relative maximum point: $(-2, 13)$
Both of the x-values are within the specified interval. Check the endpoints of the interval. From part (a), $f(-4) = -39$ and $f(2) = -3$.
Absolute maximum value $= 13$
Absolute minimum value $= -39$.

3.3   Curve Sketching

1. $\displaystyle\lim_{x \to 0} f(x) = +\infty$, so $x = 0$ is a vertical asymptote

$\displaystyle\lim_{x \to \pm\infty} f(x) = 0$, so $y = 0$ is a horizontal asymptote

3. There are no vertical asymptotes.

$\displaystyle\lim_{x \to -\infty} f(x) = 0$, so $y = 0$ is a horizontal asymptote

5. $\displaystyle\lim_{x \to -2} f(x) = +\infty$, so $x = -2$ is a vertical asymptote

$\displaystyle\lim_{x \to 2^-} f(x) = -\infty$ and $\displaystyle\lim_{x \to 2^+} f(x) = +\infty$,

so $x = 2$ is a vertical asymptote

$\displaystyle\lim_{x \to -\infty} f(x) = 0$, so $y = 0$ is a horizontal asymptote

$\displaystyle\lim_{x \to +\infty} f(x) = 2$, so $y = 2$ is a horizontal asymptote.

7. $\displaystyle\lim_{x \to 2^+} f(x) = +\infty$, so $x = 2$ is a vertical asymptote

$\displaystyle\lim_{x \to -\pm\infty} f(x) = 0$, so $y = 0$ is a horizontal asymptote

9. Since the denominator is zero when $x = -2$, $x = -2$ is a vertical asymptote.

$$\lim_{x \to \pm\infty} \frac{3x - 1}{x + 2} = \lim_{x \to \pm\infty} \frac{3 - \dfrac{1}{x}}{1 + \dfrac{2}{x}} = 3,$$

so $y = 3$ is a horizontal asymptote.

11. Since the denominator cannot be zero for any value of x, there are no vertical asymptotes.

$$\lim_{x \to \pm\infty} \frac{x^2 + 2}{x^2 + 1} = \lim_{x \to \pm\infty} \frac{1 + \dfrac{2}{x^2}}{1 + \dfrac{1}{x^2}} = 1,$$

so $y = 1$ is a horizontal asymptote.

13.
$$f(t) = \frac{t^2 + 3t - 5}{t^2 - 5t + 6} = \frac{t^2 + 3t - 5}{(t - 2)(t - 3)}$$

Since the denominator is zero when $t = 2, 3$, the vertical asymptotes are $t = 2$ and $t = 3$.

$$\lim_{x \to \pm\infty} \frac{t^2 + 3t - 5}{t^2 - 5t + 6} = \lim_{x \to \pm\infty} \frac{1 + \dfrac{3}{t} - \dfrac{5}{t^2}}{1 - \dfrac{5}{t} + \dfrac{6}{t^2}} = 1,$$

so $y = 1$ is a horizontal asymptote.

15.
$$h(x) = \frac{1}{x} - \frac{1}{x - 1} = \frac{-1}{x(x - 1)} = \frac{-1}{x^2 - x}$$

Since the denominator is zero when $x = 0, 1$, the vertical asymptotes are $x = 0$ and $x = 1$.

$$\lim_{x \to \pm\infty} \frac{-1}{x^2 - x} = 0,$$

so $y = 0$ is a horizontal asymptote.

17. $f(x) = x^3 + 3x^2 - 2$
domain: all real numbers
intercepts
   when $x = 0$, $f(0) = -2$; point $(0, -2)$
      $f(x) = 0$ is too difficult to solve
asymptotes: no vertical or horizontal asymptotes

$$f'(x) = 3x^2 + 6x = 3x(x + 2)$$
$$f'(x) = 0 \text{ when } x = -2, 0$$
$$f''(x) = 6x + 6 = 6(x + 1)$$
$$f''(x) = 0 \text{ when } x = -1$$

When $x < -2$, $f'(x) > 0$ so f is increasing
$\qquad\qquad f''(x) < 0$ so f is concave down
$-2 < x < -1$, $f'(x) < 0$ so f is decreasing
$\qquad\qquad f''(x) < 0$ so f is concave down
$-1 < x < 0$, $f'(x) < 0$ so f is decreasing
$\qquad\qquad f''(x) > 0$ so f is concave up
$x > 0$, $f'(x) > 0$ so f is increasing
$\qquad\qquad f''(x) > 0$ so f is concave up.

$(-2, 2)$ is a relative maximum, $(-1, 0)$ is an inflection point, and $(0, -2)$ is a relative minimum.

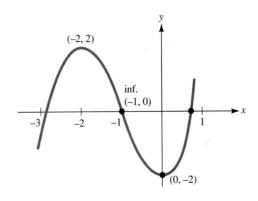

19. $f(x) = x^4 + 4x^3 + 4x^2 = x^2(x + 2)^2$
domain: all real numbers
intercepts:
   when $x = 0$, $f(0) = 0$; point $(0, 0)$
      $f(x) = 0$, $x = 0, -2$; point $(-2, 0)$
asymptotes: no vertical or horizontal asymptotes.

$$f'(x) = 4x^3 + 12x^2 + 8x = 4x(x + 1)(x + 2)$$
$$f'(x) = 0 \text{ when } x = -2, -1, 0$$
$$f''(x) = 12x^2 + 24x + 8 = 4(3x^2 + 6x + 2)$$
$$f''(x) = 0 \text{ when } x = -1.6, -0.4$$

When $x < -2$, $f'(x) < 0$ so f is decreasing

$\qquad\qquad f''(x) > 0$ so f is concave up

$-2 < x < -1.6$, $f'(x) > 0$ so f is increasing

$\qquad\qquad f''(x) > 0$ so f is concave up

$-1.6 < x < -1$, $f'(x) > 0$ so f is increasing

$\qquad\qquad f''(x) < 0$ so f is concave down

$-1 < x < -0.4$, $f'(x) < 0$ so f is decreasing

$\qquad\qquad f''(x) < 0$ so f is concave down

$-0.4 < x < 0$, $f'(x) < 0$ so f is decreasing

$\qquad\qquad f''(x) > 0$ so f is concave up

$x > 0$, $f'(x) > 0$ so f is increasing

$\qquad\qquad f''(x) > 0$ so f is concave up.

$(-2, 0)$ is a relative minimum, $(-1.6, 0.4)$ is an inflection point, $(-1, 1)$ is a relative maximum, $(-0.4, 0.4)$ is an inflection point, and $(0, 0)$ is a relative minimum.

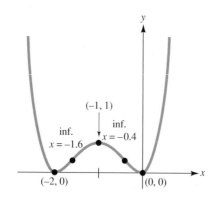

21. $f(x) = (2x - 1)^2(x^2 - 9)$

$\qquad = (2x - 1)^2(x + 3)(x - 3)$

domain: all real numbers

intercepts:

$\qquad$ when $x = 0$, $f(0) = -9$; point $(0, -9)$

$\qquad f(x) = 0$, $x = \dfrac{1}{2}$, -3, 3; points

$\qquad\qquad \left(\dfrac{1}{2}, 0\right)$, $(-3, 0)$, $(3, 0)$

asymptotes: no vertical or horizontal asymptotes.

$f'(x) = (2x - 1)^2(2x) + (x^2 - 9)[2(2x - 1)(2)]$

$\qquad = 2(2x - 1)(4x^2 - x - 18)$

$\qquad = 2(2x - 1)(4x - 9)(x + 2)$

$f'(x) = 0$ when $x = -2$, $\dfrac{1}{2}$, $\dfrac{9}{4}$

$f''(x) = \left[(2x - 1)(8x - 1) + (4x^2 - x - 18)(2)\right]$

$\qquad = 2(24x^2 - 12x - 35)$

$f''(x) = 0$ when $x = -0.98$, 1.5

When $x < -2$, $f'(x) < 0$ so f is decreasing

$\qquad\qquad f''(x) > 0$ so f is concave up

$-2 < x < -0.98$, $f'(x) > 0$ so f is increasing

$\qquad\qquad f''(x) > 0$ so f is concave up

$-0.98 < x < 0.5$, $f'(x) > 0$ so f is increasing

$\qquad\qquad f''(x) < 0$ so f is concave down

$0.5 < x < 1.5$, $f'(x) < 0$ so f is decreasing

$\qquad\qquad f''(x) < 0$ so f is concave down

$1.5 < x < 2.25$, $f'(x) < 0$ so f is decreasing

$\qquad\qquad f''(x) > 0$ so f is concave up

$x > 2.25$, $f'(x) > 0$ so f is increasing

$\qquad\qquad f''(x) > 0$ so f is concave up.

$(-2, -125)$ is a relative minimum, $(-0.98, -70.4)$ is an inflection point, $(0.5, 0)$ is a relative maximum, $(1.5, -26.2)$ is an inflection point, and $(2.25, -48.2)$ is a relative minimum.

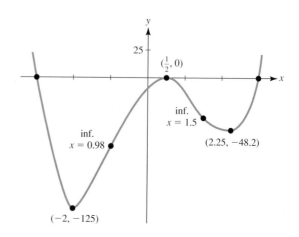

23. $f(x) = \dfrac{1}{2x+3}$

domain: $x \neq -\dfrac{3}{2}$

intercepts:

when $x = 0$, $f(0) = \dfrac{1}{3}$; point $\left(0, \dfrac{1}{3}\right)$

$f(x) \neq 0$ for any value of x

asymptotes: $x = -\dfrac{3}{2}$ is a vertical asymptote

$y = 0$ is a horizontal asymptote

$$f'(x) = -(2x+3)^{-2}(2) = \dfrac{-2}{(2x+3)^2}$$

note that $f'(x) < 0$ for all x in domain

$$f''(x) = -2\left[-2(2x+3)^{-3}(2)\right] = \dfrac{8}{(2x+3)^3}$$

When $x < -1.5$, $f'(x) < 0$ so f is decreasing

$f''(x) < 0$ so f is concave down

$x > -1.5$, $f'(x) < 0$ so f is decreasing

$f''(x) > 0$ so f is concave up.

f is undefined for $x = -1.5$, so there are no relative extrema or inflection points.

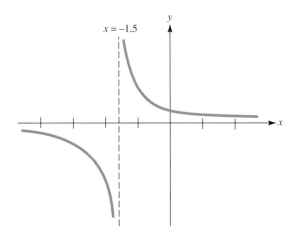

$x = -1.5$

25. $f(x) = x - \dfrac{1}{x} = \dfrac{x^2 - 1}{x} = \dfrac{(x+1)(x-1)}{x}$

domain: $x \neq 0$

intercepts:

when $x = 0$, $f(0)$ undefined

$f(x) = 0$, $x = -1, 1$; points $(-1, 0)$, $(1, 0)$

asymptotes $x = 0$ is a vertical asymptote

no horizontal asymptote

(Note: $\displaystyle\lim_{x \to \pm\infty} \dfrac{x^2 - 1}{x} = \lim_{x \to \pm\infty} \dfrac{x - \dfrac{1}{x}}{1} = x$,

so $y = x$ is an oblique asymptote)

$$f'(x) = 1 + \dfrac{1}{x^2} = \dfrac{x^2 + 1}{x}$$

$$f''(x) = -\dfrac{2}{x^3}$$

When $x < 0$, $f'(x) > 0$ so f is increasing

$f''(x) > 0$ so f is concave up

$x > 0$, $f'(x) > 0$ so f is increasing

$f''(x) < 0$ so f is concave down.

f is undefined for $x = 0$, so there are no relative extrema or inflection points.

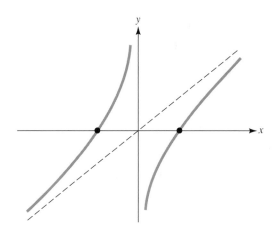

27. $f(x) = \dfrac{1}{x^2 - 9} = \dfrac{1}{(x+3)(x-3)}$

domain: $x \neq -3, 3$

intercepts:

when $x = 0$, $f(0) = -\dfrac{1}{9}$; point $\left(0, -\dfrac{1}{9}\right)$

$f(x) \neq 0$ for any value of x

asymptotes: $x = -3$ and $x = 3$ are vertical asymptotes

$y = 0$ is a horizontal asymptote

$$f'(x) = -(x^2 - 9)^2(2x) = \frac{-2x}{(x^2 - 9)^2}$$

$f'(x) = 0$ when $x = 0$

$$f''(x) = \frac{(x^2 - 9)^2(-2) - (-2x)(2(x^2 - 9)(2x))}{(x^2 - 9)^4}$$

$$= \frac{6(x^2 + 3)}{(x^2 - 9)^3}$$

When $x < -3$, $f'(x) > 0$ so f is increasing

$\qquad\qquad$ $f''(x) > 0$ so f is concave up

$-3 < x < 0$, $f'(x) > 0$ so f is increasing

$\qquad\qquad$ $f''(x) < 0$ so f is concave down

$0 < x < 3$, $f'(x) < 0$ so f is decreasing

$\qquad\qquad$ $f''(x) < 0$ so f is concave down

$x > 3$, $f'(x) < 0$ so f is decreasing

$\qquad\qquad$ $f''(x) > 0$ so f is concave up.

$\left(0, -\frac{1}{9}\right)$ is a relative maximum. Since f is undefined for $x = -3, 3$, there are no other relative extrema or inflection points.

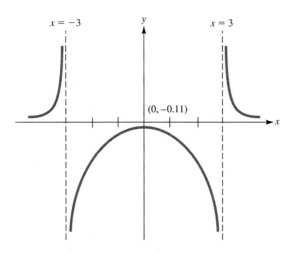

x = −3   y   x = 3

(0, −0.11)

29. $f(x) = \dfrac{x^2 - 9}{x^2 + 1} = \dfrac{(x + 3)(x - 3)}{x^2 + 1}$
domain: all real numbers
intercepts:
$\qquad$ when $x = 0$, $f(0) = -9$; point $(0, -9)$
$\qquad\qquad$ $f(x) = 0$, $x = -3, 3$; points $(-3, 0)$, $(3, 0)$

asymptotes: no vertical asymptotes
$\qquad\qquad$ $y = 1$ is a horizontal asymptote

$$f'(x) = \frac{(x^2 + 1)(2x) - (x^2 - 9)(2x)}{(x^2 + 1)^2} = \frac{20x}{(x^2 + 1)^2}$$

$f'(x) = 0$ when $x = 0$

$$f''(x) = \frac{(x^2 + 1)^2(20) - (20x)[2(x^2 + 1)(2x)]}{(x^2 + 1)^4}$$

$$= \frac{20(-3x^2 + 1)}{(x^2 + 1)^3}$$

$f''(x) = 0$ when $x = -\dfrac{1}{\sqrt{3}}, \dfrac{1}{\sqrt{3}}$

When $x < -\dfrac{1}{\sqrt{3}}$, $f'(x) < 0$ so f is decreasing

$\qquad\qquad$ $f''(x) < 0$ so f is concave down

$-\dfrac{1}{\sqrt{3}} < x < 0$, $f'(x) < 0$ so f is decreasing

$\qquad\qquad$ $f''(x) > 0$ so f is concave up

$0 < x < \dfrac{1}{\sqrt{3}}$, $f'(x) > 0$ so f is increasing

$\qquad\qquad$ $f''(x) > 0$ so f is concave up

$x > \dfrac{1}{\sqrt{3}}$, $f'(x) > 0$ so f is increasing

$\qquad\qquad$ $f''(x) < 0$ so f is concave down.

$(-0.58, -6.48)$ is an inflection point, $(0, -9)$ is a relative minimum, and $(0.58, -6.48)$ is an inflection point.

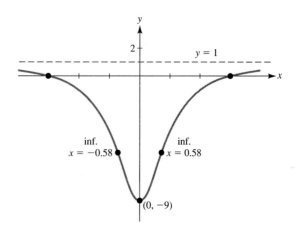

y

2   y = 1

inf.   inf.
x = −0.58   x = 0.58

(0, −9)

31. $f(x) = x^{3/2} = \sqrt{x^3}$

domain: $x \geq 0$

intercepts:

   when $x = 0$, $f(0) = 0$; point $(0, 0)$

      $f(x) = 0$, $x = 0$

asymptotes: no vertical or horizontal asymptotes

$$f'(x) = \frac{3}{2}x^{1/2} = \frac{3}{2}\sqrt{x}$$

$$f'(x) = 0 \text{ when } x = 0$$

$$f''(x) = \frac{3}{4}x^{-1/2} = \frac{3}{4\sqrt{x}}$$

When $x < 0$, f is undefined

$x > 0$, $f'(x) > 0$ so f is increasing

$f''(x) > 0$ so f is concave up.

$(0, 0)$ is a relative minimum.

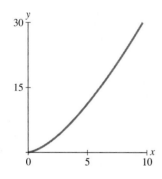

33. Answers will vary.

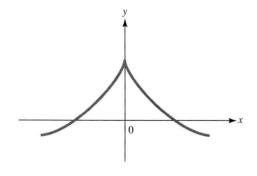

35. Answers will vary.

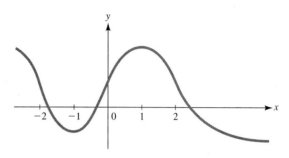

37. Answers will vary.

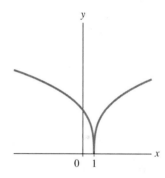

39. $f'(x) = x^3(x - 2)^2$

  (a) $f'(x) = 0$ when $x = 0, 2$

      When $x < 0$, $f'(x) < 0$ so f is decreasing

      $0 < x < 2$, $f'(x) > 0$ so f is increasing

      $x > 2$, $f'(x) > 0$ so f is increasing.

  (b) At $x = 0$, there is a relative minimum but there is no relative extrema at $x = 2$.

  (c) $f''(x) = (x^3)[2(x - 2)(1)] + (x - 2)^2(3x^2)$

          $= x^2(x - 2)(5x - 6)$

      $f''(x) = 0$ when $x = 0, \dfrac{6}{5}, 2$

      When $x < 0$, $f''(x) > 0$ so f is concave up

      $0 < x < 1.2$, $f''(x) > 0$ so f is concave up

      $1.2 < x < 2$, $f''(x) < 0$ so f is concave down

      $x > 2$, $f''(x) > 0$ so f is concave up.

Overall, f is concave up when $x < 0$, $0 < x < 1.2$, and when $x > 2$; f is concave down when $1.2 < x < 2$.

(d) At $x = 1.2$ and $x = 2$, there are inflection points.

41. $f'(x) = \dfrac{x + 3}{(x - 2)^2}$

(a) $f'(x) = 0$ when $x = -3$
$f'(x)$ is undefined when $x = 2$

When $x < -3$, $f'(x) < 0$ so f is decreasing

$-3 < x < 2$, $f'(x) > 0$ so f is increasing

$x > 2$, $f'(x) > 0$ so f is increasing.

(b) When $x = -3$, there is a relative minimum but there is no relative extrema at $x = 2$.

(c) $f''(x) = \dfrac{(x - 2)^2(1) - (x + 3) \cdot 2(x - 2)(1)}{(x - 2)^4}$

$\quad = \dfrac{(x - 2)^2\,[(x - 2) - 2(x + 3)]}{(x - 2)^4}$

$\quad = \dfrac{-x - 8}{(x - 2)^3} = \dfrac{-(x + 8)}{(x - 2)^3}$

$f''(x) = 0$ when $x = -8$
$f''(x)$ is undefined when $x = 2$

When $x < -8$, $f''(x) < 0$ so f is concave down

$-8 < x < 2$, $f''(x) > 0$ so f is concave up

$x > 2$, $f''(x) < 0$ so f is concave down.

(d) Since the concavity switches when $x = -8$, there is an inflection point when $x = -8$. The concavity switches when $x = 2$ as well, however f is undefined when $x = 2$.

43. To have a vertical asymptote of $x = 2$, the denominator must be zero for $x = 2$, so

$$5 + B(2) = 0 \rightarrow B = -\frac{5}{2}$$

To have a horizontal asymptote of $y = 4$

$$\lim_{x \to \pm\infty} \frac{Ax - 3}{5 - \frac{5}{2}x} = \lim_{x \to \pm\infty} \frac{A - \frac{3}{x}}{\frac{5}{x} - \frac{5}{2}} = \frac{A}{-\frac{5}{2}} = -\frac{2}{5}A = 4,$$

so $A = -10$.

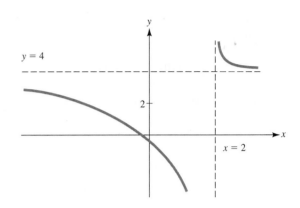

45. $\qquad C(x) = 3x^2 + x + 48$

$\qquad A(x) = 3x + 1 + \dfrac{48}{x} = \dfrac{3x^2 + x + 48}{x}$

(a) $x = 0$ is a vertical asymptote; there are no horizontal asymptotes.

(b) As $x \to \infty$, the graph of A approaches the line $y = 3x + 1$ asymptotically.

(c)

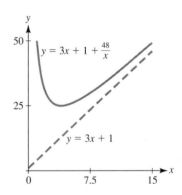

47. $W(x) = \dfrac{200x}{100 - x}$

(a) domain: $0 \le x < 100$
intercepts:
when $x = 0$, $W(0) = 0$; point $(0, 0)$
$\qquad W(x) = 0$, $x = 0$
asymptotes: $x = 100$ is a vertical asymptote
since $x \ge 0$, the is no horizontal asymptote

$$W'(x) = \frac{20,000}{(100-x)^2}$$

$$W''(x) = \frac{40,000}{(100-x)^3}$$

When $0 \le x < 100$, $W'(x) > 0$ so W is increasing

$W''(x) > 0$ so W is concave up.

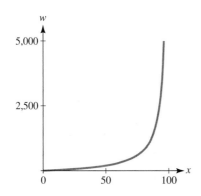

(b) $1500 = \dfrac{200x}{100-x}$; $150,000 - 1500x = 200x$;
$x \approx 88.2\%$ will receive a new book, so
$100 - 88.2 = 11.8\%$ will not receive a new book.

49. $Q(x) = \dfrac{7x}{27+x^2}$

(a) domain: $x \ge 0$
intercepts:
    when $x = 0$, $Q(0) = 0$; point $(0, 0)$
        $Q(x) = 0$, $x = 0$
asymptotes: the denominator is never zero, so there are no vertical asymptotes

$$\lim_{x \to \infty} Q(x) = \lim_{x \to \infty} \frac{\frac{7}{x}}{\frac{27}{x^2} + 1} = 0$$

so $y = 0$ is a horizontal asymptote

$$Q'(x) = \frac{(27+x^2)(7) - (7x)(2x)}{(27+x^2)^2} = \frac{189 - 7x^2}{(27+x^2)^2}$$

$$Q''(x) = \frac{(27+x^2)^2(-14x) - (189 - 7x^2) \cdot 2(27+x^2)(2x)}{(27+x^2)^4}$$

$$= \frac{2(27+x^2)\left[-7x(27+x^2) - 2x(189 - 7x^2)\right]}{(27+x^2)^4}$$

$$= \frac{2(-567x + 7x^3)}{(27+x^2)^3}$$

$Q'(x) = 0$ when $x = \sqrt{27} \approx 5.2$
$Q''(x) = 0$ when $x = 0, 9$

When $0 < x < 5.2$, $Q'(x) > 0$ so Q is increasing

$Q''(x) < 0$ so Q is concave down.

$5.2 < x < 9$, $Q'(x) < 0$ so Q is decreasing

$Q''(x) < 0$ so Q is concave down.

$x > 9$, $Q'(x) < 0$ so Q is decreasing

$Q''(x) > 0$ so Q is concave up.

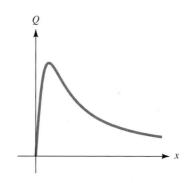

(b) Sales are maximized when $x = \sqrt{27}$, or a marketing expenditure of \$5,196. The corresponding maximum sales is
$$Q(5.196) = \frac{7(5.196)}{27+27} \approx 0.6736$$
or approximately 674 units.

51. Answers will vary.

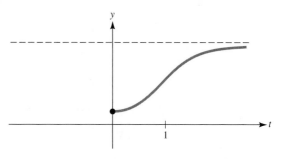

53. Answers will vary.

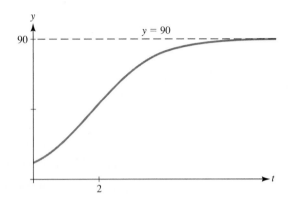

Overall, T is increasing for $0 \leq t < 7$; decreasing for $7 < t \leq 12$; concave up for $0 \leq t < \frac{3}{2}$; concave down for $\frac{3}{2} < t \leq 12$. The critical value $t = 7$ corresponds to the point $(7, 10.9)$, which is an absolute maximum. When $t = \frac{3}{2}$, the corresponding point is $(1.5, 1.7)$, which is an inflection point.

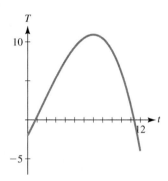

55. $T(t) = -\frac{1}{36}t^3 + \frac{1}{8}t^2 + \frac{7}{3}t - 2$

(a) domain: $0 \leq t \leq 12$

intercepts: when $t = 0$, $T(0) = -2$; point $(0, -2)$

x-intercepts too difficult to find

asymptotes: none

$$T'(t) = -\frac{1}{12}t^2 + \frac{1}{4}t + \frac{7}{3}$$

$T'(t) = 0$ when

$t^2 - 3t - 28 = 0$

$(t + 4)(t - 7) = 0$

$t = 7$ (deleting negative solution)

$$T''(t) = -\frac{1}{6}t + \frac{1}{4}$$

$T''(t) = 0$ when

$2t - 3 = 0$

$$t = \frac{3}{2}$$

When $0 \leq t < \frac{3}{2}$, $T'(t) > 0$ so T is increasing

$T''(t) > 0$ so T is concave up

$\frac{3}{2} < t < 7$, $T'(t) > 0$ so T is increasing

$T''(t) < 0$ so T is concave down

$7 < t \leq 12$, $T'(t) < 0$ so T is decreasing

$T''(t) < 0$ so T is concave down

(b) The maximum occurs when $t = 7$, or at 1:00 pm. The maximum temperature is approx. 10.9° C.

57. $S(t) = \dfrac{100(t^2 - 3t + 25)}{t^2 + 7t + 25}$

(a) domain: $0 \leq t \leq 10$

intercepts:

when $t = 0$, $S(0) = 100$; point $(0, 100)$

$f(x) \neq 0$ for any x

asymptotes: there are no vertical asymptotes

$y = 100$ is a horizontal asymptote

$$S'(t) = \frac{100}{(t^2 + 7t + 25)^2} \Big((t^2 + 7t + 25)(2t - 3)$$

$$-(t^2 - 3t + 25)(2t + 7) \Big)$$

$$= \frac{1000(t + 5)(t - 5)}{(t^2 + 7t + 25)^2} = \frac{1000(t^2 - 25)}{(t^2 + 7t + 25)^2}$$

$S'(t) = 0$ when $t = 5$

When $0 \leq t < 5$, $S'(t) < 0$ so S is decreasing

$5 < t \leq 10$, $S'(t) > 0$ so S is increasing.

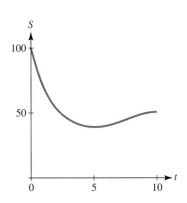

(b) When $t = 5$, there is a relative minimum, so her support is lowest when $t = 5$ and her minimum support level is $S(5) \approx 41.2\%$.

(c) When $t > 5$, $S'(t) > 0$ so $S'(10)$ is positive.

$$S''(t) = \frac{1000}{(t^2 + 7t + 25)^4} \left[(t^2 + 7t + 25)^2 (2t) \right.$$

$$\left. -(t^2 - 25)(2(t^2 + 7t + 25)(2t + 7)) \right]$$

When $t = 10$, $S''(10) < 0$ so S', or her approval rate, is decreasing.

59. $G(x) = \frac{1}{2,000} \left(\frac{800}{x} + 5x \right)$

(a) total cost = cost driver + cost gas

cost driver = (#hrs)(pay/hr)

$$= \left(\frac{\#mi}{mi/hr} \right) (pay/hr)$$

cost gas = (#mi)(gal/mi)(cost/gal)

$$C(x) = \left(\frac{400}{x} \right) (18)$$

$$+ (400) \left[\frac{1}{2,000} \left(\frac{800}{x} + 5x \right) \right] (4.25)$$

$$= \frac{7,880}{x} + 4.25x$$

domain: $30 \le x \le 65$
intercepts: none in domain
asymptotes: none in domain

$$C'(x) = -\frac{-7,880}{x^2} + 4.25$$

$C'(x) = 0$ when $x \approx 43$

When $30 \le x < 43$, $C'(x) < 0$ so C is decreasing
$43 < x \le 65$, $C'(t) > 0$ so C is increasing.

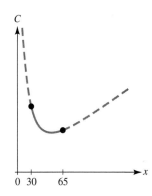

(b) When $x = 43$, there is a minimum. So cost is minimized when the driver travels at 43 mph. The minimum cost is $C(43) \approx \$366.01$.

61. $f(x) = x^{2/3}(2x - 5)$

(a)
$$f'(x) = (x^{2/3})(2) + (2x - 5) \left(\frac{2}{3} x^{-1/3} \right)$$

$$= 2x^{2/3} + \frac{2(2x - 5)}{3x^{1/3}} = \frac{10(x - 1)}{3x^{1/3}}$$

$$= \frac{10}{3} x^{2/3} - \frac{10}{3} x^{-1/3}$$

$f'(x) = 0$ when $x = 1$

When $x < 0$, $f'(x) > 0$ so f is increasing
$0 < x < 1$, $f'(x) < 0$ so f is decreasing
$x > 1$, $f'(x) > 0$ so f is increasing.

$(0, 0)$ is a relative maximum and $(1, -3)$ is a relative minimum.
Since f is defined but f' is undefined for $x = 0$, there is a vertical tangent at $x = 0$.

(b)
$$f''(x) = \frac{20}{9} x^{-1/3} + \frac{10}{9} x^{-4/3}$$

$$= \frac{10(2x + 1)}{9x^{4/3}}$$

$$f''(x) = 0 \text{ when } x = -\frac{1}{2}$$

When

$$x < -0.5, \quad f''(x) < 0 \text{ so } f \text{ is concave down}$$

$$-0.5 < x < 0, \quad f''(x) > 0 \text{ so } f \text{ is concave up}$$

$$x > 0, \quad f''(x) > 0 \text{ so } f \text{ is concave up.}$$

$(-0.5, -3.8)$ is an inflection point.

(c) When $x = 0$, $f(0) = 0$, so y-intercept is 0.
When $f(x) = 0$, $x = 0$, 2.5; so, x-intercepts are
0 and 2.5. There are no vertical or horizontal
asymptotes.

(d)

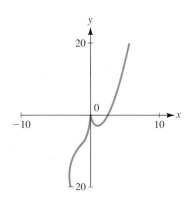

63. Let $f(x) = \dfrac{x - 1}{x^2 - 1}$ and let $g(x) = \dfrac{x - 1.01}{x^2 - 1}$.

(a) To use a graphing utility to sketch the graph of
f,
Press $\boxed{y=}$ and input $(x - 1)/(x \wedge 2 - 1)$ and
press $\boxed{\text{Graph}}$.
At first appearance, the graph appears to be
continuous at $x = 1$.
Use $\boxed{\text{2nd}}$ $\boxed{\text{calc}}$ and 1: value to evaluate $f(1)$.
We see no y-value is displayed for $x = 1$
which means $f(1)$ is undefined. From algebra,
$f(x) = \dfrac{x - 1}{(x + 1)(x - 1)}$. We can cancel the
common factor $x - 1$, which leaves a "hole" in
the graph of f at $x = 1$.

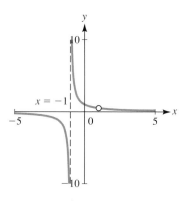

(b) To sketch a graph of g,
Press $\boxed{y=}$ and input $(x - 1.01)/(x \wedge 2 - 1)$ and
press $\boxed{\text{Graph}}$.
The graph of g appears to be the same as the
graph for f. However, by tracing and zooming
in at $x = 1$, we see the vertical asymptote
appears at $x = 1$. In addition, using $\boxed{\text{2nd}}$ $\boxed{\text{calc}}$
and 1: value to evaluate $g(1)$ also produces an
undefined y-value. The reason for this is not
due to a "hole" in the graph for g but rather the
vertical asymptote $x = 1$.

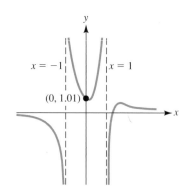

3.4   Optimization

1.
$$f(x) = x^2 + 4x + 5, \quad -3 \le x \le 1$$
$$f'(x) = 2x + 4 = 2(x + 2)$$

$f'(x) = 0$ when $x = -2$, which is in the interval

$$f(-2) = 1, \ f(-3) = 2 \text{ and } f(1) = 10$$

So, $f(1) = 10$ is the absolute maximum and $f(-2) = 1$ is the absolute minimum.

3.
$$f(x) = \frac{1}{3}x^3 - 9x + 2, \ 0 \le x \le 2$$
$$f'(x) = x^2 - 9 = (x+3)(x-3)$$

$f'(x) = 0$ when $x = -3$ and $x = 3$, which are not in the interval.
$f(0) = 2$, which is the absolute maximum and
$f(2) = -\dfrac{40}{3}$, which is the absolute minimum.

5.
$$f(t) = 3t^5 - 5t^3, \ -2 \le t \le 0$$
$$f'(t) = 15t^4 - 15t^2 = 15t^2(t+1)(t-1)$$

$f'(t) = 0$ when $t = -1$, $t = 0$ and $t = 1$, of which $t = -1$ and $t = 0$ are in the interval.
$f(-1) = 2$, $f(0) = 0$, $f(-2) = -56$
So, $f(-1) = 2$ is the absolute maximum and $f(-2) = -56$ is the absolute minimum.

7.
$$f(x) = (x^2 - 4)^5, \ -3 \le x \le 2$$
$$f'(x) = 5(x^2-4)^4(2x) = 10x(x+2)^4(x-2)^4$$

$f'(x) = 0$ when $x = -2$, $x = 0$, and $x = 2$, all of which are in the interval.
$$f(-2) = 0, \ f(0) = -1{,}024, \ f(2) = 0$$
$$\text{and } f(-3) = 3{,}125$$

So, $f(-3) = 3{,}125$ is the absolute maximum and $f(0) = -1{,}024$ is the absolute minimum.

9.
$$g(x) = x + \frac{1}{x}, \ \frac{1}{2} \le x \le 3$$
$$g'(x) = 1 - \frac{1}{x^2} = \frac{x^2 - 1}{x^2} = \frac{(x+1)(x-1)}{x^2}$$

$g'(x) = 0$ when $x = -1$ and $x = 1$, of which $x = 1$ is in the interval.
$g'(x)$ is undefined at $x = 0$, however, $x = 0$ is not in the interval
$$g(1) = 2, \ g\left(\frac{1}{2}\right) = \frac{5}{2}, \ g(3) = \frac{10}{3}$$

So, $g(3) = \dfrac{10}{3}$ is the absolute maximum and $g(1) = 2$ is the absolute minimum.

11.
$$f(u) = u + \frac{1}{u}, \ u > 0$$
$$f'(u) = 1 - \frac{1}{u^2} = \frac{u^2 - 1}{u^2} = \frac{(u+1)(u-1)}{u^2}$$

$f'(u) = 0$ when $u = -1$ and $u = 1$, of which $u = 1$ is in the interval.
$f'(u)$ is undefined when $u = 0$, which is not in the interval

When $0 < x < 1$, $f'(x) < 0$ so f is decreasing

$ x > 1$, $f'(x) > 0$ so f is increasing.

Since there are no endpoints, $f(1) = 2$ is the absolute minimum and there is no absolute maximum.

13.
$$f(x) = \frac{1}{x}, \ x > 0$$
$$f'(x) = -\frac{1}{x^2}$$

$f'(x)$ is never zero and $f'(x)$ is undefined when $x = 0$, which is not in the domain. Also, there are no endpoints. So, there is no absolute maximum or absolute minimum.

15.
$$f(x) = \frac{1}{x+1}, \ x \ge 0$$
$$f'(x) = -(x+1)^{-2}(1) = -\frac{1}{(x+1)^2}$$

$f'(x)$ is never zero and $f'(x)$ is undefined when $x = -1$, which is not in the domain.
When $x > 0$, $f'(x) < 0$ so f is decreasing. So, $f(0) = 1$ is the absolute maximum and there is no absolute minimum.

17. $p(q) = 49 - q$ and $C(q) = \dfrac{1}{8}q^2 + 4q + 200$

(a)
$$R(q) = qp(q) = 49q - q^2$$
$$R'(q) = 49 - 2q$$
$$C'(q) = \frac{1}{4}q + 4$$

The profit function is

$$P(q) = R(q) - C(q)$$

$$= -\frac{9}{8}q^2 + 45q - 200$$

$$P'(q) = -\frac{9}{4}q + 45$$

$P'(q) = 0$ when $q = 20$, so profit is maximized when 20 units are produced.

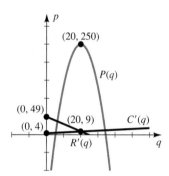

(b)
$$A(q) = \frac{C(q)}{q} = \frac{1}{8}q + 4 + \frac{200}{q}$$

$$A'(q) = \frac{1}{8} - \frac{200}{q^2}$$

$A'(q) = 0$ when $q = 40$, so the average cost is minimized when 40 units are produced.

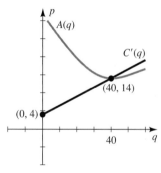

19. $p(q) = 180 - 2q$ and $C(q) = q^3 + 5q + 162$

(a)
$$R(q) = qp(q) = 180q - 2q^2$$
$$R'(q) = 180 - 4q$$
$$C'(q) = 3q^2 + 5$$

The profit function is $P(q) = R(q) - C(q)$

$$= -q^3 - 2q^2 + 175q - 162$$

$$P'(q) = -3q^2 - 4q + 175$$
$P'(q) = 0$ when $q = 7$ (rejecting negative solution), so profit is maximized when 7 units are produced.

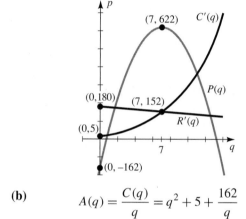

(b)
$$A(q) = \frac{C(q)}{q} = q^2 + 5 + \frac{162}{q}$$

$$A'(q) = 2q - \frac{162}{q^2}$$

$A'(q) = 0$ when $q \approx 4.327$, so the average cost is minimized when 4.327 units are produced.

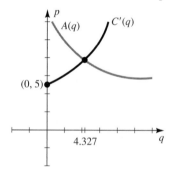

21. $p(q) = 1.0625 - 0.0025q$ and $C(q) = \dfrac{q^2 + 1}{q + 3}$

(a)
$$R(q) = qp(q) = 1.0625q - 0.0025q^2$$
$$R'(q) = 1.0625 - 0.005q$$
$$C'(q) = \frac{q^2 + 6q - 1}{(q + 3)^2}$$

The profit function is $P(q) = R(q) - C(q)$

$$= 1.0625q - 0.0025q^2 - \frac{q^2 + 1}{q + 3}$$

$$= \frac{1}{q + 3}[-0.0025q^3 + 0.055q^2 + 3.1875q - 1]$$

$$P'(q) = \frac{1}{(q + 3)^2}\left[(q + 3)\right.$$

$$(-0.0075q^2 + 0.11q + 3.1875)$$

$$\left.+0.0025q^3 - 0.055q^2 - 3.1875q + 1\right]$$

$$= \frac{1}{(q + 3)^2}\left[-0.005q^3\right.$$

$$\left.+0.0325q^2 + 0.33q + 10.5625\right]$$

Press $\boxed{y=}$ and input P, R', and C' for $y_1 =$, $y_2 =$, and $y_3 =$, respectively.
Use window dimensions [0, 45]5 by [0, 3]0.5
Press $\boxed{\text{graph}}$
Use the maximum function under the calc menu to find the relative maximum of P occurs at $x = 17.3361$.

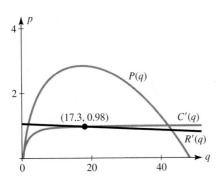

(b)

$$A(q) = \frac{C(q)}{q} = \frac{q^2 + 1}{q(q + 3)}$$

$$A'(q) = \frac{1}{(q^2 + 3q)^2}\left[2q(q^2 + 3q)\right.$$

$$\left.-(q^2 + 1)(2q + 3)\right]$$

$$= \frac{3q^2 - 2q - 3}{(q^2 + 3q)^2}$$

Press $\boxed{y=}$ and input A and C' for $y_1 =$ and $y_2 =$, respectively. Use window dimensions of [0, 6]0.5 by [0, 1.5]0.2.
Press $\boxed{\text{graph}}$
Use the minimum function under the calc menu to find the relative minimum occurs at $q = 1.3874$.

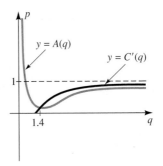

23.

$$D(p) = -1.3p + 10$$

$$E(p) = \frac{p}{D(p)} \frac{dD}{dp}$$

$$= \frac{p}{-1.3p + 10}(-1.3)$$

$$E(4) = \frac{-1.3(4)}{-1.3(4) + 10} = -\frac{13}{12}$$

$|E(4)| > 1$, so the demand is elastic.

25.

$$D(p) = 200 - p^2$$

$$E(p) = \frac{p}{D(p)} \frac{dD}{dp}$$

$$E(p) = \frac{p}{200 - p^2}(-2p)$$

$$E(10) = \frac{-2(10)^2}{200 - (10)^2} = -2$$

$|E(10)| > 1$, so the demand is elastic.

27.
$$D(p) = \frac{3{,}000}{p} - 100$$

$$E(p) = \frac{p}{D(p)} \frac{dD}{dp}$$

$$E(p) = \frac{p}{\frac{3{,}000}{p} - 100} \left(-\frac{3{,}000}{p^2} \right)$$

$$= \frac{p}{\frac{3{,}000 - 100p}{p}} \left(-\frac{3{,}000}{p^2} \right)$$

$$= \frac{p^2}{100(30 - p)} \left(-\frac{3{,}000}{p^2} \right)$$

$$= -\frac{30}{30 - p}$$

$$E(10) = -\frac{30}{30 - 10} = -\frac{3}{2}$$

$|E(10)| > 1$, so the demand is elastic.

29. Need to find the maximum absolute value of the slope of the graph. The slope is

$$f'(x) = 4x - x^2$$

To maximize $|f'|$ on the interval $-1 \le x \le 4$,

$$f''(x) = 4 - 2x = 2(2 - x)$$
$$f''(x) = 0 \text{ when } x = 2$$

Now,

$$|f'(2)| = |4| = 4$$
$$|f'(-1)| = |-5| = 5$$
$$|f'(4)| = |0| = 0$$

So, slope is steepest when $x = -1$, and its value is $f'(-1) = -5$.

31. $P(q) = -2q^2 + 68q - 128$

(a) aver profit $AP(q) = \frac{P(q)}{q}$

$$AP(q) = -2q + 68 - \frac{128}{q}$$

marginal profit is P'

$$P'(q) = -4q + 68$$

(b) $AP(q) = P'(q)$

$$-2q + 68 - \frac{128}{q} = -4q + 68$$

$$-\frac{128}{q} = -2q$$

$$64 = q^2$$

$$\bar{q} = 8 \text{ units}$$

(c) $AP(q) = -2q + 68 - \frac{128}{q}$

$$AP'(q) = -2 + \frac{128}{q^2}$$

$AP'(q) = 0$ when

$$0 = -2 + \frac{128}{q^2}$$

$$2 = \frac{128}{q^2}$$

$$q^2 = 64$$

$$q = 8$$

When $0 \le q < 8$, $AP'(q) > 0$ so AP is increasing

$q > 8$, $AP'(q) < 0$ so AP is decreasing

So, AP is a maximum when $q = 8$ units.

(d)

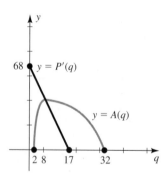

33. $P(x) = 100(2x^3 - 45x^2 + 264x)$

(a) The period of time between 1995 and 2008 corresponds to the interval $2 \le x \le 15$.

$$P'(x) = 100(6x^2 - 90x + 264)$$
$$= 600(x - 4)(x - 11)$$

$P'(x) = 0$ when $x = 4$ and $x = 11$
$P(2) = 36,400$; $P(4) = 46,400$;
$P(11) = 12,100$; $P(15) = 58,500$.
The maximum membership occurred when
$x = 15$, or in the year 2008.
The minimum membership occurred when
$x = 11$, or in the year 2004.

(b) The maximum was $P(15) = 58,500$ members
and the minimum was $P(11) = 12,100$
members.

35. $F(p) = p^n(1-p)^{m-n}$

$$F'(p) = p^n(m-n)(1-p)^{m-n-1}(-1)$$
$$+ (1-p)^{m-n}(n)(p^{n-1})$$
$$= -p^n(m-n)(1-p)^{m-n-1}$$
$$+ p^{n-1}(n)(1-p)^{m-n}$$
$$= p^{n-1}(1-p)^{m-n-1}$$
$$\left[-(m-n)p + n(1-p)\right]$$
$$= p^{n-1}(1-p)^{m-n-1}$$
$$\left[-mp + np + n - np\right]$$

$F'(p) = 0$ when $p = 0$, 1, and $\dfrac{n}{m}$

$F(0) = 0$, $F(1) = 0$
Since n, m are positive and $m > n$, $\dfrac{n}{m}$ is in interval.

$F\left(\dfrac{n}{m}\right) = \left(\dfrac{n}{m}\right)^n\left(1 - \dfrac{n}{m}\right)^{m-n}$, and $F\left(\dfrac{n}{m}\right) > 0$,

so, $p = \dfrac{n}{m}$ gives the absolute maximum.

37. $S(r) = c(R^2 - r^2)$, where c is a positive constant.
The relevant interval is $0 \le r \le R$.

$$S'(r) = -2cr$$
$$S'(r) = 0 \text{ when } r = 0$$

(the left-hand endpoint of the interval)
With $S(0) = cR^2$ and $S(r) = 0$, the speed of the
blood is greatest when $r = 0$, that is, at the central
axis.

39. $q^2 + 3pq = 22$

(a) Using implicit differentiation,

$$2q\frac{dq}{dp} + (3p)\frac{dq}{dp} + (q)(3) = 0$$
$$\frac{dq}{dp} = \frac{-3q}{2q + 3p}$$
$$E(p) = \frac{p}{q}\frac{dq}{dp}$$
$$D(p) = q$$

So,

$$E(p) = \frac{p}{q}\left(\frac{-3q}{2q + 3p}\right) = \frac{-3p}{2q + 3p}$$

(b) When $p = 3$, $q^2 + 9q = 22$, or $q = 2$ (rejecting
negative root).

$$|E(p)| = \left|\frac{-3 \cdot 3}{2 \cdot 2 + 3 \cdot 3}\right| = \left|-\frac{9}{13}\right| = \frac{9}{13}$$

Since $\dfrac{9}{13} < 1$, demand is inelastic.

41. (a) When $q = 50$, $50 = 500 - 2p$, or $p = 225$.
Further, when $q = 0$, $0 = 500 - 2p$, or $p = 250$.
So, the range for price is

$$225 \le p \le 250$$

(b)
$$E(p) = \frac{p}{q}\frac{dq}{dp} = \frac{p}{500 - 2p}(-2)$$
$$= -\frac{p}{250 - p}$$
$$\left|-\frac{p}{250 - p}\right| = 1 \text{ when } -\frac{p}{250 - p} = \pm 1$$

or, when $p = 125$ and demand is of unit
elasticity.
When $p < 125$, $|E_n| < 1$ and demand is
inelastic.
When $p > 125$, $|E_n| > 1$ and demand is elastic.

(c) When the price is less than $125, total revenue
is increasing as price increases; when the
price is $125, total revenue is unaffected by a
small change in price, when the price is more
than $125, total revenue is decreasing as price
increases.

(d) If an unlimited number of prints is available,
should charge $125 each; if only 50 prints are

available, should charge $225, the value in the price interval which is closest to $125.

43. $E(v) = \dfrac{1}{v}[0.074(v-35)^2 + 22]$

(a)

$E'(v) = \left(\dfrac{1}{v}\right)[0.148(v-35)(1)]$

$\qquad + \left[0.074(v-35)^2 + 22\right]\left(\dfrac{-1}{v^2}\right)$

$\qquad = \dfrac{1}{v}\left[0.148v - 5.18 - \dfrac{1}{v}(0.074v^2 - 5.18v + 112.65)\right]$

$\qquad = \dfrac{1}{v}\left(0.148v - 5.18 - 0.074v + 5.18 - \dfrac{112.65}{v}\right)$

$\qquad = \dfrac{1}{v}\left(0.074v - \dfrac{112.65}{v}\right)$

So, $E'(v) = 0$ when

$\qquad 0.074v - \dfrac{112.65}{v} = 0$

$\qquad 0.074v = \dfrac{112.65}{v}$

$\qquad v^2 \approx 1522.3$

$\qquad v \approx 39$

$E''(v) = \left(\dfrac{1}{v}\right)\left(0.074 + \dfrac{112.65}{v^2}\right)$

$\qquad + \left(0.074v - \dfrac{112.65}{v}\right)\left(-\dfrac{1}{v^2}\right)$

$E''(39) > 0$, so there is an absolute minimum when $v = 39$.

(b) Writing Exercise—Answers will vary.

45. The relationship between the number of Moppsy dolls and Floppsy dolls is given by

$$y = \dfrac{82 - 10x}{10 - x}$$

with the relevant interval $0 \le x \le 8$.

Let C be the amount received from the sale of Floppsy doll. Then, $2C$ is the amount received from

the sale of each Moppsy doll. The total revenue from the sale of both dolls is

$$R(x) = Cx + \dfrac{2C(82 - 10x)}{10 - x}$$

$$= C\left(\dfrac{164 - 10x - x^2}{10 - x}\right)$$

$$R'(x) = \dfrac{C}{(10 - x^2)}\left[(10 - x)(-10 - 2x)\right.$$

$$\left. -(164 - 10x - x^2)(-1)\right]$$

$$= C\left(\dfrac{x^2 - 20x + 64}{(10 - x)^2}\right)$$

$$= C\dfrac{(x - 16)(x - 4)}{(10 - x)^2}$$

$R'(x) = 0$ when $x = 4$ ($x = 16$ is not in the interval) Since $R(4) = 18C$, $R(0) = 16.4C$, and $R(8) = 10C$, revenue is maximized when 400 Floppsy and $\dfrac{82 - 10(4)}{10 - 4}$, or 700 Moppsy dolls are produced.

47. Let x be the number of hours worked after 8:00 a.m. before the coffee break. Then, $4 - x$ will be the number of hours worked after the break. The total number of units assembled will be

$$N(x) = f(x) + g(4 - x)$$

$$= -x^3 + 6x^2 + 15x - \dfrac{1}{3}(4 - x)^3$$

$$\qquad + (4 - x)^2 + 23(4 - x)$$

$$N'(x) = -3x^2 + 12x + 15 - (4 - x)^2(-1)$$

$$\qquad + 2(4 - x)(-1) + 23(-1)$$

$$N'(x) = -2x^2 + 6x = -2x(x - 3)$$

$$N'(x) = 0 \text{ when } x = 0, \ x = 3$$

Testing these values along with the interval endpoints $(0 \le x \le 4)$ gives

$$N(0) = 86.67, \ N(3) = 95.67; \ N(4) = 92$$

So, to assemble the maximum number of units, the break should be scheduled when $x = 3$. That is, at 11:00 a.m.

49.
$$R(D) = D^2\left(\frac{C}{2} - \frac{D}{3}\right) = \frac{C}{2}D^2 - \frac{1}{3}D^3$$

(a) To maximize $R'(D)$,

$$R'(D) = CD - D^2$$
$$R''(D) = C - 2D$$
$$R''(D) = 0 \text{ when } D = \frac{C}{2}$$
$$R'''(D) = -2$$

Since $R'''\left(\frac{C}{2}\right)$ is negative, $D = \frac{C}{2}$ is a maximum for sensitivity. The sensitivity when $D = \frac{C}{2}$ is

$$R'\left(\frac{C}{2}\right) = C\left(\frac{C}{2}\right) - \left(\frac{C}{2}\right)^2 = \frac{C^2}{4}$$

(b) The reaction when $D = \frac{C}{2}$ is

$$R\left(\frac{C}{2}\right) = \left(\frac{C}{2}\right)^2\left[\frac{C}{2} - \frac{C/2}{3}\right]$$
$$= \frac{C^3}{12}$$

51.
$$I = \frac{E}{r + R}, \quad P(r) = I^2R = \frac{E^2R}{(r+R)^2}$$

$$P'(R) = \frac{(r+R)^2(E^2) - (E^2R)\,[2(r+R)]}{(r+R)^4}$$
$$= \frac{E^2(r+R)\,[(r+R) - 2R]}{(r+R)^4}$$
$$= \frac{E^2(r-R)}{(r+R)^3}$$

$P'(R) = 0$ when $R = r$

When $R = 0$, $P(0) = 0$

$$0 < R < r, \quad P'(R) > 0 \text{ so } P \text{ is increasing}$$
$$R > r, \quad P'(R) < 0 \text{ so } P \text{ is decreasing.}$$

So, $R = r$ results in maximum power.

53. (a)
$$P(x) = \frac{Ax}{B + x^m}$$

$$R(x) = P'(x) = A\frac{(B + x^m) - mxx^{m-1}}{(B + x^m)^2}$$
$$= \frac{A[B + (1 - m)x^m]}{(B + x^m)^2}$$

$$R(x) = 0 \text{ when } x = \left(\frac{B}{m - 1}\right)^{1/m}$$

(b)
$$R'(x) = \frac{A}{(B + x^m)^4}\Big[(B + x^m)^2[m(1 - m)x^{m-1}]$$
$$- [B + (1 - m)x^m][2(B + x^m)(mx^{m-1})]\Big]$$
$$= \frac{A(B + x^m)nx^{m-1}}{(B + x^m)^3}\Big[(B + x^m)(1 - m)$$
$$- 2(B + (1 - m)x^m)\Big]$$
$$= \frac{-Amx^{m-1}\big[B(1 + m) + x^m(1 - m)\big]}{(B + x^m)^3}$$

$$R'(x) = 0 \text{ when } x = \left[\frac{B(m + 1)}{m - 1}\right]^{1/m}$$

(c) Assuming $m > 1$,

when $0 < x < \left[\dfrac{B(m + 1)}{m - 1}\right]^{1/m}$,

$R'(x) > 0$ so R is increasing;

when $x > \left[\dfrac{B(m + 1)}{m - 1}\right]^{1/m}$,

$R'(x) < 0$ so R is decreasing.

So there is a relative maximum when

$$x = \left[\frac{B(m + 1)}{m - 1}\right]^{1/m}$$

55. (a)
$$S(r) = ar^2(r_0 - r)$$
$$F(r) = \pi r^2 S(r) = a\pi(r_0 r^4 - r^5), \quad 0 \le r \le r_0$$

(b)
$$F'(r) = a\pi(4r_0 r^3 - 5r^4)$$
$$= a\pi r^3(4r_0 - 5r)$$
$$F'(r) = 0 \text{ when } r = \frac{4}{5}r_0$$
$$F(0) = F(r_0) = 0, \text{ and } F\left(\frac{4r_0}{5}\right) > 0,$$

so $F(r)$ is maximized for $r = \dfrac{4r_0}{5}$.

57. $q = b - ap$

(a)
$$E(p) = \frac{p}{q}\frac{dq}{dp} = \frac{p}{b-ap}(-a) = \frac{ap}{ap-b}$$

(b)
$$|E(p)| = 1 \text{ when } \left|\frac{ap}{ap-b}\right| = 1,$$

or when $\dfrac{ap}{ap-b} = \pm 1$, or $p = \dfrac{b}{2a}$

(c) $|E(p)| < 1$ when $p < \dfrac{b}{2a}$, so demand is inelastic

when $0 \leq p < \dfrac{b}{2a}$

$|E(p)| > 1$ when $p > \dfrac{b}{2a}$, so demand is elastic

when $\dfrac{b}{2a} < p \leq \dfrac{b}{a}$

59. $q = \dfrac{a}{p^m} = ap^{-m}$

The elasticity of demand is

$$E(p) = \frac{p}{q}\frac{dq}{dp}$$
$$= \frac{p}{a/p^m}(-amp^{-m-1})$$
$$= \frac{p^{m+1}}{a}\left(-\frac{am}{p^{m+1}}\right) = -m$$

When

$0 < m < 1$, $|E(p)| < 1$ and demand is inelastic

$m = 1$ $|E(p)| = 1$ and demand is of unit elasticity

$m > 1$, $|E(p)| > 1$ and demand is elastic.

3.5 Additional Applied Optimization

1. Let x denote the number that exceeds its square, x^2, by the largest amount. Then,

$$f(x) = x - x^2$$

is the function to be maximized.

$$f'(x) = 1 - 2x$$
$$f'(x) = 0 \text{ when } x = \frac{1}{2}$$
$$f''(x) = -2, \text{ so } f''\left(\frac{1}{2}\right) < 0$$

and there is a relative maximum when $x = \frac{1}{2}$. Further, since $f''(x) < 0$ for all x, it is the absolute maximum. So, $x = \frac{1}{2}$ is the desired number.

3. Let x be the first number and y be the second. Then,

$$P = xy, \text{ or since } y = 50 - x,$$
$$P(x) = x(50 - x) = 50x - x^2$$

which is the function to be maximized.

$$P'(x) = 50 - 2x$$
$$P'(x) = 0 \text{ when } x = 25$$
$$P''(x) = -2, \text{ so } P''(25) < 0$$

and there is a relative maximum when $x = 25$. Further, since $P''(x) < 0$ for all x in the domain $0 < x < 50$, it is the absolute maximum. So, $x = 25$ and $y = 50 - 25 = 25$ are the desired numbers.

5. Let x be the $1.00 price increments above $40.00. Then $40 + x$ will be the price per computer game, $50 - 3x$ will be the number of units sold per month, and the profit will be

$$P(x) = (50 - 3x)[(40 + x) - 25] = 750 + 5x - 3x^2$$

which is the function to be maximized.

$$P'(x) = 5 - 6x$$

$$P'(x) = 0 \text{ when } x = \frac{5}{6}$$

$$P''(x) = -6, \text{ so } P''\left(\frac{5}{6}\right) < 0$$

and there is a relative maximum when $x = \frac{5}{6}$. Further, since $P''(x) < 0$ for all x in the domain $x \geq 0$, it is the absolute maximum. So, the selling price for maximum profit is $40 + \frac{5}{6} \approx \$41$.

7. Let x be the number of additional trees planted per acre. The number of oranges per tree will be $400 - 4x$ and the number of trees per acre $60 + x$. The yield per acre is

$$y(x) = \left(\frac{\text{\# of oranges}}{\text{tree}}\right)\left(\frac{\text{\# of trees}}{\text{acre}}\right)$$

$$= (400 - 4x)(60 + x)$$

$$= 24{,}000 + 160x - 4x^2$$

$$y'(x) = 160 - 8x$$

$$y'(x) = 0 \text{ when } x = 20$$

$$y''(x) = -8, \text{ so } y''(20) < 0$$

and there is a relative maximum when $x = 20$. Further, since $y''(x) < 0$ for all x in the domain $x \geq 0$, it is the absolute maximum. So, the yield is maximized when there are $60 + 20 = 80$ trees per acre.

9. Profit = (#sold)(profit per card)
Let x be the number of 25 cent reductions in price. The profit per card will be
(selling price)−(cost to obtain)
$= (10 - 0.25x) - 5 = 5(1 - 0.05x)$
while the number of cards sold will be

$$25 + 5x = 5(5 + x)$$

The total profit will be

$$P(x) = 25(5 + x)(1 - 0.05x)$$

$$= 25(5 + 0.75x - 0.05x^2)$$

$$P'(x) = 18.75 - 2.5x$$

$$P'(x) = 0 \text{ when } x = 7.5$$

Since the number of 25 cent reductions must be an integer, and since $P(7) = P(8) = 195$, the store should lower the price by 8 reductions. That is, sell the cards for $10 - .25(8) = \$8$ per card. (Seven reductions yields the same profit, but using 8 reductions instead of 7 is good for the store's image.)

11. Let x be the length of the field and y be the width. The amount of fencing is the perimeter of the field, or

$$P = 2x + 2y$$

Since the area is 3,600,

$$A = xy$$

$$3{,}600 = xy, \text{ or } y = \frac{3{,}600}{x}$$

and

$$P(x) = 2x + 2\left(\frac{3{,}600}{x}\right) = 2x + \frac{7{,}200}{x}$$

which is the function to be minimized.

$$P'(x) = 2 - \frac{7{,}200}{x^2}$$

$$P'(x) = 0 \text{ when } x = 60$$

$$P''(x) = \frac{14{,}400}{x^3}, \text{ so } P''(60) > 0$$

and there is a relative minimum when $x = 60$. Further, since $P''(x) > 0$ for all x in the domain $x > 0$, it is the absolute maximum. So, the field should have a length of 60 meters and a width of 60 meters.

13. Let x be the length of the rectangle and y be the width. The area is

$$A = xy$$

Since the perimeter is fixed, let C represent its fixed value. Then,

$$P = 2x + 2y$$

$$C = 2x + 2y, \text{ so } y = \frac{C - 2x}{2}$$

and

$$A(x) = x \left(\frac{C - 2x}{2} \right) = \frac{C}{2}x - x^2$$

which is the function to be maximized.

$$A'(x) = \frac{C}{2} - 2x$$

$$A'(x) = 0 \text{ when } x = \frac{C}{4}$$

$$A''(x) = -2, \text{ so } A'' \left(\frac{C}{4} \right) < 0$$

and there is a relative maximum when $x = \frac{C}{4}$. Further, since $A''(x) < 0$ for all x in the domain $0 < x < \frac{C}{2}$, it is the absolute maximum. When $x = \frac{C}{4}$, $y = \frac{C}{4}$. So for any given perimeter, a square is the rectangle having the maximum area.

15. Let x be the length of the rectangle and let y be the vertical distance above the rectangle along the side of length 5. Then, $5 - y$ is the width of the rectangle. The area of the rectangle is

$$A = x(5 - y)$$

By similar triangles,

$$\frac{12}{5} = \frac{x}{y}, \text{ or } y = \frac{5}{12}x$$

and

$$A(x) = x \left(5 - \frac{5}{12}x \right) = 5x - \frac{5}{12}x^2$$

which is the function to be maximized.

$$A'(x) = 5 - \frac{5}{6}x$$

$$A'(x) = 0 \text{ when } x = 6$$

$$A''(x) = -\frac{5}{6}, \text{ so } A''(6) < 0$$

and there is a relative maximum when $x = 6$. Further, since $A''(x) < 0$ for all x in the domain $0 < x < 12$, it is the absolute maximum. The dimensions of the rectangle having the maximum area are $x = 6$ and $y = \frac{5}{12}(6) = \frac{5}{2}$.

17. Let x be the length of the side of the square base and y be the height of the box. The volume of the box is

$$V = x^2 y$$

The cost of the four sides is

4 (cost per unit area)(area)

$$= 4(3)(xy) = 12xy$$

The cost of the bottom of the box is

(cost per unit area)(area)

$$= 4(x^2)$$

Since there is 48 dollars available to build the box,

$$48 = 12xy + 4x^2, \text{ or}$$

$$y = \frac{48 - 4x^2}{12x} = \frac{4}{x} - \frac{x}{3}$$

and

$$V(x) = x^2 \left(\frac{4}{x} - \frac{x}{3} \right) = 4x - \frac{1}{3}x^3$$

which is the function to be maximized.

$$V'(x) = 4 - x^2$$

$$V'(x) = 0 \text{ when } x = 2 \text{ (rejecting the negative solution)}$$

$$V''(x) = -2x, \text{ so } V''(2) < 0$$

and there is a relative maximum when $x = 2$. Further, since $V''(x) < 0$ for all x in the domain $x > 0$, it is the absolute maximum. So the box has a maximum volume when its dimensions are 2 meters by 2 meters by $y = \frac{4}{2} - \frac{2}{3} = \frac{4}{3}$ meters.

19. Let x be the distance down the paved road where the jeep reaches the road. Then, the time the jeep drives in sand is given by

$$t_s = \frac{d_s}{r_s} = \frac{\sqrt{x^2 + 32^2}}{48}$$

The time the jeep drives on the road is given by

$$t_r = \frac{d_r}{r_r} = \frac{16 - x}{80}$$

The total time is given by

$$T(x) = \frac{1}{48}(x^2 + 1024)^{1/2} + \frac{1}{80}(16 - x)$$

$$T'(x) = \frac{1}{96}(x^2 + 1024)^{-1/2}(2x) + \frac{1}{80}(-1)$$

$$= \frac{x}{48\sqrt{x^2 + 1024}} - \frac{1}{80}$$

$T'(x) = 0$ when

$$0 = \frac{x}{48\sqrt{x^2 + 1024}} - \frac{1}{80}$$

$$\frac{1}{80} = \frac{x}{48\sqrt{x^2 + 1024}}$$

$$\sqrt{x^2 + 1024} = \frac{5}{3}x$$

$$x^2 + 1024 = \frac{25}{9}x^2$$

$$1024 = \frac{16}{9}x^2$$

$$576 = x^2$$

$$x = 24$$

Since the maximum value of x is 16, disregard this answer and check the endpoints ($0 \le x \le 16$).

$$T(0) \approx 0.867 \text{ hrs}$$
$$T(16) \approx 0.745 \text{ hrs}$$

So, the minimum time to reach the power plant is 0.745 hours, or approx. 44.7 minutes (making the trip entirely in the sand). Since he has 50 minutes to deliver the ransom, he can make it in time.

21. Let x be the distance down the opposite bank where the cable meets the bank. Then, the cost of the cable under the water is given by

$$C_w = 25\sqrt{x^2 + 1200^2}$$

The cost of the cable over land is

$$C_l = 20(1500 - x)$$

The total cost is given by

$$C(x) = 25(x^2 + 1,440,000)^{1/2} + 20(1500 - x)$$

$$C'(x) = \frac{25}{2}(x^2 + 1,440,000)^{-1/2}(2x) + 20(-1)$$

$$= \frac{25x}{\sqrt{x^2 + 1,440,000}} - 20$$

$C'(x) = 0$ when

$$0 = \frac{25x}{\sqrt{x^2 + 1,440,000}} - 20$$

$$20 = \frac{25x}{\sqrt{x^2 + 1,440,000}}$$

$$\sqrt{x^2 + 1,440,000} = \frac{5}{4}x$$

$$x^2 + 1,440,000 = \frac{25}{16}x^2$$

$$1,440,000 = \frac{9}{16}x^2$$

$$2,560,000 = x^2$$

$$x = 1600$$

Since the maximum value of x is 1500, disregard this answer and check the endpoints ($0 \le x \le 1500$).

$$C(0) = 60,000$$
$$C(1500) \approx 48,023$$

So, the minimum cost occurs when the cable runs entirely underwater.

23. Let x be the width (left to right) of the *printed* area and let y be the printed area's length (top to bottom). Then, the entire paper has a width of $x + 4$ and a length of $y + 8$. Need to minimize the area of the paper

$$A = (x + 4)(y + 8)$$

Since the printed area is 648 cm^2,

$$xy = 648$$

$$y = \frac{648}{x}$$

So,

$$A(x) = (x+4)\left(\frac{648}{x} + 8\right)$$

$$= 648 + 8x + \frac{2592}{x} + 32$$

$$A'(x) = 8 - \frac{2592}{x^2}$$

$A'(x) = 0$ when

$$0 = 8 - \frac{2592}{x^2}$$

$$8 = \frac{2592}{x^2}$$

$$x^2 = 324$$

$$x = 18$$

$$A''(x) = 0 + \frac{5184}{x^3}$$

Since $A''(18) > 0$, the absolute maximum occurs when $x = 18$. So, the paper shold be $18 + 4 = 22$ cm wide and $\frac{648}{18} + 8 = 44$ cm long.

25. The amount of material is the amount for the circular top and bottom, and the amount for the curved side.

$$m = 2\pi r^2 + 2\pi rh$$

Since the volume is 6.89π,

$$V = \pi r^2 h$$

$$6.89\pi = \pi r^2 h, \text{ or } h = \frac{6.89}{r^2}$$

and $m(r) = 2\pi r^2 + 2\pi r\left(\frac{6.89}{r^2}\right)$

$$= 2\pi r^2 + \frac{13.78\pi}{r}$$

which is the function to be minimized.

$$m'(r) = 4\pi r - \frac{13.78\pi}{r^2}$$

$m'(r) = 0$ when $r \approx 1.51$

$$m''(r) = 4\pi + \frac{27.56}{r^3}, \text{ so } m''(1.51) > 0$$

and there is a relative minimum when $r = 1.51$. Further, since $m''(r) > 0$ for all r in the domain $r > 0$,

it is an absolute minimum. So, the minimum material is when the can's radius is approximately 1.51 inches and its height is approximately $\frac{6.89}{(1.51)^2} \approx 3.02$ inches. (These dimensions are not used due to packaging and handling concerns.)

27. The cost of the material is the cost of the circular bottom and the cost of the curved side.

$$C = 3(\pi r^2) + 2(2\pi rh)$$

Since the volme is to be fixed, let K represent this fixed value.

$$V = \pi r^2 h$$

$$K\pi r^2 h, \text{ or } h = \frac{K}{\pi r^2}$$

and

$$C(r) = 3\pi r^2 + 4\pi r\left(\frac{K}{\pi r^2}\right) = 3\pi r^2 + \frac{4K}{r}$$

which is the function to be minimized.

$$C'(r) = 6\pi r - \frac{4K}{r^2}$$

$C'(r) = 0$ when $\frac{3\pi}{2}r^3 = K$

$$\frac{3\pi}{2}r^3 = \pi r^2 h$$

$$\text{or, } r = \frac{2}{3}h$$

$$C''(r) = 6\pi + \frac{8K}{r^3}, \text{ so } C''\left(\frac{2}{3}h\right) > 0$$

and there is a relative minimum when $r = \frac{2}{3}h$. Further, since $C''(r) > 0$ for all r in the domain $r > 0$, it is an absolute minimum. So, a can with a fixed volume has its cost minimized whenever $r = \frac{2}{3}h$.

29. Let n denote the number of floors and $A(n)$ the corresponding average cost. Since the total cost is

$$C(n) = 2n^2 + 500n + 600 \text{ thousand dollars}$$

$$A(n) = \frac{C(n)}{n} = 2n + 500 + \frac{600}{n}$$

The relevant interval is $n > 0$.

$$A'(n) = 2 - \frac{600}{n^2} = \frac{2(n^2 - 300)}{n^2}$$

$A'(n) = 0$ when $n = \sqrt{300} \approx 17.32$

When $0 < n < 17.32$, $A'(n) < 0$ so A is decreasing

$ n > 17.32$, $A'(n) > 0$ so A is increasing.

Since the number of floors must be an integer and $A(17) \approx 569.29$ and $A(18) \approx 569.33$, the average cost per floor is minimized when 17 floors are built.

31. (a) Let x be the number of bottles in each shipment. The costs include:

$$\text{purchase cost} = (800)(20) = 16{,}000$$

$$\text{ordering cost} = \left(\frac{800}{x}\right)(10)$$

$$\text{ordering cost} = \left(\frac{x}{2}\right)(0.4)$$

So, the total cost is

$$C(x) = 16{,}000 + \frac{8{,}000}{x} + 0.2x$$

which is the function to be minimized

$$C'(x) = -\frac{8{,}000}{x^2} + 0.2$$

$$C'(x) = 0 \text{ when } x = 200$$

$$C''(x) = \frac{16{,}000}{x^3}, \text{ so } C''(200) > 0$$

and there is a relative minimum when $x = 200$. $C(200) = 16{,}080$, $C(1) = 17{,}000.20$, $C(800) = 16{,}170$. So, cost is minimized when 200 bottles are ordered in each shipment.

(b) The number of shipments is $\frac{800}{200} = 4$ times a year, so the store orders every 3 months.

33. (a) Let x denote the number of machines used and $C(x)$ the corresponding total cost. Then

$$C(x) = \text{set up cost} +$$

$$\text{operating cost}$$

$$= 20 \text{ (number of machines)}$$

$$+ 15 \text{ (number of hours)}.$$

Since each machine produces 30 kickboards per hour, x machines produce $30x$ kickboards per hour and the number of hours required to produce 8,000 kickboards is $\dfrac{8{,}000}{30x}$.

So,

$$C(x) = 20x + 15\left(\frac{8{,}000}{30x}\right) = 20x + \frac{4{,}000}{x}$$

$$C'(x) = 20 - \frac{4{,}000}{x^2}$$

$$C'(x) = 0 \text{ when } x \approx 14$$

Since the company owns 10 machines, the domain of C is $1 \le x \le 10$. Further, $C(1) = 4{,}020$ and $C(10) = 600$, so cost is minimized when 10 machines are used.

(b) When 10 machines are used, the number of hours to produce the kickboards is $\dfrac{8{,}000}{30(10)}$ and the supervisor would be paid $15\left(\dfrac{8{,}000}{300}\right) = \$400$.

(c) The cost of setting up 10 machines is $20(10) = \$200$.

35. Let $P(x)$ be the profit from the sale of the wine at time x in years.

profit = value − purchase cost − storage cost

Let $V(x)$ be the value of the wine at time x, and let C be the purchase cost of the wine. Since the storage cost is $3x$,

$$P(x) = V(x) - C - 3x$$

which is the function to maximize and

$$P'(x) = V'(x) - 3$$

Since the rate of change of value is $53 - 10x$,

$$P'(x) = 50 - 10x$$

$$P'(x) = 0 \text{ when } x = 5$$

$$P''(x) = -10, \text{ so } P''(5) < 0$$

and there is a relative maximum when $x = 5$. Further, since $P''(x) < 0$ for all x in the domain $x \ge 0$, it is the absolute maximum. So, the wine should be sold 5 years from the time of purchase to maximize profit.

37. The volume of the parcel is

$$V = x^2 y$$

The restriction given is

$$4x + y = 108(\text{max}), \text{ or } y = 108 - 4x$$

and

$$V(x) = x^2(108 - 4x) = 108x^2 - 4x^3$$

which is the function to be maximized.

$$V'(x) = 216x - 12x^2 = 12x(18 - x)$$
$$V'(x) = 0 \text{ when } x = 18 \text{ (rejecting } x = 0)$$
$$V''(x) = 216 - 24x, \text{ so } V''(18) < 0$$

and there is a relative minimum when $x = 18$.

When $0 < x < 18$, $V'(x) > 0$ so V is increasing

$x > 18$, $V'(x) < 0$ so V is decreasing.

So, the relative maximum is the absolute maximum. The maximum volume is $108(18)^2 - 4(18)^3 = 11{,}664$ cubic inches.

39. Let x be the number of units and $C(x)$ be the cost of producing those units. Then,

$$C(x) = 1{,}200 + 1.2x + \frac{100}{x^2}$$

which is the function to be minimized.

$$C'(x) = 1.2 - \frac{200}{x^3}$$
$$C'(x) = 0 \text{ when } x \approx 5.503 \approx 6$$
$$C''(x) = \frac{600}{x^4}, \text{ so } C''(6) > 0$$

and there is a relative minimum when $x = 6$. Further, since $C''(x) > 0$ for all x in the domain $0 < x < 100$, it is the absolute minimum. So, producing 6 units daily minimizes the cost.

41. Let x be the distance along the shoreline from A to P. Then, the distance from B to P is the hypotenuse of a right triangle,

$$d(B, P) = \sqrt{25 + x^2}$$

The total distance along the shoreline from A to L is the leg of a right triangle,

$$d(A, L) = \sqrt{(13)^2 - (5)^2} = 12$$

So, the distance from P to L is

$$d(P, L) = 12 - x$$

The path of the bird is from B to P, and then from P to L. If e is the energy per mile to fly over land (a constant), then the energy to fly this path is

$$E(x) = 2e\sqrt{25 + x^2} + e(12 - x)$$

which is the function to be minimized.

$$E'(x) = e(25 + x^2)^{-1/2}(2x) - e$$
$$= \frac{2ex}{(25 + x^2)^{1/2}} - e$$
$$E'(x) = 0 \text{ when } \frac{2ex}{(25 + x^2)^{1/2}} = e$$
$$\frac{2x}{(25 + x^2)^{1/2}} = 1$$
$$2x = (25 + x^2)^{1/2}$$
$$4x^2 = 25 + x^2$$
$$\text{or, } x = \sqrt{\frac{25}{3}} = \frac{5\sqrt{3}}{3}$$

Since $0 \le x \le 12$,

$$E\left(\frac{5\sqrt{3}}{3}\right) \approx 20.7e; \ E(0) = 22e; \ E(12) = 26e$$

So, to minimize energy expended, the bird should fly to point P which is $\sqrt{\dfrac{25}{3}} \approx 2.9$ miles from point A.

43. Let S be the stiffness of the beam. Then,

$$S = kwh^3,$$

where k is a constant of proportionality. Since $w^2 + h^2 = 225$, or $h = \sqrt{225 - w^2}$, S can be expressed as a function of w,

$$S(w) = kw(225 - w^2)^{3/2}$$

which is the function to be maximized.

$$S'(w) = k\left[w \cdot \frac{3}{2}(225 - w^2)^{1/2}(-2w)\right.$$

$$\left. + (225 - w^2)^{3/2}(1)\right]$$

$$= k(225 - w^2)^{1/2}\left[-3w^2 + 225 - w^2\right]$$

$$= k(225 - w^2)^{1/2}(225 - 4w^2)$$

$S'(w) = 0$ when $w = \dfrac{15}{2}$ (rejecting the solution $w = 15$, which is not possible given the diameter)

When $0 < w < \dfrac{15}{2}$, $S'(w) > 0$ so C is increasing

$\dfrac{15}{2} < w < 15$, $S'(x)) < 0$ so S is decreasing.

So, the dimensions for maximum stiffness are

$w = \dfrac{15}{2}$ inches and $h = \sqrt{225 - \left(\dfrac{15}{2}\right)^2} \approx 13.0$ inches.

45. Let x be the number of miles from the house to plant A. Then, $18 - x$ is its distance from plant B, and $1 \le x \le 16$. Let $P(x)$ be the concentration of particulate matter at the house. Then,

$$P(x) = \frac{80}{x} + \frac{720}{18 - x}$$

which is the function to minimize.

$$P'(x) = -\frac{80}{x^2} + \frac{0 - (720)(-1)}{(18 - x)^2}$$

$$P'(x) = 0 \text{ when } \frac{80}{x^2} = \frac{720}{(18 - x)^2}$$

$$2x^2 + 9x - 81 = 0$$

$$\text{or, } x = \frac{9}{2} \text{ (rejecting negative solution)}$$

$P(4.5) = 0$, $P(1) \approx 122.4$, $P(16) = 365$;

So, the total pollution is minimized when the house is 4.5 miles from plant A.

47. Let $C(N)$ be the total cost of using N machines. Now, the setup cost of N machines is aN and the operating cost of N machines is $\dfrac{b}{N}$. So,

$$C(N) = aN + \frac{b}{N}$$

which is the function to minimize.

$$C'(N) = a = \frac{b}{N^2}$$

$$C'(N) = 0 \text{ when } a = \frac{b}{N^2},$$

or when $aN = \dfrac{b}{N}$ (setup cost = operating cost)

$$C''(N) = \frac{2b}{N^3},$$

which is positive for all N in the domain $N \ge 1$, so there is an absolute minimum when setup cost equals operating cost.

49. Frank is right. In the cost function,

$$C(x) = 5\sqrt{(900)^2 + x^2} + 4(3,000 - x)$$

note where the distance downstream appears. Since it is only part of the constant term in $C(x)$, it drops out when finding $C'(x)$. So, the critical value is always $x = 1,200$ (as long as the distance downstream is at least 1,200 meters).

When $0 \le x < 1,200$, $C'(x) < 0$ so C is decreasing

$x > 1,200$, $C'(x)) > 0$ so C is increasing

So, the absolute minimum cost is always when the cable reaches the bank 1,200 meters downstream.

51. (a) Let x be the number of machines and let t be the number of hours required to produce q units. The set up cost is xs and the operating cost is pt. Since each machine produces n units per hour, then $q = xnt$, or $t = \dfrac{q}{nx}$. The total cost is

$$C(x) = xs + p\frac{q}{nx}$$

which is the function to be minimized.

$$C'(x) = s - \frac{pq}{nx^2}$$

$$C'(x) = 0 \text{ when } s = \frac{pq}{nx^2}$$

$$\text{or, } x = \left(\frac{pq}{ns}\right)^{1/2}$$

$$C''(x) = \frac{2pq}{nx^3}, \text{ so } C''\left[\left(\frac{pq}{ns}\right)^{1/2}\right] > 0$$

and there is a relative minimum when $x = \left(\dfrac{pq}{ns}\right)^{1/2}$. Further, since $C''(x) > 0$ for all values of x in the domain $x \geq 1$, it is the absolute minimum.

(b) The setup cost xs, at this minimum, becomes

$$xs = s\sqrt{\frac{pq}{ns}} = \sqrt{\frac{pqs}{n}}$$

and the operating cost pt, at this minimum, becomes

$$P\frac{q}{n\sqrt{\dfrac{pq}{ns}}} = \frac{pq}{\sqrt{\dfrac{pqn}{s}}}$$

$$= pq\sqrt{\frac{s}{pqn}} = \sqrt{\frac{pqs}{n}}$$

So, the setup cost equals the operating cost when the total cost is minimized.

53. (a) Let x be the number of units produced, $p(x)$ the price per unit, t the tax per unit, and $C(x)$ the total cost.

$$C(x) = \frac{7x^2}{8} + 5x + 100$$

Since $p(x) = 15 - \dfrac{3x}{8}$, the revenue is

$$R(x) = xp(x) = 15x - \frac{3x^2}{8}$$

Now profit is

$$P(x) = \text{revenue--taxation--cost}$$

$$P(x) = 15x - \frac{3x^2}{8} - tx$$

$$- \frac{7x^2}{8} - 5x - 100$$

which is the function to be maximized.

$$P'(x) = 15 - \frac{3x}{4} - t - \frac{7x}{4} - 5$$

$$= -\frac{5}{2}x + 10 - t$$

$$P'(x) = 0 \text{ when } x = \frac{2(10 - t)}{5}$$

$$P''(x) = -\frac{5}{2}, \text{ so } P''\left(\frac{2(10 - t)}{5}\right) < 0$$

and there is a relative maximum when $x = \frac{2}{5}(10 - t)$. Further, since $P''(x) < 0$ for all x in the domain $x > 0$, it is the absolute maximum.

(b) The government share is

$$G(x) = tx = \left(\frac{2}{5}\right)(10t - t^2)$$

which is the function to be maximized.

$$G'(t) = \left(\frac{2}{5}\right)(10 - 2t)$$

$$G'(t) = 0 \text{ when } t = 5$$

$$G''(t) = -\frac{4}{5}, \text{ so } G''(5) < 0$$

and there is a relative maximum when $t = 5$. Further, since $G''(t) < 0$ for all t in the domain $t > 0$, it is the absolute maximum.

$x = 1.68$, or $(1.68, -0.23)$. There is an inflection point when $x = \frac{4}{9}$, or $(0.44, 11.1)$.

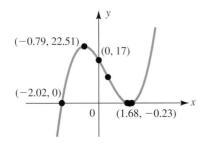

5. $f(t) = 3t^5 - 20t^3$
When $t = 0$, $f(0) = 0$ so $(0, 0)$ is an intercept.
When $f(t) = 3t^5 - 20t^3 = t^3(3t^2 - 20) = 0$ so

$$t = 0, \pm\sqrt{\frac{20}{3}} \text{ and } \left(\pm\sqrt{\frac{20}{3}}, 0\right)$$

are intercepts.
There are no asymptotes.

$$f'(t) = 15t^4 - 60t^2 = 15t^2(t + 2)(t - 2)$$

$f'(t) = 0$ when $t = -2, 0, 2$

$$f''(t) = 60t^3 - 120t = 60t(t^2 - 2)$$

$f''(t) = 0$ when $t = -\sqrt{2}, 0, \sqrt{2}$

When $t < -2$, $f'(t) > 0$ so f is increasing
$\qquad\qquad f''(t) < 0$ so f is concave down

$-2 < t < -\sqrt{2}$, $f'(t) < 0$ so f is decreasing
$\qquad\qquad f''(t) < 0$ so f is concave down

$-\sqrt{2} < t < 0$, $f'(t) < 0$ so f is decreasing
$\qquad\qquad f''(t) > 0$ so f is concave up

$0 < t < \sqrt{2}$, $f'(t) < 0$ so f is decreasing
$\qquad\qquad f''(t) < 0$ so f is concave down

$\sqrt{2} < t < 2$, $f'(t) < 0$ so f is decreasing
$\qquad\qquad f''(t) > 0$ so f is concave up

$t > 2$, $f'(t) > 0$ so f is increasing
$\qquad\qquad f''(t) > 0$ so f is concave up.

Overall,
f is decreasing when $-2 < t < 2$
f is increasing when $t < -2$ and $t > 2$
f is concave down when $t < -\sqrt{2}$ and $0 < t < \sqrt{2}$
f is concave up when $-\sqrt{2} < t < 0$ and $t > \sqrt{2}$.

There is a relative maximum when $t = -2$, or $(-2, 64)$, and a relative minimum when $t = 2$, or $(2, 64)$. There are inflection points when $t = -\sqrt{2}, \sqrt{2}$, or $(-1.4, 39.6)$ and $(1.4, -39.6)$.

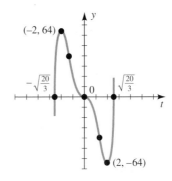

7. $g(t) = \dfrac{t^2}{t + 1}$
When $t = 0$, $g(0) = 0$ so $(0, 0)$ is an intercept.
When $g(t) = 0$, $t = 0$.
$t + 1 = 0$ when $t = -1$, so there is a vertical asymptote of $t = -1$.

$$\lim_{t \to \pm\infty} \frac{t^2}{t + 1} = \lim_{t \to \pm\infty} \frac{t}{1 + \dfrac{1}{t}} = \pm\infty,$$

so there are no horizontal asymptotes.
Note: $y = t - 1$ is an oblique asymptote.

$$g'(t) = \frac{(t + 1)(2t) - (t^2)(1)}{(t + 1)^2}$$

$$= \frac{t^2 + 2t}{(t + 1)^2} = \frac{t(t + 2)}{(t + 1)^2}$$

$g'(t) = 0$ when $t = -2, 0$ and $g'(t)$ is undefined when $t = -1$.

$$g''(t) = \frac{(t+1)^2(2t+2) - (t^2 + 2t)(2(t+1)(1))}{(t+1)^4}$$

$$= \frac{2(t+1)\left[(t+1)^2 - (t^2 + 2t)\right]}{(t+1)^4}$$

$$= \frac{2}{(t+1)^3}$$

$g''(t)$ is never zero and $g''(t)$ is undefined when $t = -1$.

When $t < -2$, $g'(t) > 0$ so g is increasing

$\qquad\qquad g''(t) < 0$ so g is concave down

$-2 < t < -1$, $g'(t) < 0$ so g is decreasing

$\qquad\qquad g''(t) < 0$ so g is concave down

$-1 < t < 0$, $g'(t) < 0$ so g is decreasing

$\qquad\qquad g''(t) > 0$ so f is concave up

$t > 0$, $g'(t) > 0$ so g is increasing

$\qquad\qquad g''(t) > 0$ so g is concave up.

Overall,

g is decreasing when $-2 < t < -1$ and $-1 < t < 0$

g is increasing when $t < -2$ and $t > 0$

g is concave down when $t < -1$

g is concave up when $t > -1$.

There is a relative maximum when $t = -2$, or $(-2, -4)$, and a relative minimum when $t = 0$, or $(0, 0)$. There are no inflection points.

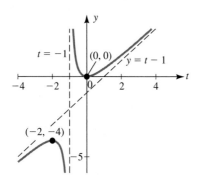

9. $F(x) = 2x + \dfrac{8}{x} + 2 = \dfrac{2x^2 + 2x + 8}{x}$

When $x = 0$, $F(0)$ is undefined.

$F(x) = 0$, $2(x^2 + x + 4) = 0$, which has no solution.

Denominator is zero 0 when $x = 0$, so there is a vertical asymptote of $x = 0$.

$$\lim_{x \to \pm\infty} \frac{2x^2 + 2x + 8}{x} = \lim_{x \to \pm\infty} \frac{2x + 2 + \dfrac{8}{x}}{1} = \pm\infty,$$

so there are no horizontal asymptotes.

Note: $y = 2x + 2$ is an oblique asymptote.

$$F'(x) = 2 - \frac{8}{x^2}$$

$F'(x) = 0$ when $x = -2$, 2 and $F'(x)$ is undefined when $x = 0$.

$$F''(x) = \frac{16}{x^3}$$

$F''(x)$ is never zero and $F''(x)$ is undefined when $x = 0$.

When $x < -2$, $F'(x) > 0$ so F is increasing

$\qquad\qquad F''(x) < 0$ so F is concave down

$-2 < x < 0$, $F'(x) < 0$ so F is decreasing

$\qquad\qquad F''(x) < 0$ so F is concave down

$0 < x < 2$, $F'(x) < 0$ so F is decreasing

$\qquad\qquad F''(x) > 0$ so F is concave up

$x > 2$, $F'(x) > 0$ so F is increasing

$\qquad\qquad F''(x) > 0$ so F is concave up.

Overall,

F is decreasing when $-2 < x < 0$ and $0 < x < 2$

F is increasing when $x < -2$ and $x > 2$

F is concave down when $x < 0$

F is concave up when $x > 0$.

There is a relative maximum when $x = -2$, or $(-2, -6)$, and a relative minimum when $x = 2$, or $(2, 10)$. There are no inflection points.

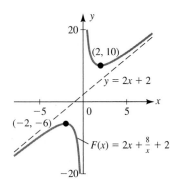

11. Graph (b) is the graph of f, and graph (a) is the graph of f'. Possible reasons include:

(i) The degree of graph (b) is one greater than the degree of graph (a).

(ii) Graph (a) is always positive, and graph (b) is always increasing.

13. $f'(x) = x^3(2x-3)^2(x+1)^5(x-7)$

$f'(x) = 0$ when $x = -1, 0, \dfrac{3}{2}, 7$

When $x < -1$, $f'(x) < 0$ so f is decreasing

$-1 < x < 0$, $f'(x) > 0$ so f is increasing

$0 < x < \dfrac{3}{2}$, $f'(x) < 0$ so f is decreasing

$\dfrac{3}{2} < x < 7$, $f'(x) < 0$ so f is decreasing

$x > 7$, $f'(x) > 0$ so f is increasing.

There is a relative minimum when $x = -1$ and $x = 7$. There is a relative maximum when $x = 0$. There is no relative extremum when $x = \frac{3}{2}$.

15. $F'(x) = \dfrac{x(x-2)^2}{x^4+1}$

$f'(x) = 0$, when $x = 0, 2$

When $x < 0$, $f'(x) < 0$ so f is decreasing

$0 < x < 2$, $f'(x) > 0$ so f is increasing

$0 > 2$, $f'(x) < 0$ so f is increasing.

There is a relative minimum when $x = 0$, but there is no relative extrema when $x = 2$.

17. (a) $f'(x) > 0$ so f is increasing when $x < 0$ and $x > 5$.

(b) $f'(x) < 0$ so f is decreasing when $0 < x < 5$.

(c) $f''(x) > 0$ so f is concave up when $-6 < x < -3$ and $x > 2$.

(d) $f''(x) < 0$ so f is concave down when $x < -6$ and $-3 < x < 2$.

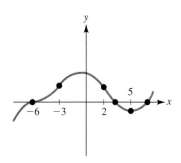

Note: since there are no points given, graphs can shift in y-direction, although not in x-direction.

19. (a) $f'(x) > 0$ so f is increasing when $1 < x < 2$

(b) $f'(x) < 0$ so f is decreasing when $x < 1$ and $x > 2$

(c) $f''(x) > 0$ so f is concave up when $x < 2$ and $x > 2$

(d) $f'(1) = 0$, so graph levels when $x = 0$
$f'(2)$ is undefined, so graph has a vertical asymptote, hole or vertical tangent when $x = 2$.

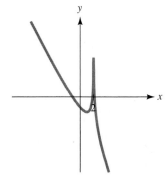

Note: since there are no points given, graphs can shift in y-direction, although not in x-direction.

21. $f(x) = -2x^3 + 3x^2 + 12x - 5$

$f'(x) = -6x^2 + 6x + 12 = -6(x + 1)(x - 2)$

$f'(x) = 0$ when $x = -1, 2$
$f''(x) = -12x + 6$
$f''(-1) = 18 > 0$, so there is a relative minimum when $x = -1$, or $(-1, -12)$; $f''(2) = -18 < 0$, so there is a relative maximum when $x = 2$, or $(2, 15)$.

23. $f(x) = \dfrac{x^2}{x + 1}$

$f'(x) = \dfrac{(x + 1)(2x) - (x^2)(1)}{(x + 1)^2} = \dfrac{x(x + 2)}{(x + 1)^2}$

$f'(x) = 0$ when $x = -2, 0$

$f''(x) = \dfrac{(x + 1)^2(2x + 2) - (x^2 + 2x)(2(x + 1)(1))}{(x + 1)^2}$

$f''(-2) = -2 < 0$, so there is a relative maximum when $x = -2$, or $(-2, -4)$; $f''(0) = 2 > 0$, so there is a relative minimum when $x = 0$, or $(0, 0)$.

25. $f(x) = -2x^3 + 3x^2 + 12x - 5$

$f(x) = -6x^2 + 6x + 12$

$f'(x) = -6(x + 1)(x - 2)$

$f'(x) = 0$ when $x = -1, 2$, both of which are in the interval $-3 \le x \le 3$.
$f(-1) = -12$, $f(2) = 15$, $f(-3) = 40$, $f(3) = 4$.
So, $f(-3) = 40$ is the absolute maximum and $f(-1) = -12$ the absolute minimum.

27. $g(s) = \dfrac{s^2}{s + 1}$

$g'(s) = \dfrac{(s + 1)(2s) - (s^2)(1)}{(s + 1)^2}$

$g'(s) = \dfrac{s(s + 2)}{(s + 1)^2}$

$g'(s) = 0$ when $s = -2, 0$, of which only $s = 0$ is in the interval $-\dfrac{1}{2} \le s \le 1$.

$g\left(-\dfrac{1}{2}\right) = \dfrac{1}{2}$, $g(0) = 0$, and $g(1) = \dfrac{1}{2}$

So, $g\left(-\dfrac{1}{2}\right) = g(1) = \dfrac{1}{2}$ is the absolute maximum and $g(0) = 0$ the absolute minimum.

29. $f'(x) = x(x - 1)^2$

(a) $f'(x) = 0$ when $x = 0, 1$

When $x < 0$, $f'(x) < 0$ so f is decreasing
$0 < x < 1$, $f'(x) > 0$ so f is increasing
$x > 1$, $f'(x)) > 0$ so f is increasing.

(b) $f''(x) = x[2(x - 1)(1)] + (x - 1)^2(1)$
$= (3x - 1)(x - 1)$

$f''(x) = 0$ when $x = \dfrac{1}{3}, 1$

When $x < \dfrac{1}{3}$, $f''(x) > 0$ so f is concave up

$\dfrac{1}{3} < x < 1$, $f''(x) < 0$ so f is concave down

$x > 1$, $f''(x) > 0$ so f is concave up

(c) There is a relative minimum when $x = 0$ and there are inflection points when $x = \dfrac{1}{3}$ and $x = 1$.

(d)

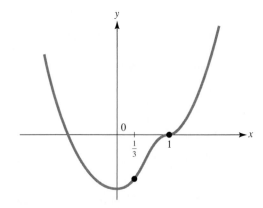

Note: since there are no points given, graph can shift in y-direction, although not in x-direction.

31. Profit = revenue − costs

= (#sold)(selling price) − (#sold)(cost per unit)

$P(x) = 100(20 - x)x - 100(20 - x)5$

$= 100(20 - x)(x - 5)$

and the relevant domain is $x \geq 5$

$P'(x) = 100[(20 - x)(1) + (x - 5)(-1)]$

$= 100(25 - 2x)$

$P'(x) = 0$ when $x = 12.50$

When $5 \leq x < 12.5$, $P'(x) > 0$ so P is increasing

$x > 12.5$, $P'(x) < 0$ so P is decreasing

So, when the price is $12.50 per unit, the profit is maximized.

33. Let r denote the radius, h the height, C the (fixed) cost (in cents), and V the volume of the container.

$$V = \pi r^2 h$$

C = cost of bottom + cost of side

= 3(area of bottom)

+ 2(area of side)

or $C = 3\pi r^2 + 4\pi r h$

Solving for h,

$$h = \frac{C - 3\pi r^2}{4\pi r}$$

and

$$V(r) = \pi r^2 \left(\frac{C - 3\pi r^2}{4\pi r} \right)$$

$$= \frac{rC}{4} - \frac{3\pi r^3}{4}$$

$$V'(r) = \frac{C}{4} - \frac{9\pi r^2}{4}$$

$V'(r) = 0$ when $\dfrac{C}{4} = \dfrac{9\pi r^2}{4}$, or $C = 9\pi r^2$. So,

$$h = \frac{9\pi r^2 - 3\pi r^2}{4\pi r}, \text{ or } h = \frac{3r}{2}.$$

$$V''(r) = -\frac{9\pi r}{2}$$

$V'' \left(\frac{3}{2} r \right) < 0$, so there is a relative maximum when $h = 1.5r$. Further, $V''(r) < 0$ for all r, so the volume is maximized when the height is 1.5 times the radius of the cylindrical container.

35. Let x be the width of the pasture and let y be its length. The area of the enclosed pasture is

$$A = xy$$

(a) Since there are 320 feet of fencing to use in enclosing the pasture,

$$2(x + y) = 320$$

$$y = 160 - x$$

So,

$$A(x) = x(160 - x) = 160x - x^2$$

$$A'(x) = 160 - 2x$$

$$A'(x) = 0 \text{ when } x = 80$$

When $0 < x < 80$, $A'(x) > 0$ so A is increasing

$80 < x < 160$, $A'(x) < 0$ so A is decreasing

So, to maximize the area, the dimensions are width = 80 feet and length = $160 - 80 = 80$ feet.

(b) Since there are 320 feet of fencing to use in enclosing the pasture and fencing is only needed on three sides (choosing the width as the side opposite the wall)

$$x + 2y = 320$$

$$y = 160 - \frac{1}{2}x$$

Now,

$$A(x) = x \left(160 - \frac{1}{2}x \right) = 160x - \frac{1}{2}x^2$$

$$A'(x) = 160 - x$$

$$A'(x) = 0 \text{ when } x = 160$$

When $0 < x < 160$, $A'(x) > 0$ so A is increasing

$160 < x < 320$, $A'(x) < 0$ so A is decreasing

So, to maximize the area, the dimensions are width (side opposite the wall) = 160 feet and length = $160 - \frac{1}{2}(160) = 80$ feet.

37. Let Q be the point on the opposite bank straight across from the starting point. With $QP = x$, the distance walked along the bank is $1 - x$. The distance across the water is given by the pythagorean theorem to be $\sqrt{1 + x^2}$. The time t is

$t = $ time in the water + time on the land

$\qquad = \dfrac{\text{distance in the water}}{\text{speed in the water}}$

$\qquad + \dfrac{\text{distance on the land}}{\text{speed on the land}}$

$\qquad = \dfrac{1}{4}(1 + x^2)^{1/2} + \dfrac{1}{5}(1 - x)$

The relevant interval is $0 \le x \le 1$ and

$$t'(x) = \frac{x}{4\sqrt{1 + x^2}} - \frac{1}{5}$$

$t'(x) = 0$ when

$$\frac{x}{4\sqrt{1 + x^2}} = \frac{1}{5}$$

$$5x = 4\sqrt{1 + x^2}$$

$$25x^2 = 16 + 16x^2, \text{ or } x = \pm\frac{4}{3}$$

Neither of these critical values is in the interval $0 \le x \le 1$. So, the absolute minimum must occur at an endpoint.

$$t(0) = 0.45; \ t(1) = \frac{\sqrt{2}}{4} \approx 0.354$$

The minimum time is when $x = 1$. That is, when you row all the way to town.

39. Let x denote the number of machines used and $C(x)$ the corresponding cost of producing the 400,000 medals. Then

$C(x) = $ set-up cost + operating cost

$\qquad = 80 \text{ (number of machines)}$

$\qquad + 5.76 \text{ (number of hours)}$

Each machine can produce 200 medals per hour, so x machines can produce $200x$ medals per hour, and it will take $\dfrac{400{,}000}{200x}$ hours to produce the 400,000 medals. So,

$$C(x) = 80x + 5.76\left(\frac{400{,}000}{200x}\right)$$

$$= 80x + \frac{11{,}520}{x}$$

$$C'(x) = 80 - \frac{11{,}520}{x^2}$$

$$= \frac{80(x - 12)(x + 12)}{x^2}$$

$C'(x) = 0$ when $x = 12$

When $0 < x < 12$, $C'(x) < 0$ so C is decreasing

$\qquad x > 12, \ C'(x) > 0$ so C is increasing.

So, the cost is minimized when 12 machines are used.

41. (a) $\qquad E(p) = \dfrac{p}{q} \cdot \dfrac{dq}{dp}$

$$= \frac{p}{200 - 2p^2}(-4p) = -\frac{2p^2}{100 - p^2}$$

(b) $E(6) = -\dfrac{2(6)^2}{100 - (6)^2} = -1.125$

A 1% increase in price will produce a decrease in demand of 1.125%.

(c) $-1 = \dfrac{-2p^2}{100 - p^2}$ or $p = \$5.77$

43. (a) $\qquad E(p) = \dfrac{p}{q}\dfrac{dq}{dp}$

$$= \frac{p}{300 - 0.7p^2} \cdot -1.4p$$

$$= \frac{-1.4p^2}{300 - 0.7p^2}$$

(b) $E(8) = \dfrac{-1.4(8)^2}{300 - 0.7(8)^2} \approx -0.351$

Since $|E(8)| = 0.35 < 1$, revenue increases as the price increases. So, the cruise line should raise the price.

45. Let A be the amount of light per square foot transmitted through stained glass. Then $2A$ is the amount transmitted through the clear glass. The total light transmitted is

$$\text{total light} = (\text{area rectangle})(2A)$$
$$+ (\text{area triangle})(A)$$

Let x be the dimension of one side of the triangle. Then the length of the rectangle is also x. Let y be the dimension of the width of the rectangle.

$$\text{area rectangle} = xy$$

but the total perimeter is 20, so

$$3x + 2y = 30, \text{ or } y = \frac{20 - 3x}{2}$$

$$\text{area triangle} = \frac{1}{2}bh$$
$$= \frac{1}{2}xh$$

Using half of the triangle, h is the leg of a right triangle, with $\dfrac{x}{2}$ as its base, so

$$h = \sqrt{x^2 - \left(\frac{1}{2}x\right)^2} = \frac{\sqrt{3}}{2}x$$

The total light function, $L(x)$, is

$$L(x) = x\left(\frac{20 - 3x}{2}\right)(2A) + \frac{1}{2}(x)\left(\frac{\sqrt{3}}{2}x\right)(A)$$

$$= A\left(20x - 3x^2 + \frac{\sqrt{3}}{4}x^2\right)$$

$$L'(x) = A\left(20 - 6x + \frac{\sqrt{3}}{2}x\right)$$

$$L'(x) = 0 \text{ when}$$

$$0 = 20 + \left(\frac{\sqrt{3}}{2} - 6\right)x, \text{ or}$$

$$x = \frac{20}{6 - \frac{\sqrt{3}}{2}} \approx 3.8956$$

When $0 < x < 3.896$, $L'(x) > 0$ so L is increasing

$$x > 3.896, \ L'(x) < 0 \text{ so } L \text{ is decreasing}$$

So, the light transmitted is maximized when the sides of the triangle and length of the rectangle are 3.896 feet, and the width of the rectangle is $\dfrac{20 - 3(3.8956)}{2} = 4.1566$ feet.

47. Let x denote the number of maps per batch and $C(x)$ the corresponding cost. Then,

$$C(x) = (\text{storage cost})$$
$$+ (\text{production cost})$$
$$+ (\text{set-up cost})$$

The relevant interval is $0 < x \leq 16,000$.

$$\text{storage cost} = \left(\begin{array}{c}\text{average} \\ \text{\#maps}\end{array}\right)\left(\begin{array}{c}\text{storage cost} \\ \text{per map}\end{array}\right)$$

$$= \left(\frac{x}{2}\right)(0.20) = 0.1x$$

$$\text{production cost} = \left(\begin{array}{c}\text{total} \\ \text{\#maps}\end{array}\right)\left(\begin{array}{c}\text{cost per} \\ \text{map}\end{array}\right)$$

$$= (16,000)(0.06) = 960$$

$$\text{set-up cost} = (\text{\#batches})\left(\begin{array}{c}\text{setup cost} \\ \text{per batch}\end{array}\right)$$

$$= \left(\frac{16,000}{x}\right)(100) = \frac{1,600,000}{x}$$

So,

$$C(x) = 0.1x + 960 + \frac{1,600,000}{x}$$

$$C'(x) = 0.1 - \frac{1,600,000}{x^2}$$

$$C'(x) = 0 \text{ when}$$

$$0.1x^2 = 1,600,000$$
$$x^2 = 16,000,000, \text{ or}$$
$$x = 4,000$$

Using the second derivative test, since

$$C''(x) = \frac{3,200,000}{x^3}$$

$$C'(4,000) > 0$$

So cost is minimized when there are 4,000 maps in each batch.

49. Let x be the number of units ordered and k_1, k_2 constants of proportionality. Since the storage cost is $C_s = k_1 x$ and the ordering cost $C_0 = \dfrac{k_2}{x}$, the total cost is

$$C(x) = k_1 x + \frac{k_2}{x}$$

$$C'(x) = k_1 - \frac{k_2}{x^2}$$

$C'(x) = 0$ when $x = \sqrt{\dfrac{k_2}{k_1}}$

Using the second derivative test, since

$$C''(x) = \frac{2k_2}{x^3}$$

$$C''\left(\sqrt{\frac{k_2}{k_1}}\right) > 0$$

So cost is minimized when

$$C_s = k_1 \sqrt{\frac{k_2}{k_1}} = \sqrt{k_1 k_2}$$

$$C_0 = \frac{k_2}{\sqrt{\dfrac{k_2}{k_1}}} = k_2 \sqrt{\frac{k_1}{k_2}} = \sqrt{k_1 k_2}$$

That is, when the storage cost equals the ordering cost.

51. $f(x) = \dfrac{K(1 + c^2 x^3)}{(1 + x)^3}$

(a)
$$f'(x) = \frac{K}{(1 + x)^6}\left[(1 + x)^3(3c^2 x^2)\right.$$
$$\left. -(1 + c^2 x^3)(3(1 + x)^2(1))\right]$$

$$= \frac{3K(c^2 x^2 - 1)}{(1 + x)^4}$$

$f'(x) = 0$ when $c^2 x^2 - 1 = 0$, or $x = \dfrac{1}{c}$

$$f''(x) = \frac{3K}{(1 + x)^8}\left[(1 + x)^4(2c^2 x)\right.$$
$$\left. -(c^2 x^2 - 1)(4(1 + x)^3(1))\right]$$

$$= 3K\frac{2(1 + x)^3(2 + c^2 x - c^2 x^2)}{(1 + x)^8}$$

$$= 6K\frac{(2 + c^2 x - c^2 x^2)}{(1 + x)^5}$$

$$f''\left(\frac{1}{c}\right) = 6K\frac{(2 + c - 1)}{\left(1 + \frac{1}{c}\right)^5}$$

$$= 6K\frac{(1 + c)}{\left(1 + \frac{1}{c}\right)^5} > 0$$

So, there is a relative minimum when $x = \dfrac{1}{c}$.

(b) With $c = 1$, $f'(x) = 0$ when $x = 1$

$$f(1) = \frac{2\pi}{3}\frac{(1 + 1)}{(1 + 1)^3} = \frac{\pi}{6} \approx 0.524$$

$$f\left(\sqrt{2} - 1\right) = \frac{2\pi}{3}\frac{\left[1 + \left(\sqrt{2} - 1\right)^3\right]}{\left[1 + \left(\sqrt{2} - 1\right)\right]^3} \approx 0.793$$

So the minimum is 0.524 and the maximum is 0.793.

(c) With $C = \sqrt{2}$, $f'(x) = 0$ when $x = \dfrac{1}{\sqrt{2}}$

$$f\left(\frac{1}{\sqrt{2}}\right) = \frac{\sqrt{3}\pi}{16}\frac{\left[1 + 2\left(\frac{1}{\sqrt{2}}\right)^3\right]}{\left[1 + \left(\frac{1}{\sqrt{2}}\right)\right]^3} \approx 0.117$$

$$f(0) = \frac{\sqrt{3}\pi}{16}\frac{(1 + 0)}{(1 + 0)^3} \approx 0.340$$

$$f(1) = \frac{\sqrt{3}\pi}{16}\frac{(1 + 2)}{(1 + 1)^3} \approx 0.128$$

So, the minimum is 0.117 and the maximum is 0.340.

Solving for P,

$$P = 5000 \left(1 + \frac{0.07}{4}\right)^{-20}$$

$$P \approx \$3,534.12$$

39. If $B(t) = \$9,000$, $r = 0.07$, $t = 5$, and

(a) $k = 4$

$$9,000 = P\left(1 + \frac{0.07}{4}\right)^{4 \cdot 5}$$

$$P = 9,000 \left(1 + \frac{0.07}{4}\right)^{-20}$$

$$P \approx \$6,361.42$$

(b) Compounded continuously

$$9,000 = Pe^{0.07(5)}$$

$$P = 9000e^{-0.35}$$

$$P \approx \$6,342.19$$

41. $p = 300e^{-0.02x}$

(a) when $x = 100$,

$$p = 300e^{-0.02(100)}$$

$$p \approx 40.60058$$

The market price is \$40.60.

(b) revenue = (#sold)(selling price)

$$R(x) = xp$$

$$R(100) = 100\left(300e^{-0.02(100)}\right)$$

$$R(100) \approx 4,060.058$$

The corresponding revenue is \$4,060.

(c) When $x = 50$,

$$R(50) = 50(300e^{-0.02(5)})$$

$$R(50) \approx 5,518.1916$$

The corresponding revenue is \$5,518.

$$R(100) - R(50)$$

$$= 4,060 - 5,518 = -1,458$$

When 100 units are produced, the revenue is \$1,458 less than when 50 units are produced.

43. $P(t) = 50e^{0.02t}$

(a) For the current population, $t = 0$ so

$$P(0) = 50e^0 = 50$$

so the current population is 50 million.

(b) When $t = 30$,

$$P(30) = 50e^{0.02(30)} \approx 91.11$$

so the population will be approx. 91.11 million

45. $C(t) = 3 \cdot 2^{-0.75t}$

(a) When $t = 0$,

$$C(0) = 3 \cdot 2^{-0.75(0)}$$

$$= 3 \cdot 2^0 = 3 \cdot 1 = 3 \text{ mg/ml}$$

When $t = 1$,

$$C(1) = 3 \cdot 2^{-0.75(1)}$$

$$\approx 1.7838 \text{ mg/ml}$$

(b) average rate of change

$$= \frac{C(t_2) - C(t_1)}{t_2 - t_1}$$

$$= \frac{C(2) - C(1)}{2 - 1}$$

$$C(2) = 3 \cdot 2^{-0.75(2)} \approx 1.0607$$
aver rate change

$$= \frac{1.0607 - 1.7838}{2 - 1}$$

$$= -0.7231 \text{ mg/ml per hour}$$

47. $P(t) = A \cdot 2^{0.001t}$

(a) Since $P(10) = 10,000$

$$10,000 = A \cdot 2^{0.001(10)}$$

$$\frac{10,000}{2^{0.01}} = A$$

$$A \approx 9,931$$

(b) When $t = 0$,

$$P(0) = 9{,}931 \cdot 2^{0.001(0)}$$

$$= 9{,}931 \cdot 2^0 = 9{,}931 \text{ bacteria}$$

When $t = 20$,

$$P(20) = 9{,}931 \cdot 2^{0.001(20)}$$

$$\approx 10{,}070 \text{ bacteria}$$

Since time is measured in minutes, one hour corresponds to $t = 60$ and

$$P(60) = 9{,}931 \cdot 2^{0.001(60)}$$

$$\approx 10{,}353 \text{ bacteria}$$

(c) Keeping t measured in minutes, the average rate of change is

$$\frac{P(120) - P(60)}{120 - 60}$$

$$P(120) = 9{,}931 \cdot 2^{0.001(120)}$$

$$\approx 10{,}792 \text{ bacteria}$$

aver rate change

$$= \frac{10{,}792 - 10{,}353}{60}$$

$$\approx 7.32 \text{ bacteria per minute}$$

49. Investing \$24 at 7% compounded continuously for 364 years would yield

$$B(t) = Pe^{rt}$$

$$B(364) = 24e^{0.07(364)}$$

$$\approx 2.7928 \times 10^{12}$$

$$\approx 2{,}792.8 \text{ billion dollars}$$

$$\underline{- \quad 25.2}$$

$$2{,}767.6$$

Investing the money would have resulted in the better deal for the sellers by \$2,767.6 billion dollars.

51. Since the pattern of daily growth is

$$P_0 \to 1.031 P_0$$

$$\to 1.031(1.031 P_0)$$

$$\to 1.031 \left[1.031(1.031 P_0) \right]$$

it can be modeled by the function

$$P(t) = P_0 (1.031)^t$$

Since the initial population is $P_0 = 10{,}000$, the population after 10 days is

$$P(10) = 10{,}000(1.031)^{10}$$

$$\approx 13{,}570 \text{ bacteria}$$

53. $C(t) = 0.065 \left(1 + e^{-0.025t} \right)$

(a) When $t = 0$,

$$C(0) = 0.065(1 + e^0)$$

$$= 0.13 \text{ g/cm}^3$$

(b) When $t = 20$,

$$C(20) = 0.065(1 + e^{-0.025(20)})$$

$$\approx 0.1044 \text{ g/cm}^3$$

Since t is measured in minutes, one hour corresponds to $t = 60$ and

$$C(60) = 0.065(1 + e^{-0.025(60)})$$

$$\approx 0.0795 \text{ g/cm}^3$$

(c) average rate of change

$$= \frac{C(1) - C(0)}{1 - 0}$$

$$C(1) = 0.065(1 + e^{-0.025(1)})$$

$$\approx 0.1284$$

aver rate change

$$= \frac{0.1284 - 0.13}{1 - 0}$$

$$\approx -0.0016 \text{ g/cm}^3 \text{ per minute}$$

(d) As $t \to \infty$,

$$\lim_{t \to \infty} C(t) = \lim_{t \to \infty} 0.065(1 + e^{-0.025t})$$

Since $\lim_{x \to \infty} e^{-x} = 0$,

$$\lim_{t \to \infty} C(t) = 0.065(1 + 0)$$

$$= 0.065 \text{ g/cm}^3$$

(e) Press $\boxed{y=}$ and input

$$0.065(1 + e \wedge (-0.025t))$$

for $y_1 =$.
Use window dimensions [0, 180]60 by
[0, 0.2].05
Press $\boxed{\text{graph}}$

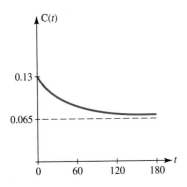

55. When interest is compounded quarterly at an annual rate of 6%,

$$r_e = \left(1 + \frac{r}{k}\right)^k - 1$$
$$= \left(1 + \frac{0.06}{4}\right)^4 - 1$$
$$\approx 0.614, \text{ or } 6.14\%$$

57. When interest is compounded continuously at an annual rate of 5%,

$$r_e = e^r - 1$$
$$= e^{0.05} - 1$$
$$\approx 0.0513, \text{ or } 5.13\%$$

59. (a) $r_e = \left(1 + \frac{r}{k}\right)^k - 1$
$$= \left(1 + \frac{0.079}{2}\right)^2 - 1$$
$$\approx 0.0806$$

(b) $r_e = \left(1 + \frac{0.078}{4}\right)^4 - 1$
$$\approx 0.0803$$

(c) $r_e = \left(1 + \frac{0.077}{12}\right)^{12} - 1$
$$\approx 0.0798$$

(d) $r_e = e^r - 1$
$$= e^{0.0765} - 1$$
$$\approx 0.0795$$

From lowest to highest,

$$d, c, b, a$$

61. The value of $500 in five years, at an annual inflation rate of 4%, will be

$$B(t) = P\left(1 + \frac{r}{k}\right)^{kt}$$

$$B(5) = 500\left(1 + \frac{0.04}{1}\right)^{1(5)}$$

$$\approx 608.326$$

To break even, he should sell the stamp for $608.33.

63. $f(t) = e^{-0.2t}$

(a) The fraction of toasters still working after 3 years is

$$f(3) = e^{-0.2(3)} \approx 0.5488.$$

(b) The fraction which fail during the first year is

$$f(0) - f(1)$$
$$= e^0 - e^{-0.2(1)} \approx 1 - 0.8187 = 0.1813$$

(c) The fraction which fail during the third year is

$$f(2) - f(3)$$
$$= e^{-0.2(2)} - e^{-0.2(3)}$$
$$\approx 0.6703 - 0.5488 = 0.1215$$

65. $D(x) = 12e^{-0.07x}$

(a) At the center of the city, the density is $D(0) = 12$, or 12,000 people per square mile.

(b) Ten miles from the center, the density is

$$D(10) = 12e^{-0.07(10)} = 12e^{-0.7} \approx 5.959,$$

or 5,959 people per square mile.

67. $I = I_0 e^{-kx}$

When $x = 3$ meters, $I = 0.1 I_0$. So

$$0.1 I_0 = I_0 e^{-k \cdot 3}, \text{ or}$$

$$0.1 = e^{-3k}$$

When $x = 1$ meter,

$$I = I_0 e^{-k \cdot 1}$$

$$= I_0 (e^{-3k})^{1/3}$$

$$= I_0 (0.1)^{1/3}$$

$$\approx 0.46 I_0$$

69. $P(t) = A e^{0.03t} - B e^{0.005t}$

(a) Since t is measured in years after 1990, $t = 2$ in 1992 and $t = 15$ in 2005. Further, $P(2) = 100$ million and $P(15) = 200$ million. So,

$$200 = A e^{0.03(15)} - B e^{0.005(15)}$$

$$200 = A e^{0.45} - B e^{0.075}$$

$$200 \approx 1.5683 A - 1.0779 B$$

And,

$$100 = A e^{0.03(2)} - B e^{0.005(2)}$$

$$100 = A e^{0.06} - B e^{0.01}$$

$$100 \approx 1.0618 A - 1.0101 B$$

This gives a system of two equations with two unknowns to solve. Multiply the first equation by 1.0101, the second by -1.0779, and add the new equations together.

$$
\begin{aligned}
202.02 &= 1.5841 A - 1.0888 B \\
-107.79 &= -1.1445 A + 1.0888 B \\
\hline
94.23 &= 0.4396 A \\
214.35 &\approx A
\end{aligned}
$$

Substituting A into the first equation gives

$$200 \approx 1.5683(214.35) - 1.0779 B$$

$$126.32 \approx B$$

(b) When $t = 0$,

$$P(0) \approx 214.35 - 126.32$$

$$\approx 88.03 \text{ million people}$$

(c) When $t = 20$,

$$P(20) \approx 214.35 e^{0.03(20)} - 126.32 e^{0.005(20)}$$

$$\approx 251 \text{ million people}$$

71. $M = \dfrac{Ai}{1 - (1+i)^{-n}}$

When $A = 150{,}000$, $i = \dfrac{0.09}{12} = 0.0075$, $n = 360$,

$$M = \frac{150{,}000(0.0075)}{1 - (1.0075)^{-360}} = \$1{,}206.93$$

for the monthly payment

73. (a) The potential buyer is offering to pay you,

$$1000 + 160(36) = \$6{,}760$$

Using the amortization formula, monthly payments would be

$$M = \frac{5{,}000 \left(\frac{0.12}{12} \right)}{1 - \left(1 + \frac{0.12}{12} \right)^{-12 \cdot 3}} \approx \$166.07$$

This way, you would receive

$$\$1{,}000 + (166.07)(36) = \$6{,}978.52$$

This is $\$6{,}978.52 - \$6{,}760 = \$218.52$ more than the potential buyer is offering.

(b) Writing Exercise—Answers will vary.

75. $f(x) = \dfrac{1}{2} \left(\dfrac{1}{4} \right)^x$

x	-2.2	-1.5	0	1.5	2.3
$f(x)$	10.5561	4	0.5	0.0625	0.02062

Press $\boxed{y=}$ and input $.5(.25 \wedge x)$ for $y_1 =$.
Press $\boxed{\text{2nd}}$ $\boxed{\text{TBLSET}}$ and enter ask independent with auto dependent. Press $\boxed{\text{2nd}}$ $\boxed{\text{table}}$ and enter $x = -2.2$, -1.5, 0, 1.5, and 2.3. The output values are displayed automatically.

77. To use a calculator to evaluate $\left(1 + \dfrac{1}{n} \right)^n$ for $n = -1{,}000, -2{,}000 \ldots -50{,}000$, press $\boxed{y=}$ and input $(1 + (1 \div x)) \wedge x$ for $y_1 =$.

Press 2nd TBLSET and input TblStart $= -1{,}000$, Δ Tbl $= -1{,}000$ and auto independent with auto dependent. Press 2nd table.
Following are some values from this table:

x	y_1
$-1{,}000$	2.7196
$-2{,}000$	2.719
$-3{,}000$	2.7187
$-4{,}000$	2.7186
$-5{,}000$	2.7186
$\vdots$	$\vdots$
$-48{,}000$	2.7183
$-49{,}000$	2.7183
$-50{,}000$	2.7183

As n decreases without bound, $\left(1 + \dfrac{1}{n}\right)^n$ approaches $e \approx 2.71828$.

79. To use a calculator to estimate $\displaystyle\lim_{x \to \infty} \left(2 - \dfrac{5}{2n}\right)^{n/3}$,

Press y= and input
$(2 - (5 \div (2x))) \wedge (x \div 3)$ for $y_1 =$.
Press 2nd TBLSET and input Tblstart $= 10$ and Δ Tbl $= 10$. Use auto independent with auto dependent. Press 2nd table. The following are a few values from the table:

x	y
10	6.4584
20	66.071
$\vdots$	$\vdots$
100	7.12×10^9

These values suggest that

$$\lim_{n \to +\infty} \left(2 - \frac{5}{2n}\right)^{n/3} = +\infty.$$

4.2 Logarithmic Functions

1. Using the TI-84 Plus, press LN, the number, a right parenthesis, and then ENTER. When combined with powers of e, press LN, 2nd, e^x, the power of e, right parenthesis, and then ENTER. So, $\ln 1 = 0$, $\ln 2 \approx 0.693$, $\ln e = 1$, $\ln 5 \approx 1.609$, $\ln(1/5) \approx -1.609$, $\ln e^2 = 2$. Since $\ln x$ has a domain of $x > 0$, $\ln 0$ and $\ln(-2)$ yield ERR: DOMAIN.

3. Since $\ln x$ and e^x are inverse operations, $\ln e^3 = 3$.

5. Since e^x and $\ln x$ are inverse operations, $e^{\ln 5} = 5$.

7.
$$
\begin{aligned}
e^{3\ln 2 - 2\ln 5} &= e^{\ln 2^3 - \ln 5^2} \\
&= e^{\ln 8 - \ln 25} \\
&= e^{\ln\left(\frac{8}{25}\right)} \\
&= \frac{8}{25}.
\end{aligned}
$$

9.
$$
\begin{aligned}
\log_3 270 &= \log_3 27 + \log_3 10 \\
&= \log_3 27 + \log_3 5 + \log_3 2 \\
&= \log_3 3^3 + \log_3 5 + \log_3 2
\end{aligned}
$$
Since $\log_3 x$ and 3^x are inverse operations,
$$= 3 + \log_3 5 + \log_3 2.$$

11.
$$
\begin{aligned}
\log_3 100 &= \log_3 (10)^2 \\
&= 2\log_3 10 \\
&= 2\log_3 (2 \cdot 5) \\
&= 2(\log_3 2 + \log_3 5) \\
&= 2\log_3 2 + 2\log_3 5.
\end{aligned}
$$

13. $\log_2(x^4 y^3) = \log_2 x^4 + \log_2 y^3$
$$= 4\log_2 x + 3\log_2 y.$$

15.
$$
\begin{aligned}
\ln \sqrt[3]{x^2 - x} &= \ln(x^2 - x)^{1/3} \\
&= \frac{1}{3}\ln(x^2 - x) \\
&= \frac{1}{3}\ln[x(x-1)] \\
&= \frac{1}{3}[\ln x + \ln(x-1)] \\
&= \frac{1}{3}\ln x + \frac{1}{3}\ln(x-1).
\end{aligned}
$$

17.
$$\ln\left[\frac{x^2(3-x)^{2/3}}{\sqrt{x^2+x+1}}\right]$$
$$= \ln\left[x^2(3-x)^{2/3}\right] - \ln\sqrt{x^2+x+1}$$
$$= \ln x^2 + \ln(3-x)^{2/3} - \ln(x^2+x+1)^{1/2}$$
$$= 2\ln x + \frac{2}{3}\ln(3-x) - \frac{1}{2}\ln(x^2+x+1).$$

19.
$$\ln(x^3 e^{-x^2}) = \ln x^3 + \ln e^{-x^2}$$
$$= 3\ln x - x^2.$$

21. $4^x = 53$
Taking the natural log of both sides gives
$\ln 4^x = \ln 53$.
Using a rule of logarithms gives
$x\ln 4 = \ln 53$
$$x = \frac{\ln 53}{\ln 4} \approx 2.864$$

23. $\log_3(2x-1) = 2$
Rewriting in exponential form gives
$2x - 1 = 3^2$
or $x = 5$

25. $2 = e^{0.06x}$
Taking the natural log of both sides gives
$$\ln 2 = 0.06x, \quad \text{or}$$
$$x = \frac{\ln 2}{0.06} \approx 11.552$$

27. $3 = 2 + 5e^{-4x}$
$$1 = 5e^{-4x}$$
$$\frac{1}{5} = e^{-4x}$$
Taking the natural log of both sides gives
$$\ln\frac{1}{5} = -4x, \quad \text{or}$$
$$x = \frac{\ln(1/5)}{-4}$$
Since $\ln\frac{1}{5} = \ln 1 - \ln 5 = 0 - \ln 5 = -\ln 5$,
$$x = \frac{-\ln 5}{-4} = \frac{\ln 5}{4} \approx 0.402.$$

29.
$$-\ln x = \frac{t}{50} + C$$
$$\ln x = \frac{-t}{50} - C$$
$$e^{\ln x} = e^{(-t/50)-C}, \quad \text{or}$$
$$x = e^{(-t/50)-C}$$

31.
$$\ln x = \frac{1}{3}(\ln 16 + 2\ln 2)$$
$$= \frac{1}{3}(\ln 16 + \ln 4)$$
$$= \frac{1}{3}\ln(16 \cdot 4)$$
$$= \ln 64^{1/3}$$
$$\text{So,} \quad \ln x = \ln 4$$
$$e^{\ln x} = e^{\ln 4}$$
or $x = 4$.

33. $3^x = e^2$
Taking the natural log of both sides gives
$$\ln 3^x = \ln e^2$$
$$\text{So, } x\ln 3 = 2$$
$$x = \frac{2}{\ln 3} \approx 1.820.$$

35.
$$\frac{25e^{0.1x}}{e^{0.1x}+3} = 10$$
$$25e^{0.1x} = 10(e^{0.1x}+3)$$
$$25e^{0.1x} = 10e^{0.1x}+30$$
$$15e^{0.1x} = 30$$
$$e^{0.1x} = 2$$
$$\ln e^{0.1x} = \ln 2$$
$$0.1x = \ln 2$$
$$x = \frac{\ln 2}{0.1} = 10\ln 2 \approx 6.9315$$

37. $\log_2 x = 5$
Rewriting in exponential form,
$$x = 2^5$$
$$\ln x = \ln 2^5$$
$$\ln x = 5\ln 2 \approx 3.4657$$

39. $\log_5(2x) = 7$

Rewriting in exponential form,

$$2x = 5^7$$

$$x = \frac{5^7}{2}$$

$$\ln x = \ln\left(\frac{5^7}{2}\right)$$

$$= \ln 5^7 - \ln 2$$

$$= 7\ln 5 - \ln 2 \approx 10.5729.$$

41.

$$\ln\frac{1}{\sqrt{ab^3}} = \ln 1 - \ln\left(\sqrt{ab^3}\right)$$

$$= 0 - \ln(ab^3)^{1/2}$$

$$= -\frac{1}{2}\ln(ab^3)$$

$$= -\frac{1}{2}[\ln a + \ln b^3]$$

$$= -\frac{1}{2}\ln a - \frac{1}{2}\ln b^3$$

$$= -\frac{1}{2}\ln a - \frac{3}{2}\ln b$$

Since $\ln a = 2$ and $\ln b = 3$,

$$= -\frac{1}{2}(2) - \frac{3}{2}(3) = -\frac{11}{2}.$$

43. $B(t) = Pe^{rt}$

After a certain time, the investment will have grown to $B(t) = 2P$ at the interest rate of 0.06. So,

$$2P = Pe^{0.06t}$$

$$2 = e^{0.06t}$$

$$\ln 2 = \ln e^{0.06t}$$

$$\ln 2 = 0.06t$$

and $t = \dfrac{\ln 2}{0.06} = 11.55$ years.

45. $B(t) = Pe^{rt}$

Since money doubles in 13 years,

$$2P = B(13) = Pe^{13r}$$

$$2 = e^{13r}$$

$$\ln 2 = \ln e^{13r}$$

$$\ln 2 = 13r$$

and $r = \dfrac{\ln 2}{13} = 0.0533$. The annual interest rate is 5.33%.

47. $B(t) = Pe^{rt}$

Since money doubles in 12 years,

$$2P = B(12) = Pe^{12r}$$

$$2 = e^{12r}$$

$$\ln 2 = 12r$$

and $r = \dfrac{\ln 2}{12} \approx 0.05776.$

To find t when money triples,

$$3P = B(t) = Pe^{0.05776t}$$

$$3 = e^{0.5776t}$$

$$\ln 3 = 0.05776t$$

$$t = \frac{\ln 3}{0.05776} \approx 19.02 \text{ years}$$

49. At 6% compounded annually, the effective interest rate is

$$\left(1 + \frac{r}{k}\right)^k - 1 = \left(1 + \frac{0.06}{1}\right)^1 - 1$$

$$= 0.06.$$

At r% compounded continuously, the effective interest rate is $e^r - 1$. Setting the two effective rates equal to each other yields

$$e^r - 1 = 0.06,$$

$$e^r = 1.06, \ r = \ln 1.06 = 0.0583 \text{ or } 5.83\%.$$

51. $C(t) = 0.4(2 - 0.13e^{-0.02t})$

(a) After 20 seconds, the drug concentration is

$$C(20) = 0.4(2 - 0.13e^{-0.02(20)})$$

$$\approx 0.765 \text{ g/cm}^3$$

After 60 seconds, it is

$$C(60) = 0.4(2 - 0.13e^{-0.02(60)})$$

$$\approx 0.784 \text{ g/cm}^3$$

(b) To find the time for the given concentration,

$$0.75 = 0.4(2 - 0.13e^{-0.02t})$$

$$1.875 = 2 - 0.13e^{-0.02t}$$

$$0.13e^{-0.02t} = 0.125$$

$$e^{-0.02t} \approx 0.9615$$

$$-0.02t \approx \ln 0.9615$$

$$t \approx \frac{\ln 0.9615}{-0.02} \approx 1.96 \text{ seconds}$$

53. The decay function is of the form

$$Q(t) = Q_0 e^{-kt}$$

Since the half-life is 1,690 years, $Q(1690) = \frac{1}{2} Q_0$

$$\text{and } \frac{1}{2} Q_0 = Q_0 e^{-k(1,690)}$$

$$\frac{1}{2} = e^{-1,690k}$$

$$\ln \frac{1}{2} = \ln e^{-1,690k}$$

$$\ln \frac{1}{2} = -1,690k$$

$$\frac{\ln \frac{1}{2}}{-1,690} = k$$

or $k = \dfrac{\ln 2}{1,690}$

The initial amount, $Q_0 = 50$ grams, will reduce to 5 grams when

$$5 = 50e^{-kt}$$

$$\frac{1}{10} = e^{-kt}$$

$$\ln \frac{1}{10} = \ln e^{-kt},$$

$$\ln \frac{1}{10} = -kt$$

$$\frac{\ln \frac{1}{10}}{-k} = t$$

or $t = \dfrac{\ln 10}{k}$

Substituting k from above,

$$t = \frac{\ln 10}{\left(\frac{\ln 2}{1,690}\right)} = \frac{1,690 \ln 10}{\ln 2} \approx 5,614 \text{ years.}$$

55. $Q(t) = Q_0 e^{kt}$

Since initial amount, $Q_0 = 6,000$,

$$Q(t) = 6,000 e^{kt}$$

When $t = 20$ minutes, $Q(20) = 9,000$.

So, $\qquad 9,000 = 6,000 e^{k(20)}$

$$\frac{3}{2} = e^{20k}$$

$$\ln \frac{3}{2} = \ln e^{20k}$$

$$\ln \frac{3}{2} = 20k$$

$$\frac{\ln \frac{3}{2}}{20} = k$$

In general, $Q(t) = 6,000 e^{\frac{\ln 1.5}{20} t}$

When $t = 60$ minutes,

$$Q(60) = 6,000 e^{\frac{\ln 1.5}{20}(60)}$$

$$= 20,250 \text{ bacteria.}$$

57. $Q(t) = 500 - Ae^{-kt}$

When $t = 0$, $Q(0) = 300$ and

$$300 = 500 - Ae^{-k(0)}$$

$$300 = 500 - A, \text{ or } A = 200$$

So, $\qquad Q(t) = 500 - 200 e^{-kt}$

When $t = 6$ months, $Q(6) = 410$ and

$$410 = 500 - 200 e^{-k(6)}$$

$$200 e^{-6k} = 90$$

$$e^{-6k} = \frac{9}{20}$$

$$\ln e^{-6k} = \ln \frac{9}{20}$$

$$-6k = \ln \frac{9}{20}$$

$$k = \frac{\ln \frac{9}{20}}{-6}$$

So, $Q(t) = 500 - 200e^{\frac{\ln 0.45}{6}t}$

When $t = 12$ months,

$$Q(12) = 500 - 200e^{\frac{\ln 0.45}{6}(12)}$$
$$= 459.5 \text{ units}$$

59. The decay function is of the form $R(t) = R_0 e^{-kt}$. From the text page 306, the half-life of ^{14}C is 5,730 years, so

$$\frac{1}{2}R_0 = R_0 e^{-k(5,730)}$$

$$\frac{1}{2} = e^{-5,730k}$$

$$\ln\frac{1}{2} = \ln e^{-5,730k}$$

$$\ln\frac{1}{2} = -5,730k$$

$$\frac{\ln\frac{1}{2}}{-5,730} = k$$

$$\text{or } k = \frac{\ln 2}{5,730}$$

When 28% of the original amount remains,

$$0.28R_0 = R_0 e^{-kt}$$
$$0.28 = e^{-kt}$$
$$\ln 0.28 = \ln e^{-kt}$$
$$\ln 0.28 = -kt$$
$$\frac{\ln 0.28}{-k} = t$$

Substituting k from above,

$$t = \frac{\ln 0.28}{-\left(\frac{\ln 2}{5,730}\right)} = \frac{-5,730 \ln 0.28}{\ln 2} \approx 10,523 \text{ years.}$$

61. The decay function is of the form $R(t) = R_0 e^{-kt}$. From the text page 306, the half-life of ^{14}C is 5,730 years, so

$$\frac{1}{2}R_0 = R_0 e^{-k(5,730)}$$

$$\frac{1}{2} = e^{-5,730k}$$

$$\ln\frac{1}{2} = \ln e^{-5,730k}$$

$$\ln\frac{1}{2} = -5,730k$$

$$\frac{\ln\frac{1}{2}}{-5,730} = k$$

$$\text{or } k = \frac{\ln 2}{5,730}$$

When 99.7% of the original amount remains,

$$0.997R_0 = R_0 e^{-kt}$$
$$0.997 = e^{-kt}$$
$$\ln 0.997 = \ln e^{-kt}$$
$$\ln 0.997 = -kt$$
$$\frac{\ln 0.997}{-k} = t$$

Substituting k from above,

$$t = \frac{\ln 0.997}{-\left(\frac{\ln 2}{5,730}\right)} = \frac{-5,730 \ln 0.997}{\ln 2} \approx 24.8 \text{ years.}$$

So, the painting in question was painted only 24.8 years ago. If the painting was actually $2003 - 1640 = 363$ years old, and p represents the percentage of ^{14}C currently present,

$$pR_0 = R_0 e^{-\left(\frac{\ln 2}{5,730}\right)(363)}$$

$$p = e^{-\left(\frac{\ln 2}{5,730}\right)(363)}$$

$$p \approx 0.957, \quad \text{or} \quad 95.7\%$$

63. $f(t) = 70 - Ae^{-kt}$
When $t = 0$, $f(0) = 212$

So, $212 = 70 - Ae^{-k(0)}$
$$212 = 70 - A, \text{ or}$$
$$A = -142$$

and $f(t) = 70 + 142e^{-kt}$

Now, let t_i be the ideal drinking temperature. Then,
$$t_i + 15 = f(2) = 70 + 142e^{-k(2)}$$

or, $t_i = 55 + 142e^{-2k}$
Also, $t_i = f(4) = 70 + 142e^{-k(4)}$
so, $70 + 142e^{-4k} = 55 + 142e^{-2k}$
$142e^{-4k} - 142e^{-2k} + 15 = 0$
Letting $u = e^{-2k}$,
$142u^2 - 142u + 15 = 0$
Using the quadratic formula,

$$u = \frac{142 \pm \sqrt{(-142)^2 - (4)(142)(15)}}{2(142)}$$

so, $u \approx 0.1200445$
or, $e^{-2k} \approx 0.1200445$ and

$$t_i = 55 + 142(0.1200445)$$
$$\approx 72.05°F.$$

65. $S(x) = \ln(x + 2)$
$D(x) = 10 - \ln(x + 1)$

(a) When $x = 10$,

$$D(10) = 10 - \ln(10 + 1)$$
$$\approx \$7.60$$

(b) When $x = 100$,

$$S(100) = \ln(100 + 2)$$
$$\approx \$4.62$$

(c) $\ln(x + 2) = 10 - \ln(x + 1)$
$\ln(x + 2) + \ln(x + 1) = 10$
$\ln(x^2 + 3x + 2) = 10$
$e^{\ln(x^2+3x+2)} = e^{10}$
$x^2 + 3x + 2 = e^{10}$
$x^2 + 3x + (2 - e^{10}) = 0$

$$x_e = \frac{-3 + \sqrt{(3)^2 - 4(1)(2 - e^{10})}}{2(1)}$$

$x_e \approx 147$ units
$P_e = \ln(147 + 2)$
$\approx \$5.00$

67. $T = T_a + (98.6 - T_a)(0.97)^t$

When $T = 40°F$ and $T_a = 10°F$,

$$40 = 10 + (98.6 - 10)(0.97)^t,$$

$$\frac{30}{88.6} = (0.97)^t$$

$$\ln \frac{30}{88.6} = \ln(0.97)^t$$

$$\ln \frac{30}{88.6} = t \ln(0.97)$$

so, $$t = \frac{\ln \frac{30}{88.6}}{\ln(0.97)} \approx 35.55 \text{ hrs}$$

This means the murder occurred around 1:27 a.m. on Wednesday. Blohardt was in jail at this time, so Scélérat must have committed the murder.

69.
$$R = \frac{2}{3} \log_{10} \left(\frac{E}{10^{4.4}} \right)$$

(a) When $E = 5.96 \times 10^{16}$,

$$R = \frac{2}{3} \log_{10} \left(\frac{5.96 \times 10^{16}}{10^{4.4}} \right)$$
$$\approx 8.25$$

(b) When $R = 6.4$,

$$6.4 = \frac{2}{3} \log_{10} \left(\frac{E}{10^{4.4}} \right)$$

$$9.6 = \log_{10} \left(\frac{E}{10^{4.4}} \right)$$

$$10^{9.6} = 10^{\log_{10} \left(\frac{E}{10^{4.4}} \right)}$$

$$10^{9.6} = \frac{E}{10^{4.4}}$$

$$E = (10^{9.6})(10^{4.4}) = 10^{14} \text{ joules}$$

71. $p(t) = 0.89[0.01 + 0.99(0.85)^t]$

(a) When $t = 0$,

$$P(0) = 0.89[0.01 + 0.99(0.85)^0]$$
$$= 0.89[0.01 + 0.99]$$
$$= 0.89$$

(b) To find t when $p(t) = 0.5$,

$$0.5 = 0.89[0.01 + 0.99(0.85)^t]$$

$$0.5618 \approx 0.01 + 0.99(0.85)^t$$

$$0.5518 \approx 0.99(0.85)^t$$

$$0.5574 \approx (0.85)^t$$

$$\ln 0.5574 \approx \ln(0.85)^t$$

$$\ln 0.5574 \approx t \ln(0.85)$$

$$t \approx \frac{\ln 0.5574}{\ln 0.85} \approx 3.6 \text{ seconds}$$

(c) Press $\boxed{y=}$ and input

$$0.89(0.01 + 0.99(0.85 \wedge t))$$

for $y_1 =$.
Use window dimensions [0, 20]4 by [0, 1].25
Press $\boxed{\text{graph}}$

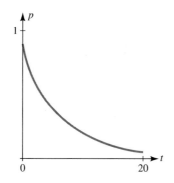

73. Intensity function is of the form $I(t) = I_0 e^{-kt}$
When $t = 20.9$ hours,
$I(20.9) = \frac{1}{2}I_0$

$$\text{So,} \quad \frac{1}{2}I_0 = I_0 e^{-k(20.9)}$$

$$\frac{1}{2} = e^{-20.9k}$$

$$\ln \frac{1}{2} = \ln e^{-20.9k}$$

$$\ln \frac{1}{2} = -20.9k$$

$$\frac{\ln \frac{1}{2}}{-20.9} = k$$

or $k = \dfrac{\ln 2}{20.9}$

(a) When $t = 24$ hours,

$$I(24) = I_0 e^{-\left(\frac{\ln 2}{20.9}\right)(24)}$$

$$\approx I_0 \cdot 0.451$$

So approximately 45.1% of the original amount should be detected.

(b)
$$I(25) = I_0 e^{\left(\frac{\ln 0.5}{20.9}\right)(25)}$$

$$\approx I_0 \cdot 0.436$$

A total of 43.6% should remain in the entire body, and $43.6\% - 41.3\% = 2.3\%$ remains outside of the thyroid gland.

75. (a)

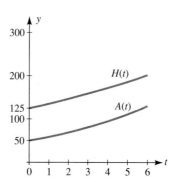

(b)
$$H = 125e^{0.08t}$$

$$\frac{H}{125} = e^{0.08t}$$

$$\ln \frac{H}{125} = \ln e^{0.08t}$$

$$\ln \frac{H}{125} = 0.08t$$

$$t = \frac{\ln \frac{H}{125}}{0.08}$$

Now, $A(t) = 50e^{0.16t}$

So, $A(H) = 50^{0.16(\ln(H/125)/0.08)}$

$= 50e^{2\ln(H/125)}$

$= 50e^{\ln(H/125)^2}$

$= 50\dfrac{H^2}{15,625}$

$= \dfrac{2H^2}{625}$.

77. $P(t) = 51 + 100\ln(t+3)$

(a) When $t = 0$,

$$P(0) = 51 + 100\ln(0+3)$$
$$\approx 160.86 \text{ thousand, or}$$
$$160,860 \text{ people}$$

(b) To find t when $P(t) = 2(160.86) = 321.72$ solve

$$321.72 = 51 + 100\ln(t+3)$$
$$270.72 = 100\ln(t+3)$$
$$2.7072 = \ln(t+3)$$
$$e^{2.7072} = e^{\ln(t+3)}$$
$$e^{2.7072} = t + 3$$
$$t = e^{2.7072} - 3 \approx 12 \text{ years}$$

(c) average rate of growth

$$= \frac{P(10) - P(0)}{10 - 0}$$
$$P(10) = 51 + 100\ln(10+3)$$
$$\approx 307.49$$

aver rate growth

$$= \frac{307.49 - 160.86}{10 - 0}$$
$$\approx 14.66 \text{ thousand, or}$$
$$14,660 \text{ people per year}$$

79. The midpoint of the segment joining the points (a, b) and (b, a) is

$$\left(\frac{a+b}{2}, \frac{b+a}{2}\right)$$

This point is on the line $y = x$; the slope of the line joining the points is

$$\frac{a-b}{b-a} = \frac{-(b-a)}{b-a} = -1$$

So the line is perpendicular to the line $y = x$, which has slope $= 1$. Now, using the midpoint found above, the distance from (a, b) to the line $y = x$ is

$$\sqrt{\left(a - \frac{a+b}{2}\right)^2 + \left(b - \frac{a+b}{2}\right)^2}$$

Similarly, the distance from (b, a) to the line $y = x$ is

$$\sqrt{\left(b - \frac{a+b}{2}\right)^2 + \left(a - \frac{a+b}{2}\right)^2}$$

which is the same distance. So, the reflection of the point (a, b) in the line $y = x$ is (b, a).

81.
$$y = Cx^k$$
$$\ln y = \ln(Cx^k)$$
$$= \ln C + \ln x^k$$
$$= \ln C + k\ln x$$
$$\ln y = k\ln x + \ln c$$

is of form $Y = mX + b$

So, $\ln y$ is a linear function of $\ln x$.

83.
$$x = \ln(3.42 \times 10^{-8.1})$$

Input $\ln(3.42 * 10 \wedge -8.1)$ and see that the output is approximately -17.4213. So $x \approx -17.4213$. Note: Do not input $\ln(3.42 \boxed{\text{2nd}} \boxed{\text{EE}} - 8.1)$ as this results in an error.

85. $e^{0.113x} + 4.72 = 7.031 - x$
$x + e^{0.113x} - 2.311 = 0$
Press $\boxed{y=}$ and input $x + e \wedge (0.113x) - 2.311$ for $y_1 =$
Press $\boxed{\text{graph}}$
Press $\boxed{\text{2nd}}$ $\boxed{\text{calc}}$ and use the zero function to find $x \approx 1.1697$.

87. (a) $(\log_a b)(\log_b a)$

$$= \left(\frac{\ln b}{\ln a}\right)\left(\frac{\ln a}{\ln b}\right) = 1$$

(b)

$$\frac{\log_b x}{\log_b a} = \frac{\frac{\ln x}{\ln b}}{\frac{\ln a}{\ln b}}$$

$$= \frac{\ln x}{\ln b} \cdot \frac{\ln b}{\ln a}$$

$$= \frac{\ln x}{\ln a} = \log_a x$$

4.3 Differentiation of Logarithmic and Exponential Functions

1. $f(x) = e^{5x}$

$$f'(x) = e^{5x}\frac{d}{dx}(5x) = 5e^{5x}$$

3. $\qquad f(x) = xe^x$

$$f'(x) = x\frac{d}{dx}e^x + e^x\frac{d}{dx}x$$

$$= x\left[e^x\frac{d}{dx}x\right] + e^x \cdot 1$$

$$= xe^x + e^x = e^x(x+1)$$

5. $f(x) = 30 + 10e^{-0.05x}$

$$f'(x) = 0 + 10e^{-0.05x}\frac{d}{dx}(-0.05x) = -0.5e^{-0.05x}$$

7. $f(x) = (x^2 + 3x + 5)e^{6x}$

$$f'(x) = (x^2 + 3x + 5)\frac{d}{dx}e^{6x} + e^{6x}\frac{d}{dx}(x^2 + 3x + 5)$$

$$= (x^2 + 3x + 5)\left[e^{6x}\frac{d}{dx}6x\right] + e^{6x}(2x + 3)$$

$$= 6(x^2 + 3x + 5)(e^{6x}) + (2x + 3)e^{6x}$$

$$= e^{6x}\left[(6x^2 + 18x + 30) + (2x + 3)\right]$$

$$= (6x^2 + 20x + 33)e^{6x}$$

9. $f(x) = (1 - 3e^x)^2$

$$f'(x) = 2(1 - 3e^x)\frac{d}{dx}(1 - 3e^x)$$

$$= 2(1 - 3e^x)(0 - 3e^x)$$

$$= -6e^x(1 - 3e^x)$$

11. $f(x) = e^{\sqrt{3x}}$

$$f'(x) = e^{\sqrt{3x}}\frac{d}{dx}\left(\sqrt{3x}\right)$$

$$= e^{\sqrt{3x}}\left(\sqrt{3}\frac{d}{dx}\sqrt{x}\right)$$

$$= \sqrt{3}e^{\sqrt{3x}}\left(\frac{1}{2}x^{-1/2}\right)$$

$$= \frac{\sqrt{3}}{2\sqrt{x}}e^{\sqrt{3x}} = \frac{3}{2\sqrt{3x}}e^{\sqrt{3x}}$$

13. $f(x) = \ln x^3 = 3\ln x$

$$f'(x) = 3\left(\frac{1}{x}\right) = \frac{3}{x}$$

15. $\qquad f(x) = x^2 \ln x$

$$f'(x) = x^2\frac{d}{dx}(\ln x) + \ln x\frac{d}{dx}(x^2)$$

$$= x^2 \cdot \frac{1}{x} + 2x \ln x$$

$$= x + 2x \ln x$$

$$= x(1 + 2\ln x)$$

17. $f(x) = \sqrt[3]{e^{2x}} = e^{2x/3}$

$$f'(x) = e^{2x/3}\frac{d}{dx}\left(\frac{2x}{3}\right)$$

$$= \frac{2}{3}e^{2x/3}$$

19. $f(x) = \ln\left(\dfrac{x+1}{x-1}\right)$

$$f'(x) = \frac{1}{\left(\frac{x+1}{x-1}\right)} \frac{d}{dx}\left(\frac{x+1}{x-1}\right)$$

$$= \frac{x-1}{x+1}\left[\frac{(x-1)(1)-(x+1)(1)}{(x-1)^2}\right]$$

$$= \frac{-2}{(x+1)(x-1)}$$

21. $\qquad f(x) = e^{-2x} + x^3$

$$f'(x) = e^{-2x}\frac{d}{dx}(-2x) + 3x^2$$

$$= -2e^{-2x} + 3x^2$$

23. $g(s) = (e^s + s + 1)(2e^{-s} + s)$

$$g'(s) = (e^s + s + 1)\left(2e^{-s}\frac{d}{ds}(-s) + 1\right)$$

$$+ (2e^{-s} + s)(e^s + 1)$$

$$= (e^s + s + 1)(-2e^{-s} + 1) + (2e^{-s} + s)(e^s + 1)$$

$$= -2e^0 - 2se^{-s} - 2e^{-s} + e^s + s + 1$$

$$+ 2e^0 + se^s + 2e^{-s} + s$$

$$= 1 + 2s + e^s + se^s - 2se^{-s}$$

25. $\qquad h(t) = \dfrac{e^t + t}{\ln t}$

$$h'(t) = \frac{(\ln t)\frac{d}{dt}(e^t + t) - (e^t + t)\frac{d}{dt}(\ln t)}{(\ln t)^2}$$

$$= \frac{(\ln t)(e^t + 1) - (e^t + t)\left(\frac{1}{t}\right)}{(\ln t)^2}$$

$$= \frac{t(\ln t)(e^t + 1) - e^t - t}{t(\ln t)^2}$$

27. $\qquad f(x) = \dfrac{e^x + e^{-x}}{2} = \dfrac{1}{2}(e^x + e^{-x})$

$$f'(x) = \frac{1}{2}(e^x - e^{-x})$$

29. $\qquad f(t) = \sqrt{\ln t + t} = (\ln t + t)^{1/2}$

$$f'(t) = \frac{1}{2}(\ln t + t)^{-1/2}\frac{d}{dt}(\ln t + t)$$

$$= \frac{\frac{1}{t} + 1}{2(\ln t + t)^{1/2}} = \frac{1+t}{2t\sqrt{\ln t + t}}$$

31. $\qquad f(x) = \ln(e^{-x} + x)$

$$f'(x) = \frac{1}{e^{-x} + x}\frac{d}{dx}(e^{-x} + x)$$

$$= \frac{-e^{-x} + 1}{e^{-x} + x}$$

33. $g(u) = \ln\left(u + \sqrt{u^2 + 1}\right) = \ln\left(u + (u^2 + 1)^{1/2}\right)$

$$g'(u) = \frac{1}{u + (u^2 + 1)^{1/2}}\frac{d}{du}\left(u + (u^2 + 1)^{1/2}\right)$$

$$= \frac{1 + \frac{1}{2}(u^2 + 1)^{-1/2}(2u)}{u + (u^2 + 1)^{1/2}}$$

$$= \frac{1 + u(u^2 + 1)^{-1/2}}{u + (u^2 + 1)^{1/2}} \cdot \frac{u - (u^2 + 1)^{1/2}}{u - (u^2 + 1)^{1/2}}$$

$$= \frac{u + u^2(u^2 + 1)^{-1/2} - (u^2 + 1)^{1/2} - u}{u^2 - (u^2 + 1)}$$

$$= \frac{\frac{u^2}{(u^2+1)^{1/2}} - (u^2 + 1)^{1/2}}{-1}$$

$$= \frac{-u^2}{(u^2 + 1)^{1/2}} + (u^2 + 1)^{1/2}\frac{(u^2 + 1)^{1/2}}{(u^2 + 1)^{1/2}}$$

$$= \frac{-u^2 + u^2 + 1}{(u^2 + 1)^{1/2}} = \frac{1}{(u^2 + 1)^{1/2}}$$

35. $f(x) = \dfrac{2^x}{x}$

$$f'(x) = \frac{x\frac{d}{dx}(2^x) - (2^x)(1)}{x^2}$$

$$= \frac{x(\ln 2)2^x - 2^x}{x^2}$$

$$\frac{2^x(x\ln 2 - 1)}{x^2}$$

37. $f(x) = x \log_{10} x$

$$f'(x) = (x)\frac{d}{dx}(\log_{10} x) + (\log_{10} x)(1)$$

$$= x \cdot \frac{1}{\ln 10} \cdot \frac{1}{x} + \log_{10} x$$

$$= \frac{1}{\ln 10} + \log_{10} x$$

$$= \frac{1}{\ln 10} + \frac{\ln x}{\ln 10} = \frac{1 + \ln x}{\ln 10}$$

39.

$$f(x) = e^{1-x}; \ 0 \le x \le 1$$

$$f'(x) = (e^{1-x})(-1) = -e^{1-x}$$

So, $f'(x) = 0$ when

$$-e^{1-x} = 0$$

$$e^{1-x} = 0 \to \text{no solution}$$

$$f(0) = e^{1-0} = e \approx 2.718$$

$$f(1) = e^{1-1} = e^0 = 1$$

abs max $= e$; abs min $= 1$

41.

$$f(x) = (3x - 1)e^{-x}; \ 0 \le x \le 2$$

$$f'(x) = (3x - 1)(e^{-x})(-1) + (e^{-x})(3)$$

$$= e^{-x}[-1(3x - 1) + 3]$$

$$= e^{-x}(4 - 3x)$$

So, $f'(x) = 0$ when

$$e^{-x} = 0 \to \text{no solution}$$

$$4 - 3x = 0 \to x = \frac{4}{3}$$

$$f(0) = [3(0) - 1]e^{-0} = -1$$

$$f\left(\frac{4}{3}\right) = \left[3\left(\frac{4}{3}\right) - 1\right]e^{-4/3}$$

$$= 3e^{-4/3} \approx 0.791$$

$$f(2) = [3(2) - 1]e^{-2} = 5e^{-2} \approx 0.677$$

abs max $= 3e^{-4/3}$; abs min $= -1$

43.

$$g(t) = t^{3/2}e^{-2t}; \ 0 \le t \le 1$$

$$g'(t) = (t^{3/2})(e^{-2t} \cdot -2) + (e^{-2t})\left(\frac{3}{2}t^{1/2}\right)$$

$$= t^{1/2}e^{-2t}\left[-2t + \frac{3}{2}\right]$$

So, $g'(t) = 0$ when

$$t^{1/2} = 0 \to t = 0$$

$$e^{-2t} = 0 \to \text{no solution}$$

$$-2t + \frac{3}{2} = 0 \to t = \frac{3}{4}$$

$$g\left(\frac{3}{4}\right) = \left(\frac{3}{4}\right)^{3/2}\left(e^{-2\left(\frac{3}{4}\right)}\right) = \frac{3\sqrt{3}}{8}e^{-3/2} \approx 0.1449$$

$$g(0) = 0; \ g(1) = e^{-2} \approx 0.1353$$

abs. max. $= \frac{3\sqrt{3}}{8}e^{-3/2}$; abs. min. $= 0$

45.

$$f(x) = \frac{\ln(x + 1)}{x + 1}, \ 0 \le x \le 2$$

$$f'(x) = \frac{(x + 1) \cdot \frac{1}{x+1} - \ln(x + 1) \cdot 1}{(x + 1)^2}$$

$$= \frac{1 - \ln(x + 1)}{(x + 1)^2}$$

So, $f'(x) = 0$ when

$$1 - \ln(x + 1) = 0$$

$$1 = \ln(x + 1)$$

$$e^1 = e^{\ln(x+1)}$$

$$e = x + 1, \text{ or}$$

$$x = e - 1$$

$$f(e - 1) = \frac{\ln(e - 1 + 1)}{(e - 1) + 1} = \frac{1}{e} \approx 0.3679$$

$$f(0) = \frac{\ln(0 + 1)}{(0 + 1)^2} = 0$$

$$f(2) = \frac{\ln(2 + 1)}{2 + 1} \approx 0.3662$$

abs. max. $= \frac{1}{e}$; abs. min. $= 0$

47. $f(x) = xe^{-x}$; $x = 0$

$$f'(x) = (x)(e^{-x} \cdot -1) + (e^{-x})(1)$$
$$= e^{-x}(1 - x)$$

So, $m = f'(0) = e^0(1 - 0) = 1$

Also, $f(0) = 0$, so point $(0, 0)$ is on tangent line and

$$y - 0 = 1(x - 0), \quad \text{or} \quad y = x.$$

49. $f(x) = \dfrac{e^{2x}}{x^2}$, $x = 1$

$$f'(x) = \frac{(x^2)(e^{2x} \cdot 2) - (e^{2x})(2x)}{x^4}$$
$$= \frac{2xe^{2x}(x - 1)}{x^4} = \frac{2e^{2x}(x - 1)}{x^3}$$

so, $m = f'(1) = \dfrac{2e^2(1 - 1)}{1^3} = 0$

Since the slope of the line tangent is zero, the tangent line is horizontal and of the form $y = b$.
Since $f(1) = e^2$, the tangent line is $y = e^2$.

51. $f(x) = x^2 \ln \sqrt{x}$; $x = 1$

$$f(x) = x^2 \ln x^{1/2} = \frac{1}{2}x^2 \ln x$$

$$f'(x) = \left(\frac{1}{2}x^2\right)\left(\frac{1}{x}\right) + (\ln x)(x)$$
$$= \frac{x}{2} + x \ln x$$

So, $m = f'(1) = \dfrac{1}{2} + \ln 1 = \dfrac{1}{2}$. Also, $f(1) = 1 \ln 1 = 0$, so the point $(1, 0)$ is on tangent line and

$$y - 0 = \frac{1}{2}(x - 1), \text{ or } y = \frac{1}{2}x - \frac{1}{2}.$$

53. $f(x) = e^{2x} + 2e^{-x}$

$$f'(x) = e^{2x} \cdot 2 + 2e^{-x} \cdot -1$$
$$= 2e^{2x} - 2e^{-x}$$
$$f''(x) = 2e^{2x} \cdot 2 - 2e^{-x} \cdot -1 = 4e^{2x} + 2e^{-x}$$

55. $f(t) = t^2 \ln t$

$$f'(t) = (t^2)\left(\frac{1}{t}\right) + (\ln t)(2t)$$
$$= t(1 + 2 \ln t)$$

$$f''(t) = (t)\left(2 \cdot \frac{1}{t}\right) + (1 + 2 \ln t)(1)$$
$$= 2 + 1 + 2 \ln t = 3 + 2 \ln t$$

57. $f(x) = (2x + 3)^2(x - 5x^2)^{1/2}$

$$\ln f(x) = \ln\left[(2x + 3)^2(x - 5x^2)^{1/2}\right]$$
$$= \ln(2x + 3)^2 + \ln(x - 5x^2)^{1/2}$$
$$= 2\ln(2x + 3) + \frac{1}{2}\ln(x - 5x^2)$$

Differentiating,

$$\frac{f'(x)}{f(x)} = 2\left(\frac{1}{2x + 3}\right)(2) + \frac{1}{2}\left(\frac{1}{x - 5x^2}\right)(1 - 10x)$$
$$= \frac{4}{2x + 3} + \frac{1 - 10x}{2(x - 5x^2)}$$

Multiplying both sides by $f(x)$,

$$f'(x) = (2x + 3)^2(x - 5x^2)^{1/2}\left[\frac{4}{2x + 3} + \frac{1 - 10x}{2(x - 5x^2)}\right]$$

59. $f(x) = \dfrac{(x + 2)^5}{\sqrt[6]{3x - 5}}$.

$$\ln f(x) = \ln\left[\frac{(x + 2)^5}{(3x - 5)^{1/6}}\right]$$
$$= \ln(x + 2)^5 - \ln(3x - 5)^{1/6}$$
$$= 5\ln(x + 2) - \frac{1}{6}\ln(3x - 5)$$

Differentiating,

$$\frac{f'(x)}{f(x)} = \frac{5}{x + 2} - \frac{3}{6(3x - 5)}$$

Multiplying both sides by $f(x)$

$$f'(x) = \frac{(x + 2)^5}{(3x - 5)^{1/6}}\left[\frac{5}{x + 2} - \frac{1}{2(3x - 5)}\right]$$

27. $T(t) = -5 + Ae^{-kt}$

(a) When $t = 0$, $T(0) = 80$, so $80 = -5 + Ae^0$, or $A = 85$.

When $t = 20$, $T(20) = 25$, so

$$25 = -5 + 85e^{-k \cdot 20}$$

$$30 = 85e^{-20k}$$

$$\frac{6}{17} = e^{-20k}$$

$$\ln \frac{6}{17} = \ln e^{-20k}$$

$$\ln \frac{6}{17} = -20k, \text{ or}$$

$$k = \frac{\ln \frac{6}{17}}{-20} = \frac{-\ln \frac{6}{17}}{20} = \frac{\ln \frac{17}{6}}{20}$$

(b) $T(t) = -5 + 85e^{-0.052t}$
When $t = 0$, $T(0) = 80$, so $(0, 80)$ is an intercept.

When $T(t) = 0$, $0 = -5 + 85e^{-0.052t}$

$$5 = 85e^{-0.052t}$$

$$\frac{1}{17} = e^{-0.052t}$$

$$\ln \frac{1}{17} = \ln e^{-0.052t}$$

$$\ln \frac{1}{17} = -0.052t, \text{ so}$$

$$t = \frac{\ln \frac{1}{17}}{-0.052} = \frac{-\ln \frac{1}{17}}{0.052} = \frac{\ln 17}{0.052} \approx 54.5$$

So $(54.5, 0)$ is an intercept
$\lim_{t \to +\infty} -5 + 85e^{-0.052t} = -5$, so $y = -5$ is a
horizontal asymptote. $T'(t) = -4.42e^{-0.052t}$
$T'(t) < 0$ for all values of t, so T is always
decreasing.
$T''(t) = 0.23e^{-0.052t}$
$T''(t) > 0$ for all values of t, so T is always
concave up.

As $t \to +\infty$, the temperature approaches $-5°C$.

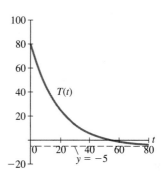

(c) $T(30) = -5 + 85e^{-0.052(30)} \approx 12.8°C$

(d) The temperature will be $0°C$ after approximately 54.5 minutes (see part a).

29. $f(t) = \dfrac{2}{1 + 3e^{-0.8t}}$

(a) When $t = 0$, $f(0) = \dfrac{1}{2}$, so $\left(0, \dfrac{1}{2}\right)$ is an intercept. $f(t) = 0$ has no solution.

$$\lim_{t \to \infty} \frac{2}{1 + 3e^{-0.8t}} = 2, \text{ so } y = 2$$

is a horizontal asymptote.

$$f'(t) = \frac{0 - (2)(-2.4e^{-0.8t})}{(1 + 3e^{-0.8t})^2} = \frac{4.8e^{-0.8t}}{(1 + 3e^{-0.8t})^2}$$

$f'(t) > 0$ for all values of t, so f is always increasing. Using logarithmic differentiation,

$$\ln f'(t) = \ln \left[\frac{4.8e^{-0.8t}}{(1 + 3e^{-0.8t})^2} \right]$$

$$= \ln 4.8 + \ln e^{-0.8t} - \ln(1 + 3e^{-0.8t})^2$$

$$= \ln 4.8 - 0.8t - 2\ln(1 + 3e^{-0.8t})$$

$$\frac{f''(t)}{f'(t)} = -0.8 - 2 \cdot \frac{-2.4e^{-0.8t}}{1 + 3e^{-0.8t}}$$

$$f''(t) = \left[\frac{-0.8(1 + 3e^{-0.8t}) + 4.8e^{-0.8t}}{1 + 3e^{-0.8t}} \right] f'(t)$$

$$= \left[\frac{-0.8 + 2.4e^{-0.8t}}{1 + 3e^{-0.8t}} \right] \left[\frac{4.8e^{-0.8t}}{(1 + 3e^{-0.8t})^2} \right]$$

$$= (-0.8 + 2.4e^{-0.8t}) \left[\frac{4.8e^{-0.8t}}{(1 + 3e^{-0.8t})^3} \right]$$

$f''(t) = 0$ when $-0.8 + 2.4e^{-0.8t} = 0$

$$e^{-0.8t} = \frac{1}{3}$$

$$\ln e^{-0.8t} = \ln \frac{1}{3}$$

$$-0.8t = \ln \frac{1}{3}, \text{ or}$$

$$t = \frac{\ln \frac{1}{3}}{-0.8} = \frac{-\ln \frac{1}{3}}{0.8} = \frac{\ln 3}{0.8} = \frac{5 \ln 3}{4}$$

When $0 < t < \dfrac{5 \ln 3}{4}$, $f''(t) > 0$, so f is concave up

$t > \dfrac{5 \ln 3}{4}$, $f''(t) < 0$, so f is concave down.

The point $(1.37, 1)$ is an inflection point.

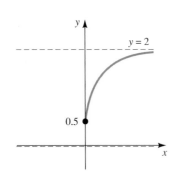

(b) $f(0) = 0.5$ thousand people, or 500 people.

(c) $f(3) = \dfrac{2}{1 + 3\,(0.907)} = 1.572$, so 1,572 people have caught the disease.

(d) $\displaystyle\lim_{t \to \infty} \frac{2}{1 + 3e^{-0.8t}} = 2$, so in the long run, approximately 2,000 people will contract the disease.

31. $Q(t) = 40 - Ae^{-kt}$
When $t = 0$, $Q(0) = 20$, so
$20 = 40 - Ae^{-k \cdot 0}$, or $A = 20$.
Now, $Q(t) = 40 - 20e^{-kt}$.
When $t = 1$, $Q(1) = 30$, so
$30 = 40 - 20e^{-k \cdot 1}$
$20e^{-k} = 10$; $e^{-k} = \frac{1}{2}$; $-k = \ln \frac{1}{2}$
$k = -\ln \frac{1}{2} = \ln 2$
Now, $Q(t) = 40 - 20e^{-(\ln 2)t}$.
When $t = 3$,
$Q(3) = 40 - 20e^{-(\ln 2)(3)} = 37.5$ units per day.

33. $f(x) = 15 - 20e^{-0.3x}$

(a) $\Delta f \approx f'(x)$, where x is the current number of complimentary copies. $f'(x) = 6e^{-0.3x}$
$\Delta f \approx f'(9) = 6e^{-0.3(9)} \approx 0.403$
So, approximately 403 additional copies will be sold.

(b)
$$\Delta f = f(x_2) - f(x_1)$$
$$= f(10) - f(9)$$
$$f(10) = 15 - 20e^{-0.3(10)} \approx 14.004$$
$$f(9) = 15 - 20e^{-0.3(9)} \approx 13.656$$
$$\Delta f = 0.348, \text{ or } 348 \text{ additional copies.}$$

The approximation is off by 55 copies, or $\dfrac{55}{348} \approx 16\%$.

35. $L(t) = \dfrac{\ln(t + 1)}{t + 1}$

(a)
$$L'(t) = \frac{(t + 1)\left(\frac{1}{t+1} \cdot 1\right) - \ln(t + 1)(1)}{(t + 1)^2}$$
$$= \frac{1 - \ln(t + 1)}{(t + 1)^2}$$

So, $L'(t) = 0$ when $1 - \ln(t + 1) = 0$
$\ln(t + 1) = 1$
$e^{\ln(t+1)} = e^1$
$t + 1 = e$, or $t = e - 1$.

When $0 \le t < e - 1$, $L'(t) > 0$, so L is increasing. When $e - 1 < t \le 5$, $L'(t) < 0$, so L is decreasing.

$$L(e - 1) = \frac{\ln(e - 1 + 1)}{e - 1 + 1} = \frac{\ln e}{e} = \frac{1}{e} \approx 0.368$$

$$L(0) = \frac{\ln(1)}{1} = 0$$

$$L(1) = \frac{\ln 2}{2} \approx 0.347$$

So, at the age $e - 1 \approx 1.7$ years of age, a child's learning capacity is the greatest.

(b) Need to maximize the rate of learning, or maximize the first derivative.

$$L''(t) = \frac{(t + 1)^2 \left(\frac{-1}{t+1}\right) - [1 - \ln(t + 1)][2(t + 1)(1)]}{(t + 1)^4}$$

$$= \frac{-(t + 1) - 2(t + 1)[1 - \ln(t + 1)]}{(t + 1)^4}$$

$$= \frac{(t + 1)[-1 - 2(1 - \ln(t + 1))]}{(t + 1)^4}$$

$$= \frac{-1 - 2[1 - \ln(t + 1)]}{(t + 1)^3}$$

So $L''(t) = 0$ when
$-1 - 2[1 - \ln(t + 1)] = 0$, or

$$-2[1 - \ln(t + 1)] = 1$$

$$1 - \ln(t + 1) = -\frac{1}{2}$$

$$1 + \frac{1}{2} = \ln(t + 1)$$

$$e^{1.5} = e^{\ln(t+1)}$$

$$e^{1.5} = t + 1, \text{ or}$$

$$t = e^{1.5} - 1$$

When $0 \le t < e^{1.5} - 1$, $L''(t) < 0$, so $L'(t)$ is decreasing.
$e^{1.5} - 1 < t \le 5$, $L''(t) > 0$, so $L'(t)$ is increasing.

$$L'(e^{1.5} - 1) = \frac{1 - \ln(e^{1.5} - 1 + 1)}{(e^{1.5} - 1 + 1)^2} = \frac{1 - \ln e^{1.5}}{(e^{1.5})^2}$$

$$= \frac{1 - 1.5}{e^3} \approx -0.025$$

$$L'(0) = \frac{1 - \ln(0 + 1)}{(0 + 1)^2} = 0$$

$$L'(5) = \frac{1 - \ln(5 + 1)}{(5 + 1)^2} \approx -0.022$$

So, a child's learning capability is increasing most rapidly at birth.

37. $p(t) = \dfrac{Ce^{kt}}{1 + Ce^{kt}}$

Since

$$p(0) = \frac{1}{200},$$

$$\frac{1}{200} = \frac{Ce^{k \cdot 0}}{1 + Ce^{k \cdot 0}}$$

$$\frac{1}{200} = \frac{C}{1 + C}$$

$$1 + C = 200C, \text{ or } C = \frac{1}{199}$$

So, $p(t) = \dfrac{\frac{1}{199}e^{kt}}{1 + \frac{1}{199}e^{kt}} = \dfrac{e^{kt}}{199 + e^{kt}}$

Since $\quad p(4) = \dfrac{1}{100}$,

$$\frac{1}{100} = \frac{e^{k \cdot 4}}{199 + e^{k \cdot 4}}$$

$$199 + e^{4k} = 100e^{4k}$$

$$\frac{199}{99} = e^{4k}$$

$$\ln \frac{199}{99} = 4k$$

$$k = \frac{\ln \frac{199}{99}}{4} \approx 0.1745$$

So, $p(t) = \dfrac{e^{0.1745t}}{199 + e^{0.1745t}}.$

Using logarithmic differentiation to find the rate of change,

$$\ln p(t) = \ln \left[\frac{e^{0.1745t}}{199 + e^{0.1745t}} \right]$$

$$= 0.1745t - \ln(199 + e^{0.1745t})$$

$$\frac{p'(t)}{p(t)} = 0.1745 - \frac{0.1745e^{0.1745t}}{199 + e^{0.1745t}}$$

$$= \frac{(0.1745)(199)}{199 + e^{0.1745t}} = \frac{34.7255}{199 + e^{0.1745t}}$$

So,

$$p'(t) = \frac{34.7255}{199 + e^{0.1745t}} \left(\frac{e^{0.1745t}}{199 + e^{0.1745t}} \right)$$

$$= \frac{34.7255e^{0.1745t}}{(199 + e^{0.1745t})^2}.$$

To maximize this rate, use logarithmic differentiation again.

$$\ln p'(t) = \ln \left[\frac{34.7255e^{0.1745t}}{(199 + e^{0.1745t})^2} \right]$$

$$= \ln 34.7255 + 0.1745t - 2\ln(199 + e^{0.1745t})$$

$$\frac{p''(t)}{p'(t)} = 0 + 0.1745 - 2\left(\frac{0.1745e^{0.1745t}}{199 + e^{0.1745t}} \right)$$

$$= \frac{(0.1745)(199) - 0.1745e^{0.1745t}}{199 + e^{0.1745t}}$$

$$= \frac{34.7255 - 0.1745e^{0.1745t}}{199 + e^{0.1745t}}$$

and,

$$p''(t) = \left[\frac{34.7255 - 0.1745e^{0.1745t}}{199 + e^{0.1745t}} \right]$$

$$\left[\frac{34.7255e^{0.1745t}}{(199 + e^{0.1745t})^2} \right]$$

$p''(t) = 0$ when $34.7255 - 0.1745e^{0.1745t} = 0$

$$\frac{34.7255}{0.1745} = e^{0.1745t}$$

$\ln 199 = 0.1745t$,

or $t = \dfrac{\ln 199}{0.1745} \approx 30.33$ weeks

$p(30.33) \approx 0.5$, so roughly half of the trading volume is due to day trading.

39. (a) Profit = (# sold) (profit on each)

$$P(x) = (1,000e^{-0.02x})(x - 125)$$

When $x = 0$, $P(0) = -125,000$ which is not in the practical domain. When $P(x) = 0$, $x = 125$ so (125,0) is an intercept.
$\lim\limits_{x \to \infty} (1000e^{-0.02x})(x - 125) = 0$, so $y = 0$ is a horizontal asymptote.

$$P'(x) = 1000 \left[(e^{-0.02x})(1) + (x - 125)(-0.02^{-0.02x}) \right]$$

$$= 1000e^{-0.02x}\,[1 - 0.02(x - 125)]$$

$$= 1000e^{-0.02x}(3.5 - 0.02x)$$

So, $P'(x) = 0$ when $3.5 - 0.02x = 0$
$3.5 = 0.02x$, or $x = 175$.
When $125 < x < 175$, $P'(x) > 0$, so P is increasing. When $x > 175$, $P'(x) < 0$, so P is decreasing.
The point (175,1510) is a relative maximum.
Using logarithmic differentiation,

$$\ln P'(x) = \ln \left[1,000e^{-0.02x}(3.5 - 0.02x) \right]$$

$$= \ln 1,000 + \ln e^{-0.02x} + \ln(3.5 - 0.02x)$$

$$= \ln 1,000 - 0.02x + \ln(3.5 - 0.02x)$$

$$\frac{P''(x)}{P'(x)} = -0.02 + \frac{-0.02}{3.5 - 0.02x}$$

$$P''(x) = \left(\frac{-0.02(3.5 - 0.02x) - 0.02}{3.5 - 0.02x} \right) P'(x)$$

$$= \left[\frac{0.0004x - 0.09}{3.5 - 0.02x} \right] \left[1,000e^{-0.02x}(3.5 - 0.02x) \right]$$

$$= (0.4x - 90)e^{-0.02x}$$

So $P''(x) = 0$ when $0.4x - 90 = 0$, or $x = 225$.
When $125 < x < 225$, $P''(x) < 0$, so P is concave down
$x > 225$, $P''(x) > 0$, so P is concave up.
The point (225, 1111) is an inflection point.

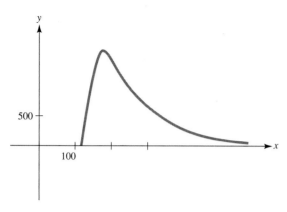

(b) Since $P''(175) < 0$, the relative maximum is the absolute maximum, so the selling price should be $175.

41. $Q(t) = Q_0 e^{-0.0015t}$

(a) The percentage rate is

$$100 \frac{Q'(t)}{Q(t)}$$

$$= 100 \frac{-0.0015 Q_0 e^{-0.0015t}}{Q_0 e^{-0.0015t}} = -0.15\% \text{ per year}$$

(b) When 10% is depleted, 90% remains, so

$$0.9 Q_0 = Q_0 e^{-0.0015t}$$

$$0.9 = e^{-0.0015t}$$

$$\ln 0.9 = -0.0015t, \text{ or}$$

$$t = \frac{\ln 0.9}{-0.0015} \approx 70.24 \text{ years}$$

The percentage rate of change is constant, so the rate at this time is 0.15%.

43. $V(t) = 8,000 e^{\sqrt{t}}$

The prevailing interest rate of 6% is the same as the percentage rate of change of V, so

$$6 = 100 \frac{V'(t)}{V(t)}$$

Now, $V'(t) = 8,000 e^{\sqrt{t}} \left(\frac{1}{2} t^{-1/2} \right)$

So, $100 \dfrac{V'(t)}{V(t)} = 100 \dfrac{8,000 e^{\sqrt{t}} \left(\frac{1}{2} t^{-1/2} \right)}{8,000 e^{\sqrt{t}}} = \dfrac{50}{t^{1/2}}$

and

$$6 = \frac{50}{t^{1/2}}, \quad t^{1/2} = \frac{25}{3}, \text{ or}$$

$$t = \left(\frac{25}{3} \right)^2 \approx 69.44$$

When $0 < t < \dfrac{625}{9}$, the percentage rate of growth $100 \dfrac{V'(t)}{V(t)} > 6\%$. When $t > \dfrac{625}{9}$, the percentage rate of growth is $100 \dfrac{V'(t)}{V(t)} < 6\%$. So, the land should be sold approximately 69.44 years from now.

45. $p(x) = e^{-0.2x}; f(x) = 5x^{0.9}$

The per capita rate of increase function is

$$R(x) = \frac{\ln \left[e^{-0.2x} (5x^{0.9}) \right]}{x}$$

$$= -0.2 + [\ln 5 + 0.9 \ln x] \frac{1}{x}$$

So,

$$R'(x) = 0 + [\ln 5 + 0.9 \ln x] \left(\frac{-1}{x^2} \right) + \left(\frac{1}{x} \right) \left(0 + \frac{0.9}{x} \right)$$

$$= \frac{-\ln 5 - 0.9 \ln x + 0.9}{x^2}$$

So, $R'(x) = 0$ when

$$0 = -\ln 5 - 0.9 \ln x + 0.9$$

$$0.9 \ln x = -\ln 5 + 0.9$$

$$\ln x = \frac{-\ln 5 + 0.9}{0.9}$$

$$e^{\ln x} = e^{(-\ln 5 + 0.9)/0.9}$$

$$x = e^{(-\ln 5 + 0.9)/0.9} \approx 0.45$$

Since

$$R''(x) = \frac{(x^2) \left(\frac{-0.9}{x} \right) + [-\ln 5 - 0.9 \ln x + 0.9](2x)}{x^4}$$

$$= \frac{x \left[-0.9 + 2(-\ln 5 - 0.9 \ln x + 0.9) \right]}{x^4}$$

$$= \frac{-2 \ln 5 - 1.8 \ln x + 0.9}{x^3}$$

and $R''(0.45) < 0$, so $x = 0.45$ corresponds to the absolute maximum. The ideal reproductive age is 0.45 years.

47. $E(C) = C\left(aR + \dfrac{b}{C}\right)^2$

(a)
$$E'(C) = (C)\left[2\left(aR + \frac{b}{C}\right)\left(\frac{-b}{C^2}\right)\right] + \left(aR + \frac{b}{C}\right)^2 \quad (1)$$

$$= \frac{-2b}{C}\left(aR + \frac{b}{C}\right) + \left(aR + \frac{b}{C}\right)^2$$

$$= \left(aR + \frac{b}{C}\right)\left[\frac{-2b}{C} + aR + \frac{b}{C}\right]$$

$$= \left(aR + \frac{b}{C}\right)\left(aR - \frac{b}{C}\right)$$

So $E'(C) = 0$ when

$$aR - \frac{b}{C} = 0 \text{ (rejecting the negative solution)}$$

$$aR = \frac{b}{C}$$

$$C = \frac{b}{aR}$$

$$E''(C) = \left(aR + \frac{b}{C}\right)\left(\frac{b}{C^2}\right) + \left(aR - \frac{b}{C}\right)\left(\frac{-b}{C^2}\right)$$

$$= \frac{b}{C^2}\left[\left(aR + \frac{b}{C}\right) - \left(aR - \frac{b}{C}\right)\right]$$

$$= \frac{b}{C^2}\left(\frac{2b}{C}\right) = \frac{2b^2}{C^3}$$

When $C = \dfrac{b}{aR}$,

$$E''\left(\frac{b}{aR}\right) = \frac{2b^2}{\left(\frac{b}{aR}\right)^3}$$

Since a, b, R are all positive,

$$E''\left(\frac{b}{aR}\right) > 0$$

So, the absolute minimum occurs when

$$C = \frac{b}{aR}.$$

(b) $E(C) = mCe^{k/C}$

Using logarithmic differentiation,

$$\ln E(C) = \ln mCe^{k/C}$$

$$\ln E(C) = \ln m + \ln C + \ln e^{k/C}$$

$$\ln E(C) = \ln m + \ln C + k/C$$

$$\frac{E'(C)}{E(C)} = \frac{1}{C} - \frac{k}{C^2}$$

or, $E'(C) = \dfrac{C - k}{C^2}E(C)$

$$= \frac{C - k}{C^2}(mCe^{k/C})$$

$$= \frac{(C - k)m}{C}e^{k/C}$$

So, $E'(C) = 0$ when $C - k = 0$, or $C = k$. We want the same value of C for a minimum in both models, so

$$k = \frac{b}{aR}$$

From the first model, the minimum value is

$$E\left(\frac{b}{aR}\right) = \frac{b}{aR}\left(aR + b \cdot \frac{aR}{b}\right)^2$$

$$= \frac{b}{aR}(2aR)^2$$

$$= 4abR.$$

For the second model to have this same minimum,

$$E(k) = mke^{k/k}$$

$$4abR = m\left(\frac{b}{aR}\right)e, \text{ so } m = 4a^2R^2e^{-1}.$$

49. $w(t) = \dfrac{10}{1 + 15e^{-0.05t}}$; $p(t) = e^{-0.01t}$

(a) Total weight
    =(weight per fish) (number of fish)
    =(weight per fish) [(beginning number fish) (proportion remaining)]

$$E(t) = \left(\frac{10}{1 + 15e^{-0.05t}}\right)(1,000e^{-0.01t})$$

$$E(t) = 10,000\frac{e^{-0.01t}}{1 + 15e^{-0.05t}}$$

(b) Using logarithmic differentiation,

$$\ln E(t) = \ln\left[10{,}000\frac{e^{-0.01t}}{1+15e^{-0.05t}}\right]$$

$$= \ln 10{,}000 + \ln e^{-0.01t} - \ln(1+15e^{-0.05t})$$

$$= \ln 10{,}000 - 0.01t - \ln(1+15e^{-0.05t})$$

$$\frac{E'(t)}{E(t)} = -0.01 - \frac{-0.75e^{-0.05t}}{1+15e^{-0.05t}}$$

$$E'(t) = \left[\frac{-0.01(1+15e^{-0.05t})+0.75e^{-0.05t}}{1+15e^{-0.05t}}\right]E(t)$$

$$= \left[\frac{-0.01+0.6e^{-0.05t}}{1+15e^{-0.05t}}\right]\left[10{,}000\frac{e^{-0.01t}}{1+15e^{-0.05t}}\right]$$

$$= \left[-0.01+0.6e^{-0.05t}\right]\left[10{,}000\frac{e^{-0.01t}}{(1+15e^{-0.05t})^2}\right]$$

So, $E((t) = 0$ when $-0.01+0.6e^{-0.05t}=0$

$$0.6e^{-0.05t} = 0.01$$

$$e^{-0.05t} = \frac{1}{60}$$

$$\ln e^{-0.05t} = \ln\frac{1}{60}$$

$$-0.05t = \ln\frac{1}{60}, \text{ or}$$

$$t = \frac{\ln\frac{1}{60}}{-0.05} = \frac{-\ln\frac{1}{60}}{0.05} = \frac{\ln 60}{0.05} \approx 81.9$$

For the domain $t \geq 0$,

when $0 \leq t < \dfrac{\ln 60}{0.05}$, $E'(t) > 0$, so E is increasing

$t > \dfrac{\ln 60}{0.05}$, $E'(t) < 0$, so E is decreasing.

So, the relative maximum is also the absolute maximum.
When $t \approx 81.9$ days, the yield is the maximum, namely

$$E(81.9) = 10{,}000\frac{e^{-0.01(81.9)}}{1+15e^{-0.05(81.9)}}$$

$$\approx 3{,}527 \text{ pounds}$$

(c)

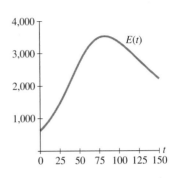

51.

$$N(t) = \frac{B}{1+Ce^{-kt}}$$

(a) When $t = 0$, $N(0) = 0.1B$ so

$$0.1B = \frac{B}{1+Ce^{-k\cdot 0}}$$

$$0.1 = \frac{1}{1+C}$$

$$1+C = \frac{1}{0.1}$$

$$C = 9$$

When $t = 2$, $N(2) = 0.25B$, so

$$0.25B = \frac{B}{1+9e^{-k(2)}}$$

$$0.25 = \frac{1}{1+9e^{-2k}}$$

$$1+9e^{-2k} = \frac{1}{0.25}$$

$$9e^{-2k} = 3$$

$$e^{-2k} = \frac{1}{3}$$

$$\ln e^{-2k} = \ln\frac{1}{3}$$

$$-2k = \ln\frac{1}{3}, \text{ or}$$

$$k = \frac{\ln\frac{1}{3}}{-2} = \frac{-\ln\frac{1}{3}}{2} = \frac{\ln 3}{2}$$

(b)
$$N(t) = \frac{B}{1 + 9e^{-\left(\frac{\ln 3}{2}\right)t}}$$

$$0.5B = \frac{B}{1 + 9e^{(-t/2)(\ln 3)}}$$

$$1 + 9e^{(-t/2)(\ln 3)} = \frac{1}{0.5}$$

$$9e^{(-t/2)(\ln 3)} = 1$$

$$e^{\ln 3^{-t/2}} = \frac{1}{9}$$

$$3^{-t/2} = \frac{1}{9}$$

$$\ln 3^{-t/2} = \ln \frac{1}{9}$$

$$-\frac{t}{2} \ln 3^{-t/2} = \ln \frac{1}{9}$$

$$-\frac{t}{2} = \frac{\ln \frac{1}{9}}{\ln 3}, \text{ or }$$

$$t = \frac{-2 \ln \frac{1}{9}}{\ln 3} = \frac{2 \ln 9}{\ln 3} = 4 \text{ hours}$$

(c) Need to maximize the rate at which news is spreading (maximize the first derivative).

$$N(t) = \frac{B}{1 + 9e^{-(\ln 3/2)t}}$$

To use the result from page 331, consider

$$\frac{\ln 3}{2} = B\left(\frac{\ln 3}{2B}\right) = Bk$$

Then, $N''(t) = 0$ when

$$t = \frac{\ln 9}{\ln \frac{3}{2}} = \frac{2 \ln 9}{\ln 3}$$

$$= \frac{\ln 81}{\ln 3} = \log_3 81 = 4$$

So, the news is spreading most rapidly after 4 hours.

53. $N(t) = 500(0.03)^{(0.4)^t}$

(a) When $t = 0$, $N(0) = 500(0.03)^{(0.4)^0} = 15$ employees.

When $t = 5$, $N(5) = 500(0.03)^{(0.4)^5} \approx 482$ employees.

$$300 = 500(0.03)^{(0.4)^t}$$

$$\frac{3}{5} = (0.03)^{(0.4)^t}$$

$$\ln 0.6 = \ln(0.03)^{(0.4)^t}$$

$$\ln 0.6 = (0.4)^t \ln(0.03)$$

$$\frac{\ln 0.6}{\ln 0.03} = (0.4)^t$$

$$0.145677 \approx (0.4)^t$$

$$\ln 0.145677 \approx \ln(0.4)^t$$

$$\ln 0.145677 \approx t \ln(0.4), \text{ so }$$

$$t \approx \frac{\ln 0.145677}{\ln 0.4} \approx 2.10 \text{ years}$$

Since $\lim_{t \to +\infty} (0.4)^t = 0$,

$$\lim_{t \to +\infty} 500(0.03)^{(0.4)^t} = 500 \text{ employees.}$$

(b) To sketch the graphs of N and $F(t) = 500(0.03)^{-(0.4)^{-t}}$ on the same graph, Press $\boxed{y=}$ and input N for $Y_1 =$.
Use window dimensions of $[-6, 6]2$ by $[0,1000]100$
Press $\boxed{\text{graph}}$.
Press $\boxed{y=}$ and input F for $Y_2 =$.
Press $\boxed{\text{graph}}$.

Writing Exercise—Answers will vary.

55. $C(t) = Ate^{-kt}$

(a)
$$C'(t) = A\left[(t)(-ke^{-kt}) + (e^{-kt})(1)\right]$$
$$= Ae^{-kt}(1 - kt)$$

So $C'(t) = 0$ when $1 - kt = 0$, or $t = \dfrac{1}{k}$.

When $0 \le t < \dfrac{1}{k}$, $C'(t) > 0$, so C is increasing

$t > \dfrac{1}{k}$, $C'(t) < 0$, so C is decreasing.

$$C''(t) = A\left[(e^{-kt})(-k) + (1 - kt)(-ke^{-kt})\right]$$
$$= Ake^{-kt}(kt - 2)$$

$C''\left(\dfrac{1}{k}\right) < 0$, so the absolute maximum

concentration occurs when $t = \dfrac{1}{k}$ and has a value of

$$C\left(\frac{1}{k}\right) = A\left(\frac{1}{k}\right)e^{-k(1/k)} = \frac{A}{ke}.$$

(b) From above, $C''(t) = Ake^{-kt}(kt - 2)$, so
$C''(t) = 0$ when $kt - 2 = 0$, or $t = \dfrac{2}{k}$.

When $0 \le t < \dfrac{2}{k}$, $C''(t) < 0$, so C is concave down;

$t > \dfrac{2}{k}$, $C''(t) > 0$, so C is concave up.

The point $\left(\dfrac{2}{k}, \dfrac{2A}{ke^2}\right)$ is an inflection point.
The zeros of the second derivative are relative extrema of the first derivative, or in this case, the rate of change of drug concentration.

When $0 < t < \dfrac{2}{k}$, $C''(t) < 0$, so C' is decreasing;

$t > \dfrac{2}{k}$, $C''(t) > 0$, so C' is increasing.

So the inflection point corresponds to the minimum rate of change of drug concentration.

(c) The maximum point shifts to the left and the height of the curve decreases.

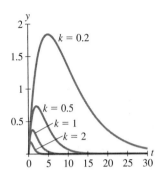

57. (a) Assuming continuous growth, the situation can be modeled by a function of the form

$$Q(t) = Q_0 e^{kt}$$

Let $t = 0$ be the year 1947. Since $r = 0.06$ and $Q_0 = 1{,}139$,

$$Q(t) = 1{,}139e^{0.06t}$$

In the year 1954, $t = 7$ and

$$Q(7) = 1{,}139e^{0.06(7)}$$
$$\approx 1{,}733 \text{ staff members}$$

(b) Let the original size of the staff be Q_0 and double the staff be $2Q_0$. Then,

$$2Q_0 = Q_0 e^{0.06t}$$
$$2 = e^{0.06t}$$
$$\ln 2 = \ln e^{0.06t}$$
$$\ln 2 = 0.06t, \text{ or } t = \frac{\ln 2}{0.06} = 11.55$$

So, any size staff doubles in approximately 11.55 years.

(c) Writing Exercise—Answers will vary.

59. $p(x) = Ax^s c^{-sx/r}$

(a)
$$p'(x) = A\left[(x^s)\left(\frac{-s}{r} e^{-sx/r} \right) + \left(e^{-sx/r} \right)\left(sx^{s-1} \right) \right]$$

$$= sAx^{s-1}e^{-sx/r}\left[\frac{-x}{r} + 1 \right]$$

So $p'(x) = 0$ when $\dfrac{-x}{r} + 1 = 0$, or $x = r$.

When $0 \le x < r$, $p'(x) > 0$, so p is increasing

$x > r$, $p'(x) < 0$ so p is decreasing.

Since the domain of p is $p \ge 0$, this means the absolute maximum occurs when $x = r$.

(b) Rewrite $p'(x)$ as

$$p'(x) = sAe^{-sx/r}\left(\frac{-x^s}{r} + x^{s-1} \right)$$

Then $p''(x) =$

$$sA\left[\left(e^{-sx/r} \right)\left(\frac{-sx^{s-1}}{r} + (s-1)x^{s-2} \right) \right.$$

$$\left. + \left(\frac{-x^s}{r} + x^{s-1} \right)\left(\frac{-s}{r} e^{-sx/r} \right) \right]$$

$$= sAx^{s-2}e^{-sx/r}\left[\frac{-sx}{r} + s - 1 + \left(\frac{-x^2}{r} + x \right)\frac{-s}{r} \right]$$

$$= sAx^{s-2}e^{-sx/r}\left(\frac{-s}{r}x + s - 1 + \frac{s}{r^2}x^2 - \frac{s}{r}x \right)$$

$$= sAx^{s-2}e^{-sx/r}\left[\frac{s}{r^2}x^2 - \frac{2s}{r}x + (s-1) \right]$$

$$= r^2 sA e^{s-2}e^{-sx/r}\left[sx^2 - 2rsx + r^2(s-1) \right]$$

Using the quadratic formula,

$$x = \frac{2rs \pm \sqrt{(2rs)^2 - (4)(s)r^2(s-1)}}{2(s)}$$

$$x = \frac{2rs \pm 2r\sqrt{s^2 - s(s-1)}}{2s}$$

$$x = \frac{rs \pm r\sqrt{s}}{s} = \frac{r}{s}\left(s \pm \sqrt{s} \right)$$

So, there are two possible inflection points. (Checking with $p''(x)$ shows that they both are inflection points.)

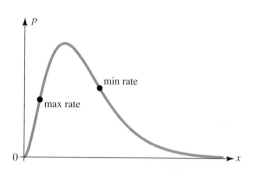

(c) When $0 < s < 1$, $s - \sqrt{s} < 0$, so $x < 0$. Since the practical domain is $x > 0$, this value is rejected and there is only one inflection point.

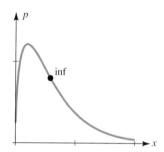

61. $f(t) = \dfrac{A}{1 + Ce^{-kt}}$

The epidemic is spreading most rapidly when the rate of change, or derivative, is maximized

$$f'(t) = \frac{0 - (A)(-kCe^{-kt})}{(1 + Ce^{-kt})^2}$$

$$= \frac{kACe^{-kt}}{(1 + Ce^{-kt})^2} = kAC\frac{e^{-kt}}{(1 + Ce^{-kt})^2}$$

The possible min/max of f' are the zeros of f''.

$$f''(t) = kAC\left[\frac{(1 + Ce^{-kt})^2(-ke^{-kt})}{(1 + Ce^{-kt})^4} \right.$$

$$\left. - \frac{(e^{-kt})\left[2(1 + Ce^{-kt})(-kCe^{-kt}) \right]}{(1 + Ce^{-kt})^4} \right]$$

$$= -k^2 ACe^{-kt}(1 + Ce^{-kt})\left[\frac{1 + Ce^{-kt} - 2Ce^{-kt}}{(1 + Ce^{-kt})^4} \right]$$

So, $f''(t) = 0$ when

$$1 - Ce^{-kt} = 0$$

$$1 = Ce^{-kt}$$

$$\frac{1}{C} = e^{-kt}$$

$$\ln \frac{1}{C} = \ln e^{-kt}$$

$$\ln \frac{1}{C} = -kt, \text{ or }$$

$$t = \frac{\ln \frac{1}{C}}{-k} = \frac{-\ln \frac{1}{C}}{k} = \frac{\ln C}{k}$$

Checking with f''' shows this value of t corresponds to the absolute maximum. The absolute maximum is

$$f\left(\frac{\ln C}{k}\right) = \frac{A}{1 + Ce^{-k(\ln C/k)}}$$

$$= \frac{A}{1 + Ce^{-\ln C}}$$

$$= \frac{A}{1 + Ce^{\ln(1/C)}}$$

$$= \frac{A}{1 + C \cdot \frac{1}{C}} = \frac{A}{2}$$

So the epidemic is spreading most rapidly when half of those susceptible are infected.

63. $N(t) = 2(1 - e^{-.037t})$

To graph this function and see what happens as $t \to \infty$, press $\boxed{y=}$ and input N for $y_1 =$.
Use window dimensions of $[0, 200]10$ by $[0, 3]1$.
Press $\boxed{\text{graph}}$.
The value of N approaches the maximum of 2 million viewers.

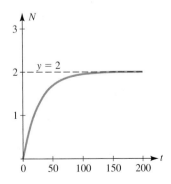

65. $y(t) = \dfrac{c}{b - a}(e^{-at} - e^{-bt})$

(a) $y'(t) = \dfrac{c}{b - a}(-ae^{-at} + be^{-bt})$
So, $y'(t) = 0$ when

$$-ae^{-at} + be^{-bt} = 0$$

$$be^{-bt} = ae^{-at}$$

$$\frac{e^{-bt}}{e^{-at}} = \frac{a}{b}$$

$$e^{-bt+at} = \frac{a}{b}$$

$$\ln e^{-bt+at} = \ln \frac{a}{b}$$

$$(a - b)t = \ln \frac{a}{b}$$

$$t = \frac{\ln \frac{a}{b}}{a - b} = \frac{\ln \frac{b}{a}}{b - a}$$

$$y''(t) = \frac{c}{b - a}(a^2 e^{-at} - b^2 e^{-bt})$$

$$y''\left(\frac{\ln \frac{a}{b}}{a - b}\right) < 0, \text{ so the maximum occurs}$$

when $t = \dfrac{\ln \dfrac{a}{b}}{a - b}$.

In the long run,

$$\lim_{t \to +\infty} \frac{c}{b - a}(e^{-at} - e^{-kt}) = \frac{c}{b - a}(0 - 0) = 0.$$

So, the concentration approaches zero.

(b)

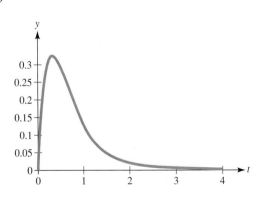

(c) Writing Exercise—Answers will vary.

67. $V(t) = V_0 \left(1 - \dfrac{2}{L}\right)^t$

   (a) When $L = 8$, $\ V(t) = 875 \left(1 - \dfrac{2}{8}\right)^t =$

      $875(0.75)^t$.
      When $t = 5$, $V(5) = 875(0.75)^5 \approx \$207.64$
      The annual rate of depreciation is the derivative,
      and logarithmic differentiation must be used.

$$\ln V = \ln[8.75(0.75)^t]$$
$$= \ln 8.75 + \ln(0.75)^t$$
$$= \ln 8.75 + t \ln 0.75$$

      Differentiating,

$$\frac{V'(t)}{V(t)} = 0 + \ln 0.75$$
$$V'(t) = (\ln 0.75) V(t) = (\ln 0.75)(875)(0.75^t)$$

   (b) In general, the percentage rate of change is

$$100 \frac{V'(t)}{V(t)} = 100 \frac{\ln\left(1 - \frac{2}{L}\right) V(t)}{V(t)}$$
$$= 100 \ln\left(1 - \frac{2}{L}\right).$$

69. $f(x) = \dfrac{1}{\sigma\sqrt{2\pi}} e^{-(x-\mu)^2/2\sigma^2}$

   (a) Noting that σ, $\sqrt{2\pi}$ and μ are all constants, and
      that

$$-\frac{(x-\mu)^2}{2\sigma^2} = -\frac{1}{2\sigma^2}(x^2 - 2\mu x + \mu^2)$$
$$= -\frac{1}{2\sigma^2}x^2 + \frac{\mu}{\sigma^2}x - \frac{\mu^2}{2\sigma^2}$$
$$f'(x) = \frac{1}{\sigma\sqrt{2\pi}}\left[\left(e^{-(x-\mu)^2/2\sigma^2}\right)\left(-\frac{1}{\sigma^2}x + \frac{\mu}{\sigma^2}\right)\right]$$

      So, $f'(x) = 0$ when

$$\frac{1}{\sigma\sqrt{2\pi}} = 0 \rightarrow \text{no solution}$$
$$e^{-(x-\mu)^2/2\sigma^2} = 0 \rightarrow \text{no solution}$$

$$-\frac{1}{\sigma^2}x + \frac{\mu}{\sigma^2} = 0$$
$$-x + \mu = 0$$
$$x = \mu$$

$$f''(x) = \frac{1}{\sigma\sqrt{2\pi}}\left[\left(e^{-(x-\mu)^2/2\sigma^2}\right)\left(-\frac{1}{\sigma^2}\right)\right.$$
$$\left. + \left(-\frac{1}{\sigma^2}x + \frac{\mu}{\sigma^2}\right)\left(e^{-(x-\mu)^2/2\sigma^2}\right)\left(-\frac{1}{\sigma^2}x + \frac{\mu}{\sigma^2}\right)\right]$$
$$= \frac{1}{\sigma\sqrt{2\pi}}e^{-(x-\mu)^2/2\sigma^2}$$
$$\cdot \left[-\frac{1}{\sigma^2} + \left(\frac{1}{\sigma^4}x^2 - \frac{2\mu}{\sigma^4}x + \frac{\mu^2}{\sigma^4}\right)\right]$$

So, $f''(x) = 0$ when

$$\frac{1}{\sigma\sqrt{2\pi}} = 0 \rightarrow \text{no solution}$$

$$e^{-(x-\mu)^2/2\sigma^2} = 0 \rightarrow \text{no solution}$$

$$\frac{1}{\sigma^4}x^2 - \frac{2\mu}{\sigma^4}x + \frac{\mu^2}{\sigma^4} - \frac{1}{\sigma^2} = 0$$
$$\frac{1}{\sigma^4}(x^2 - 2\mu x + \mu^2 - \sigma^2) = 0$$
$$x^2 - 2\mu x + (\mu^2 - \sigma^2) = 0$$
$$(x - (\mu - \sigma))(x - (\mu + \sigma)) = 0$$
$$x - (\mu - \sigma) = 0, \ \text{or}$$
$$x = \mu - \sigma$$
$$x - (\mu + \sigma) = 0, \ \text{or}$$
$$x = \mu + \sigma$$

So, there are inflection points at $x = \mu - \sigma$ and
$x = \mu + \sigma$. To test the critical value $x = \mu$ from
the first derivative, note that

$$f''(\mu) = \frac{1}{\sigma\sqrt{2\pi}}e^{-(\mu-\mu)^2/2\sigma^2}$$
$$\cdot \left(\frac{1}{\sigma^4}\mu^2 - \frac{2\mu}{\sigma^4}\mu + \frac{\mu^2}{\sigma^4} - \frac{1}{\sigma^2}\right)$$
$$= \frac{1}{\sigma\sqrt{2\pi}} \cdot e^0 \left(-\frac{1}{\sigma^2}\right) < 0$$

The function is concave down and there is an
absolute max at $x = \mu$.

(b)

$$f(\mu + c) = \frac{1}{\sigma\sqrt{2\pi}}e^{-[(\mu+c)-\mu]^2/2\sigma^2}$$

$$f(\mu - c) = \frac{1}{\sigma\sqrt{2\pi}}e^{-[(\mu-c)-\mu]^2/2\sigma^2}$$

$$-[(\mu + c) - \mu]^2 = -c^2$$

$$-[(\mu - c) - \mu]^2 = -c^2$$

So, $f(\mu + c) = f(\mu - c)$

(c) This means that the graph of f is symmetric about the line $\mu = c$.

Checkup for Chapter 4

1. (a)

$$\frac{(3^{-2})(9^2)}{(27)^{2/3}} = \frac{\left(\frac{1}{3^2}\right)(9^2)}{\left(\sqrt[3]{27}\right)^2} = \frac{\left(\frac{1}{9}\right)(81)}{(3)^2} = 1$$

(b)

$$\sqrt[3]{(25)^{1.5}\left(\frac{8}{27}\right)} = \sqrt[3]{(25)^{1.5}}\sqrt[3]{\frac{8}{27}}$$

$$= \left[(25)^{1.5}\right]^{1/3}\frac{\sqrt[3]{8}}{\sqrt[3]{27}} = (25)^{0.5}\left(\frac{2}{3}\right)$$

$$= \sqrt{25}\left(\frac{2}{3}\right) = \frac{10}{3}$$

(c) $\log_2 4 + \log_4 16^{-1}$

$\log_2 4 = a$ if and only if $2^a = 4$, so $a = 2$

$\log_4 16^{-1} = \log_4\left(\frac{1}{16}\right)$. Now,

$\log_4\left(\frac{1}{16}\right) = b$ if and only if $4^b = \frac{1}{16}$, so $b = -2$

$\log_2 4 + \log_4 16^{-1} = 2 - 2 = 0$

(d)

$$\left(\frac{8}{27}\right)^{-2/3}\left(\frac{16}{81}\right)^{3/2} = \left(\frac{27}{8}\right)^{2/3}\left(\frac{16}{81}\right)^{3/2}$$

$$= \left(\sqrt[3]{\frac{27}{8}}\right)^2\left(\sqrt{\frac{16}{81}}\right)^3 = \left(\frac{3}{2}\right)^2\left(\frac{4}{9}\right)^3$$

$$= \left(\frac{9}{4}\right)\left(\frac{64}{729}\right) = \frac{16}{81}$$

2. (a) $(9x^4y^2)^{3/2} = 9^{3/2}(x^4)^{3/2}(y^2)^{3/2}$

$$= \left(\sqrt{9}\right)^3(x^6)(y^3)$$

$$= 27x^6y^3$$

(b) $(3x^2y^{4/3})^{-1/2} = \left(\frac{1}{3x^2y^{4/3}}\right)^{1/2}$

$$= \frac{(1)^{1/2}}{(3)^{1/2}(x^2)^{1/2}(y^{4/3})^{1/2}} = \frac{\sqrt{1}}{\left(\sqrt{3}\right)(x)(y^{2/3})}$$

$$= \frac{1}{\sqrt{3}xy^{2/3}}$$

(c)

$$\left(\frac{y}{x}\right)^{3/2}\left(\frac{x^{2/3}}{y^{1/6}}\right)^2 = \left(\frac{y^{3/2}}{x^{3/2}}\right)\left(\frac{x^{4/3}}{y^{1/3}}\right)$$

$$= \left(x^{4/3-3/2}\right)\left(y^{3/2-1/3}\right)$$

$$= x^{-1/6}y^{7/6} = \frac{y^{7/6}}{x^{1/6}}$$

(d)

$$\left(\frac{x^{0.2}y^{-1.2}}{x^{1.5}y^{0.4}}\right)^5 = \left[\left(x^{0.2-1.5}\right)\left(y^{-1.2-0.4}\right)\right]^5$$

$$= \left(x^{-1.3}y^{-1.6}\right)^5 = (x^{-1.3})^5(y^{-1.6})^5$$

$$= x^{-6.5}y^{-8} = \frac{1}{x^{6.5}y^8}$$

3. (a) $4^{2x-x^2} = \frac{1}{64}$

$$4^{2x-x^2} = 4^{-3}$$

So, $2x - x^2 = -3$

$$0 = x^2 - 2x + 3$$

$$0 = (x - 3)(x + 1)$$

$$x = 3, -1$$

(b)

$$e^{1/x} = 4$$

$$\ln e^{1/x} = \ln 4$$

$$\frac{1}{x} = \ln 4$$

$$x = \frac{1}{\ln 4}$$

(c) $\log_4 x^2 = 2$ if and only if $4^2 = x^2$,
so, $x = \pm 4$.

(d) $\dfrac{25}{1 + 2e^{-0.5t}} = 3$

$$\frac{25}{3} = 1 + 2e^{-0.5t}$$

$$\frac{22}{3} = 2e^{-0.5t}$$

$$\frac{11}{3} = e^{-0.5t}$$

$$\ln \frac{11}{3} = \ln e^{-0.5t}$$

$$\ln \frac{11}{3} = -0.5t, \text{ or}$$

$$t = \frac{\ln \frac{11}{3}}{-0.5} = -2 \ln \frac{11}{3} = 2 \ln \frac{3}{11}$$

4. **(a)** (a) $y = \dfrac{e^x}{x^2 - 3x}$

$$\frac{dy}{dx} = \frac{(x^2 - 3x)(e^x \cdot 1) - (e^x)(2x - 3)}{(x^2 - 3x)^2}$$

$$= \frac{e^x \left[(x^2 - 3x) - (2x - 3)\right]}{(x^2 - 3x)^2}$$

$$= \frac{e^x(x^2 - 5x + 3)}{(x^2 - 3x)^2}$$

(b) $y = \ln(x^3 + 2x^2 - 3x)$

$$\frac{dy}{dx} = \frac{1}{x^3 + 2x^2 - 3x}(3x^2 + 4x - 3)$$

$$= \frac{3x^2 + 4x - 3}{x^3 + 2x^2 - 3x}$$

(c) $y = x^3 \ln x$

$$\frac{dy}{dx} = (x^3)\left(\frac{1}{x} \cdot 1\right) + (\ln x)(3x^2)$$

$$= x^2 + 3x^2 \ln x$$

$$= x^2(1 + 3 \ln x)$$

(d) $y = \dfrac{e^{-2x}(2x - 1)^3}{1 - x^2}$

Using logarithmic differentiation,

$$\ln y = \ln \left[\frac{e^{-2x}(2x - 1)^3}{1 - x^2}\right]$$

$$= \ln e^{-2x} + \ln(2x - 1)^3 - \ln(1 - x^2)$$

$$= -2x + 3 \ln(2x - 1) - \ln(1 - x^2)$$

$$\frac{y'}{y} = -2 + 3 \cdot \frac{2}{2x - 1} - \frac{-2x}{1 - x^2}$$

$$y' = \left(-2 + \frac{6}{2x - 1} + \frac{2x}{1 - x^2}\right) y$$

$$= \left(-2 + \frac{6}{2x - 1} + \frac{2x}{1 - x^2}\right)\left[\frac{e^{-2x}(2x - 1)^3}{1 - x^2}\right]$$

$$= \left(-1 + \frac{3}{2x - 1} + \frac{x}{1 - x^2}\right)\left[\frac{2e^{-2x}(2x - 1)^3}{1 - x^2}\right]$$

5. **(a)** $y = x^2 e^{-x}$

When $x = 0$, $y = 0$ so $(0, 0)$ is an intercept.
When $y = 0$, $x = 0$.
Also, $\displaystyle\lim_{x \to -\infty} x^2 e^{-x} = +\infty$

$$\lim_{x \to +\infty} x^2 e^{-x} = \lim_{x \to +\infty} \frac{x^2}{e^x} = \lim_{x \to +\infty} \frac{2x}{e^x} =$$

$$\lim_{x \to +\infty} \frac{2}{e^x} = 0 \text{ so } y = 0 \text{ is a horizontal}$$

asymptote. $y' = (x^2)(-e^{-x}) + (e^{-x})(2x)$
$= xe^{-x}(2 - x)$
so $y' = 0$ when $x = 0, 2$.
Rewriting, $y' = e^{-x}(2x - x^2)$, so

$$y'' = (e^{-x})(2 - 2x) + (2x - x^2)(-e^{-x})$$

$$= e^{-x}\left[(2 - 2x) - (2x - x^2)\right]$$

$$= e^{-x}(2 - 4x + x^2)$$

So, $y'' = 0$ when $2 - 4x + x^2 = 0$.
Using the quadratic formula,

$$x = 2 \pm \sqrt{2}$$

When $x < 0$, $y' < 0$, so y is decreasing,

$$y'' > 0, \text{ so } y \text{ is concave up;}$$

$0 < x < 2 - \sqrt{2}$, $y' > 0$, so y is increasing,

$y'' > 0$, so y is concave up;

$2 - \sqrt{2} < x < 2$, $y' > 0$, so y is increasing,

$y'' < 0$, so y is concave down;

$2 < x < 2 + \sqrt{2}$, $y' < 0$, so y is decreasing,

$y'' < 0$, so y is concave down;

$x > 2 + \sqrt{2}$, $y' < 0$, so y is decreasing,

$y'' > 0$, so y is concave up.

Overall, y is increasing when $0 < x < 2$;
y is decreasing when $x < 0$ and $x > 2$;
y is concave up when $x < 2 - \sqrt{2}$ and $x > 2 + \sqrt{2}$;
y is concave down when $2 - \sqrt{2} < x < 2 + \sqrt{2}$.
The point $(0, 0)$ is a relative minimum, the point $\left(2, \dfrac{4}{e^2}\right)$ is a relative maximum, and the points $(0.59, 0.19)$, $(3.41, 0.38)$ are inflection points.

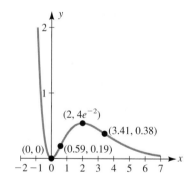

(b) (b)
$$y = \frac{\ln \sqrt{x}}{x^2} = \frac{\ln x^{1/2}}{x^2} = \frac{\frac{1}{2} \ln x}{x^2} = \frac{\ln x}{2x^2}$$

Note that the domain of y is $x > 0$, and $x = 0$ is a vertical asymptote.
When $y = 0$, $x = 1$ so $(1, 0)$ is an intercept.

$$\lim_{x \to \infty} \frac{\ln x}{2x^2} = \lim_{x \to \infty} \frac{\frac{1}{x}}{4x} = \lim_{x \to \infty} \frac{1}{4x^2} = 0$$

so $y = 0$ is a horizontal asymptote.

$$y' = \frac{(2x^2)\left(\frac{1}{x}\right) - (\ln x)(4x)}{(2x^2)^2}$$

$$= \frac{2x(1 - 2 \ln x)}{4x^4} = \frac{1 - 2 \ln x}{2x^3}$$

So $y' = 0$ when

$$1 - 2 \ln x = 0$$
$$1 = 2 \ln x$$
$$\frac{1}{2} = \ln x$$
$$e^{1/2} = e^{\ln x}, \text{ or}$$
$$x = e^{1/2}$$

$$y'' = \frac{(2x^3)\left(-2 \cdot \frac{1}{x}\right) - (1 - 2 \ln x)(6x^2)}{(2x^3)^2}$$

$$= \frac{2x^2\left[(-2 - 3(1 - 2 \ln x)\right]}{4x^6}$$

$$= \frac{-2 - 3 + 6 \ln x}{4x^6} = \frac{-5 + 6 \ln x}{4x^6}$$

So, $y'' = 0$ when

$$-5 + 6 \ln x = 0$$
$$6 \ln x = 5$$
$$\ln x = \frac{5}{6}$$
$$e^{\ln x} = e^{5/6}$$
$$x = e^{5/6}$$

When $0 < x < e^{1/2}$, $y' > 0$, so y is increasing,

$y'' < 0$, so y is concave down;

$e^{1/2} < x < e^{5/6}$, $y' < 0$, so y is decreasing,

$y'' < 0$, so y is concave down;

$x > e^{5/6}$, $y' < 0$, so y is decreasing,

$y'' > 0$, so y is concave up.

Overall, y is increasing when $0 < x < e^{1/2}$;
y is decreasing when $x > e^{1/2}$;
y is concave up when $x > e^{5/6}$;
y is concave down when $0 < x < e^{5/6}$.

The point $\left(e^{1/2}, \dfrac{1}{4e}\right)$ is a relative maximum and the point $\left(e^{5/6}, \dfrac{5}{12e^{5/3}}\right)$ is an inflection point.

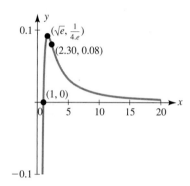

(c) (c) $y = \ln\left(\sqrt{x} - x\right)^2 = 2\ln(x^{1/2} - x)$
Note that the domain of y is $x > 0$ and $x \neq 1$.
When $y = 0$, $\ln(x^{1/2} - x)^2 = 0$
$x^{1/2} - x = \pm 1$
$0 = x - x^{1/2} + 1$ has no solution.
$0 = x - x^{1/2} - 1$ is solved by
letting $u = x^{1/2}$, so $0 = u^2 - u - 1$

$$u = \frac{1 \pm \sqrt{1 + 4}}{2} \approx 1.62$$

(rejecting the negative solution)
$x^{1/2} \approx 1.62$ so $x \approx 2.6$
So, $(2.6, 0)$ is an intercept. Since y is undefined when $x = 1$, there is a vertical asymptote at $x = 1$. Similarly, there is a vertical asymptote at $x = 0$.

Since $\displaystyle\lim_{x \to +\infty} \left(\sqrt{x} - x\right)^2 = +\infty$,

$$\lim_{x \to +\infty} \ln\left(\sqrt{x} - x\right)^2 = +\infty$$

$$y' = 2 \cdot \frac{1}{x^{1/2} - x}\left(\frac{1}{2}x^{-1/2} - 1\right)$$

$$= \frac{\frac{1}{x^{1/2}} - 2}{x^{1/2} - x} \cdot \frac{x^{1/2}}{x^{1/2}}$$

$$= \frac{1 - 2x^{1/2}}{x - x^{3/2}}$$

So $y' = 0$ when $1 - 2x^{1/2} = 0$

$$1 = 2x^{1/2}$$

$$\frac{1}{2} = x^{1/2}, \text{ or}$$

$$x = \frac{1}{4}$$

$$y'' = \frac{(x - x^{3/2})(-x^{-1/2}) - (1 - 2x^{1/2})\left(1 - \frac{3}{2}x^{1/2}\right)}{(x - x^{3/2})^2}$$

$$= \frac{-x^{1/2} + x - \left(1 - 2x^{1/2} - \frac{3}{2}x^{1/2} + 3x\right)}{(x - x^{3/2})^2}$$

$$= \frac{-2x + \frac{5}{2}x^{1/2} - 1}{(x - x^{3/2})^2}$$

So $y'' = 0$ when $-2x + \frac{5}{2}x^{1/2} - 1 = 0$.
To solve, let $u = x^{1/2}$, so $-2u^2 + \frac{5}{2}u - 1 = 0$.
Using the quadratic formula, there are no solutions.

When $0 < x < \dfrac{1}{4}$, $y' > 0$, so y is increasing,

$\quad\quad y'' < 0$, so y is concave down;

$\dfrac{1}{4} < x < 1$, $y' < 0$, so y is decreasing,

$\quad\quad y'' < 0$, so y is concave down;

$\quad x > 1$, $y' > 0$, so y is increasing,

$\quad\quad y'' < 0$, so y is concave down.

Overall, y is increasing when $0 < x < \frac{1}{4}$ and $x > 1$;
y is decreasing when $\frac{1}{4} < x < 1$;
y is concave down when $0 < x < 1$ and $x > 1$.
The point $\left(\dfrac{1}{4}, \ln\dfrac{1}{16}\right)$ is a relative maximum and there are no inflection points.

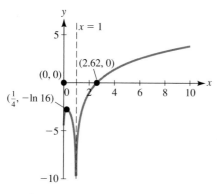

(d) $y = \dfrac{4}{1+e^{-x}}$

When $x = 0$, $y = 2$ so $(0, 2)$ is an intercept.

$y = 0$, has no solution.

$\displaystyle\lim_{x\to-\infty} \dfrac{4}{1+e^{-x}} = 0$ so $y = 0$ is a horizontal asymptote.

$\displaystyle\lim_{x\to+\infty} \dfrac{4}{1+e^{-x}} = 4$ so $y = 4$ is a horizontal asymptote.

$y' = \dfrac{0 - (4)(-e^{-x})}{(1+e^{-x})^2} = \dfrac{4e^{-x}}{(1+e^{-x})^2}$

So y' is never zero. Further, $y' > 0$ for all values of x, so y is always increasing.

Using logarithmic differentiation,

$$\ln y' = \ln\left[\dfrac{4e^{-x}}{(1+e^{-x})^2}\right]$$

$$= \ln 4 + \ln e^{-x} - \ln(1+e^{-x})^2$$

$$= \ln 4 - x - 2\ln(1+e^{-x})$$

$$\dfrac{y''}{y'} = -1 - 2\cdot\dfrac{-e^{-x}}{1+e^{-x}}$$

$$= -1 + \dfrac{2e^{-x}}{1+e^{-x}}$$

$$y'' = \left[\dfrac{-(1+e^{-x}) + 2e^{-x}}{1+e^{-x}}\right]y'$$

$$= \left[\dfrac{-1+e^{-x}}{1+e^{-x}}\right]\left[\dfrac{4e^{-x}}{(1+e^{-x})^2}\right]$$

$$= (-1+e^{-x})\left[\dfrac{4e^{-x}}{(1+e^{-x})^3}\right]$$

So, $y'' = 0$ when

$$-1 + e^{-x} = 0$$
$$e^{-x} = 1$$
$$-x = \ln 1$$
$$\text{or } x = 0$$

When $x < 0$, $y'' > 0$ so y is concave up

$x > 0$, $y'' < 0$ so y is concave down.

The point $(0, 2)$ is an inflection point.

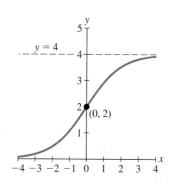

6. In general, $B(t) = Pe^{rt}$.
Here, $B(t) = 2000e^{0.05(t)}$.
When

$$t = 3, \quad B(3) = 2000e^{0.05(3)}$$
$$= 2000e^{0.15}$$
$$\approx \$2{,}323.67$$

For a balance of $3,000,

$$3000 = 2000e^{0.05t}$$
$$\dfrac{3}{2} = e^{0.05t}$$
$$\ln\dfrac{3}{2} = \ln e^{0.05t}$$
$$\ln\dfrac{3}{2} = 0.05t, \text{ or}$$
$$t = \dfrac{\ln(3/2)}{0.05} \approx 8.1 \text{ years}$$

7.   (a)
$$8{,}000 = (P)\left(1 + \frac{0.0625}{2}\right)^{2(10)}$$

$$P = \frac{8{,}000}{(1.03125)^{20}} = \$4{,}323.25$$

(b)
$$8{,}000 = Pe^{0.0625(10)}$$

$$P = 8{,}000e^{-0.625} = \$4{,}282.09$$

8. $p = \dfrac{\ln(t+1)}{t+1} + 5$

Note that the domain is $t > -1$.

(a)
$$p'(t) = \frac{(t+1)\left(\frac{1}{t+1} \cdot 1\right) - [\ln(t+1)](1)}{(t+1)^2} + 0$$

$$= \frac{1 - \ln(t+1)}{(t+1)^2}$$

So, $p'(t) = 0$ when

$$1 - \ln(t+1) = 0$$
$$1 = \ln(t+1)$$
$$e^1 = e^{\ln(t+1)}$$
$$e = t+1, \text{ or}$$
$$t = e - 1$$

When $-1 < t < e - 1$, $p' > 0$ so p is increasing

$t > e - 1$, $p' < 0$ so p is decreasing.

(b) The price is decreasing most rapidly when the first derivative is maximized.

$$p'' = \frac{(t+1)^2\left(\frac{-1}{t+1} \cdot 1\right) - [1 - \ln(t+1)][2(t+1)(1)]}{(t+1)^4}$$

$$= \frac{(t+1)[-1 - 2(1 - \ln(t+1))]}{(t+1)^4}$$

$$= \frac{-3 + 2\ln(t+1)}{(t+1)^3}$$

So, $p'' = 0$ when
$$-3 + 2\ln(t+1) = 0$$
$$2\ln(t+1) = 3$$
$$\ln(t+1) = \frac{3}{2}$$
$$e^{\ln(t+1)} = e^{3/2}$$
$$t + 1 = e^{3/2}, \text{ or}$$
$$t = e^{3/2} - 1$$

$$p''' = \frac{(t+1)^3\left(\frac{2}{t+1}\right) - [-3 + 2\ln(t+1)]\left[3(t+1)^2\right]}{(t+1)^6}$$

$$= \frac{(t+1)^2\,[2 - 3(-3 + 2\ln(t+1))]}{(t+1)^6}$$

$$= \frac{11 - 6\ln(t+1)}{(t+1)^6}$$

So, when $t = e^{3/2} - 1$,

$$p''' = \frac{11 - 6\ln(e^{3/2} - 1 + 1)}{(e^{3/2} - 1 + 1)^6}$$

$$= \frac{11 - 6e^{3/2}}{e^9}$$

Since $p''' < 0$, $t = e^{3/2} - 1$ is a maximum.

(c) $\displaystyle \lim_{t \to \infty} \frac{\ln(t+1)}{t+1} + 5$

$$= \lim_{t \to \infty} \frac{\ln(t+1)}{t+1} + \lim_{t \to \infty} 5$$

$$= \lim_{t \to \infty} \frac{\frac{1}{t+1} \cdot 1}{1} + 5$$

$$= \lim_{t \to \infty} \frac{1}{t+1} + 5 = 0 + 5 = 5$$

So, in the long run, the price approaches $500.

9. $D = q(p) = 1{,}000(p+2)e^{-p}$

(a) $q'(p) = 1{,}000\left[(p+2)(-e^{-p}) + (e^{-p})(1)\right]$

$$= -1{,}000e^{-p}\left[(p+2) - 1\right]$$

$$= -1{,}000e^{-p}(p+1)$$

So, $q'(p) = 0$ when $p = -1$.

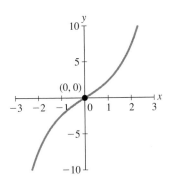

33. $f(t) = t + e^{-t}$

When $t = 0$, $f(0) = 1$ so $(0, 1)$ is an intercept.

$f(t) = 0$ has no solution.

$\lim\limits_{t \to -\infty} t + e^{-t} = +\infty$ (since e^{-t} increases more rapidly than t decreases).

$\lim\limits_{t \to +\infty} t + e^{-t} = t$, so $y = t$ is an oblique asymptote.

$f'(t) = 1 - e^{-t}$

So $f'(t) = 0$ when $1 - e^{-t} = 0$

$$1 = e^{-t}$$
$$\ln 1 = t, \text{ or } t = 0.$$

When $t < 0$, $f'(t) < 0$ so f is decreasing

$t > 0$, $f'(t) > 0$ so f is increasing.

The point $(0, 1)$ is a relative minimum.

$f''(t) = e^{-t}$

So, $f''(t)$ is never zero; further $f''(t) > 0$ for all values of t, so f is always concave up.

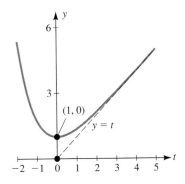

35. $F(u) = u^2 + 2\ln(u + 2)$

Note that the domain is $u > -2$, so $u = -2$ is a vertical asymptote.

When $u = 0$, $F(0) = 2\ln 2$ so $(0, 2\ln 2)$ is an intercept.

$F(u) = 0$ is too difficult to solve.

$\lim\limits_{u \to +\infty} u^2 + 2\ln(u + 2) = +\infty$ so F increases without bound as u increases.

$$F'(u) = 2u + 2 \cdot \frac{1}{u + 2} \cdot 1 = 2\left(u + \frac{1}{u + 2}\right)$$
$$= 2\frac{u^2 + 2u + 1}{u + 2} = 2\frac{(u + 1)^2}{u + 2}$$

So, $F'(u) = 0$ when $u = -1$.

When $-2 < u < -1$, $F'(u) > 0$ so F increases

$u > -1$, $F'(u) > 0$ so F increases.

$$F''(u) = 2\left[\frac{(u + 2)(2u + 2) - (u^2 + 2u + 1)(1)}{(u + 2)^2}\right]$$
$$= 2(u + 1)\left[\frac{2(u + 2) - (u + 1)}{(u + 2)^2}\right]$$
$$= 2(u + 1)\left[\frac{u + 3}{(u + 2)^2}\right]$$

So, $F''(u) = 0$ when $u = -1$ (rejecting $u = -3$ since it is not in the domain of F).

When

$-2 < u < -1$, $F''(u) < 0$ so F is concave down

$u > -1$, $F''(u) > 0$ so F is concave up.

The point $(-1, 1)$ is an inflection point.

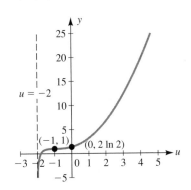

37. $G(x) = \ln(e^{-2x} + e^{-x})$
When $x = 0$, $G(0) = \ln 2$ so $(0, \ln 2)$ is an intercept.
When $G(x) = 0$, $\ln(e^{-2x} + e^{-x}) = 0$;
$e^{-2x} + e^{-x} = 1$;
$e^{-2x} + e^{-x} - 1 = 0$
Letting $u = e^{-x}$,

$$u^2 + u - 1 = 0$$
$$u = \frac{-1 \pm \sqrt{1 + (4)(1)(1)}}{2(1)} = \frac{-1 \pm \sqrt{5}}{2}$$

So,

$$e^{-x} = \frac{-1 \pm \sqrt{5}}{2}$$

$$\ln e^{-x} = \ln\left(\frac{-1 + \sqrt{5}}{2}\right) \text{ (rejecting negative value)}$$

$$-x = \ln\left(\frac{-1 + \sqrt{5}}{2}\right), \text{ or}$$

$$x = -\ln\left(\frac{-1 + \sqrt{5}}{2}\right) \approx 0.48$$

So, $(0.48, 0)$ is an intercept.
$\lim\limits_{x \to -\infty} \ln(e^{-2x} + e^{-x}) = +\infty$ so G increases without bound as x decreases.
$\lim\limits_{x \to +\infty} \ln(e^{-2x} + e^{-x}) = \lim\limits_{x \to 0^+} \ln x = -\infty$
so G decreases without bound as x increases.
$G'(x) = \dfrac{1}{e^{-2x} + e^{-x}}(-2e^{-2x} - e^{-x})$
So, $G'(x) = 0$ when

$$-2e^{-2x} - e^{-x} = 0$$
$$-e^{-x}(2e^{-x} + 1) = 0$$
$$2e^{-x} + 1 = 0 \quad \text{(since } e^{-x} \text{ is never zero)}$$
$$e^{-x} = -\frac{1}{2} \text{ has no solution.}$$

$G'(x)$ is never zero; further, $G'(x) < 0$ for all x so G is always decreasing.

$$G''(x) = \left[\frac{(e^{-2x} + e^{-x})(4e^{-2x} + e^{-x})}{(e^{-2x} + e^{-x})^2}\right.$$
$$\left. - \frac{(-2e^{-2x} - e^{-x})(-2e^{-2x} - e^{-x})}{(e^{-2x} + e^{-x})^2}\right]$$
$$= \frac{4e^{-4x} + 5e^{-3x} + e^{-2x} - (4e^{-4x} + 4e^{-3x} + e^{-2x})}{(e^{-2x} + e^{-x})^2}$$
$$= \frac{e^{-3x}}{(e^{-2x} + e^{-x})^2}$$

Since e^{-3x} is never zero, $G''(x)$ is never zero; further $G''(x) > 0$ for all x so G is always concave up.

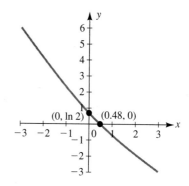

39.
$$f(x) = \ln(4x - x^2), \quad 1 \le x \le 3$$
$$f'(x) = \frac{4 - 2x}{4x - x^2}$$

So, $f'(x) = 0$ when $4 - 2x = 0$, or $x = 2$.
$f(2) = \ln 4$; $f(1) = \ln 3$; $f(3) = \ln 3$
The function's largest value is $\ln 4$ and its smallest value is $\ln 3$.

41.
$$h(t) = (e^{-t} + e^t)^5, \quad -1 \le t \le 1$$
$$h'(t) = 5(e^{-t} + e^t)^4(-e^{-t} + e^t)$$

So, $h'(t) = 0$ when

$$-e^{-t} + e^t = 0 \text{ (since } e^{-t} + e^t \text{ is never zero)}$$
$$e^{-t}(-1 + e^{2t}) = 0$$
$$e^{2t} = 1, \text{ or } t = 0$$

$h(0) = 32; h(-1) = \left(e + \dfrac{1}{e}\right)^5 \approx 280, h(1) = \left(e + \dfrac{1}{e}\right)^5$

So, the function's largest value is $\left(e + \dfrac{1}{e}\right)^5$ and its smallest value is 32.

43. $y = \ln x^2,\ x = 1$

When $x = 1$, $y = \ln 1 = 0$ so point $(1, 0)$ is on the tangent line.

$$y' = (x)\left(\frac{2x}{x^2}\right) + (\ln x^2) = 2 + \ln x^2$$

$$\text{slope } = y' = 2 + \ln(1)^2 = 2$$

So, the equation of the tangent line is

$$y - 0 = 2(x - 1), \text{ or}$$
$$y = 2x - 2.$$

45. $y = x^3 e^{2-x},\ x = 2$

When $x = 2$, $y = 8$ so point $(2, 8)$ is on the tangent line.
$y' = (x^3)(-e^{2-x}) + (e^{2-x})(3x^2)$
$\text{slope} = y' = (2)^3(-e^0) + (e^0)(3 \cdot 4) = 4$
So, the equation of the tangent line is

$$y - 8 = 4(x - 2), \text{ or}$$
$$y = 4x.$$

47. $f(x) = e^{kx}$

Since $f(3) = 2$, $2 = e^{3k}$. Now, $f(9) = e^{9k}$. Using the facts that $(e^{3k})^3 = e^{9k}$,

$$f(9) = (e^{3k})^3 = (2)^3 = 8$$

49. Since the money doubles in 15 years,

$$B(15) = P\left(1 + \frac{r}{4}\right)^{4 \cdot 15}$$
$$= P\left(1 + \frac{r}{4}\right)^{60} = 2P$$

Now,

$$B(30) = P\left(1 + \frac{r}{4}\right)^{4 \cdot 30}$$
$$= \left[P\left(1 + \frac{r}{4}\right)^{60}\right]^2 = (2P)^2 = 4P$$

So the money quadruples in 30 years.

51. Since the decay is exponential and 500 grams were present initially,

$$Q(t) = 500e^{-kt}$$

Also, $Q(50) = 500e^{-50k} = 400$, so $e^{-50k} = \dfrac{4}{5}$

Now, $Q(200) = 500e^{-200k}$
$$= 500(e^{-50k})^4$$
$$= 500\left(\frac{4}{5}\right)^4$$
$$= 204.8 \text{ grams}$$

53. Since the growth is exponential, $P(t) = P_0 e^{kt}$ where the initial number of bacteria is $P_0 = 5{,}000$ Also,

$$P(10) = 5{,}000e^{10k} = 8{,}000, \text{ so } e^{10k} = \frac{8}{5}$$

Now, $P(30) = 5000(e^{30k})$
$$= 5000(e^{10k})^3$$
$$= 5000\left(\frac{8}{5}\right)^3$$
$$= 20{,}480 \text{ bacteria}$$

55. $Q(x) = 50 - 40e^{-0.1x}$

(a) When $x = 0$, $Q(0) = 10$ so $(0, 10)$ is an intercept.

$$Q(x) = 0 \text{ when } 50 - 40e^{-0.1x} = 0$$
$$50 = 40e^{-0.1x}$$
$$\frac{5}{4} = e^{-0.1x}$$
$$\ln \frac{5}{4} = -0.1x, \text{ or}$$
$$x = \frac{\ln \frac{5}{4}}{-0.1}$$

Since the relevant domain is $x \geq 0$, this intercept will not be on graph.
$\displaystyle\lim_{x \to \infty} 50 - 40e^{-0.1x} = 50$, so $y = 50$ is a horizontal asymptote.
$Q'(x) = 4e^{-0.1x}$

Now, $Q'(x)$ is never zero. Further, $Q'(x) > 0$ for all x so Q is always increasing.
$Q''(x) = -0.4e^{-0.1x}$
which is never zero. Further, $Q''(x) < 0$ for all x so Q is always concave down.

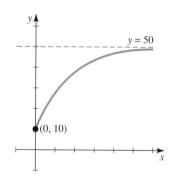

(b) When no money is spent on advertising,
$Q(0) = 50 - 40e^0 = 10$
So, 10,000 units will be sold.

(c) If 8 thousand dollars are spent on advertising,
$Q(8) = 50 - 40e^{-0.1(8)} \approx 32.027$
So, approximately 32,027 units will be sold.

(d) For sales of 35 thousand units,

$$35 = 50 - 40e^{-0.1x}$$
$$40e^{-0.1x} = 15$$
$$e^{-0.1x} = \frac{3}{8}$$
$$-0.1x = \ln \frac{3}{8}$$
$$x = \frac{\ln \frac{3}{8}}{-0.1} = 10 \ln \frac{8}{3} \approx 9.81$$

So, approximately $9,810 dollars must be spent on advertising.

(e) $\lim\limits_{x \to \infty} 50 - 40e^{-0.1x} = 50$
So, approximately (just less than) 50,000 units is the optimal sales projection.

57. $B(t) = P \left(1 + \frac{r}{k}\right)^{kt}$

(a) compounded quarterly, with $P = 2,000$, $B(t) = 5,000$ and $r = 0.08$,

$$5,000 = 2,000 \left(1 + \frac{0.08}{4}\right)^{4t}$$
$$2.5 = \left(1 + \frac{0.08}{4}\right)^{4t}$$
$$\ln 2.5 = \ln \left(1 + \frac{0.08}{4}\right)^{4t}$$
$$\ln 2.5 = 4t \cdot \ln \left(1 + \frac{0.08}{4}\right)$$
$$t = \frac{\ln 2.5}{4 \ln \left(1 + \frac{0.08}{4}\right)} \approx 11.57 \text{ years}$$

(b) Using the same values but compounded continuously,

$$5,000 = 2,000e^{0.08t}$$
$$2.5 = e^{0.08t}$$
$$\ln 2.5 = \ln e^{0.08t}$$
$$\ln 2.5 = 0.08t$$
$$t = \frac{\ln 2.5}{0.08} \approx 11.45 \text{ years}$$

59. The present value of $10,000 payable after 10 years

(a) at 7% compounded monthly is

$$P = B \left(1 + \frac{r}{k}\right)^{-kt}$$
$$= 10,000 \left(1 + \frac{0.07}{12}\right)^{-12(10)}$$
$$\approx \$4,975.96$$

(b) at 6% compounded continuously is

$$P = Be^{-rt}$$
$$= 10,000e^{-0.06(10)}$$
$$\approx \$5,488.12$$

61. When interest is compounded quarterly, the effective rate is
$$\left(1 + \frac{.0825}{4}\right)^4 - 1 \approx 0.08509, \text{ or } 8.51\%.$$
When interest is compounded continuously, the effective rate is

$e^{.082} - 1 \approx 0.08546$, or 8.55%.
So, 8.20% compounded continuously has the greater effective interest rate.

63. $P(t) = \dfrac{30}{1 + 2e^{-0.05t}}$

(a) When $t = 0$, $P(0) = 10$ so $(0, 10)$ is an intercept.
$P(t) = 0$ has no solution.
$\lim\limits_{x \to \infty} \dfrac{30}{1 + 2e^{-0.05t}} = 30$, so $y = 30$ is a horizontal asymptote.

$P'(t) = \dfrac{0 - (30)(-0.1e^{-0.05t})}{(1 + 2e^{-0.05t})^2} = \dfrac{3e^{-0.05t}}{(1 + 2e^{-0.05t})^2}$

Since $3e^{-0.05t}$ is never zero, $P'(t)$ is never zero. Further, $P'(t) > 0$ for all t, so P is always increasing. Using logarithmic differentiation,

$\ln P'(t) = \ln \left[\dfrac{3e^{-0.05t}}{(1 + 2e^{-0.05t})^2} \right]$

$= \ln 3 + \ln e^{-0.05t} - \ln(1 + 2e^{-0.05t})^2$

$= \ln 3 - 0.05t - 2\ln(1 + 2e^{-0.05t})$

$\dfrac{P''(t)}{P(t)} = -0.05 - 2 \cdot \dfrac{-0.1e^{-0.05t}}{1 + 2e^{-0.05t}}$

$P''(t) = \left[\dfrac{-0.05(1 + 2e^{-0.05t}) + 0.2e^{-0.05t}}{1 + 2e^{-0.05t}} \right] P'(t)$

$= \left[\dfrac{-0.05 + 0.1e^{-0.05t}}{1 + 2e^{-0.05t}} \right] \left[\dfrac{3e^{-0.05t}}{(1 + 2e^{-0.05t})^2} \right]$

$= (-0.05 + 0.1e^{-0.05t}) \left[\dfrac{3e^{-0.05t}}{(1 + 2e^{-0.05t})^3} \right]$

So $P''(t) = 0$ when

$-0.05 + 0.1e^{-0.05t} = 0$

$e^{-0.05t} = 0.5$

$-0.05t = 0.5$, or

$t = \dfrac{\ln 0.5}{-0.05} = 20 \ln 2 \approx 13.9$

When $0 < t < 13.9$, $P''(t) > 0$, so P is concave up. When $t > 13.9$, $P''(t) < 0$ so P is concave down. The point $(13.9, 15.0)$ is an inflection point.

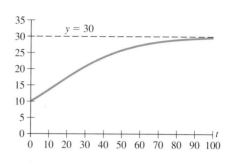

(b) The current population is
$P(0) = \dfrac{30}{1 + 2e^0} = 10$, or 10,000,000 people.

(c) The population in 20 years will be
$P(20) = \dfrac{30}{1 + 2e^{-0.05(20)}}$
$= \dfrac{30}{1 + 2e^{-1}} = 17.2835$
or 17,283,500 people.

(d) $\lim\limits_{x \to \infty} \dfrac{30}{1 + 2e^{-0.05t}} = 30$
So, the population approaches 30,000,000 in the long run.

65. (a) The rate of change of the carbon monoxide level t years from now is $Q'(t) = 0.12e^{0.03t}$. The rate two years from now is $Q'(2) = 0.12e^{0.03(2)} = 0.13$ parts per million per year.

(b) The percentage rate of change of the carbon monoxide level t years from now is
$100 \left[\dfrac{Q'(t)}{Q(t)} \right] = 100 \left(\dfrac{0.12e^{0.03t}}{4e^{0.03t}} \right) = 3\%$ per year, which is a constant (independent of time).

67. $V(t) = 2{,}000e^{\sqrt{2t}}$
The percentage rate of change of the value of the asset is

$100 \dfrac{V'(t)}{V(t)} = 100 \dfrac{2000e^{\sqrt{2t}} \left[\frac{1}{2}(2t)^{-1/2}(2) \right]}{2{,}000e^{\sqrt{2t}}}$

$= 1000 \dfrac{1}{\sqrt{2t}}$

Which will equal the prevailing interest rate when

$$\frac{1}{\sqrt{2t}} = 0.05$$

$$\sqrt{2t} = \frac{1}{0.05} = 20$$

$$2t = 400$$

$$t = 200 \text{ years}$$

When $0 < t < 200$, the percentage rate is more than the prevailing rate. When $t > 200$, the prevailing rate is greater, so, it's best to sell the asset after 200 years.

69. $Q(t) = Q_0 e^{-kt}$

(a) When $t = \lambda$, $Q(\lambda) = \frac{1}{2}Q_0$, so

$$\frac{1}{2}Q_0 = Q_0 e^{-k(\lambda)}$$

$$\frac{1}{2} = e^{-k(\lambda)}$$

$$\ln\frac{1}{2} = -k\lambda, \text{ or}$$

$$k = \frac{\ln\frac{1}{2}}{-\lambda} = \frac{\ln 2}{\lambda}$$

So, $Q(t) = Q_0 e^{-\left(\frac{\ln 2}{\lambda}\right)t}$

(b)
$$Q_0 e^{-\left(\frac{\ln 2}{\lambda}\right)t} = Q_0(0.5)^{kt}$$

$$e^{-\left(\frac{\ln 2}{\lambda}\right)t} = (0.5)^{kt}$$

$$-\frac{\ln 2}{\lambda}t = kt \ln 0.5$$

$$k = \frac{-\ln 2}{\lambda \ln 0.5} = \frac{\ln\frac{1}{2}}{\lambda \ln\frac{1}{2}} = \frac{1}{\lambda}$$

71. $R(t) = R_0 e^{-\left(\frac{\ln 2}{5,730}\right)t}$

Since the Bronze age began about 5,000 years ago, the maximum percentage is

$$\frac{R(5,000)}{R_0} = \frac{R_0 e^{-(\ln 2/5,730)(5,000)}}{R_0}$$

$$\approx 0.5462, \text{ or } 54.62\%.$$

73. $T(t) = 35e^{-0.32t}$

$27 = 35e^{-0.32t}$ or $t = 0.811 \text{ min}$.

Rescuers have about 49 seconds before the girl looses consciousness.

$$\frac{dT}{dt} = -35(0.32)e^{-0.32t}$$

So, when $t = 0.811$,

$$\frac{dT}{dt} = (-35)(0.32)(e^{-0.32(0.811)}) \approx -8.64$$

So, the girl's temperature is dropping at a rate of 8.64 °C per minute.

75. $C(t) = Ate^{-kt}$

(a)
$$C'(t) = A\left[(t)(-ke^{-kt}) + (e^{-kt})(1)\right]$$

$$= Ae^{-kt}(-kt + 1)$$

So, $C'(t) = 0$ when $-kt + 1 = 0$, or $t = \frac{1}{k}$

When $0 < t < \frac{1}{k}$, $C'(t) > 0$, so C is increasing

$t > \frac{1}{k}$, $C'(t) < 0$, so C is decreasing.

So, the maximum occurs when $t = \frac{1}{k}$. Since the maximum occurs after 2 hours,

$$2 = \frac{1}{k}, \text{ or } k = \frac{1}{2}$$

The maximum is 10, so

$$10 = A(2)e^{-\frac{1}{2}(2)}, \text{ or}$$

$$A = 5e$$

(b) To find when the concentration falls to 1 microgram / ml,

$$C(t) = 5ete^{-0.5t}$$

$$5ete^{-0.5t} = 1$$

$$5ete^{-0.5t} - 1 = 0$$

Press $\boxed{y=}$ and input
$5e \wedge (1)xe \wedge (-.5x) - 1$ for $y_1 =$.
Use window dimensions of
$[-5, 20]2$ by $[-10, 10]1$
Press $\boxed{\text{graph}}$.

Press 2nd calc and use the zero function to find $t \approx 9.78$ hours.

77. $P(t) = \frac{40}{1+Ce^{-kt}}$

Let $t = 0$ in the year 1960. Then,

$$P(0) = \frac{40}{1+Ce^{-k(0)}}$$

$$3 = \frac{40}{1+C}$$

$$1 + C = \frac{40}{3}$$

$$C = \frac{37}{3}$$

and $P(t) = \frac{40}{1+\frac{37}{3}e^{-kt}}$

In the year 1975, $t = 15$ and $P(15) = 4$ billion, so

$$4 = \frac{40}{1+\frac{37}{3}e^{-k(15)}}$$

$$1 + \frac{37}{3}e^{-15k} = 10$$

$$e^{-15k} = \frac{27}{37}$$

$$\ln e^{-15k} = \ln\frac{27}{37}$$

$$-15k = \ln\frac{27}{37}$$

$$k = \frac{\ln\frac{27}{37}}{-15} \approx 0.0210$$

The predicted population in 2000, when $t = 40$, would be

$$P(40) = \frac{40}{1+\frac{37}{3}e^{-0.0210(40)}}$$

$$\approx 6.3 \text{ billion people}$$

79. $pH = -\log_{10}[H_3O^+]$
For milk and lime,
$pHm = 3pH_l$.
For lime and orange,

$pH_l = \frac{1}{2}pH_0$.
If $pH_0 = 3.2$,
$pH_l = \frac{1}{2}(3.2) = 1.6$
Then,

$$1.6 = -\log_{10}[H_3O^+]_l$$

$$-1.6 = \log_{10}[H_3O^+]_l$$

$$10^{-1.6} = 10^{\log_{10}[H_3O^+]_l} \text{ or}$$

$$[H_3O^+]_l = 10^{-1.6} \approx 0.0251$$

81. (a) $D(t) = (D_0 - 0.00046)e^{-0.162t} + 0.00046$
With

$D_0 = 0.008$,

$D(10) = (0.008 - 0.00046)e^{-0.162(10)} + 0.00046$
$= 0.00195$, or 1.95 deaths per 1,000 women.

$D(25) = 0.000590$, or 0.59 deaths per 1,000 women.

(b) When $t = 0$, $D(0) = 0.008$ so $(0, 0.008)$ is an intercept.
When $D(t) = 0$, $0.00754e^{-0.162t} + 0.00046 = 0$
$e^{-0.162t} = -0.061008$, which has no solution.
$D'(t) = -0.00122e^{-0.162t}$
So $D'(t)$ is never zero. Further, $D'(t) < 0$ for all t, so D is always decreasing.
$D''(t) = 0.000198e^{-0.162t}$
$D''(t)$ is never zero. Further, $D''(t) > 0$ for all t, so D is always concave up.

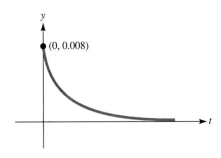

83. $R(t) = R_0 e^{-\left(\frac{\ln 2}{5,730}\right)t}$

(a) $R(3.8 \times 10^6) = R_0 e^{-\left(\frac{\ln 2}{5,730}\right)(3.8 \times 10^6)}$
$= R_0 e^{-459.7}$

Note: different calculators evaluate $e^{-459.7}$ differently; as a result, you may get 0 or you may get $\dfrac{1}{(2.3)^{200}}$. In either case, $R(3.8 \times 10^6) \approx 0$. Since $\lim\limits_{t \to +\infty} e^{-t} = 0$, we can't distinguish ages for large values of t.

(b) Writing Exercise—Answers will vary.

85. $P(t) = \dfrac{202.31}{1 + e^{3.938 - 0.314t}}$

(a) To use this formula to compute the population of US for the years 1790, 1800, 1830, 1860, 1880, 1900, 1920, 1940, 1960, 1980, 1990, and 2000,
Press $\boxed{y=}$ and input $P(t)$ for $y_1 =$.
Press $\boxed{\text{2nd}}$ $\boxed{\text{tblset}}$ and use Tblstart $= 0$, ΔTbl $= 1$, auto independent and auto dependent.
Press $\boxed{\text{2nd}}$ $\boxed{\text{table}}$.
Given below are the parts of the table corresponding to the years above.

Year	t	Population (in millions)
1790	0	3.8671
1800	1	5.2566
1830	4	12.957
1860	7	30.207
1880	9	50.071
1900	11	77.142
1920	13	108.43
1940	15	138.37
1960	17	162.29
1980	19	178.78
1990	20	184.57
2000	21	189.03

(b) Press $\boxed{y=}$ and input $P(t)$ for $y_1 =$.
Use window dimensions [0,28]4 by [0,200]25
Press $\boxed{\text{graph}}$.
The rate the population is growing is given by
$$P'(t) = \dfrac{63.52534 e^{3.938 - 0.314t}}{(1 + e^{3.938 - 0.314t})^2}$$
Press $\boxed{y=}$ and input $P'(t)$ for $y_2 =$.
Deselect $y_1 =$ so only $P'(t)$ is active.
Use window dimensions [0, 28]4 by [0, 20]2

Use the maximum function under the calc menu to find that the maximum of $P'(t)$ occurs at $x \approx 12.5$. So, the population is growing most rapidly when $t = 12.5$ or in 1915.

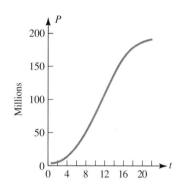

(c) Writing Exercise—Answers will vary.

87. To draw graphs of $y = \sqrt{3^x}$ $y = \sqrt{3^{-x}}$ and $y = 3^{-x}$ on the same axes,
Press $\boxed{y=}$ and input $\sqrt{\ }(3 \wedge x)$ for $y_1 =$, $\sqrt{\ }(3 \wedge (-x))$ for $y_2 =$, and $3 \wedge (-x)$ for $y_3 =$.
Use window dimensions $[-3, 3]1$ by $[-3, 3]1$.
Press $\boxed{\text{graph}}$.
The graph of $y = \sqrt{3^{-x}}$ is a reflection of the graph of $y = \sqrt{3^x}$ across the y-axis. The graph of $y = \sqrt{3^{-x}}$ is the graph of $y = 3^{-x}$ vertically compressed. Similarly, the graph of $y = \sqrt{3^x}$ is vertically compressed in addition to being reflected across the y-axis.

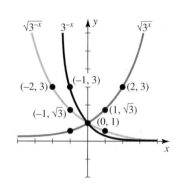

89. Using the conversion formula for logarithms, we will change all logarithms to natural logarithms:

$$\log_5(x+5) - \log_2 x - \log_{10}(x^2+2x)^2 = 0$$

$$\frac{\ln(x+5)}{\ln 5} - \frac{\ln(x)}{\ln 2} - \frac{\ln(x^2+2x)^2}{\ln 10} = 0$$

Press $\boxed{y=}$ and input
$\ln(x+5)/\ln(5) - \ln(x)/\ln(2) - \ln\left((x^2+2x)^2\right)/\ln(10)$ for $y_1 =$.
Press $\boxed{\text{graph}}$.
Use the zero function under the calc menu to find that $x \approx 1.066$ is a root. There is no other real root because x^2 increases much more rapidly than any other argument, making $y_1 =$ monotonically decreasing.

91. To make a table for $\left(\sqrt{n}\right)^{\sqrt{n+1}}$ and $\left(\sqrt{n+1}\right)^{\sqrt{n}}$ with $n = 8, 9, 12, 20, 25, 31, 37, 38, 43, 50, 100,$ and $1,000$, press $\boxed{y=}$ and input $\sqrt{n} \wedge \sqrt{n+1}$ for $y_1 =$ and $\sqrt{n+1} \wedge \sqrt{n}$ for $y_2 =$.
Press $\boxed{\text{2nd}}$ $\boxed{\text{tblset}}$ and use ask independent and auto dependent.
Press $\boxed{\text{2nd}}$ $\boxed{\text{table}}$ and input each value of n given.

n	$\left(\sqrt{n}\right)^{\sqrt{n+1}}$	$\left(\sqrt{n+2}\right)^{\sqrt{n}}$
8	22.63	22.36
9	32.27	31.62
12	88.21	85.00
20	957.27	904.84
25	3,665	3,447
31	16,528	15,494
37	68,159	63,786
38	85,679	80,166
43	261,578	244,579
50	1.17×10^6	1.09×10^6
1000	1.1×10^{10}	1.1×10^{10}
1000	2.9×10^{47}	2.8×10^{47}

$$\left(\sqrt{n}\right)^{\sqrt{n+1}} \geq \left(\sqrt{n+1}\right)^{\sqrt{n}}$$

This inequality holds for all $n \geq 8$. To confirm, since $(n+1)^{\sqrt{n}} \leq (n+1)^{\sqrt{n+1}}$

$$\lim_{n\to\infty} \frac{(n+1)^{\sqrt{n}}}{n^{\sqrt{n+1}}} \leq \lim_{n\to\infty} \frac{(n+1)^{\sqrt{n+1}}}{n^{\sqrt{n+1}}}$$

$$\leq \lim_{n\to\infty} \left(\frac{n+1}{n}\right)^{\sqrt{n+1}}$$

$$\leq \lim_{n\to\infty} e^{\ln\left(\frac{n+1}{n}\right)^{\sqrt{n+1}}}$$

$$\leq \lim_{n\to\infty} e^{\sqrt{n+1}\ln\left(\frac{n+1}{n}\right)}$$

$$\leq \lim_{n\to\infty} e^{[\ln(n+1)/n)/(n+1)^{-1/2}]}$$

$$\leq e^{\lim_{n\to\infty} \frac{\ln\left(\frac{n+1}{n}\right)}{(n+1)^{-1/2}}}$$

Using l'Hopital's rule,

$$\leq e^{\lim_{n\to\infty} \frac{\left(\frac{n}{n+1}\right)\frac{n(1)-(n+1)(1)}{n^2}}{-\frac{1}{2}(n+1)^{-3/2}(1)}}$$

$$\leq e^{\lim_{n\to\infty} \frac{-\frac{1}{n}}{-\frac{1}{2}(n+1)^{-3/2}(n+1)}}$$

$$\leq e^{\lim_{n\to\infty} \frac{2(n+1)^{1/2}}{n}}$$

Using l'Hopital's rule again,

$$\leq e^{\lim_{n\to\infty} \frac{1}{(n+1)^{1/2}}}$$

$$\leq e^0$$

$$\leq 1$$

Since the ratio of $(n+1)^{\sqrt{n}}$ to $n^{\sqrt{n+1}}$ is less than or equal to one,

$$(n+1)^{\sqrt{n}} \leq n^{\sqrt{n+1}}.$$

Chapter 5

Integration

5.1 Antidifferentiation; the Indefinite Integral

1.
$$I = \int -3\,dx = -3x + C.$$

3.
$$I = \int x^5\,dx = \frac{x^6}{6} + C.$$

5.
$$I = \int \frac{1}{x^2}\,dx = \int x^{-2}\,dx$$
$$= -x^{-1} + C = -\frac{1}{x} + C.$$

7.
$$I = \int \frac{2}{\sqrt{t}}\,dt = 2\int t^{-1/2}\,dt$$
$$= 2\frac{t^{1/2}}{1/2} + C$$
$$= 4t^{\frac{1}{2}} + C = 4\sqrt{t} + C.$$

9.
$$I = \int u^{-2/5}\,du$$
$$= \frac{u^{3/5}}{3/5} + C = \frac{5}{3}u^{3/5} + C.$$

11.
$$I = \int (3t^2 - \sqrt{5t} + 2)\,dt$$
$$= 3\int t^2\,dt - \sqrt{5}\int t^{1/2}\,dt + 2\int dt$$
$$= 3\left(\frac{t^3}{3}\right) - \sqrt{5}\left(\frac{t^{3/2}}{\frac{3}{2}}\right) + 2t + C$$
$$= t^3 - \frac{2\sqrt{5}}{3}t^{3/2} + 2t + C.$$

13.
$$I = \int \left(3\sqrt{y} - 2y^{-3}\right)\,dy$$
$$= 3\int y^{1/2}\,dy - 2\int y^{-3}\,dy$$
$$= 3\frac{y^{3/2}}{3/2} - 2\frac{y^{-2}}{-2} + C$$
$$= 2y^{3/2} + y^{-2} + C$$
$$= 2y^{3/2} + \frac{1}{y^2} + C.$$

15.
$$I = \int \left(\frac{e^x}{2} + x\sqrt{x}\right)\,dx$$
$$= \frac{1}{2}\int e^x\,dx + \int x^{3/2}\,dx$$
$$= \frac{1}{2}e^x + \frac{x^{5/2}}{5/2} + C$$
$$= \frac{e^x}{2} + \frac{2}{5}x^{5/2} + C.$$

17.
$$I = \int u^{1.1}\left(\frac{1}{3u} - 1\right)\,du$$
$$= \int \left(\frac{u^{1.1}}{3u} - u^{1.1}\right)\,du$$
$$= \int \left(\frac{u^{0.1}}{3} - u^{1.1}\right)\,du$$
$$= \frac{1}{3}\int u^{0.1}\,du - \int u^{1.1}\,du$$
$$= \frac{1}{3}\cdot\frac{u^{1.1}}{1.1} - \frac{u^{2.1}}{2.1} + C$$
$$= \frac{u^{1.1}}{3.3} - \frac{u^{2.1}}{2.1} + C.$$

19.

$$I = \int \frac{x^2 + 2x + 1}{x^2} \, dx$$

$$= \int \left(1 + \frac{2}{x} + \frac{1}{x^2}\right) dx$$

$$= \int dx + 2 \int \frac{1}{x} \, dx + \int x^{-2} \, dx$$

$$= x + 2 \ln |x| + \frac{x^{-1}}{-1} + C$$

$$= x + 2 \ln |x| - \frac{1}{x} + C$$

$$= x + \ln x^2 - \frac{1}{x} + C.$$

21.

$$I = \int (x^3 - 2x^2)\left(\frac{1}{x} - 5\right) dx$$

$$= \int (x^2 - 2x - 5x^3 + 10x^2) \, dx$$

$$= \int \left(-5x^3 + 11x^2 - 2x\right) dx$$

$$= -5 \int x^3 \, dx + 11 \int x^2 \, dx - 2 \int x \, dx$$

$$= -\frac{5x^4}{4} + \frac{11x^3}{3} - \frac{2x^2}{2} + C$$

$$= -\frac{5}{4}x^4 + \frac{11}{3}x^3 - x^2 + C.$$

23.

$$I = \int \sqrt{t}(t^2 - 1) \, dt$$

$$= \int (t^{5/2} - t^{1/2}) \, dt$$

$$= \int t^{5/2} \, dt - \int t^{1/2} \, dt$$

$$= \frac{2t^{7/2}}{7} - \frac{2t^{3/2}}{3} + C$$

$$= \frac{2}{7}t^{7/2} - \frac{2}{3}t^{3/2} + C.$$

25.

$$I = \int (e^t + 1)^2 \, dt$$

$$= \int (e^{2t} + 2e^t + 1) \, dt$$

$$= \int e^{2t} \, dt + 2 \int e^t \, dt + \int dt$$

$$= \frac{1}{2}e^{2t} + 2e^t + t + C.$$

27.

$$I = \int \left(\frac{1}{3y} - \frac{5}{\sqrt{y}} + e^{-y/2}\right) dy$$

$$= \frac{1}{3} \int \frac{1}{y} \, dy - 5 \int y^{-1/2} \, dy + \int e^{-\frac{1}{2}y} \, dy$$

$$= \frac{1}{3} \ln |y| - 5\frac{y^{1/2}}{1/2} + \frac{1}{-1/2}e^{-\frac{1}{2}y} + C$$

$$= \frac{1}{3} \ln |y| - 10\sqrt{y} - 2e^{-y/2} + C.$$

29.

$$I = \int t^{-1/2}(t^2 - t + 2) \, dt$$

$$= \int (t^{3/2} - t^{1/2} + 2t^{-1/2}) \, dt$$

$$= \int t^{3/2} \, dt - \int t^{1/2} \, dt + 2 \int t^{-1/2} \, dt$$

$$= \frac{t^{5/2}}{5/2} - \frac{t^{3/2}}{3/2} + 2\frac{t^{1/2}}{1/2} + C$$

$$= \frac{2}{5}t^{5/2} - \frac{2}{3}t^{3/2} + 4t^{1/2} + C.$$

31.

$$\frac{dy}{dx} = 3x - 2$$

$$\int \frac{dy}{dx} \, dx = \int (3x - 2) \, dx$$

$$\int \frac{dy}{dx} \, dx = 3 \int x \, dx - 2 \int dx$$

$$y = 3\frac{x^2}{2} - 2x + C$$

$$y = \frac{3}{2}x^2 - 2x + C$$

Since $y = 2$ when $x = -1$,

$$2 = \frac{3}{2}(-1)^2 - 2(-1) + C$$

$$2 = \frac{3}{2} + 2 + C, \text{ or}$$

$$C = -\frac{3}{2}$$

So, $y = \frac{3}{2}x^2 - 2x - \frac{3}{2}$.

33.

$$\frac{dy}{dx} = \frac{2}{x} - \frac{1}{x^2}$$

$$\int \frac{dy}{dx}\,dx = \int \left(\frac{2}{x} - \frac{1}{x^2}\right)dx$$

$$\int \frac{dy}{dx}\,dx = 2\int \frac{1}{x}\,dx - \int x^{-2}\,dx$$

$$y = 2\ln|x| - \frac{x^{-1}}{-1} + C$$

$$= \ln x^2 + \frac{1}{x} + C$$

Since $y = -1$ when $x = 1$,

$$-1 = \ln 1 + \frac{1}{1} + C$$

$$-1 = 0 + 1 + C, \text{ or}$$

$$C = -2$$

So, $y = \ln x^2 + \frac{1}{x} - 2$.

35.

$$f'(x) = 4x + 1$$

$$\int f'(x)\,dx = \int (4x + 1)\,dx$$

$$\int f'(x)\,dx = 4\int x\,dx + \int dx$$

$$f(x) = 4\frac{x^2}{2} + x + C$$

$$= 2x^2 + x + C$$

Since the function goes through the point $(1, 2)$,

$$2 = 2(1)^2 + 1 + C, \text{ or}$$

$$C = -1$$

So, $f(x) = 2x^2 + x - 1$.

37.

$$f'(x) = -x(x + 1) = -x^2 - x; (-1, 5)$$

$$\int f'(x)\,dx = \int (-x^2 - x)\,dx$$

$$= \int -x^2\,dx - \int x\,dx$$

$$= -\int x^2\,dx - \int x\,dx$$

$$f(x) = -\frac{x^3}{3} - \frac{x^2}{2} + C$$

Since the function goes through the point $(-1, 5)$,

$$5 = -\frac{(-1)^3}{3} - \frac{(-1)^2}{2} + C$$

$$5 = \frac{1}{3} - \frac{1}{2} + C, \text{ or}$$

$$C = \frac{31}{6}$$

So, $f(x) = -\frac{x^3}{3} - \frac{x^2}{2} + \frac{31}{6}$

39.

$$f'(x) = x^3 - \frac{2}{x^2} + 2$$

$$\int f'(x)\,dx = \int \left(x^3 - \frac{2}{x^2} + 2\right)dx$$

$$\int f'(x)\,dx = \int x^3\,dx - 2\int x^{-2}\,dx + 2\int dx$$

$$f(x) = \frac{x^4}{4} - 2\frac{x^{-1}}{-1} + 2x + C$$

$$= \frac{1}{4}x^4 + \frac{2}{x} + 2x + C$$

Since the function goes through the point $(1, 3)$,

$$3 = \frac{1}{4}(1)^4 + \frac{2}{1} + 2(1) + C, \text{ or}$$

$$C = -\frac{5}{4}$$

So, $f(x) = \frac{1}{4}x^4 + \frac{2}{x} + 2x - \frac{5}{4}$.

41.

$$f'(x) = e^{-x} + x^2$$

$$\int f'(x)\, dx = \int (e^{-x} + x^2)\, dx$$

$$\int f'(x)\, dx = \int e^{-x}\, dx + \int x^2\, dx$$

$$f(x) = \frac{1}{-1}e^{-x} + \frac{x^3}{3} + C$$

$$= -e^{-x} + \frac{1}{3}x^3 + C$$

Since the function goes through the point (0, 4),

$$4 = -e^0 + \frac{1}{3}(0) + C, \text{ or}$$

$$C = 5$$

So, $f(x) = -e^{-x} + \frac{1}{3}x^3 + 5$.

43.

$$C(q) = \int C'(q)\, dq$$

$$= \int (3q^2 - 24q + 48)\, dq$$

$$= 3\int q^2\, dq - 24\int q\, dq + 48\int dq$$

$$= 3\frac{q^3}{3} - 24\frac{q^2}{2} + 48q + C$$

$$= q^3 - 12q^2 + 48q + C$$

Since the cost is \$5,000 for producing 10 units,

$$5000 = (10)^3 - 12(10)^2 + 48(10) + C, \text{ or}$$

$$C = 4720$$

So, $C(q) = q^3 - 12q^2 + 48q + 4720$.

When 30 units are produced, the cost is

$$C(30) = (30)^3 - 12(30)^2 + 48(30) + 4720$$
$$= \$22,360.$$

45.

$$R'(q) = 100q^{-1/2}$$

$$\int R'(q)\, dq = \int 100q^{-1/2}\, dq = 100\int q^{-1/2}\, dq$$

$$R(q) = 100 \cdot 2q^{1/2} + R(0) = 200q^{1/2} + R(0)$$

$$C'(q) = 0.4q\, dq$$

$$\int C'(q)\, dq = \int 0.4q\, dq = 0.4\int q\, dq$$

$$C(q) = 0.4 \cdot \frac{q^2}{2} + C(0) = 0.2q^2 + C(0)$$

Now, profit = revenues − costs so

$$P(q) = R(q) - C(q)$$
$$= 200q^{1/2} + R(0) - 0.2q^2 - C(0)$$

When $q = 16$, $P(16) = 520$, so

$$520 = 200\sqrt{16} + R(0) - 0.2(16)^2 - C(0)$$
$$520 = 800 - 51.2 + R(0) - C(0)$$
$$-228.8 = R(0) - C(0)$$

This makes the profit function

$$P(q) = 200\sqrt{q} - 0.2q^2 - 228.8$$

When $q = 25$,

$$P(25) = 200\sqrt{25} - 0.2(25)^2 - 228.8$$
$$= \$646.20$$

47.

$$N(t) = \int N'(t)\, dt$$

$$= \int (154t^{2/3} + 37)\, dt$$

$$= 154\int t^{2/3}\, dt + 37\int dt$$

$$= 154\frac{t^{5/3}}{5/3} + 37t + C$$

$$= \frac{462}{5}t^{5/3} + 37t + C$$

Since there are no subscribers when $t = 0$,

$$C = 0$$

So, $N(t) = \frac{462}{5}t^{5/3} + 37t$.

Eight months from now, the number of subscribers will be

$$N(8) = \frac{462}{5}(8)^{5/3} + 37(8)$$

$$\approx 3{,}253 \text{ subscribers.}$$

49. Let $P(t)$ be the population of the town t months from now. Since

$$\frac{dP}{dt} = 4 + 5t^{2/3},$$

then, $P(t) = \displaystyle\int \frac{dP}{dt}\, dt$

$$= \int (4 + 5t^{2/3})\, dt$$

$$= 4 \int dt + 5 \int t^{2/3}\, dt$$

$$= 4t + 5\frac{t^{5/3}}{5/3} + C$$

$$= 4t + 3t^{5/3} + C$$

Since the population is 10,000 when $t = 0$,

$$10{,}000 = 4(0) + 3(0) + C, \text{ or}$$

$$C = 10{,}000$$

So, $P(t) = 4t + 3t^{5/3} + 10{,}000$.

When $t = 8$,

$$P(8) = 4(8) + 3(8)^{5/3} + 10{,}000$$
$$= 10{,}128 \text{ people.}$$

51. $\qquad M'(t) = 0.4t - 0.005t^2$

(a) $\qquad M(t) = \displaystyle\int M'(t)\, dt$

$$= \int (0.4t - 0.005t^2)\, dt$$

$$= 0.4 \int t\, dt - 0.005 \int t^2\, dt$$

$$= 0.4\frac{t^2}{2} - 0.005\frac{t^3}{3} + C$$

$$= 0.2t^2 - \frac{0.005}{3}t^3 + C$$

Since $M(t) = 0$ when $t = 0$, $C = 0$.

So, $M(t) = 0.2t^2 - \dfrac{0.005}{3}t^3$.

In ten minutes, Bob can memorize

$$M(10) = 0.2(10)^2 - \frac{0.005}{3}(10)^3$$

$$= 18\frac{1}{3} \text{ items.}$$

(b) $\qquad M(20) - M(10)$

$$= \left[0.2(20)^2 - \frac{0.005}{3}(20)^3\right] - 18\frac{1}{3}$$

$$= 66\frac{2}{3} - 18\frac{1}{3} = 48\frac{1}{3} \text{ items.}$$

53. $\qquad T'(t) = 7e^{-0.35t}$

(a) $\qquad T(t) = \displaystyle\int T'(t)\, dt$

$$= \int 7e^{-0.35t}\, dt$$

$$= 7 \int e^{-0.35t}\, dt$$

$$= 7 \cdot \frac{1}{-0.35}e^{-0.35t} + C$$

$$= -20e^{-0.35t} + C$$

Since the temperature was $-4°C$ when $t = 0$,

$$-4 = -20e^0 + C, \text{ or}$$

$$C = 16$$

So, $T(t) = -20e^{-0.35t} + 16$.

(b) After two hours,

$$T(2) = -20e^{-0.35(2)} + 16$$
$$\approx 6.07°C.$$

(c) For the temperature to reach 10°C,

$$10 = -20e^{-0.35t} + 16$$

$$6 = 20e^{-0.35t}$$

$$\frac{3}{10} = e^{-0.35t}$$

$$\ln \frac{3}{10} = \ln e^{-0.35t}$$

$$\ln \frac{3}{10} = -0.35t, \text{ or}$$

$$t - \frac{\ln \frac{3}{10}}{-0.35} = \frac{-20}{7} \ln \frac{3}{10}$$

$$= \frac{20}{7} \ln \frac{10}{3} \approx 3.44 \text{ hours.}$$

55.
$$R'(q) = 100 - 2q$$

(a) Since $P'(q) = R'(q)$,

$$P(q) = \int R'(q) \, dq$$

$$= \int (100 - 2q) \, dq$$

$$= 100 \int dq - 2 \int q \, dq$$

$$= 100q - 2\frac{q^2}{2} + C$$

$$= 100q - q^2 + C$$

Since the profit is $700 when 10 units are produced,

$$700 = 100(10) - (10)^2 + C, \text{ or}$$

$$C = -200$$

So, $P(q) = 100q - q^2 - 200$.

(b) Since $R'(q) = P'(q)$, to maximize P,

$$R'(q) = 0 \text{ when } 100 - 2q = 0, \text{ or } q = 50$$

Further, $R''(q) = -2$, so $R''(50) < 0$ and the maximum profit occurs when $q = 50$. The maximum profit is

$$P(50) = 100(50) - (50)^2 - 200$$

$$= \$2,300.$$

57.
$$c(x) = \int c'(x) \, dx$$

$$= \int (0.9 + 0.3\sqrt{x}) \, dx$$

$$= 0.9 \int dx + 0.3 \int x^{1/2} \, dx$$

$$= 0.9x + 0.3\frac{x^{3/2}}{3/2} + C$$

$$= 0.9x + 0.2x^{3/2} + C$$

Since the consumption is 10 billion when $x = 0$,

$$10 = 0.9(0) + 0.2(0) + C, \text{ or}$$

$$C = 10$$

So, $c(x) = 0.9x + 0.2x^{3/2} + 10$.

59. In the 0.7 seconds it takes for our spy to react, the car travels $(88)(0.7) = 61.6$ feet. Once he reacts, the speed of the car will be zero when

$$88 + \int -28 \, dt = 0$$

$$88 - 28t = 0$$

$$t = \frac{22}{7} \text{ seconds}$$

During this time, the car travels an additional

$$\int_0^{22/7} (88 - 28t) \, dt$$

$$= 88t - 14t^2 \Big|_0^{22/7}$$

$$= 88 \left(\frac{22}{7}\right) - 14 \left(\frac{22}{7}\right)^2 \approx 138.29 \text{ feet}$$

So, the car travels $61.6 + 138.29 = 199.89$ feet. If the camel remains in the road during the entire $\frac{22}{7} + 0.7 = 3.84$ seconds, the camel will be hit.

61.
$$f'(x) = 0.1(10 + 12x - 0.6x^2)$$

(a) To maximize the rate of learning,

$$f''(x) = 0.1(12 - 1.2x)$$

So $f''(x) = 0$ when $12 - 1.2x = 0$, or

$$x = 10$$

Further, $f''(x) = 0.1(-1.2) = -0.12$ so $f'''(10) < 0$ and the absolute maximum occurs when $x = 10$. The maximum rate is

$$f'(10) = 0.1[10 + 12(10) - 0.6(10)^2]$$
$$= 7 \text{ items per minute.}$$

(b) $f(x) = \displaystyle\int f'(x)\,dx$

$$= \int [0.1(10 + 12x - 0.6x^2)]\,dx$$

$$= \int (1 + 1.2x - 0.06x^2)\,dx$$

$$= \int dx + 1.2 \int x\,dx - 0.06 \int x^2\,dx$$

$$= x + 1.2\frac{x^2}{2} - 0.06\frac{x^3}{3} + C$$

$$= x + 0.6x^2 - 0.02x^3 + C$$

Since no items are memorized when $t = 0$,

$$C = 0$$

So, $f(x) = x + 0.6x^2 - 0.02x^3$.

(c) $\qquad f'(x) = 0.1(10 + 12x - 0.6x^2)$

$$= 1 + 1.2x - 0.06x^2$$

So, $f'(x) = 0$ when

$$x = \frac{-1.2 \pm \sqrt{(1.2)^2 - 4(-0.06)(1)}}{2(-0.06)}$$

or, $x \approx 20.8$ (rejecting the negative solution)

$f''(20.8) < 0$, so the absolute maximum is

$$f(20.8) = (20.8) + 0.6(20.8)^2 - 0.02(20.8)^3$$
$$\approx 100 \text{ items}$$

63. $\qquad v'(r) = -ar$

$$v(r) = \int v'(r)\,dr$$

$$= \int -ar\,dr = -a \int r\,dr$$

$$= -a\frac{r^2}{2} + C = -\frac{a}{2}r^2 + C$$

Since $v(R) = 0$,

$$0 = -\frac{a}{2}(R)^2 + C, \text{ or}$$

$$C = \frac{aR^2}{2}$$

So, $v(r) = -\dfrac{a}{2}r^2 + \dfrac{aR^2}{2} = \dfrac{a}{2}(R^2 - r^2)$.

65. $\qquad v(t) = 3 + 2t + 6t^2$

Since velocity is the derivative of distance,

$$s(t) = \int v(t)\,dt$$

$$= \int (3 + 2t + 6t^2)\,dt$$

$$= 3 \int dt + 2 \int t\,dt + 6 \int t^2\,dt$$

$$= 3t + 2\frac{t^2}{2} + 6\frac{t^3}{3} + C$$

$$= 3t + t^2 + 2t^3 + C$$

The distance traveled during the second minute is

$$s(2) - s(1)$$

$$= [3(2) + (2)^2 + 2(2)^3 + C] - [3(1) + (1)^2 + 2(1)^3 + C]$$

$$= 20 \text{ meters.}$$

67. $\displaystyle\int b^x\,dx = \int e^{x \ln b}\,dx = \int e^{(\ln b)x}\,dx$

$$= \frac{1}{\ln b}e^{x \ln b} + C = \frac{1}{\ln b}b^x + C$$

69. $\qquad a(t) = -23$

(a) Since acceleration is the derivative of velocity,

$$v(t) = \int -23\,dt$$

$$= -23t + C$$

The velocity when the brakes are applied is 67 ft/sec, so

$$67 = -23(0) + C, \text{ or } C = 67$$

$$\text{and } v(t) = -23t + 67$$

Since velocity is the derivative of distance,

$$s(t) = \int v(t)\,dt$$

$$= \int (-23t + 67)\,dt$$

$$= -23\int t\,dt + 67\int dt$$

$$= -23\frac{t^2}{2} + 67t + C$$

$$= -\frac{23}{2}t^2 + 67t + C$$

Since the distance is to be measured from the point the brakes are applied, $s(0) = 0$ and

$$0 = -\frac{23}{2}(0) + 67(0) + C,$$

$$\text{or } C = 0$$

So, $s(t) = -\frac{23}{2}t^2 + 67t$.

(b) To use the graphing utility to sketch graphs of $v(t)$ and $s(t)$ on same screen,
Press $\boxed{\text{y=}}$ and input $v(t)$ for $y_1 =$ and input $s(t)$ for $y_2 =$.
Use window dimensions [0, 5]1 by [0, 200]10.
Press $\boxed{\text{graph}}$.

(c) The car comes to a complete stop when $v(t) = 0$.
Press $\boxed{\text{trace}}$ and verify that the cross-hairs are on the line $y_1 = -23t + 67$.
Move along line until it appears to be at the t-intercept.
Use the zoom-in function under the zoom menu to find that the velocity $= 0$ when $t \approx 2.9$ seconds.

To find how far the car travels in 2.9 seconds, go back to the original graphing screen. Use the value function under the calc menu and input 2.9 for x and press enter. Use the ↑ arrow to verify that $y_2 = -\frac{23}{2}t^2 + 67t$ is displayed. The car travels 97.6 feet in 2.9 seconds.

To find how fast the car travels when $s = 45$ feet, trace along the parabola $s(t)$ and use the zoom-in function to find that it takes approximately

0.77 seconds and 5.05 seconds to travel 45 feet. Next, go back to the original graphing screen and use the value fucntion under the calc menu. Input $x = 0.77$ and verify $y_1 = -23t + 67$ is displayed. The car is traveling 49.2 feet/sec when it has traveled 45 feet. Repeat this process with $x = 5.05$ to find the velocity at 5.05 is 49.15 (decelerating).

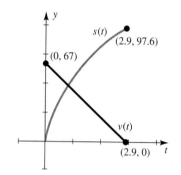

5.2   Integration by Substitution

1. **(a)** $u = 3x + 4$
   (b) $u = 3 - x$
   (c) $u = 2 - t^2$
   (d) $u = 2 + t^2$

3. Let $u = 2x + 6$. Then $du = 2\,dx$ or $dx = \dfrac{du}{2}$.

So $\displaystyle\int (2x + 6)^5\,dx = \frac{1}{2}\int u^5\,du$

$$= \frac{(2x + 6)^6}{12} + C.$$

5. Let $u = 4x - 1$. Then $du = 4\,dx$ or $dx = \dfrac{du}{4}$.

So $\displaystyle\int \sqrt{4x - 1}\,dx = \frac{1}{4}\int u^{1/2}\,du$

$$= \frac{1}{4}\frac{2u^{3/2}}{3} + C$$

$$= \frac{(4x - 1)^{3/2}}{6} + C.$$

7. Let $u = 1 - x$. Then $du = -dx$ or $dx = -du$.

So $\displaystyle\int e^{1-x}\, dx = -\int e^u\, du = -e^{1-x} + C$.

9. Let $u = x^2$. Then $\dfrac{du}{dx} = 2x$ or $\dfrac{1}{2}\, du = x\, dx$.

$$\int xe^{x^2}\, dx = \int e^{x^2} \cdot x\, dx$$

$$= \int e^u \cdot \frac{1}{2}\, du$$

$$= \frac{1}{2}\int e^u\, du = \frac{1}{2}e^{x^2} + C.$$

11. Let $u = t^2 + 1$. Then $\dfrac{du}{dt} = 2t$ or $\dfrac{1}{2}\, du = t\, dt$.

$$\int t(t^2 + 1)^5\, dt = \int (t^2 + 1)^5 t\, dt$$

$$= \int u^5 \cdot \frac{1}{2}\, du$$

$$= \frac{1}{2}\int u^5\, du = \frac{(t^2 + 1)^6}{12} + C.$$

13. Let $u = x^3 + 1$. Then $\dfrac{du}{dx} = 3x^2$ or $\dfrac{1}{3}\, du = x^2\, dx$.

$$\int x^2(x^3 + 1)^{3/4}\, dx = \int (x^3 + 1)^{3/4} x^2\, dx$$

$$= \int u^{3/4} \cdot \frac{1}{3}\, du = \frac{1}{3}\int u^{3/4}\, du$$

$$= \frac{4(x^3 + 1)^{7/4}}{21} + C.$$

15. Let $u = y^5 + 1$. Then $\dfrac{du}{dy} = 5y^4$, or $\dfrac{1}{5}\, du = y^4\, dy$.

$$\int \frac{2y^4}{y^5 + 1}\, dy = 2\int \frac{1}{y^5 + 1} y^4\, dy = 2\int \frac{1}{u} \cdot \frac{1}{5}\, du$$

$$= \frac{2}{5}\int \frac{1}{u}\, du = \frac{2}{5}\ln|y^5 + 1| + C.$$

17. Let $u = x^2 + 2x + 5$. Then $\dfrac{du}{dx} = 2x + 2$

$= 2(x + 1)$, or $\dfrac{1}{2}\, du = (x + 1)\, dx$.

$$\int (x + 1)(x^2 + 2x + 5)^{12}\, dx$$

$$= \int (x^2 + 2x + 5)^{12}(x + 1)\, dx$$

$$= \int u^{12} \cdot \frac{1}{2}\, du = \frac{1}{2}\int u^{12}\, du$$

$$= \frac{(x^2 + 2x + 5)^{13}}{26} + C.$$

19. Let $u = x^5 + 5x^4 + 10x + 12$. Then
$\dfrac{du}{dx} = 5x^4 + 20x^3 + 10 = 5(x^4 + 4x^3 + 2)$, or
$\dfrac{1}{5}\, du = (x^4 + 4x^3 + 2)\, dx$.

$$\int \frac{3x^4 + 12x^3 + 6}{x^5 + 4x^3 + 2}\, dx = \int \frac{3(x^4 + 4x^3 + 2)}{x^5 + 4x^3 + 2}\, dx$$

$$= 3\int \frac{1}{x^5 + 4x^3 + 2}(x^4 + 4x^3 + 2)\, dx$$

$$= 3\int \frac{1}{u} \cdot \frac{1}{5}\, du = \frac{3}{5}\int \frac{1}{u}\, du$$

$$= \frac{3}{5}\ln|x^5 + 5x^4 + 10x + 12| + C.$$

21. Let $t = u^2 - 2u + 6$. Then $\dfrac{dt}{du} = 2u - 2 = 2(u - 1)$,

or $\dfrac{1}{2}\, dt = (u - 1)\, du$.

$$\int \frac{3u - 3}{(u^2 - 2u + 6)^2}\, du = \int \frac{3(u - 1)}{(u^2 - 2u + 6)^2}\, du$$

$$= 3\int \frac{1}{(u^2 - 2u + 6)^2}(u - 1)\, du$$

$$= 3\int \frac{1}{t^2} \cdot \frac{1}{2}\, dt = \frac{3}{2}\int t^{-2}\, dt$$

$$= \frac{-3}{2(u^2 - 2u + 6)} + C.$$

23. Let $u = \ln 5x$. Then $\dfrac{du}{dx} = \dfrac{1}{5x} \cdot 5 = \dfrac{1}{x}$, or

$du = \dfrac{1}{x}\, dx$.

$$\int \frac{\ln 5x}{x}\, dx = \int \ln 5x \cdot \frac{1}{x}\, dx$$

$$= \int u\, du = \frac{(\ln 5x)^2}{2} + C.$$

25. Let $u = \ln x$. Then $\dfrac{du}{dx} = \dfrac{1}{x}$, or $du = \dfrac{1}{x}\, dx$.

$$\int \frac{1}{x(\ln x)^2}\, dx = \int \frac{1}{(\ln x)^2} \cdot \frac{1}{x}\, dx$$

$$= \int \frac{1}{u^2}\, du = -\frac{1}{\ln x} + C.$$

27. Let $u = x^2 + 1$. Then $\dfrac{du}{dx} = 2x$, or $\dfrac{1}{2}\, du = x\, dx$.

$$\int \frac{2x \ln(x^2 + 1)}{x^2 + 1}\, dx = 2 \int \frac{\ln(x^2 + 1)}{x^2 + 1} \cdot x\, dx$$

$$= 2 \int \frac{\ln u}{u} \cdot \frac{1}{2}\, du = \int \frac{\ln u}{u}\, du$$

Substitution must be used a second time. Let $t = \ln u$. Then $\dfrac{dt}{du} = \dfrac{1}{u}$, or $dt = \dfrac{1}{u}\, du$.

$$\int \frac{\ln u}{u}\, du = \int \ln u \cdot \frac{1}{u}\, du$$

$$= \int t\, dt = \frac{t^2}{2} + C$$

$$= \frac{(\ln u)^2}{2} + C = \frac{[\ln(x^2 + 1)]^2}{2} + C.$$

29. Let $u = e^x - e^{-x}$. Then $\dfrac{du}{dx} = e^x + e^{-x}$, or $du = (e^x + e^{-x})\, dx$.

$$\int \frac{e^x + e^{-x}}{e^x - e^{-x}}\, dx = \int \frac{1}{e^x - e^{-x}}(e^x + e^{-x})\, dx$$

$$= \int \frac{1}{u}\, du = \ln |e^x - e^{-x}| + C.$$

31. Let $u = 2x + 1$. Then $\dfrac{du}{dx} = 2$, or $\dfrac{1}{2}\, du = dx$.
Further, $x = \dfrac{u - 1}{2}$.

$$\int \frac{x}{2x + 1}\, dx = \frac{1}{4} \int \frac{u - 1}{u}\, du$$

$$= \frac{1}{4} \int \left(1 - \frac{1}{u}\right) du = \frac{1}{4} \int du - \frac{1}{4} \int \frac{1}{u}\, du$$

$$= \frac{1}{4} u - \frac{1}{4} \ln |u| + C = \frac{1}{4}(2x + 1) - \frac{1}{4} \ln |2x + 1| + C.$$

This can also be written as

$$= \frac{1}{2}x + \frac{1}{4} - \frac{1}{4} \ln |2x + 1| + C$$

$$= \frac{1}{2}x - \frac{1}{4} \ln |2x + 1| + C,$$

where the $\frac{1}{4}$ has been added to the constant C. (In mathematics, the same C is often used for the original constant and for the constant after it is changed.)

33. Let $u = 2x + 1$. Then $\dfrac{du}{dx} = 2$, or $\dfrac{1}{2}\, du = dx$.
Further, $x = \dfrac{u - 1}{2}$.

$$\int x\sqrt{2x - 1}\, dx = \frac{1}{4} \int (u - 1)u^{1/2}\, du$$

$$= \frac{1}{4} \int (u^{3/2} - u^{1/2})\, du$$

$$= \frac{1}{4} \left(\frac{2}{5}(2x + 1)^{5/2} - \frac{2}{3}(2x + 1)^{3/2}\right) + C$$

$$= \frac{1}{10}(2x + 1)^{5/2} - \frac{1}{6}(2x + 1)^{3/2} + C.$$

35. Let $u = \sqrt{x} + 1$. Then $\dfrac{du}{dx} = \dfrac{1}{2}x^{-1/2} = \dfrac{1}{2x^{1/2}}$, or
$2\, du = \dfrac{1}{\sqrt{x}}\, dx$.

$$\int \frac{1}{\sqrt{x}(\sqrt{x} + 1)}\, dx = \int \frac{1}{\sqrt{x} + 1} \cdot \frac{1}{\sqrt{x}}\, dx$$

$$= 2 \int \frac{1}{u}\, du = 2 \ln |\sqrt{x} + 1| + C$$

$$= 2 \ln(\sqrt{x} + 1) + C.$$

37. $y = \int \dfrac{dy}{dx}\, dx = \int (3 - 2x)^2\, dx$
Let $u = 3 - 2x$. Then, $\dfrac{du}{dx} = -2$, or $-\dfrac{1}{2}\, du = dx$.

Using substitution for the second term with $u = t - 5$, $du = dt$, $u_1 = -3$ and $u_2 = 6$,

$$= \frac{1}{9} \left[3t \Big|_2^{11} - \frac{1}{9} u^3 \Big|_{-3}^6 \right]$$

$$= \frac{1}{9} \left[(33 - 6) - \frac{1}{9}(216 + 27) \right]$$

$$= 0°C$$

(b) Need to find t when $T(t) = 0$, so

$$0 = -\frac{1}{3}(t - 5)^2$$

$$\frac{1}{3}(t - 5)^2 = 3$$

$$(t - 5)^2 = 9$$

$$t - 5 = \pm 3$$

$$t = 2.8$$

When $t = 2$, the time is 8:00 a.m. and when $t = 8$, the time is 2:00 p.m.

53. (a)

$$S_{av} = \frac{1}{6 - 1} \int_1^6 (t^3 - 10.5t^2 + 30t + 20) \, dt$$

$$= \frac{1}{5} \left(\frac{t^4}{4} - 3.5t^3 + 15t^2 + 20t \right) \Big|_1^6$$

$$= 39.25 \text{ mph.}$$

(b) Need to find t when $S(t) = 39.25$, so
$39.25 = t^3 - 10.5t^2 + 30t + 20$
$0 = t^3 - 10.5t^2 + 30t - 19.25$
To solve $t^3 - 10.5t^2 + 30t - 19.25 = 0$, press
$\boxed{y=}$ and enter $x \wedge 3 - 10.5x \wedge 2 + 30x - 19.25$
for $y_1 =$. Use zstandard under the zoom menu
and the graph of $y_1 =$ is displayed. The graph
has 3 x-intercepts. To find the first, use the zero
function under the calc menu. Enter a left bound
close to the first x-intercept, a right bound, and
a guess. The first x-intercept is approximately
$x \approx 0.902$. Repeat this process to find the other
two x-intercepts are $x = 3.5$ and $x \approx 6.10$. The
only intercept corresponding to a time between
1:00 and 6:00 p.m. is $x = 3.5$, which is 3:30
p.m.

55. (a)

$$M_{av} = \frac{1}{12 - 0} \int_0^{12} (M_0 + 50te^{-0.1t^2}) \, dt$$

$$= \frac{1}{12} \left[\int_0^{12} M_0 \, dt + 50 \int_0^{12} (te^{-0.1t^2}) \, dt \right]$$

Using substitution with $u = -0.1t^2$,

$$= \frac{1}{12} \left[\int_0^{12} M_0 \, dt - 250 \int_0^{-14.4} e^u \, du \right]$$

$$= \frac{1}{12} \left[\int_0^{12} M_0 \, dt + 250 \int_{-14.4}^0 e^u \, du \right]$$

$$= \frac{1}{12} \left[M_0 t \Big|_0^{12} + 250(e^u) \Big|_{-14.4}^0 \right]$$

$$= M_0 + 20.83 \text{ kilo-Joules per hour.}$$

(b) When $t = 0$, $M(0) = M_0$ so $(0, M_0)$ is an
intercept.
$\lim_{t \to +\infty} (M_0 + 50te^{-0.1t^2}) = M_0$, so $y = M_0$ is a
horizontal asymptote.

$$M'(t) = 50 \left[(t)(e^{-0.1t^2} \cdot -0.2t) + (e^{-0.1t^2})(1) \right]$$

$$= 50e^{-0.1t^2}(-0.2t^2 + 1).$$

So $M'(t) = 0$ when $-0.2t^2 + 1 = 0$, or $t = \sqrt{5}$.
The peak metabolic rate is

$$M\left(\sqrt{5}\right) = M_0 + 50\sqrt{5}e^{-0.5}$$

$$= M_0 + 50\sqrt{\frac{5}{e}}$$

$$M''(t) = 50 \left[(e^{-0.1t^2})(-0.4) \right.$$

$$\left. + (-0.2t^2 + 1)(e^{-0.1t^2} \cdot -0.2t) \right]$$

$$= -10e^{-0.1t^2} \left[2 + (-0.2t^2 + 1) \right]$$

So $M''(t) = 0$ when $3 - 0.2t^2 = 0$, or $t = \sqrt{15}$.

When $0 < t < \sqrt{5}$, $M'(t) > 0$ so m is increasing

$M''(t) < 0$ so m is concave down

$\sqrt{5} < t < \sqrt{15}$, $M'(t) < 0$ so m is decreasing

$M''(t) < 0$ so m is concave down

$t > \sqrt{15}$, $M'(t) < 0$ so m is decreasing

$M''(t) > 0$ so m is concave up.

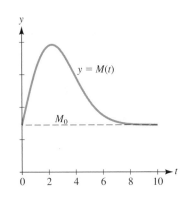

57.
$$GI_1 = 2 \int_0^1 \left(x - \frac{2}{3}x^3 - \frac{1}{3}x \right) dx$$

$$= 2 \left(\frac{x^2}{3} - \frac{x^4}{6} \right) \Big|_0^1 = \frac{1}{3} \approx 0.33$$

$$GI_2 = 2 \int_0^1 \left(x - \frac{5}{6}x^2 - \frac{1}{6}x \right) dx$$

$$= 2 \left(\frac{5}{12}x^2 - \frac{5}{18}x^3 \right) \Big|_0^1 = \frac{5}{18} \approx 0.28$$

$$GI_3 = 2 \int_0^1 \left(x - \frac{3}{5}x^4 - \frac{2}{5}x \right) dx$$

$$= 2 \left(\frac{3}{10}x^2 - \frac{3}{25}x^5 \right) \Big|_0^1 = \frac{9}{25} = 0.36$$

So, football is the most equitable, basketball is the least equitable.

59.
$$\text{Excess} = \int_0^{10} \left(10e^{0.02t} - \frac{20e^{0.02t}}{1 + e^{0.02t}} \right) dt$$

$$= 10 \int_0^{10} e^{0.02t} dt - 20 \int_0^{10} \frac{e^{0.02t}}{1 + e^{0.02t}} dt$$

Using substitution with $u = 1 + e^{0.02t}$,

$$= 10 \int_0^{10} e^{0.02t} dt - 1{,}000 \int_2^{1+e^{0.2}} \frac{1}{u} du$$

$$= 500(e^{0.02t}) \Big|_0^{10} - 1{,}000(\ln |u|) \Big|_2^{1+e^{0.2}}$$

$$\approx 5.710, \text{ or } 5{,}710 \text{ people.}$$

61.   Total cost = cost of cabin + cost of land

cost of cabin = (area of cabin)(price per sq. yard)

$$= (64)(2{,}000) = \$128{,}000$$

cost of land = (area of land)(price per sq. yard)

area of land = area under curve $-$ area of cabin

$$= \int_0^{15} 10e^{0.04x} dx - 64$$

$$= 250(e^{0.04x}) \Big|_0^{15} - 64 \approx 141.53$$

cost of land = (141.53)(800) = \$113,224

So, the total cost is \$241,224.

63. (a) $S = F'(M) = \frac{1}{3}(2kM - 3M^2)$

We need to maximize S.

$$F''(M) = \frac{1}{3}(2k - 6M)$$

So $F''(M) = 0$ when $2k - 6M = 0$, or $M = \frac{k}{3}$.

$F'''(M) = -2$, so $F''' \left(\frac{k}{3} \right) < 0$, so the absolute

maximum occurs when $M = \frac{k}{3}$.

(b)
$$F_{av} = \frac{1}{k/3 - 0} \int_0^{k/3} \frac{1}{3}(kM^2 - M^3) \, dM$$

$$= \frac{1}{k} \left(\frac{kM^3}{3} - \frac{M^4}{4} \right) \Big|_0^{k/3} = \frac{k^3}{108}$$

65. Press $\boxed{y=}$ and input $\sqrt{\frac{2}{5}x^2 - 2}$ for $y_1 =$,

input $-\sqrt{\frac{2}{5}x^2 - 2}$ for $y_2 =$,

and input $x \wedge 3 - 8.9x^2 + 26.7x - 27$ for $y_3 =$.

Use window dimensions $[-5, 5]1$ by $[-4, 4]0.5$
Press [graph].
Use trace and zoom-in to find the points of
intersection are $(4.2, 2.25)$ and $(2.34, -0.44)$.
An alternative to using trace and zoom is to use
the intersect function under the calc menu. To
find the first point, use ↑ and ↓ arrows to verify
$y_1 = \sqrt{\dfrac{2}{5}x^2 - 2}$ is displayed. Enter and value close
to the point of intersection.
Then, verify $y_3 = x^3 - 8.9x^2 + 26.7x - 27$ is
displayed and enter a value close and finally, enter a
guess. This gives the point $(4.2, 2.25)$
Repeat this process using $y_2 = -\sqrt{\dfrac{2}{5}x^2 - 2}$ and
$y_3 = x^3 - 8.9x^2 + 26.7x - 27$ to find the second
point $(2.34, -0.44)$.
To find the area bounded by the curves, we also
find the positive x-intercept of $\dfrac{x^2}{5} - \dfrac{y^2}{2} = 1$ to be
$x = 2.236$
The area is given by

$$\int_{2.236}^{2.34} y_1 - y_2 + \int_{2.34}^{4.2} y_1 - y_3 = \int_{2.236}^{2.34} y_1 - \int_{2.236}^{2.34} y_2$$

$$+ \int_{2.34}^{4.2} y_1 - \int_{2.34}^{4.2} y_3$$

Use the $\int f(x)\,dx$ function under the calc menu
making sure the correct y equation is displayed in
the upper left corner for each integral to find the
area is $0.03008441 - (-0.0300844) + 2.7254917 -$
$0.68880636 \approx 2.097$
An easier alternative to evaluating each separate
integral is to use the f_nInt function. From the
home screen, select f_nInt from the math menu and
enter $f_n\text{Int}(y_1 - y_2, x, 2.236, 2.34) + f_n\text{Int}(y_1 -$
$y_3, x, 2.34, 4.2)$ to find the area. You input the y
equations by pressing [vars] and selecting which y
equation you want from the function window under
y-vars.

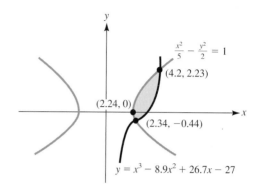

67. Let t_1 represent the starting time of an arbitrary time
interval and let t_2 represent the ending time. Also,
let $S(t)$ represent the distance function. Then, the
average value of the velocity is

$$\frac{S(t_2) - S(t_1)}{t_2 - t_1}$$

The averagae velocity is

$$\frac{1}{t_2 - t_1} \int_{t_1}^{t_2} v(t)\,dt$$

Since distance is the integral of velocity,

$$= \frac{1}{t_2 - t_1} \left[S(t) \Big|_{t_1}^{t_2} \right]$$

$$= \frac{1}{t_2 - t_1} \left[S(t_2) - S(t_1) \right]$$

$$= \frac{S(t_2) - S(t_1)}{t_2 - t_1}$$

5.5 Additional Applications to Business and Economics

1. (a)
$$D(q) = 2(64 - q^2)$$

$$A(6) = 2 \int_0^6 (64 - q^2)\,dq$$

$$= 2\left(64q - \frac{q^3}{3} \right) \Big|_0^6 = \$624$$

(b) The consumer's willingness to spend in part (a) is the area under the demand curve from $q = 0$ to $q = 6$.

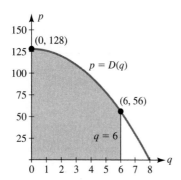

(b) The consumer's willingness to spend in part (a) is the area under the demand curve from $q = 0$ to $q = 10$.

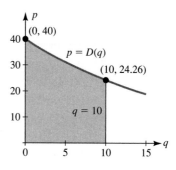

3. (a)

$$D(q) = \frac{400}{0.5q + 2}$$

$$A(12) = 2 \int_0^{12} \frac{400}{0.5q + 2} \, dq$$

$$= 800 \ln |0.5q + 2| \Big|_0^{12}$$

$$= 800 \ln 4 = \$1{,}109.04$$

(b) The consumer's willingness to spend in part (a) is the area under the demand curve from $q = 0$ to $q = 12$.

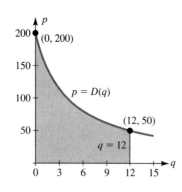

5. (a)

$$D(q) = 40e^{-0.05q}$$

$$A(10) = 40 \int_0^{10} e^{-0.05q} \, dq$$

$$= -800e^{-0.05q} \Big|_0^{10} = \$314.78$$

7. $D(q) = p_0$ if $110 = 2(64 - q^2)$ or $q = 3$. The consumer's surplus is

$$CS = \int_0^3 2(64 - q^2) \, dq - 3(110)$$

$$= 2 \left(64q - \frac{q^3}{3} \right) \Big|_0^3 - 330 = \$36$$

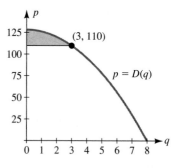

9. $D(q) = p_0$ if $31.15 = 40e^{-0.25}$ or $q = 5$. The consumer's surplus is

$$CS = \int_0^5 (40e^{-0.05q}) \, dq - 5(31.15)$$

$$= -800e^{-0.05q} \Big|_0^5 - 93.45$$

$$= \$21.20$$

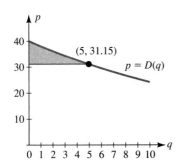

11. $S(q) = 0.3q^2 + 30$, $p_0 = S(4) = \$34.80$. The producer's surplus is

$$PS = 4(34.80) - \int_0^4 (0.3q^2 + 30)\, dq$$

$$= 139.20 - (0.1q^3 + 30q)\Big|_0^4$$

$$= \$12.80$$

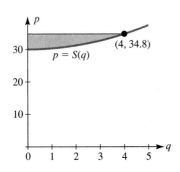

13. $S(q) = 10 + 15e^{0.03q}$, $p_0 = S(3) = \$26.41$. The producer's surplus is

$$PS = 3(26.41) - \int_0^3 (10 + 15e^{0.3q})\, dq$$

$$= 79.23 - (10q + 500e^{0.03q})\Big|_0^3$$

$$= \$2.14$$

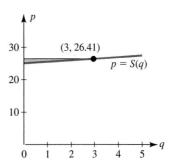

15. (a) The supply equals demand when

$$50 + \frac{2}{3}q^2 = 131 - \frac{1}{3}q^2$$

$$q^2 = 81, \text{ or } q = 9$$

So, the equilibrium price is

$$p_e = D(9) = 131 - \frac{1}{3}(9)^2 = \$104$$

(b) The corresponding consumer's surplus is

$$CS = \int_0^9 \left(131 - \frac{1}{3}q^2\right) dq - 9(104)$$

$$= \left(131q - \frac{1}{9}q^3\right)\Big|_0^9 - 936$$

$$= 162, \text{ or } \$162,000$$

since $q_0 = 9$ means 9,000 units will be supplied and the corresponding producer's surplus is

$$PS = (9)(104) - \int_0^9 \left(50 + \frac{2}{3}q^2\right) dq$$

$$= 936 - \left(50q + \frac{2}{9}q^3\right)\Big|_0^9$$

$$= 324, \text{ or } \$324,000$$

17. (a) The supply equals demand when

$$-0.3q^2 + 70 = 0.1q^2 + q + 20$$

$$0 = 0.4q^2 + q - 50$$

$$q = \frac{-1 \pm \sqrt{1 + 4(0.4)(50)}}{2(0.4)} = 10$$

So, the equilibrium price is

$$p_e = D(10) = -0.3(10)^2 + 70 = \$40$$

(b) The corresponding consumer's surplus is

$$CS = \int_0^{10} (-0.3q^2 + 70)\, dq - 10(40)$$

$$= (-0.1q^3 + 70q)\Big|_0^{10} - 400$$

$$= 200, \text{ or } \$200,000$$

since $q_0 = 10$ means 10,000 units will be supplied and the corresponding producer's surplus is

$$PS = 10(40) - \int_0^{10} (0.1q^2 + q + 20)\, dq$$

$$= 400 - \left(\frac{0.1}{3}q^3 + \frac{q^2}{2} + 20q\right)\Big|_0^{10}$$

$$\approx 116.67, \text{ or } \$116,670$$

19. (a) The supply equals demand when

$$\frac{1}{3}(q + 1) = \frac{16}{q + 2} - 3$$

$$\frac{(q + 1)}{3} = \frac{10 - 3q}{q + 2}$$

$$0 = q^2 + 12q - 28$$

$$q = \frac{-12 \pm \sqrt{(12)^2 + 4(1)(28)}}{2(1)}$$

or, $q = 2$

So, the equilibrium price is

$$p_e = D(2) = \frac{16}{2 + 2} - 3 = \$1$$

(b) The corresponding consumer's surplus is

$$\int_0^2 \left(\frac{16}{q + 2} - 3\right) dq - 2(1)$$

$$= (16 \ln|q + 2| - 3q)\Big|_0^2 - 2$$

$$= 3.09, \text{ or } \$3,090$$

since $q_0 = 2$ means 2,000 units will be supplied and the corresponding producer's surplus is

$$PS = 2(1) - \int_0^2 \frac{1}{3}(q + 1)\, dq$$

$$= 2 - \frac{1}{3}\left(\frac{q^2}{2} + q\right)\Big|_0^2$$

$$= 0.67, \text{ or } \$670$$

21. (a) The use of the machine will be profitable as long as the rate at which revenue is generated is greater than the rate at which costs accumulate. That is, until

$$R'(t) = C'(t)$$

$$7,250 - 18t^2 = 3,620 + 12t^2$$

or $t = 11$ years.

(b) The rate at which net earnings are generated by the machine is

$$R'(t) = C'(t)$$

So, the net earnings over the next 11 years is

$$\int_0^{11} \left[R'(t) - C'(t)\right] dt$$

$$= \int_0^{11} \left[(7,250 - 18t^2) - (3,620 + 12t^2)\right] dt$$

$$= \int_0^{11} (3,630 - 30t^2)\, dt$$

$$= (3,630t - 10t^3)\Big|_0^{11} = \$26,620$$

(c)

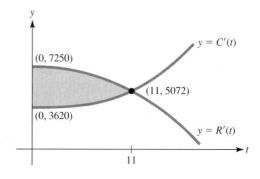

23. (a) The drive is profitable as long as rate of revenue exceeds weekly expenses.

$$e^{-0.3t} = \frac{593}{6,537}$$

$$= 0.090714,$$

$$-0.3t = \ln 0.090714,$$

$$\text{or } t = 8 \text{ weeks.}$$

(b) The net earnings during the first 8 weeks are

$$N = \int_0^8 (6{,}537e^{-0.3t} - 593)\, dt$$

$$= \left(-\frac{6{,}537}{0.3} e^{-0.3t} - 593t \right) \Big|_0^8$$

$$= \frac{6{,}537}{0.3}(1 - 0.09072) - (593)(8)$$

$$= 19{,}813.26 - 4{,}744 = \$15{,}069.26.$$

(c) In geometric terms, the net earnings in part (b) is the area of the region between the curves

$$y = R'(t) \text{ and } y = E'(t)$$

rewrite as: $y = R'(t) = 6{,}537e^{-0.3t}$

and $y = E'(t) = 593$

25.

$$\text{amount} = \int_0^{10} 1000e^{0.1(10-t)}\, dt$$

$$= 1000e^1 \int_0^{10} e^{-0.1t}\, dt$$

$$= -10{,}000e(e^{-0.1t}) \Big|_0^{10}$$

$$= -10{,}000e(e^{-1} - e^0)$$

$$\approx \$17{,}182.82$$

27. At age 60, Tom would have

$$\int_0^{35} 2500e^{0.05(35-t)}\, dt$$

$$= 2500e^{1.75} \int_0^{35} e^{-0.05t}\, dt$$

$$= -50{,}000e^{1.75}(e^{-0.05t}) \Big|_0^{35}$$

$$= -50{,}000e^{1.75}(e^{-1.75} - e^0)$$

$$\approx \$237{,}730.13$$

At age 65, Tom would have

$$\int_0^{40} 2500e^{0.05(40-t)}\, dt$$

$$= 2500e^2 \int_0^{40} e^{-0.05t}\, dt$$

$$= -50{,}000e^2(e^{-0.05t}) \Big|_0^{40}$$

$$= -50{,}000e^2(e^{-2} - e^0)$$

$$\approx \$319{,}452.80$$

29.

$$PV = \int_0^5 1200e^{-0.05t}\, dt$$

$$= -24{,}000(e^{-0.05t}) \Big|_0^5$$

$$= -24{,}000(e^{-0.25} - e^0)$$

$$\approx \$5{,}308.78$$

31. The net income of the first investment is

$$\int_0^5 15{,}000e^{0.06(5-t)}\, dt - 50{,}000$$

$$= 15{,}000e^{0.3} \int_0^5 e^{-0.06t}\, dt - 50{,}000$$

$$= 87{,}464.70 - 50{,}000 = \$37{,}464.70$$

The net income of the second investment is

$$\int_0^5 9000e^{0.06(5-t)}\, dt - 30{,}000$$

$$= 9000e^{0.3} \int_0^5 e^{-0.06t}\, dt - 30{,}000$$

$$= 52{,}478.82 - 30{,}000 = \$22{,}478.82$$

So, the first investment will generate more income.

33. (a) The profit function is

$$P(q) = (110 - q)q - (q^3 - 25q^2 + 2q + 3{,}000)$$

$$= 110q - q^2 - q^3 + 25q^2 - 2q - 3{,}000$$

$$= -q^3 + 24q^2 + 108q - 3{,}000$$

(b)
$$P'(q) = -3q^2 + 48q + 108$$
$$= -3(q^2 - 16q - 36)$$

So, $P'(q) = 0$ when

$$q = \frac{24 \pm \sqrt{24^2 + 3(108)}}{3} = 18$$

$$P''(q) = -6q + 48$$

and $P''(18) < 0$, so $q = 18$ corresponds to the maximum profit.

(c) When $q = 18$, the price is

$$p = 110 - 18 = 92$$

and the corresponding consumer's surplus is

$$CS = \int_0^{18} (110 - q)\, dq - 18(92)$$

$$= \left(110q - \frac{q^2}{2}\right)\bigg|_0^{18} - 1656$$

$$= \$162$$

35. (a)
$$P(t) = \int P'(t)\, dt$$

$$= \int 1.3e^{0.04t}\, dt$$

$$= 1.3 \int e^{0.04t}\, dt$$

$$= 32.5e^{0.04t} + C$$

When $t = 0$, $P(0) = 0$ so $C = -32.5$ and $P(t) = 32.5e^{0.04t} - 32.5$.
When $t = 3$, $P(3) = 32.5e^{0.04(3)} - 32.5 \approx 4.14$ billion barrels.
Over the following three years, the amount pumped is $P(6) - P(3)$, or

$$= (32.5e^{0.04(6)} - 32.5) - 4.14$$
$$\approx 4.68 \text{ billion barrels}$$

(b) The field stops operating when it uses up the 20 billion barrels it holds, or when

$$20 = 32.5e^{0.04t} - 32.5$$

$$\frac{21}{13} = e^{0.04t}$$

$$\ln \frac{21}{13} = \ln e^{0.04t}, \text{ or}$$

$$t - \frac{\ln \frac{21}{13}}{0.04}, \text{ or approximately 12 years}$$

(c)
$$PV = \int V(t)e^{-rt}\, dt$$

$$= \int 112 P'(t)e^{-rt}\, dt$$

$$= \int_0^{12} 112(1.3e^{0.04t})e^{-0.05t}\, dt$$

$$= 145.6 \int_0^{12} e^{-0.01t}\, dt$$

$$= -14{,}560 \left(e^{-0.01t}\right)\bigg|_0^{12}$$

$$= -14{,}560 \left(e^{-0.12} - e^0\right)$$

$$\approx 1{,}646.44 \text{ billion dollars}$$

(d) Writing exercise—Answers will vary.

37. (a)
$$P(t) = \int P'(t)\, dt$$

$$= \int 1.2e^{0.02t}\, dt$$

$$= 1.2 \int e^{0.02t}\, dt$$

$$= 60e^{0.02t} + C$$

When $t = 0$, $P(0) = 0$ so $C = -60$ and $P(t) = 60e^{0.02t} - 60$.
When $t = 3$, $P(3) = 60e^{0.02(3)} - 60$
$$\approx 3.71 \text{ billion barrels}$$
$$P(6) - P(3) = (60e^{0.02(6)} - 60) - 3.71$$
$$\approx 3.94 \text{ billion barrels}$$

(b)
$$12 = 60e^{0.02t} - 60$$

$$\frac{6}{5} = e^{0.02t}$$

$$\ln \frac{6}{5} = \ln e^{0.02t}$$

$$\ln \frac{6}{5} = 0.02t, \text{ or}$$

$$t = \frac{\ln \frac{6}{5}}{0.02}, \text{ or approximately 9.12 years}$$

(c) Since the annual revenue is $A(t)P(t)$, the rate of annual revenue is, using the product rule,

$$A(t)P'(t) + A'(t)P(t)$$

$$= (56e^{0.015t})(1.2e^{0.02t})$$

$$+ (60e^{0.02t} - 60)(0.39e^{0.015t})$$

$$= 67.2e^{0.035t} + 23.4e^{0.035t} - 23.4e^{0.015t}$$

$$= 90.6e^{0.035t} - 23.4e^{0.015t}$$

$$PV = \int_0^{9.12} (90.6e^{0.035t} - 23.4e^{0.015t})e^{-0.05t} \, dt$$

$$= \int_0^{9.12} \left(90.6e^{-0.015t} - 23.4e^{-0.035t}\right) dt$$

$$= \left[\frac{90.6}{-0.015}e^{-0.015t} + \frac{23.4}{0.035}e^{-0.035t}\right]_0^{9.12}$$

$$= \left[\frac{90.6}{-0.015}e^{-0.015(9.12)} + \frac{23.4}{0.035}e^{-0.035(9.12)}\right]$$

$$- \left[\frac{90.6}{-0.015}e^0 + \frac{23.4}{0.035}e^0\right]$$

$$\approx 589.55 \text{ billion years}$$

(d) Writing exercise—Answers will vary.

39.
$$PV = 10 \text{ million} = \int_0^6 Ae^{-0.05t} \, dt$$

$$10 = -20A(e^{-0.05t})\Big|_0^6$$

$$10 = -20A(e^{-0.3} - e^0)$$

$$\frac{1}{-2(e^{-0.3} - 1)} = A \approx 1.929148 \text{ million, or}$$

$$\$1,929,148$$

41. $A(t) = 10e^{1-0.05t}$

(a)
$$FV = \int_0^5 10e^{1-0.05t} \cdot e^{1-0.05(5-t)} \, dt$$

$$= 10 \int_0^5 e^{(1-0.05t)+(0.25-0.05t)} \, dt$$

$$= 10 \int_0^5 e^{1.25-0.1t} \, dt$$

$$= 10e^{1.25} \int_0^5 e^{-0.1t} \, dt$$

$$= 10e^{1.25} \left(-10e^{-0.1t}\Big|_0^5\right)$$

$$= -100e^{1.25} \left(e^{-0.1t}\Big|_0^5\right)$$

$$= -100e^{1.25} \left(e^{-0.5} - e^0\right)$$

$$= -100e^{1.25} \left(e^{0.5} - 1\right)$$

$$\approx 137.33429$$

or $137,334.29

(b)
$$PV \int_1^3 10e^{1-0.05t} \cdot e^{-0.05t} \, dt$$

$$= 10 \int_1^3 e^{(1-0.05t)-0.05t} \, dt$$

$$= 10 \int_1^3 e^{1-0.1t} \, dt$$

$$= 10e^1 \int_1^3 e^{-0.1t} \, dt$$

$$= 10e \left(-10e^{-0.1t}\Big|_1^3\right)$$

$$= -100e \left(e^{-0.1t}\Big|_1^3\right)$$

$$= -100e \left(e^{-0.3} - e^0\right)$$

$$= -100e \left(e^{-0.3} - 1\right)$$

$$\approx 70.45291$$

or $70,452.91

43. (a)
$$R'(t) = 300(18 + 0.3t^{1/2})$$

$$FV = \int_0^{36} 300(18 + 0.3t^{1/2})\, dt$$

$$= 300 \int_0^{36} (18 + 0.3t^{1/2})\, dt$$

$$= 300(18t + 0.2t^{3/2})\Big|_0^{36}$$

$$= 300(648 + 43.2) = \$207,360$$

(b) Writing exercise—Answers will vary.

45.
$$FV = \int_0^T f(t)e^{r(T-t)}\, dt$$

$$= \int_0^T Me^{r(T-t)}\, dt = \int_0^T Me^{rT} \cdot e^{-rt}\, dt$$

$$= Me^{rt} \int_0^T e^{-rt}\, dt$$

$$= \frac{Me^{rt}}{-r}\left(e^{-rt}\Big|_0^T\right)$$

$$= -\frac{Me^{rt}}{r}\left(e^{-rt} - e^0\right)$$

$$-\frac{M}{r}\left(e^0 - e^{rT}\right) = \frac{M}{r}\left(e^{rt} - 1\right)$$

5.6 Additional Applications to the Life and Social Sciences

1. After 5 months, the number of the original population surviving is

$$50,000e^{-0.1(5)}.$$

The number of new members surviving after 5 months is

$$\int_0^5 40e^{-0.1(5-t)}\, dt.$$

So, the total will be

$$= 50,000e^{-0.5} + 40e^{-0.5}\int_0^5 e^{0.1t}\, dt$$

$$= e^{-0.5}\left[50,000 + 400(e^{0.1t})\Big|_0^5\right]$$

$$\approx 30,484 \text{ members.}$$

3. After 3 years, the number of the original population surviving is

$$500,000e^{-0.011(3)}.$$

The number of new members surviving after 3 years is

$$\int_0^3 800e^{-0.011(3-t)}\, dt.$$

So, the total will be

$$500,000e^{-0.033} + 800e^{-0.033}\int_0^3 e^{0.011t}\, dt$$

$$= 800e^{-0.033}\left[625 + \frac{1}{0.011}(e^{0.011t})\Big|_0^3\right]$$

$$\approx 486,130 \text{ members}$$

5. After 8 years, the number of the original population surviving is $500,000e^{-0.013(8)}$

The number of new members surviving after 8 years is

$$\int_0^8 100e^{0.01t} - e^{-0.013(8-t)}dt$$

$$= 100\int_0^8 e^{0.01t - 0.104 + 0.013t}dt$$

$$= 100e^{-0.104}\int_0^8 e^{0.023t}dt$$

So, the total will be

$$500{,}000e^{-0.104} + 100e^{-0.104} \int_0^8 e^{0.023t}\,dt$$

$$= 100e^{-0.104}\left[5000 + \frac{1}{0.023}e^{0.023t}\Big|_0^8\right]$$

$$= 100e^{-0.104}\left[5000 + \frac{1000}{23}\left(e^{0.023t}\Big|_0^8\right)\right]$$

$$= 100{,}000e^{-0.104}\left[5 + \frac{1}{23}\left(e^{0.184} - e^0\right)\right]$$

$$= 100{,}000e^{-0.104}\left[5 + \frac{1}{23}\left(e^{0.184} - 1\right)\right]$$

$$\approx 451{,}404 \text{ members}$$

7. Volum of $S = \pi \int_0^1 (3x+1)^2 dx$

$$= \pi \int_0^1 (9x^2 + 6x + 1)\,dx$$

$$= \pi \left(3x^3 + 3x^2 + x\Big|_0^1\right)$$

$$= \pi\,[(3+3+1) - (0)] = 7\pi$$

9. Volume of $S = \pi \int_{-1}^3 (x^2+2)^2 dx$

$$= \pi \int_{-1}^3 (x^4 + 4x^2 + 4)\,dx$$

$$= \left(\frac{x^5}{5} + \frac{4x^3}{3} + 4x\Big|_{-1}^3\right)$$

$$= \pi \left[\left(\frac{243}{5} + \frac{108}{3} + 12\right) - \left(-\frac{1}{5} - \frac{4}{3} - 4\right)\right]$$

$$= \pi \left(\frac{729}{15} + \frac{540}{15} + \frac{180}{15} + \frac{3}{15} + \frac{20}{15} + \frac{60}{15}\right)$$

$$= \frac{1532}{15}\pi$$

11. Volume of $S = \pi \int_{-2}^2 \left(\sqrt{4-x^2}\right)^2 dx$

$$= \pi \int_{-2}^2 (4-x)\,dx = \pi \left(4x - \frac{x^3}{3}\Big|_{-2}^2\right)$$

$$= \left[\left(8 - \frac{8}{3}\right) - \left(-8 + \frac{8}{3}\right)\right]$$

$$= \pi \left(\frac{24}{3} - \frac{8}{3} + \frac{24}{3} - \frac{8}{3}\right)$$

$$= \frac{32}{3}\pi$$

13. Volume of $S = \pi \int_1^{e^2} \left(\frac{1}{\sqrt{x}}\right)^2 dx$

$$= \pi \int_1^{e^2} \frac{1}{x} = \pi \left(\ln x\Big|_1^{e^2}\right)$$

$$= \pi \left(\ln e^2 - \ln 1\right)$$

$$= \pi(2-0) = 2\pi$$

15.
$$P(t) = \int P'(t)\,dt$$

$$= \int e^{0.02t}\,dt$$

$$= 50e^{0.02t} + C$$

When $t = 0$, $P(0) = 50$

$$50 = 50e^0 + C, \text{ or } C = 0.$$

So, $P(t) = 50e^{0.02t}$ and

$$P(10) = 50e^{0.02(10)} \approx 61.07 \text{ million,}$$

or 61,070,138 people.

17. After 8 months, the number of the original members remaining is

$$200e^{-0.2(8)}$$

The number of new members remaining is

$$\int_0^8 10e^{-0.2(8-t)}\,dt.$$

So, the total will be

$$200e^{-1.6} + 10e^{-1.6} \int_0^8 e^{0.2t} \, dt$$

$$= 10e^{-1.6}[20 + 5(e^{0.2t}) \Big|_0^8]$$

$$\approx 80 \text{ members}$$

19. After 30 days, the number of those originally infected who still have the disease is

$$5000e^{-0.02(30)}$$

The number of those since infected who still have the disease is

$$\int_0^{30} 60e^{-0.02(30-t)} \, dt.$$

So, the total still infected will be

$$20e^{-0.6} \left(250 + 3 \int_0^{30} e^{0.02t} \, dt \right)$$

$$= 20e^{-0.6} \left[250 + 150(e^{0.02t}) \Big|_0^{30} \right]$$

$$= 1,000e^{-0.6} \left[5 + 3(e^{0.02t}) \Big|_0^{30} \right]$$

$$\approx 4,098 \text{ people}$$

21.
$$\int_0^{10} 30e^{0.1t} \, dt = 300(e^{0.1t}) \Big|_0^{10}$$

$$\approx 515.48 \quad \text{billion barrels.}$$

23. After 10 months, the number of the origianl members remaining is

$$8,000e^{-10/10}.$$

The number of new members remaining is

$$\int_0^{10} 200e^{-(10-t)/10} \, dt$$

So, the total will be

$$200e^{-1}(40 + \int_0^{10} e^{t/10} \, dt)$$

$$= 200e^{-1}[40 + 10(e^{t/10}) \Big|_0^{10}]$$

$$\approx 4,207 \text{ members}$$

25. (a)
$$\int_0^{24} (-0.028t^2 + 0.672t) \, dt$$

$$= \left(\frac{-0.028}{3}t^3 + 0.336t^2 \right) \Big|_0^{24}$$

$$= 64.512.$$

So, the cardiac output is

$$R = \frac{5}{64.512} \approx 0.0775 \text{ liters/sec.}$$

(b) When $t = 0$, $C = 0$ so $(0, 0)$ is an intercept. $C(t) = 0$, $0 = -0.028t(t - 24)$, or $t = 24$, so $(24, 0)$ is an intercept. The vertex is

$$\left(-\frac{b}{2a}, f\left(-\frac{b}{2a} \right) \right)$$

$$h = -\frac{b}{2a} = -\frac{0.672}{2(-0.028)} = 12$$

$$k = C(12) = -0.028(12)^2 + 0.672(12) \approx 4.03.$$

So, the vertex is $(12, 4.03)$.

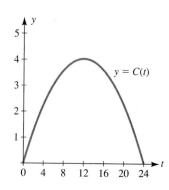

(c) Writing exercise—Answers will vary.

27. (a)

$$\int_0^{24} \frac{1}{12,312} \left(t^4 - 48t^3 + 378t^2 + 4,752t \right) dt$$

$$= \frac{1}{12,312} \left(\frac{t^5}{5} - 12t^4 + 126t^3 + 2,376t^2 \right) \Big|_0^{24}$$

$$\approx 58.611.$$

So, the cardiac output is

$$R = \frac{5}{58.611} \approx 0.0853 \text{ liters/sec.}$$

(b) To sketch the graph of $C(t)$,
Press $\boxed{y=}$ and input $C(t)$ for $y_1 = .$
Use window dimensions [0, 24]4 by [0, 5]l.

Writing exercise—Answers will vary.

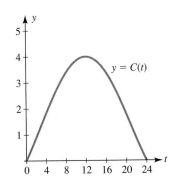

29.

$$\# \text{ people} = \int_1^2 2\pi r (25,000 e^{-0.05r^2}) \, dr$$

$$= 50,000\pi \int_1^2 r e^{-0.05r^2} \, dr$$

Let $u = -0.05r^2$; then $-10 \, du = r \, dr$ and the limits of integration become $-0.05(1)^2 = -0.05$ and $-0.05(2)^2 = -0.2$ So,

$$= 50,000\pi \int_{-0.05}^{-0.2} e^u \cdot -10 \, du$$

$$= 500,000\pi \int_{-0.2}^{-0.05} e^u \, du$$

$$= 500,000\pi \left(e^u \Big|_{-0.2}^{-0.05} \right)$$

$$= 500,000\pi (e^{-0.05} - e^{-0.2})$$

$$\approx 208,128 \text{ people}$$

31. (a)

$$\int_0^3 0.3t (49 - t^2)^{0.4} \, dt$$

Using substitution with $u = 49 - t^2$,

$$= \frac{-0.3}{2} \int_{49}^{40} u^{0.4} \, du$$

$$= \frac{0.3}{2} \int_{40}^{49} u^{0.4} \, du$$

$$= \frac{0.3}{2.8} (u^{1.4}) \Big|_{40}^{49}$$

$$\approx 6.16,$$

so LDL decreases by approximately 6.16 units.

(b)

$$L(t) = \int L'(t) \, dt$$

$$= \int 0.3t (49 - t^2)^{0.4} \, dt$$

$$= \frac{3}{28} (49 - t^2)^{1.4} + C$$

When $t = 0$, $L(t) = 120$ so

$$120 = \frac{3}{28} (49)^{1.4} + C,$$

$$\text{or } C = 120 - \frac{3}{28} (49)^{1.4}$$

So,

$$L(t) = \frac{3}{28} (49 - t^2)^{1.4} + 120 - \frac{3}{28} (49)^{1.4}$$

$$= \frac{3}{28} (49 - t^2)^{1.4} + 120 - \frac{21}{4} (49)^{0.4}$$

(c) To find how many days it takes for patient's LDL level to be safe,
Press $\boxed{y=}$
Input $(3/28)(49 - x^2) \wedge (1.4) + 120 - (21/4)(49) \wedge (0.4)$ for $y_1 =.$
Use window dimensions [0, 10]1 by [0, 200]20.
Press $\boxed{\text{graph}}$.
Use $\boxed{\text{trace}}$ and zoom-in to find that $y = 100$ when $x \approx 5.8$
Therefore, it takes approximately 5.8 days for the LDL level to be safe.

33. For the first colony, the number of bacteria after 50 days will be

$$100{,}000e^{-0.011(50)} + \int_0^{50} 50e^{-0.011(50-t)}\, dt$$

$$= 100{,}000e^{-0.55} + 50e^{-0.55} \int_0^{50} e^{0.011t}\, dt$$

$$= 50e^{-0.55}\left[2{,}000 + \frac{1}{0.011}(e^{0.011t})\Big|_0^{50}\right]$$

$$\approx 59{,}618$$

The number in the second colony will be

$$P(50) = \frac{5{,}000}{1 + 49e^{0.009(50)}}$$

$$\approx 64.228, \text{ or } 64{,}228$$

So, after 50 days, the population is larger in the second colony.
Similarly, after 100 days, the first colony's population will be

$$100{,}000e^{-0.011(100)} + \int_0^{100} 50e^{-0.011(100-t)}\, dt$$

$$\approx 36{,}320$$

and the second colony will be

$$P(100) = \frac{5{,}000}{1 + 49e^{0.009(100)}}$$

$$\approx 41.145, \text{ or } 41{,}145$$

So, the second colony is still larger after 100 days.
Similarly, after 300 days, the first will be

$$100{,}000e^{-0.011(300)} + \int_0^{300} 50e^{-0.011(300-t)}\, dt$$

$$\approx 8{,}066$$

and the second will be

$$P(300) = \frac{5{,}000}{1 + 49e^{0.009(300)}}$$

$$\approx 6{,}848$$

So, after 300 days, the first colony is now larger.

35. Using the result of problem #24,

$$P(10) = 3{,}000e^{-0.07(10)} + \int_0^{10} 10e^{0.01t}e^{-0.07(10-t)}\, dt$$

$$= 3{,}000e^{-0.7} + 10e^{-0.7}\int_0^{10} e^{0.08t}\, dt$$

$$= 10e^{-0.7}\left[300 + \frac{1}{0.08}(e^{0.08t})\Big|_0^{10}\right]$$

$$\approx 1{,}566 \text{ members of the species.}$$

37. Using the result of problem #24,

$$P(10) = 85{,}000\left(\frac{1}{10+1}\right)$$

$$+ \int_0^{10} 1{,}000\frac{1}{(10-t)+1}\, dt$$

$$= \frac{85{,}000}{11} + 1{,}000\int_0^{10} \frac{1}{11-t}\, dt$$

$$= \frac{85{,}000}{11} - 1{,}000\int_{11}^{1} \frac{1}{u}\, du$$

$$= \frac{85{,}000}{11} + 1{,}000\int_1^{11} \frac{1}{u}\, du$$

$$= \frac{85{,}000}{11} + 1{,}000\ln|u|\Big|_1^{11}$$

$$\approx 10{,}125 \text{ people.}$$

39.
$$D(t) = \int D'(t)\, dt$$

$$= \int 0.12 + \frac{0.08}{t+1}\, dt$$

$$= 0.12t + 0.08\ln|t+1| + C$$

When $t = 0$, $D(0) = 0$ so $C = 0$ and

$$D(t) = 0.12t + 0.08\ln|t+1|$$

When $t = 12$ months (1 year),

$$D(12) = 0.12(12) + 0.08\ln|12+1|$$

$$\approx 1.65, \text{ or } 165 \text{ infected people}$$

of those inoculated.

Of those not inoculated,

$$W(t) = \int W'(t)\, dt$$

$$= \int \frac{0.8e^{0.13t}}{(1+e^{0.13t})^2}\, dt$$

Using substitution, with $u = 1 + e^{0.13t}$,

$$= 0.8 \int \frac{1}{(1+e^{0.13t})^2} e^{0.13t}\, dt$$

$$= \frac{0.8}{0.13} \int u^{-2}\, du$$

$$= \frac{80}{13}\left[\frac{-1}{(1+e^{0.13t})}\right] + C$$

When $t = 0$, $W(0) = 0$, so

$$0 = \frac{80}{13}\left(\frac{-1}{2}\right) + C,$$

$$\text{or } C = \frac{40}{13}$$

$$\text{and } W(t) = \frac{-80}{13(1+e^{0.13t})} + \frac{40}{13}.$$

So, after 12 months,

$$W(12) = \frac{-80}{13(1+e^{0.13(12)})} + \frac{40}{13}$$

$$\approx 2.01, \text{ or approximately 201 people infected.}$$

So, approximately $201 - 165 = 36$ people protected by the drug, or

$$\frac{W(12) - D(12)}{W(12)} \approx 18.1\%.$$

41. (a) At birth,

$$L(0) = \frac{110e^0}{1+e^0} = 55 \text{ years of age}$$

(b)

$$L_{av} = \frac{1}{70-10} \int_{10}^{70} \frac{110e^{0.015t}}{1+e^{0.015t}}\, dt$$

Using substitution, with $u = 1 + e^{0.015t}$,

$$= \frac{110}{60} \int_{10}^{70} \frac{1}{1+e^{0.015t}} e^{0.015t}\, dt$$

$$= \frac{11}{6(0.015)} \int_{1+e^{0.15}}^{1+e^{1.05}} \frac{1}{u}\, du$$

$$= \frac{11}{0.09} (\ln|u|)\Big|_{1+e^{0.15}}^{1+e^{1.05}}$$

$$\approx 70.78 \text{ years of age}$$

(c) To find the age T such that $L(T) = T$, we must find T such that

$$\frac{110e^{0.015T}}{1+e^{0.015T}} = T$$

$$110e^{0.015T} - T(1+e^{0.015T}) = 0$$

Press $\boxed{\text{y=}}$ and input $110e \wedge (0.015x) - (x * (1 + e \wedge (0.015x)))$ for $y_1 =$.
Use window dimensions $[0, 100]10$ by $[-10, 120]20$.
Press $\boxed{\text{graph}}$.
Use the zero function under the calc menu to find that $T \approx 86.4$ years.
On the average, this is how long people in this country live.

(d) $$L_e = \frac{1}{86.4 - 0} \int_0^{86.4} \frac{110e^{0.015t}}{1+e^{0.015t}}\, dt$$

Using substitution as before,

$$= \frac{110}{(86.4)(0.015)} \int_2^{1+e^{1.296}} \frac{1}{u}\, du$$

$$= \frac{110}{1.296}\left[\ln(1+e^{1.296}) - \ln 2\right]$$

$$\approx 71.7 \text{ years of age}$$

43. (a)

$$0 = -0.41t^2 + 0.97t$$
$$= t(0.97 - 0.41t)$$

so $R(t) = 0$ when $t = 0$ and when $t \approx 2.37$ sec.

(b)
$$\text{Volume} = \int_0^{2.37} (-0.41t^2 + 0.97t)\, dt$$

$$= \left(\frac{-0.41}{3} t^3 + \frac{0.97}{2} t^2 \right) \Big|_0^{2.37}$$

$$\approx 0.905 \text{ liters}$$

(c)
$$R_{av} = \frac{1}{2.37 - 0} \int_0^{2.37} (-0.41t^2 + 0.97t)\, dt$$

$$\approx \frac{0.905}{2.37} \approx 0.382 \text{ liters/sec.}$$

45. $T(r) = \dfrac{3}{2+r} = 3(2+r)^{-1}$

(a) domain: $[0, \infty)$

intercepts: when $r = 0$, $T(0) = \dfrac{3}{2}$; point $\left(0, \dfrac{3}{2}\right)$

when $T(r) = 0$, no solution

vertical asymptote outside of domain ($r = -2$)

horizontal aymptote

$$\lim_{r \to \infty} \frac{\dfrac{3}{r}}{\dfrac{2}{r} + 1} = 0, \text{ or } y = 0$$

$$T'(r) = -\frac{3}{(2+r)^2} = -3(2+r)^{-2}$$

$$T''(r) = \frac{6}{(2+r)^3}$$

When $r \geq 0$, $T'(r) < 0$ so T is decreasing

$T''(r) > 0$ so T is concave up.

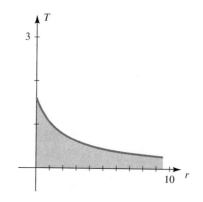

(b)
$$T(r) = \frac{3}{2+r}$$

$$2 + r = \frac{3}{T}$$

$$r(T) = \frac{3}{t} - 2$$

Graph is relection of graph in part(a) over the line $y = x$.

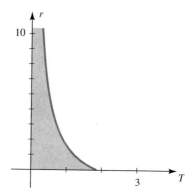

(c) When $r = 0$, $T = \dfrac{3}{2}$ and when $r = 7$, $T = \dfrac{1}{3}$.

Volume

$$= \pi \int_{1/3}^{3/2} \left(\frac{3}{T} - 2 \right)^2 dT$$

$$= \pi \int_{1/3}^{3/2} \left(\frac{9}{T^2} - \frac{12}{T} + 4 \right) dT$$

$$= \pi \left[-\frac{9}{T} - 12 \ln T + 4T \right]_{1/3}^{3/2}$$

$$= \pi \left[\left(-6 - 12 \ln \frac{3}{2} + 6 \right) - \left(-27 - 12 \ln \frac{1}{3} + \frac{4}{3} \right) \right]$$

$$= \pi \left[-12 \ln \frac{3}{2} + \frac{81}{3} + 12 \ln \frac{1}{3} - \frac{4}{3} \right]$$

$$= \pi \left[12 \ln \frac{1}{3} - 12 \ln \frac{3}{2} + \frac{77}{3} \right] \approx 23.93 \text{ft}^3$$

47. $p(r) = \dfrac{200}{5 + 2r^2}$

(a) Since the pollution is distributed in a circular fashion about the smoke stack,

$$\text{pollution} = 2\pi \int_0^3 r \left(\frac{200}{5 + 2r^2} \right) dr$$

$$= 400\pi \int_0^3 \frac{r}{5 + 2r^2} dr$$

Using substitution with $u = 5 + 2r^2$, $\frac{1}{4} du = r \, dr$ and limits of integration $u_1 = 5$ and $u_2 = 23$,

$$= 400\pi \int_5^{23} \frac{1}{u} \cdot \frac{1}{4} du$$

$$= 100\pi \int_5^{23} \frac{1}{u} du$$

$$= 100\pi \left(\ln u \Big|_5^{23} \right)$$

$$= 100\pi (\ln 23 - \ln 5)$$

$$= 100\pi \ln \frac{23}{5} \approx 479.42 \text{ units}$$

(b) $\quad 4 = \dfrac{200}{5 + 2r^2}$

$$L = r = \sqrt{\frac{45}{2}} = \frac{3\sqrt{10}}{2} \approx 4.74 \text{ miles}$$

$$\text{amt of pollution} = 2\pi \int_0^{\frac{3\sqrt{10}}{2}} r \left(\frac{200}{5 + 2r^2} \right) dr$$

$$= 100\pi \left(\ln u \Big|_5^{50} \right)$$

$$= 100\pi (\ln 50 - \ln 5)$$

$$= 100\pi \ln 10 \approx 723.38 \text{ units}$$

49. Volume $= \displaystyle\int_0^h \pi y^2 dx$

Since the hypotenuse of the triangle is along the line $y = \dfrac{r}{h} x$,

$$= \pi \int_0^h \left(\frac{r}{h} x \right)^2 dx$$

$$= \frac{\pi r^2}{h^2} \int_0^h x^2 dx$$

$$= \frac{\pi r^2}{h^2} \left(\frac{x^3}{3} \Big|_0^h \right)$$

$$= \frac{\pi r^2}{h^2} \left(\frac{h^3}{3} - 0 \right)$$

$$= \frac{1}{3} \pi r^2 h$$

Checkup for Chapter 5

1. **(a)** $\quad \displaystyle\int \left(x^3 - \sqrt{3x} + 5e^{-2x} \right) dx$

$$= \int x^3 \, dx - \sqrt{3} \int x^{1/2} \, dx + 5 \int e^{-2x} \, dx$$

$$= \frac{x^4}{4} - \frac{2\sqrt{3}}{3} x^{3/2} - \frac{5}{2} e^{-2x} + C$$

(b) $\quad \displaystyle\int \frac{x^2 - 2x + 4}{x} \, dx$

$$= \int \left(x - 2x + \frac{4}{x} \right) dx$$

$$= \int x \, dx - 2 \int dx + 4 \int \frac{1}{x} \, dx$$

$$= \frac{x^2}{2} - 2x + 4 \ln |x| + C$$

(c) $\quad \displaystyle\int \sqrt{x} \left(x^2 - \frac{1}{x} \right) dx$

$$= \int \left(x^{5/2} - x^{-1/2} \right) dx$$

$$= \frac{2}{7} x^{7/2} - 2x^{1/2} + C$$

(d) $\displaystyle\int \frac{x \, dx}{(3 + 2x^2)^{3/2}}$

Let $u = 3 + 2x^2$; then $\dfrac{1}{4} du = x \, dx$

$$= \frac{1}{4} \int u^{-3/2} \, du = \frac{1}{4} (-2u^{-1/2}) + C$$

$$= \frac{-1}{2\sqrt{3 + 2x^2}} + C$$

(e)

$$\int \frac{\ln \sqrt{x}}{x}\, dx$$

$$= \int \frac{\frac{1}{2}\ln x}{x}\, dx$$

let $u = \ln x$; then $du = \frac{1}{x}\, dx$

$$\frac{1}{2}\int (\ln x)\frac{1}{x}\, dx$$

$$= \frac{1}{2}\int u\, du = \frac{1}{4}(\ln x)^2 + C$$

(f) $\displaystyle\int xe^{1+x^2}\, dx$

Let $u = 1 + x^2$; then $\frac{1}{2}\, du = x\, dx$

$$= \int (e^{1+x^2})x\, dx$$

$$= \frac{1}{2}\int e^u\, du = \frac{1}{2}e^{1+x^2} + C$$

2. (a)

$$\int_1^4 \left(x^{3/2} + \frac{2}{x}\right) dx$$

$$= \int_1^4 x^{3/2}\, dx + 2\int_1^4 \frac{1}{x}\, dx$$

$$= \frac{2}{5}x^{5/2}\Big|_1^4 + 2(\ln|x|)\Big|_1^4$$

$$= \frac{2}{5}\left[(4)^{5/2} - (1)^{5/2}\right] + 2[\ln 4 - \ln 1]$$

$$= \frac{62}{5} + 2\ln 4$$

$$= \frac{62}{5} + 2\ln 2^2 = \frac{62}{5} + 4\ln 2$$

(b) $\displaystyle\int_0^3 e^{3-x}\, dx$

Let $u = 3 - x$; then $-du = dx$ and the limits of integration become $3 - 3 = 0$ and $3 - 0 = 3$

$$= -\int_3^0 e^u\, du$$

$$= \int_0^3 e^u\, du = e^3 - e^0 = e^3 - 1$$

(c) $\displaystyle\int_0^1 \frac{x}{x+1}\, dx$

Let $u = x + 1$; then $du = dx$ and $x = u - 1$. Further, the limits of integration become $0 + 1 = 1$ and $1 + 2 = 2$

$$= \int_1^2 \frac{u-1}{u}\, du$$

$$= \int_1^2 \left(1 - \frac{1}{u}\right) du$$

$$= (u - \ln|u|)\Big|_1^2$$

$$= (2 - \ln 2) - (1 - \ln 1) = 1 - \ln 2$$

(d) $\displaystyle\int_0^3 \frac{(x+3)\, dx}{\sqrt{x^2 + 6x + 4}}$

Let $u = x^2 + 6x + 4$; then $du = (2x + 6)\, dx$ or, $\dfrac{du}{2} = (x+3)\, dx$. Further, the limits of integration become $0 + 6(0) + 4 = 4$ and $(3)^2 + 6(3) + 4 = 31$

$$= \frac{1}{2}\int_4^{31} u^{-1/2}\, du = \frac{1}{2}(2u^{1/2})\Big|_4^{31}$$

$$= u^{1/2}\Big|_4^{31} = \sqrt{31} - 2$$

3. (a)

$$\text{Area} = \int_1^4 \left[(x + \sqrt{x}) - 0\right] dx$$

$$= \int_1^4 x + x^{1/2}\, dx$$

$$= \left(\frac{x^2}{2} + \frac{2}{3}x^{3/2}\right)\Big|_1^4$$

$$= \left[\frac{(4)^2}{2} + \frac{2}{3}(4)^{3/2}\right] - \left[\frac{1}{2} + \frac{2}{3}(1)^{3/2}\right]$$

$$= \frac{73}{6}\ \text{sq. units.}$$

Chapter 6

Additional Topics in Integration

6.1 Integration by Parts; Integral Tables

1. Both terms are easy to integrate; however, the derivative of x becomes simpler while the derivative of e^{-x} does not. So,

$$u = x \quad \text{and} \quad dV = e^{-x}\, dx$$
$$du = dx \qquad V = -e^{-x}$$

and

$$\int xe^{-x}\, dx = -xe^{-x} - \int -e^{-x}\, dx$$

$$= -xe^{-x} + \int e^{-x}\, dx$$

$$= -xe^{-x} - e^{-x} + C$$

$$= -(x+1)e^{-x} + C$$

3. Both terms are easy to integrate; however, the derivative of $1 - x$ becomes simpler while the derivative of e^x does not. So,

$$u = 1 - x \qquad dV = e^x\, dx$$
$$du = -dx \qquad V = e^x$$

and

$$\int (1-x)e^x\, dx = (1-x)e^x - \int e^x - dx$$

$$= (1-x)e^x + \int e^x\, dx$$

$$= (1-x)e^x + e^x + C$$

$$= [(1-x)+1]e^x + C$$

$$= (2-x)e^x + C$$

5. $\ln 2t$ cannot be easily integrated. So,

$$u = \ln 2t \qquad \text{and} \quad dV = t\, dt$$
$$du = \frac{1}{2t} \cdot 2dt \qquad\quad V = \frac{t^2}{2}$$
$$= \frac{1}{t}\, dt$$

and

$$\int t \ln 2t\, dt = \frac{t^2}{2} \ln 2t - \int \frac{t^2}{2} \cdot \frac{1}{t}\, dt$$

$$= \frac{t^2}{2} \ln 2t - \frac{1}{2} \int t\, dt$$

$$= \frac{t^2}{2} \ln 2t - \frac{1}{4}t^2 + C$$

$$= \frac{t^2}{2} \left(\ln 2t - \frac{1}{2} \right) + C$$

7. Both terms are easy to integrage; however, the derivative of v becomes simpler while the derivative of $e^{-v/5}$ does not. So,

$$u = v \qquad \text{and} \quad dV = e^{-v/5}dv$$
$$du = dv \qquad\quad V = -5e^{-v/5}$$

and

$$\int ve^{-v/5}dv = -5ve^{-v/5} - \int -5e^{-v/5}dv$$

$$= -5ve^{-v/5} + 5 \int e^{-v/5}dv$$

$$= -5ve^{-v/5} - 25e^{-v/5} + C$$

$$= -5(v+5)e^{-v/5} + C$$

9. Both terms are easy to integrate; however, the derivative of x becomes simpler while the derivative of $\sqrt{x-6}$ does not. So,

$$u = x \quad \text{and} \quad dV = (x-6)^{1/2}\,dx$$

$$du = dx \qquad V = \frac{2}{3}(x-6)^{3/2}$$

and

$$\int x\sqrt{x-6}\,dx = \frac{2}{3}x(x-6)^{3/2} - \int \frac{2}{3}(x-6)^{3/2}\,dx$$

$$= \frac{2}{3}x(x-6)^{3/2} - \frac{2}{3}\int (x-6)^{3/2}\,dx$$

$$= \frac{2}{3}x(x-6)^{3/2} - \frac{4}{15}(x-6)^{5/2} + C$$

11. Both terms are easy to integrate; however, the derivative of x becomes simpler while the derivative of $(x+1)^8$ does not. So,

$$u = x \quad \text{and} \quad dV = (x+1)^8\,dx$$

$$du = dx \qquad V = \frac{1}{9}(x+1)^9$$

and

$$\int x(x+1)^8\,dx = \frac{1}{9}x(x+1)^9 - \int \frac{1}{9}(x+1)^9\,dx$$

$$= \frac{1}{9}x(x+1)^9 - \frac{1}{9}\int (x+1)^9\,dx$$

$$= \frac{1}{9}x(x+1)^9 - \frac{1}{90}(x+1)^{10} + C$$

13. Rewriting, $\displaystyle\int \frac{x}{\sqrt{x+2}}\,dx = \int x(x+2)^{-1/2}\,dx$, both terms are easy to integrate; however, the derivative of x becomes simpler while the derivative of $(x+2)^{-1/2}$ does not. So,

$$u = x \quad \text{and} \quad dV = (x+2)^{-1/2}\,dx$$

$$du = dx \qquad V = 2(x+2)^{1/2}$$

and

$$\int \frac{x}{\sqrt{x+2}}\,dx = 2x(x+2)^{1/2} - \int 2(x+2)^{1/2}\,dx$$

$$= 2x(x+2)^{1/2} - 2\int (x+2)^{1/2}\,dx$$

$$= 2x\sqrt{x+2} - \frac{4}{3}(x+2)^{3/2} + C$$

15. Rewriting, $\displaystyle\int_{-1}^{4} \frac{x}{\sqrt{x+5}}\,dx = \int_{-1}^{4} x(x+5)^{-1/2}\,dx$, both terms are easy to integrate; however, the derivative of x becomes simpler while the derivative of $(x+5)^{-1/2}$ does not. So,

$$u = x \quad \text{and} \quad dV = (x+5)^{-1/2}\,dx$$

$$du = dx \qquad V = 2(x+5)^{1/2}$$

and

$$\int_{-1}^{4} \frac{x}{\sqrt{x+5}}\,dx = 2x(x+5)^{1/2}\Big|_{-1}^{4} - \int_{-1}^{4} 2(x+5)^{1/2}\,dx$$

$$= 2x(x+5)^{1/2}\Big|_{-1}^{4} - 2\int_{-1}^{4} (x+5)^{1/2}\,dx$$

$$= \left[2x\sqrt{x+5} - \frac{4}{3}(x+5)^{3/2}\right]\Big|_{-1}^{4}$$

$$= \left[2(4)\sqrt{4+5} - \frac{4}{3}(4+5)^{3/2}\right]$$

$$\quad - \left[2(-1)\sqrt{-1+5} - \frac{4}{3}(-1+5)^{3/2}\right]$$

$$= \frac{8}{3}$$

17. Rewriting, $\displaystyle\int_{0}^{1} \frac{x}{e^{2x}}\,dx = \int_{0}^{1} xe^{-2x}\,dx$, both terms are easy to integrate; however, the derivative of x becomes simpler while the derivative of e^{-2x} does not. So,

$$u = x \quad \text{and} \quad dV = e^{-2x}\,dx$$

$$du = dx \qquad V = -\frac{1}{2}e^{-2x}$$

and

$$\int_0^1 \frac{x}{e^{2x}}\,dx = -\frac{x}{2}e^{-2x}\Big|_0^1 - \int_0^1 -\frac{1}{2}e^{-2x}\,dx$$

$$= -\frac{x}{2}e^{-2x}\Big|_0^1 + \frac{1}{2}\int_0^1 e^{-2x}\,dx$$

$$= \left[-\frac{x}{2}e^{-2x} - \frac{1}{4}e^{-2x}\right]\Big|_0^1$$

$$= \left[-\frac{1}{2}e^{-2} - \frac{1}{4}e^{-2}\right] - \left[0 - \frac{1}{4}e^0\right]$$

$$= -\frac{3}{4}e^{-2} + \frac{1}{4} = \frac{1}{4}(1 - 3e^{-2})$$

19. $\ln \sqrt[3]{x}$ cannot be easily integrated. So,

$$u = \ln \sqrt[3]{x} \qquad \text{and} \quad dV = x\,dx$$

$$= \ln(x)^{1/3} \qquad\qquad V = \frac{x^2}{2}$$

$$= \frac{1}{3}\ln x$$

$$du = \frac{1}{3x}\,dx$$

and

$$\int_1^{e^2} x \ln \sqrt[3]{x}\,dx = \frac{x^2}{6}\ln x\Big|_1^{e^2} - \int_1^{e^2} \frac{x^2}{2}\cdot\frac{1}{3x}\,dx$$

$$= \frac{x^2}{6}\ln x\Big|_1^{e^2} - \frac{1}{6}\int_1^{e^2} x\,dx$$

$$= \left(\frac{x^2}{6}\ln x - \frac{x^2}{12}\right)\Big|_1^{e^2}$$

$$= \left[\frac{(e^2)^2}{6}\ln(e^2) - \frac{(e^2)^2}{12}\right]$$

$$\qquad - \left[\frac{1}{6}\ln 1 - \frac{1}{12}\right]$$

$$= \frac{1}{12}\left(3e^4 + 1\right)$$

21. $\ln 2t$ cannot be easily integrated. So,

$$u = \ln 2t \qquad \text{and} \qquad dV = t\,dt$$

$$du = \frac{1}{2t}\cdot 2dt \qquad\qquad V = \frac{t^2}{2}$$

$$= \frac{1}{t}\,dt$$

and

$$\int_{1/2}^{e/2} t \ln 2t\,dt = \frac{t^2}{2}\ln 2t\Big|_{1/2}^{e/2} - \int_{1/2}^{e/2} \frac{t^2}{2}\cdot\frac{1}{t}\,dt$$

$$= \frac{t^2}{2}\ln 2t\Big|_{1/2}^{e/2} - \frac{1}{2}\int_{1/2}^{e/2} t\,dt$$

$$= \left(\frac{t^2}{2}\ln 2t - \frac{t^2}{4}\right)\Big|_{1/2}^{e/2}$$

$$= \left[\frac{\left(\frac{e}{2}\right)^2}{2}\ln 2\left(\frac{e}{2}\right) - \frac{\left(\frac{e}{2}\right)^2}{4}\right]$$

$$\qquad - \left[\frac{\left(\frac{1}{2}\right)^2}{2}\ln 2\left(\frac{1}{2}\right) - \frac{\left(\frac{1}{2}\right)^2}{4}\right]$$

$$= \frac{1}{16}(e^2 + 1)$$

23. Rewriting, $\int \frac{\ln x}{x^2}\,dx = \int x^{-2}\ln x\,dx$, $\ln x$ cannot be easily integrated. So,

$$u = \ln x \qquad \text{and} \quad dV = x^{-2}\,dx$$

$$du = \frac{1}{x}\,dx \qquad\qquad V = -\frac{1}{x}$$

and

$$\int \frac{\ln x}{x^2}\,dx = -\frac{1}{x}\ln x - \int -\frac{1}{x}\cdot\frac{1}{x}\,dx$$

$$= -\frac{1}{x}\ln x + \int x^{-2}\,dx$$

$$= -\frac{1}{x}\ln x - \frac{1}{x} + C$$

$$= -\frac{1}{x}(\ln x + 1) + C$$

25. Using the hint,

$$u = x^2 \quad \text{and} \quad dV = xe^{x^2}\, dx$$

$$du = 2x\, dx \qquad \text{let } u = x^2; \frac{1}{2}\, du = x\, dx$$

$$V = \frac{1}{2}e^{x^2}$$

and

$$\int x^3 e^{x^2}\, dx = \frac{x^2}{2}e^{x^2} - \int \frac{1}{2}e^{x^2} \cdot 2x\, dx$$

$$= \frac{x^2}{2}e^{x^2} - \frac{1}{2}e^{x^2} + C$$

$$= \frac{1}{2}e^{x^2}(x^2 - 1) + C$$

27. Rewriting, $\displaystyle\int \frac{x\, dx}{3 - 5x} = \int \frac{x\, dx}{3 + -5x}$ which is of the

form $\displaystyle\int \frac{u\, du}{a + bu}$ (formula #1). Using $u = x, du = dx$,

$a = 3$, and $b = -5$, the formula yields

$$\int \frac{x\, dx}{3 - 5x} = \frac{1}{(-5)^2}[3 + -5x - 3\ln|3 + -5x|] + C$$

$$= \frac{1}{25}(3 - 5x - 3\ln|3 - 5x|) + C$$

29. Rewriting, $\displaystyle\int \frac{\sqrt{4x^2 - 9}}{x^2}\, dx = \int \frac{\sqrt{(2x)^2 - (3)^2}}{x^2}\, dx$

most closely resembles $\displaystyle\int \frac{\sqrt{u^2 - a^2}}{u^2}\, du$ (formula

#19). Now,

$$\int \frac{\sqrt{(2x)^2 - (3)^2}}{x^2}\, dx = \int \frac{4\sqrt{(2x)^2 - (3)^2}}{4x^2}\, dx$$

$$= 2\int \frac{\sqrt{(2x)^2 - (3)^2}}{(2x)^2}\, 2\, dx$$

and formula #19 can be used with $u = 2x, du = 2\, dx$,
and $a = 3$. So,

$$\int \frac{\sqrt{4x^2 - 9}}{x^2}\, dx$$

$$= 2\left[\frac{-\sqrt{4x^2 - 9}}{2x} + \ln\left|2x + \sqrt{4x^2 - 9}\right|\right] + C$$

$$= \frac{-\sqrt{4x^2 - 9}}{x} + 2\ln\left|2x + \sqrt{4x^2 - 9}\right| + C$$

31. As written, $\displaystyle\int \frac{dx}{x(2 + 3x)}$ is of the form $\displaystyle\int \frac{du}{u(a + bu)}$
(formula #6). Using $u = x, du = dx, a = 2$,
and $b = 3$, the formula yields $\displaystyle\int \frac{dx}{x(2 + 3x)} =$

$$\frac{1}{2}\ln\left|\frac{x}{2 + 3x}\right| + C.$$

33. Rewriting, $\displaystyle\int \frac{du}{16 - 3u^2} = \int \frac{du}{3\left(\frac{16}{3} - u^2\right)} =$

$$\frac{1}{3}\int \frac{du}{\frac{16}{3} - u^2} = \frac{1}{3}\int \frac{du}{\left(\frac{4}{\sqrt{3}}\right)^2 - u^2} \text{ which is of the}$$

form $\displaystyle\int \frac{du}{a^2 - u^2}$ (formula #16). Using $a = \frac{4}{\sqrt{3}}$, the
formula yields

$$\int \frac{du}{16 - 3u^2} = \frac{1}{3}\left[\frac{1}{2\left(\frac{4}{\sqrt{3}}\right)}\ln\left|\frac{\frac{4}{\sqrt{3}} + u}{\frac{4}{\sqrt{3}} - u}\right|\right] + C$$

$$= \frac{\sqrt{3}}{24}\ln\left|\frac{\frac{4 + \sqrt{3}u}{\sqrt{3}}}{\frac{4 - \sqrt{3}u}{\sqrt{3}}}\right| + C$$

$$= \frac{\sqrt{3}}{24}\ln\left|\frac{4 + \sqrt{3}u}{4 - \sqrt{3}u}\right| + C$$

35. $\displaystyle\int (\ln x)^3\, dx$ is of the form $\displaystyle\int (\ln u)^n\, du$ (formula
#27). Using $u = x$, the formula yields

$$\int (\ln x)^3\, dx = x(\ln x)^3 - 3\int (\ln x)^2\, dx$$

Applying the formula again to the last term

$$= x(\ln x)^3 - 3\left[x(\ln x)^2 - 2\int \ln x\, dx \right]$$

$$= x(\ln x)^3 - 3x(\ln x)^2 + 6\int \ln x\, dx$$

Applying the formula one more time (or using formula #23),

$$= x(\ln x)^3 - 3x(\ln x)^2 + 6[x \ln x - x] + C$$

$$= x(\ln x)^3 - 3x(\ln x)^2 + 6x \ln x - 6x + C$$

37. $\displaystyle \int \frac{dx}{x^2(5+2x)^2}$ is of the form $\displaystyle \int \frac{du}{u^2(a+bu)^2}$
(formula #8). Using $u = x$, $du = dx$, $a = 5$, and $b = 2$, the formula yields

$$\int \frac{dx}{x^2(5+2x)^2}$$

$$= -\frac{1}{25}\left[\frac{5+4x}{x(5+2x)} + \frac{4}{5}\ln\left| \frac{x}{5+2x} \right| \right] + C$$

39.   Slope $= y' = (x+1)e^{-x}$

$$y = \int y'\, dx$$

$$= \int (x+1)e^{-x}\, dx$$

$u = x+1$ and $dV = e^{-x}\, dx$
$du = dx$ $V = -e^{-x}$

$$y = -(x+1)e^{-x} - \int -e^{-x}\, dx$$

$$= -(x+1)e^{-x} + \int e^{-x}\, dx$$

$$= -(x+1)e^{-x} - e^{-x} + C$$

Since the graph of y passes through the point $(1,5)$,
$5 = -(1+1)e^{-1} - e^{-1} + C$ or, $C = 5 + \frac{3}{e}$. So,

$$y = -(x+1)e^{-x} - e^{-x} + 5 + \frac{3}{e}$$

$$= 5 + \frac{3}{e} - \frac{x+2}{e^x}$$

41. $\displaystyle Q(t) = \int Q'(t)\, dt$

$$= \int_0^5 2000t e^{-0.2t}\, dt$$

$$= 2000 \int_0^5 t e^{-0.2t}\, dt$$

$u = t$ and $dV = e^{-0.2t}\, dt$
$du = dt$ $V = -5e^{-0.2t}$

$$Q(t) = 2000\left[-5t e^{-0.2t}\Big|_0^5 - \int_0^5 -5e^{-0.2t}\, dt \right]$$

$$= 2000\left[-5t e^{-0.2t}\Big|_0^5 + 5\int_0^5 e^{-0.2t}\, dt \right]$$

$$= 2000\left[-5t e^{-0.2t} - 25e^{-0.2t} \right]\Big|_0^5$$

$$= 2000\left[\left(-25e^{-1} - 25e^{-1}\right) - \left(0 - 25e^0\right) \right]$$

$$= 2000\left(\frac{-50}{e} + 25 \right) \approx \$13,212.06$$

43.
$$Q(t) = \int_0^3 100t e^{-0.5t}\, dt$$

$$= 100 \int_0^3 t e^{-0.5t}\, dt$$

$u = t$ $dV = e^{-0.5t}\, dt$
$du = dt$ $V = -\dfrac{1}{-0.5}e^{-0.5t} = -2e^{-0.5t}$

$$Q(t) = 100\left[-2t e^{-0.5t}\Big|_0^3 - \int_0^3 -2e^{-0.5t}\, dt \right]$$

$$= 100\left[-2t e^{-0.5t}\Big|_0^3 + 2\int_0^3 e^{-0.5t}\, dt \right]$$

$$= 100\left[-2t e^{-0.5t} - 4e^{-0.5t} \right]\Big|_0^3$$

$$= 100\left[\left(-6e^{-1.5} - 4e^{-1.5}\right) - \left(0 - 4e^0\right) \right]$$

$$= 100\left(\frac{-10}{e^{1.5}} + 4 \right) \approx \$176.87,$$

or approx 176 units

45.
$$P(t) = \int P'(t)\, dt$$

$$= \int t \ln \sqrt{t+1}\, dt$$

$$u = \ln \sqrt{t+1} \quad \text{and} \quad dV = t \, dt$$

$$= \ln(t+1)^{1/2} \quad \text{and} \quad dV = \frac{t^2}{2}$$

$$= \frac{1}{2}\ln(t+1)$$

$$du = \frac{1}{2(t+1)} \, dt$$

$$P(t) = \frac{t^2}{4}\ln(t+1) - \int \frac{t^2}{2} \cdot \frac{1}{2(t+1)} \, dt$$

$$= \frac{t^2}{4}\ln(t+1) - \frac{1}{4}\int \frac{t^2}{t+1} \, dt$$

Rewriting,

$$\int \frac{t^2}{t+1} \, dt = \int \frac{1 + t^2 - 1}{t+1} \, dt$$

$$= \int \frac{1 + (t+1)(t-1)}{t+1} \, dt$$

$$= \int \frac{1}{t+1} \, dt + \int (t-1) \, dt$$

So,

$$P(t) = \frac{t^2}{4}\ln(t+1) - \frac{1}{4}\left[\ln|t+1| + \frac{(t-1)^2}{2}\right] + C$$

$$= \frac{t^2}{4}\ln(t+1) - \frac{1}{4}\ln|t+1| - \frac{(t-1)^2}{8} + C$$

When $t = 0$, $P(0) = 2000$ thousand, so

$$2000 = 0 - \frac{1}{4}\ln 1 - \frac{1}{8} + C,$$

$$\text{or } C = 2000.125$$

So,

$$P(t) = \frac{t^2}{4}\ln(t+1) - \frac{1}{4}\ln|t+1| - \frac{(t-1)^2}{8} + 2000.125$$

and when $t = 5$,

$$P(5) = \frac{25}{4}\ln 6 - \frac{1}{4}\ln 6 - 2 + 2000.125$$

$$= 6\ln 6 + 1998.125 \approx 2{,}008.8756 \text{ thousand.}$$

The population will be approximately 2,008,876 people.

47.

$$C_{av} = \frac{1}{6-0}\int_0^6 4te^{(2-0.3t)} \, dt$$

$$= \frac{2}{3}e^2\int_0^6 te^{-0.3t} \, dt$$

$$u = t \quad \text{and} \quad dV = e^{-0.3t} \, dt$$

$$du = dt \qquad\qquad V = -\frac{10}{3}e^{-0.3t}$$

So,

$$C_{av} = \frac{2}{3}e^2\left[-\frac{10}{3}te^{-0.3t}\Big|_0^6 - \int_0^6 -\frac{10}{3}e^{-0.3t} \, dt\right]$$

$$= \frac{2}{3}e^2\left[-\frac{10}{3}te^{-0.3t}\Big|_0^6 + \frac{10}{3}\int_0^6 e^{-0.3t} \, dt\right]$$

$$= \frac{2}{3}e^2\left[-\frac{10}{3}te^{-0.3t} - \frac{100}{9}e^{-0.3t}\right]\Big|_0^6$$

$$= \frac{2}{3}e^2\left[\left(-\frac{10}{3}(6)e^{-1.8} - \frac{100}{9}e^{-1.8}\right) - \left(0 - \frac{100}{9}e^0\right)\right]$$

$$= \frac{2}{3}e^2\left(-\frac{280}{9}e^{-1.8} + \frac{100}{9}\right) \approx 29.4 \text{ mg/ml}$$

49.

$$FV = \int_0^{10}(3{,}000 + 5t)e^{0.05(10-t)} \, dt$$

$$= e^{0.5}\int_0^{10}(3{,}000 + 5t)e^{-0.05t} \, dt$$

$$u = 3{,}000 + 5t \quad \text{and} \quad dV = e^{-0.05t} \, dt$$

$$du = 5 \, dt \qquad\qquad V = -20e^{-0.05t}$$

So,

$$FV = e^{0.5}\left[-20(3{,}000 + 5t)e^{-0.05t}\Big|_0^{10}\right.$$

$$\left. - \int_0^{10} -20e^{-0.05t} \cdot 5 \, dt\right]$$

$$= e^{0.5}\left[-20(3{,}000 + 5t)e^{-0.05t}\Big|_0^{10} + 100\int_0^{10} e^{-0.05t} \, dt\right]$$

$$= e^{0.5}\left[-20(3{,}000+5t)e^{-0.05t}-2{,}000e^{-0.05t}\right]\Big|_0^{10}$$

$$= e^{0.5}\left(\left[-20(3{,}000+5(10))e^{-0.5t}-2{,}000e^{-0.5}\right]\right.$$

$$\left.\quad -\left[-20(3{,}000+0)e^0-2{,}000e^0\right]\right)$$

$$= e^{0.5}\left(-63{,}000e^{-0.5}+62{,}000\right)\approx\$39{,}220.72$$

51.
$$PV=\int_0^5(20+3t)e^{-0.07t}\,dt$$

$$u=20+3t\qquad\text{and}\quad dV=e^{-0.07t}\,dt$$

$$du=3\,dt\qquad\qquad V=-\frac{100}{7}e^{-0.07t}$$

So,

$$PV=-\frac{100}{7}(20+3t)e^{-0.07t}\Big|_0^5$$

$$\quad -\int_0^5-\frac{100}{7}e^{-0.07t}\cdot3\,dt$$

$$=-\frac{100}{7}(20+3t)e^{-0.07t}\Big|_0^5$$

$$\quad +\frac{300}{7}\int_0^5 e^{-0.07t}\,dt$$

$$=\left[-\frac{100}{7}(20+3t)e^{-0.07t}-\frac{30{,}000}{49}e^{-0.07t}\right]\Big|_0^5$$

$$=\left[-\frac{100}{7}(20+3(5))e^{-0.35}-\frac{30{,}000}{49}e^{-0.35}\right]$$

$$\quad -\left[-\frac{100}{7}(20+0)e^0-\frac{30{,}000}{49}e^0\right]$$

$$=\left(-500e^{-0.35}-\frac{30{,}000}{49}e^{-0.35}\right)$$

$$\quad -\left(-\frac{2{,}000}{7}-\frac{30{,}000}{49}\right)$$

$$\approx 114.17345\text{ hundred, or }\$11{,}417.35$$

53. From section 5.6, problem #24,

$$= P_0 S(N)+\int_0^N R(t)S(N-t)\,dt$$

Here,

members $= 5{,}000e^{-0.02(9)}+\int_0^9 5te^{-0.02(9-t)}\,dt$

$$= 5{,}000e^{-0.18}+5e^{-0.18}\int_0^9 te^{0.02t}\,dt$$

$$= 5e^{-0.18}\left[1{,}000+\int_0^9 te^{0.02t}\,dt\right]$$

$$u=t\qquad\text{and}\quad dV=e^{0.02t}\,dt$$
$$du=dt\qquad\qquad V=50e^{0.02t}$$

$$= 5e^{-0.18}\left(1{,}000+50te^{0.02t}\Big|_0^9-\int_0^9 50e^{0.02t}\,dt\right)$$

$$= 5e^{-0.18}\left(1{,}000+50te^{0.02t}\Big|_0^9-50\int_0^9 e^{0.02t}\,dt\right)$$

$$= 5e^{-0.18}\left[1{,}000+\left(50te^{0.02t}-2{,}500e^{0.02t}\right)\Big|_0^9\right]$$

$$= 5e^{-0.18}\left[1{,}000+\left(50(9)e^{0.02(9)}-2{,}500e^{0.02(9)}\right)\right.$$

$$\left.\quad -\left(0-2{,}500e^0\right)\right]$$

$$\approx 4{,}367\text{ members}$$

55. (a)
$$p=D(q)$$
$$D(q)=10-qe^{0.02q}$$
$$D(5)=10-(5)e^{0.02(5)}=\$4.47\text{ each}$$

(b)
$$CS=\int_0^5\left(10-qe^{0.02q}\right)dq-5(4.47)$$

$$=\int_0^5 10\,dq-\int_0^5 qe^{0.02q}\,dq-22.35$$

$$u=q\qquad\text{and}\quad dV=e^{0.02q}\,dq$$
$$du=dq\qquad\qquad V=50e^{0.02q}$$

$$= 10q \Big|_0^5 - \left[50qe^{0.02q} \Big|_0^5 - \int_0^5 50e^{0.02q} \, dq \right] - 22.35$$

$$= 10q \Big|_0^5 - 50qe^{0.02q} \Big|_0^5 + 50 \int_0^5 e^{0.02q} \, dq - 22.35$$

$$= \left(10q - 50qe^{0.02q} + 2{,}500e^{0.02q} \right) \Big|_0^5 - 22.35$$

$$= \left[10(5) - 50(5)e^{0.02(5)} + 2{,}500e^{0.02(5)} \right]$$

$$\quad - \left[0 - 0 + 2{,}500e^0 \right] - 22.35$$

$$\approx 14.28456 \text{ thousand, or } \$14{,}284.56$$

57.
$$GI = 2 \int_0^1 \left(x - xe^{x-1} \right) \, dx$$

$$= 2 \left[\int_0^1 x \, dx - \int_0^1 xe^{x-1} dx \right]$$

$$u = x \qquad \text{and} \qquad dV = e^{x-1} \, dx$$
$$du = dx \qquad\qquad V = e^{x-1}$$

$$= 2 \left[\frac{x^2}{2} \Big|_0^1 - \left(xe^{x-1} \Big|_0^1 - \int_0^1 e^{x-1} \, dx \right) \right]$$

$$= 2 \left(\frac{x^2}{2} - xe^{x-1} + e^{x-1} \right) \Big|_0^1$$

$$= 2 \left[\left(\frac{1}{2} - 1e^0 + e^0 \right) - \left(0 - 0 + e^{-1} \right) \right]$$

$$= 1 - \frac{2}{e} \approx 0.2642$$

59. From section 5.6, cardiac output is

$$R = \frac{D}{\displaystyle\int_0^{T_0} C(t) \, dt}$$

Here,

$$R = \frac{5}{\displaystyle\int_0^{20} \left(1.54te^{-0.12t} - 0.007t^2 \right) \, dt}$$

where the denominator can be written as

$$1.54 \int_0^{20} te^{-0.12t} \, dt - \int_0^{20} 0.007t^2 \, dt$$

$$u = t \qquad \text{and} \qquad dV = e^{-0.12t} \, dt$$
$$du = dt \qquad\qquad V = -\frac{100}{12}e^{-0.12t}$$

$$= 1.54 \left[-\frac{25}{3}te^{-0.12t} \Big|_0^{20} - \int_0^{20} -\frac{25}{3}e^{-0.12t} \, dt \right]$$
$$\quad - \frac{0.007}{3}t^3 \Big|_0^{20}$$

$$= 1.54 \left[-\frac{25}{3}te^{-0.12t} \Big|_0^{20} + \frac{25}{3} \int_0^{20} e^{-0.12t} \, dt \right]$$
$$\quad - \frac{0.007}{3}t^3 \Big|_0^{20}$$

$$= 1.54 \left(-\frac{25}{3}te^{-0.12t} - \frac{625}{9}e^{-0.12t} \right) \Big|_0^{20}$$
$$\quad - \frac{0.007}{3}t^3 \Big|_0^{20}$$

$$= 1.54 \left[\left(-\frac{25}{3}(20)e^{-0.12(20)} - \frac{625}{9}e^{-0.12(20)} \right) \right.$$
$$\quad \left. - \left(0 - \frac{625}{9}e^0 \right) \right] - \left[\frac{0.007}{3}(20)^3 - 0 \right]$$

$$\approx 55.2917$$

So, $R \approx \dfrac{5}{55.2917} \approx 0.0904 \text{ bit/sec}$

61. $\displaystyle\int u^n e^{au} \, du$

Let

$$f = u^n \qquad \text{and} \qquad dV = e^{au} \, du$$
$$df = nu^{n-1} \, du \qquad\qquad V = \frac{1}{a}e^{au}$$

$$= \frac{1}{a}u^n e^{au} - \int \frac{1}{a}e^{au} \cdot nu^{n-1} \, du$$

$$= \frac{1}{a}u^n e^{au} - \frac{n}{a} \int u^{n-1}e^{au} \, du$$

63. $\text{area} = \displaystyle\int_0^{\ln 2} \left(2 - e^x\right) \, dx$

$= \left(2x - e^x\right) \Big|_0^{\ln 2}$

$= \left(2 \ln 2 - e^{\ln 2}\right) - \left(0 - e^0\right)$

$= 2 \ln 2 - 1 \approx 0.38629$

$\bar{x} = \dfrac{1}{0.38629} \displaystyle\int_0^{\ln 2} x \left(2 - e^x\right) \, dx$

$= 2.5887 \left[\displaystyle\int_0^{\ln 2} 2x \, dx - \int_0^{\ln 2} x e^x \, dx \right]$

Let $u = x$ and $dV = e^x \, dx$

$= 2.5887 \left[x^2 \Big|_0^{\ln 2} - \left(x e^x \Big|_0^{\ln 2} - \int_0^{\ln 2} e^x \, dx \right) \right]$

$= 2.5887 \left(x^2 - x e^x + e^x \right) \Big|_0^{\ln 2}$

$= 2.5887 \left[\left((\ln 2)^2 - (\ln 2)(e^{\ln 2}) + e^{\ln 2} \right) \right.$

$\left. - \left(0 - 0 + e^0 \right) \right] \approx 0.244$

$\bar{y} = \dfrac{1}{2(0.38629)} \displaystyle\int_0^{\ln 2} \left(2 - e^x\right)^2 \, dx$

$= 1.2944 \displaystyle\int_0^{\ln 2} \left(4 - 4e^x + e^{2x} \right) \, dx$

$= 1.2944 \left(4x - 4e^x + \dfrac{1}{2} e^{2x} \right) \Big|_0^{\ln 2}$

$= 1.2944 \left[\left(4 \ln 2 - 4 e^{\ln 2} + \dfrac{1}{2} e^{2(\ln 2)} \right) \right.$

$\left. - \left(0 - 4e^0 + \dfrac{1}{2} e^0 \right) \right] \approx 0.353$

So, the centroid is $(0.244, 0.353)$.

65. (a) The kiosk should be located at the centroid.
Using $y = \sqrt{2x^2 - 1}$,

$\text{Area} = \displaystyle\int_1^5 \sqrt{2x^2 - 1} \, dx$

$= \displaystyle\int_1^5 \sqrt{(\sqrt{2}x)^2 - (1)^2} \, dx$

which most closely resembles $\int \sqrt{u^2 - a^2} \, du$ (formula #18). Rewriting,

$\displaystyle\int_1^5 \sqrt{(\sqrt{2}x)^2 - (1)^2} \, dx$

$= \dfrac{1}{\sqrt{2}} \displaystyle\int_1^5 \sqrt{(\sqrt{2}x)^2 - (1)^2} \cdot \sqrt{2} \, dx$

The formula can be used with $u = \sqrt{2}x$, $du = \sqrt{2} \, dx$, and $a = 1$.

$= \dfrac{1}{\sqrt{2}} \left[\dfrac{\sqrt{2}x}{2} \sqrt{2x^2 - 1} - \dfrac{1}{2} \ln \left| \sqrt{2}x + \sqrt{2x^2 - 1} \right| \right]_1^5$

$= \dfrac{1}{\sqrt{2}} \left[\left(\dfrac{\sqrt{2}(5)}{2} \sqrt{2(5)^2 - 1} - \dfrac{1}{2} \ln \left| \sqrt{2}(5) + \sqrt{2(5)^2 - 1} \right| \right) \right.$

$\left. - \left(\dfrac{\sqrt{2}(1)}{2} \sqrt{2(1)^2 - 1} - \dfrac{1}{2} \ln \left| \sqrt{2}(1) + \sqrt{2(1)^2 - 1} \right| \right) \right]$

$= \dfrac{1}{\sqrt{2}} \left[\dfrac{35\sqrt{2}}{2} - \dfrac{1}{2} \ln \left| 5\sqrt{2} + 7 \right| - \dfrac{\sqrt{2}}{2} + \dfrac{1}{2} \ln \left(\sqrt{2} + 1 \right) \right]$

≈ 16.3768

$\bar{x} = \dfrac{1}{16.3768} \displaystyle\int_1^5 x \sqrt{2x^2 - 1} \, dx$

Using substitution with $u = 2x^2 - 1$, $\dfrac{1}{4} \, du = x \, dx$, and limits of integration of $2(1)^2 - 1 = 1$ and $2(5)^2 - 1 = 49$,

$\bar{x} = 0.06106 \left(\dfrac{1}{4} \displaystyle\int_1^{49} u^{1/2} \, du \right)$

$= 0.01527 \left(\dfrac{2}{3} u^{3/2} \right) \Big|_1^{49}$

$= 0.010177 \left[(49)^{3/2} - (1)^{3/2} \right] \approx 3.48$

$$\bar{y} = \frac{1}{2(16.3768)} \int_1^5 \left(\sqrt{2x^2 - 1}\right)^2 dx$$

$$= 0.030531 \int_1^5 (2x^2 - 1)\, dx$$

$$= 0.030531 \left[\frac{2x^3}{3} - x\right]_1^5$$

$$= 0.030531 \left[\left(\frac{2(5)^3}{3} - 5\right) - \left(\frac{2(1)^3}{3} - 1\right)\right]$$

$$\approx 2.40$$

So, the kiosk should be located at the coordinates (3.48, 2.40).

(b) Writing Exercise—Answers will vary.

67. To use graphing utility to find where curves intersect and compute the area of region bounded by the curves,

Press [y=] and input $\sqrt{\left(\left(\frac{2}{5}\right)x^2 - 2\right)}$ for $y_1 =$.

Input $-\sqrt{\left(\left(\frac{2}{5}\right)x^2 - 2\right)}$ for $y_2 =$,

and input $x^\wedge 3 - 3.5x^2 + 2x$ for $y_3 =$.

Use window dimensions $[-1, 4]1$ by $[-3, 5]1$ for a good view of where the graphs intersect.
Use trace and zoom to find the points of intersection or use the intersect function under the calc menu to find $(2.966, 1.232)$ and $(2.608, -0.850)$ are the two points of intersection.
To find the area bounded by the curves, we must find that the x-intercept of the hyperbola is $x \approx 2.236$. Then we need

$$\int_{2.236}^{2.608} y_1 - y_2 + \int_{2.608}^{2.966} y_1 - y_3 = \int_{2.236}^{2.608} y_1$$

$$- \int_{2.236}^{2.608} y_2 + \int_{2.608}^{2.966} y_1 - \int_{2.608}^{2.966} y_3$$

Use the $\int f(x)\, dx$ function under the calc menu making sure the current equation is activated for each integral. The area is approximately 0.75834. Alternatively, you can use the *fnInt* function from the home screen under the math menu and enter:

$$fnInt(y_1 - y_2, x, 2.236, 2.608)$$
$$+ fnInt(y_1 - y_3, x, 2.608, 2.966)$$

You can insert y_1, y_2, y_3 by pressing [vars] and select Function under $Y - vars$ and then select which y function to insert.

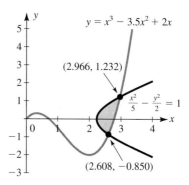

69. Press [y=]. Input $e \wedge (2x) + 4$ for $y_1 =$ and $5e \wedge (x)$ for y_2.
Use window dimensions $[-1, 3]1$ by $[-5, 25]5$.
Press [graph].
Use the intersect function under the calc menu to find the two points of intersection. Enter a value close to the first point of intersection on $y_1 =$ and also on $y_2 =$. Then enter a guess. The first point of intersection is $(0, 5)$. Repeat this process for the second point of intersection to find $(1.386, 20)$. To find the area boounded by these two curves, we must find

$$\int_0^{1.386} y_2 - y_1 = \int_0^{1.386} y_2 - \int_0^{1.386} y_1.$$

Use the $\int f(x)dx$ function under the calc menu making sure the current equation is activated for each integral. The area is approximately 1.9548. Alternatively, you can use the *fnInt* function from the home screen under the math menu and enter

$fnInt(y_2 - y_1, x, 0, 1.386)$
You can insert y_1 and y_2 by pressing $\boxed{\text{vars}}$ and selecting function under the y-vars.

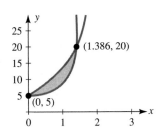

71. To use the numeric integration feature to evaluate the integral,

Press $\boxed{\text{y=}}$ and input $\sqrt{(4x^2 - 7)}$ for $y_1 =$.
Use window dimensions $[-1, 4]1$ by $[-3, 5]1$.
Press $\boxed{\text{Graph}}$.

Use the $\int f(x)\, dx$ function under the calc menu. Enter $x = 2$ for the lower limit and $x = 3$ for the upper limit. We see that $\int_2^3 \sqrt{4x^2 - 7}\, dx \simeq 4.227$. To verify, we use formula #18 on the table of integrals with

$$u = 2x$$
$$du = 2\, dx$$
$$dx = \frac{1}{2}\, du$$

When $x = 2$, $u = 4$;
when $x = 3$, $u = 6$.
So,

$$\int_2^3 \sqrt{4x^2 - 7}\, dx$$

$$= \frac{1}{2} \int_4^6 \sqrt{u^2 - 7}\, du$$

$$= \frac{1}{2} \left[\frac{u}{2}\sqrt{u^2 - 7} - \frac{7}{2} \ln \left| u + \sqrt{u^2 - 7} \right| \right] \Big|_4^6$$

$$= \frac{1}{2} \left[3\sqrt{29} - \frac{7}{2} \ln(6 + \sqrt{29}) - 2(3) + \frac{7}{2} \ln 7 \right]$$

$$= \frac{1}{2}(8.45309083)$$

$$\approx 4.227$$

73. To use the numeric integration feature to evaluate the integral,

Press $\boxed{\text{y=}}$ and input $\sqrt{\left((x^2 + 2x)\right) / \left((x + 1)^2\right)}$
for $y_1 =$.
Use window dimensions $[-1, 3]1$ by $[-1, 2]1$.
Press $\boxed{\text{graph}}$.

Use the $\int f(x)\, dx$ function under the calc menu with $x = 0$ as the lower limit and $x = 1$ the upper limit. We see that

$$\int_0^1 \frac{\sqrt{x^2 + 2x}}{(x + 1)^2}\, dx \approx 0.4509$$

To verify, we use formula #19 on the table of integrals:

$$\int_0^1 \frac{\sqrt{x^2 + 2x}}{(x + 1)^2}\, dx = \int_0^1 \frac{\sqrt{(x + 1)^2 - 1}}{(x + 1)^2}\, dx$$

Let

$$u = x + 1$$
$$du = dx$$

When $x = 0$, $u = 1$;
when $x = 1$, $u = 2$.
So,

$$\int_1^2 \frac{\sqrt{u^2 - 1}}{u^2}\, du$$

$$= \left[-\frac{\sqrt{u^2 - 1}}{u} + \ln \left| u + \sqrt{u^2 - 1} \right| \right] \Bigg|_1^2$$

$$= -\frac{\sqrt{3}}{2} + \ln \left| 2 + \sqrt{3} \right| - \left(-\frac{\sqrt{0}}{1} + \ln \left| 1 + \sqrt{0} \right| \right)$$

$$= -\frac{\sqrt{3}}{2} + \ln(2 + \sqrt{3}) - \ln 1$$

$$\approx 0.4509$$

6.2   Introduction to Differential Equations

1.
$$\frac{dy}{dx} = 3x^2 + 5x - 6$$

$$y = \int \frac{dy}{dx}\, dx$$

$$y = \int (3x^2 + 5x - 6)\, dx$$

$$= x^3 + \frac{5}{2}x^2 - 6x + C.$$

3.   Separate the variables
$$\frac{dy}{dx} = 3y$$

$$\frac{1}{y}\, dy = 3\, dx$$

and integrate
$$\int \frac{1}{y}\, dy = \int 3\, dx,$$

$$\ln |y| = 3x + C_1,$$

$$|y| = e^{3x + C_1} = e^{C_1} e^{3x}, \text{ or } y = C e^{3x}$$

where C is the constant $\pm e^{C_1}$.

5.   Separate the variables of

$$\frac{dy}{dx} = e^y$$

$$\frac{1}{e^y}\, dy = dx$$

and integrate

$$\int e^{-y}\, dy = \int dx,$$

$$-e^{-y} = x + C_1 \text{ or } e^{-y} = C - x$$

where C is the constant $-C_1$. So,

$$\ln e^{-y} = \ln(C - x),$$

$$-y = \ln(C - x), \text{ or } y = -\ln(C - x)$$

7.   Separate the variables of
$$\frac{dy}{dx} = \frac{x}{y}$$

$$y\, dy = x\, dx$$

and integrate
$$\int y\, dy = \int x\, dx,$$

$$\frac{y^2}{2} = \frac{x^2}{2} + C_1 \text{ or } y^2 = x^2 + C$$

$$y = \pm\sqrt{x^2 + C}, \text{ where } C \text{ is the constant } 2C_1.$$

9.   Separate the variables of
$$\frac{dy}{dx} = \sqrt{xy} = \sqrt{x}\sqrt{y}$$

$$\frac{1}{\sqrt{y}}\, dy = \sqrt{x}\, dx$$

and integrate
$$\int y^{-1/2}\, dy = \int x^{1/2}\, dx$$

$$2y^{1/2} = \frac{2}{3}x^{3/2} + C_1$$

$$y = \left(\frac{1}{3}x^{3/2} + C \right)^2$$

where C is the constant $2C_1$.

11.   Separate the variables of

$$\frac{dy}{dx} = \frac{y}{x-1}$$

$$\frac{1}{y} \, dy = \frac{1}{x-1} \, dx$$

and integrate

$$\int \frac{1}{y} \, dy = \int \frac{1}{x-1} \, dx$$

$$\ln |y| = \ln |x-1| + C_1$$

$$\ln |y| - \ln |x-1| = C_1$$

$$\ln \frac{|y|}{|x-1|} = C_1$$

$$\frac{|y|}{|x-1|} = e^{C_1}$$

$$|y| = e^{C_1} |x-1|$$

$$y = \pm e^{C_1} |x-1|$$

$$y = C |x-1|$$

where C is the constant $\pm e^{C_1}$.

13. Separate the variables of

$$\frac{dy}{dx} = \frac{y+3}{(2x-5)^6}$$

$$\frac{1}{y+3} \, dy = \frac{1}{(2x-5)^6} \, dx$$

and integrate

$$\int \frac{1}{y+3} \, dy = \int (2x-5)^{-6} \, dx$$

$$\ln |y+3| = -\frac{1}{10}(2x-5)^{-5} + C_1$$

$$|y+3| = e^{-1/10(2x-5)^{-5} + C_1}$$

$$|y+3| = e^{C_1} e^{-1/10(2x-5)^{-5}}$$

$$y+3 = \pm e^{C_1} e^{-1/10(2x-5)^{-5}}$$

$$y = -3 + C e^{-1/10(2x-5)^{-5}}$$

where C is the constant $\pm e^{C_1}$.
Note: $\ln |y+3| = -\frac{1}{10}(2x-5)^{-5} + C_1$

$$\ln |y+3|^{10} = -(2x-5)^{-5} + C_1.$$

15. Separate the variables of

$$\frac{dx}{dt} = \frac{xt}{2t+1}$$

$$\frac{1}{x} \, dx = \frac{t}{2t+1} \, dt$$

and integrate

$$\int \frac{1}{x} \, dx = \int \frac{t}{2t+1} \, dt$$

using substitution with $u = 2t+1$,

$$\int \frac{1}{x} \, dx = \frac{1}{2} \int \frac{\frac{u-1}{2}}{u} \, du$$

$$= \frac{1}{4} \int \frac{u-1}{u} \, du$$

$$= \frac{1}{4} \int 1 - \frac{1}{u} \, du$$

$$\ln |x| = \frac{1}{4} u - \frac{1}{4} \ln |u| + C_1$$

$$= \frac{1}{4}(2t+1) - \frac{1}{4} \ln |2t+1| + C_1$$

$$= \frac{t}{2} - \frac{1}{4} \ln |2t+1| + C_2$$

$$= \frac{t}{2} + \ln(2t+1)^{-1/4} + C_2$$

where C_2 is the constant $\frac{1}{4} + C_1$.

$$|x| = e^{t/2 + \ln(2t+1)^{-1/4} + C_2}$$

$$|x| = e^{t/2}(2t+1)^{-1/4} \cdot e^{C_2}$$

$$x = \frac{\pm e^{C_2} e^{t/2}}{(2t+1)^{1/4}}$$

$$x = \frac{C e^{t/2}}{(2t+1)^{1/4}}$$

where C is the constant $\pm e^{C_2}$.

17. Separate the variables of

$$\frac{dy}{dx} = xe^{x-y} = x \cdot \frac{e^x}{e^y}$$

$$e^y \, dy = xe^x \, dx$$

and integrate

$$\int e^y \, dy = \int x e^x \, dx$$

Let

$$u = x \quad \text{and} \quad dV = e^x \, dx$$
$$du = dx \qquad\qquad V = e^x$$

$$\int e^y \, dy = x e^x - \int e^x \, dx$$

$$e^y = x e^x - e^x + C_1$$

$$y = \ln\left(x e^x - e^x + C_1\right)$$

19. Separate the variables of

$$\frac{dy}{dt} = y \ln \sqrt{t} = y \ln t^{1/2} = y \frac{1}{2} \ln t$$

$$\frac{1}{y} \, dy = \frac{1}{2} \ln t \, dt$$

and integrate

$$\int \frac{1}{y} \, dy = \frac{1}{2} \int \ln t \, dt$$

Let

$$u = \ln t \quad \text{and} \quad dV = dt$$
$$du = \frac{1}{2} \, dt \qquad\qquad V = t$$

$$\int \frac{1}{y} \, dy = \frac{1}{2} \left[t \ln t - \int t \cdot \frac{1}{t} \, dt \right]$$

$$\ln |y| = \frac{1}{2} \left[t \ln t - t \right] + C_1$$

$$|y| = e^{t/2(\ln t - 1) + C_1}$$

$$|y| = e^{C_1} \cdot e^{t/2(\ln t - 1)}$$

$$y = \pm e^{C_1} \cdot e^{t/2(\ln t - 1)}$$

$$y = C e^{t(\ln t - 1)/2}$$

where C is the constant $\pm e^{C_1}$.

21.

$$\frac{dy}{dx} = e^{5x}$$

$$\int \frac{dy}{dx} \, dx = \int e^{5x} \, dx$$

$$y = \frac{1}{5} e^{5x} + C$$

Since $y = 1$ when $x = 0$,

$$1 = \frac{1}{5} e^0 + C, \text{ or } C = \frac{4}{5}$$

So,

$$y = \frac{1}{5} e^{5x} + \frac{4}{5}$$

23.

$$\frac{dy}{dx} = \frac{x}{y^2}$$

$$y^2 \, dy = x \, dx$$

$$\int y^2 \, dy = \int x \, dx$$

$$\frac{y^3}{3} = \frac{x^2}{2} + C_1$$

$$y^3 = \frac{3}{2} x^2 + C_2$$

where C_2 is the constant $3C_1$,

$$y = \left(\frac{3}{2} x^2 + C_2 \right)^{1/3}$$

since $y = 3$ when $x = 2$,

$$3 = \left[\frac{3}{2} (2)^2 + C_2 \right]^{1/3}$$

$$3 = (6 + C_2)^{1/3}$$

$$27 = 6 + C_2, \text{ or } C_2 = 21$$

So,

$$y = \left(\frac{3}{2} x^2 + 21 \right)^{1/3}$$

$$= \left(\frac{3x^2 + 42}{2} \right)^{1/3}$$

25.
$$\frac{dy}{dx} = y^2 (4 - x)^{1/2}$$

$$\frac{1}{y^2}\, dy = (4 - x)^{1/2}\, dx$$

$$\int y^{-2}\, dy = \int (4 - x)^{1/2}\, dx$$

$$\frac{y^{-1}}{-1} = \frac{-2}{3}(4 - x)^{3/2} + C_1$$

$$\frac{1}{y} = \frac{2}{3}(4 - x)^{3/2} - C_1$$

Since $y = 2$ when $x = 4$,

$$\frac{1}{2} = \frac{2}{3}(0) - C_1, \text{ or } C_1 = -\frac{1}{2}$$

$$\frac{1}{y} = \frac{2}{3}(4 - x)^{3/2} + \frac{1}{2} = \frac{4(4 - x)^{3/2} + 3}{6}$$

$$y = \frac{6}{4(4 - x)^{3/2} + 3}$$

27.
$$\frac{dy}{dt} = \frac{y + 1}{t(y - 1)}$$

$$\frac{y - 1}{y + 1}\, dy = \frac{1}{t}\, dt$$

$$\left(1 - \frac{2}{y + 1}\right) dy = \frac{1}{t}\, dt$$

$$y - 2\ln|y + 1| = \ln|t| + C_1$$

Since $y = 2$ when $t = 1$,

$$2 - 2\ln 3 = 0 + C_1,$$
$$\text{or } C_1 = 2(1 - \ln 3)$$
$$y - 2\ln|y + 1| = \ln|t| + 2(1 - \ln 3)$$

29. Let V denote the value of the investment. Then, $\frac{dV}{dt}$ is the rate of change of V, and since this rate is equal to 7% of its size,

$$\frac{dV}{dt} = 0.07V$$

31. The rate of change of p, $\frac{dp}{dt}$, is jointly proportional to p and t, so

$$\frac{dp}{dt} = kpt$$

where k is a negative constant of proportionality (since p is decreasing)

33. Let C denote the cost per unit x. Then, $\frac{dc}{dx}$ is the rate of change of C, and since this rate is a constant 60,

$$\frac{dC}{dx} = 60$$

35. Let Q denote the number of bacteria. Then, $\frac{dQ}{dt}$ is the rate of change of Q, and since this rate of change is proportional to Q,

$$\frac{dQ}{dt} = kQ$$

where k is a positive constant of proportionality.

37. Let P denote the population. Then $\frac{dP}{dt}$ is the rate of change of P, and since this rate of change is the constant 500,

$$\frac{dP}{dt} = 500$$

39. Let $T_m =$ temperature of the surrounding medium

$$T(t) = \text{object's temperature at time } t$$

Then, $\frac{dT}{dt}$ is the rate of change of T and since this rate is proportional to $T_m - T$,

$$\frac{dT}{dt} = k\left(T_m - T\right)$$

41. Let $F =$ total number of facts and

$$R(t) = \text{number of facts recalled at time } t.$$

Then, $\frac{dR}{dt}$ is the rate of change of R and since this rate is proportional to $F - R$,

$$\frac{dR}{dt} = k(F - R)$$

43. Let $N =$ number of people involved and

$$P(t) = \text{number of people implicated at time } t.$$

Then, $\frac{dP}{dt}$ is the rate of change of P and since this rate is proportional to $(P)(N - P)$,

$$\frac{dP}{dt} = kP(N - P)$$

45. If $y = Ce^{kx}$, the derivative of y is

$$\frac{dy}{dx} = Ce^{kx} \cdot k = kCe^{kx} = ky,$$

the given differential equation.

47.
$$y = C_1 e^x + C_2 x e^x$$

$$\frac{dy}{dx} = C_1 e^x + C_2 (x e^x + e^x)$$

$$= (C_1 + C_2) e^x + C_2 x e^x$$

$$\frac{d^2 y}{dx^2} = (C_1 + C_2) e^x + C_2 (x e^x + e^x)$$

$$= (C_1 + 2C_2) e^x + C_2 x e^x$$

$$\frac{d^2 y}{dx^2} - 2\frac{dy}{dx} + y = (C_1 + 2C_2) e^x + C_2 x e^x$$

$$- 2C_1 e^x - 2C_2 x e^x - 2C_2 e^x$$

$$+ C_1 e^x + C_2 x e^x$$

$$= (C_1 + 2C_2 - 2C_1 - 2C_2 + C_1) e^x$$

$$+ (C_2 - 2C_2 + C_2) x e^x$$

$$= 0 \cdot e^x + 0 \cdot x e^x = 0$$

49. Rate revenue changes = (# barrels)(rate selling price changes).

$$\frac{dR}{dt} = 400(98 + 0.04t), \text{ where } t \text{ is in months.}$$

$$\text{Revenue} = \int_0^{24} 400(98 + 0.04t)\, dt$$

$$= 400(98t + 0.02t^2)\Big|_0^{24}$$

$$= 400\left[\left(98(24) + 0.2(24)^2\right) - 0\right]$$

$$\approx \$986,880$$

51. Let S_0 = amount of sugar placed in the container and
$D(t)$ = amount of sugar dissolved after time t.

$$\frac{dD}{dt} = k(S_0 - D)$$

$$\frac{1}{S - D} dD = k\, dt$$

$$-\ln|S_0 - D| = kt + C_1$$

$$\ln|S_0 - D| = -kt - C_1$$

$$|S_0 - D| = e^{kt - C_1}$$

$$|S_0 - D| = e^{-C_1} e^{-kt}$$

$$S_0 - D = Ce^{-kt}$$

$$D(t) = S_0 - Ce^{kt}$$

When $t = 0$, $D(0) = 0$, so

$$0 = S_0 - Ce^0, \text{ or } C = S_0.$$

So, $D(t) = S_0 - S_0 e^{-kt}$

$$= S_0\left(1 - e^{-kt}\right)$$

$$\lim_{t \to \infty} S_0\left(1 - e^{-kt}\right) = S_0,$$

so $y = S_0$ is a horizontal asymptote. Since $k > 0$ and $S_0 \geq D(t)$ for all t,

$$\frac{dD}{dt} > 0 \text{ for all } t > 0,$$

so D is always concave down.

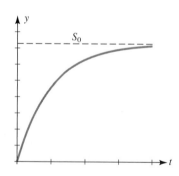

53. Let T_m = temperature of the surrounding medium and
$T(t)$ = object's temperature.

$$\frac{dT}{dt} = -k(T - T_m), \text{ where } k > 0.$$

$$\frac{1}{T - T_m} dT = -k \, dt$$

$$\ln |T - T_m| = -kt + C_1$$

$$\ln(T - T_m) = -kt + C_1$$

$$T - T_m = e^{-kt + C_1}$$

$$T - T_m = e^{C_1} \cdot e^{-kt}$$

$$T - T_m = Ce^{-kt}$$

$$T = T_m + Ce^{-kt}$$

When $t = 0$, $T(0) = T_0$, the initial temperature of the object. So,

$$T_0 = T)m + Ce^0$$

$$\text{or } C = T_0 - T_m$$

$$\text{and } T(t) = T_m + (T_0 - T_m)e^{-kt}$$

$$\lim_{t \to \infty} T_m + (T_0 - T_m)e^{-kt} = T_m.$$

so, $y = T_m$ is a horizontal asymptote. Since $\frac{dT}{dt} < 0$ for all $t > 0$, T is always decreasing. Since $\frac{d^2T}{dt^2} > 0$ for all $t > 0$, T is always concave up.

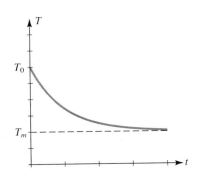

55. (a) rate salt flows out
$$= (\text{salt/gal}) \text{ flowing out})(\text{gal/min flowing out})$$
$$= \left(\frac{S(t)}{200} \right)(5) = \frac{S(t)}{40} \text{ gal/min}$$

(b) $\frac{dS}{dt} = (\text{rate salt enters}) - (\text{rate salt leaves})$

$$= (\text{salt/gal flowing in})(\text{gal/min flowing in}) - \frac{S}{40}$$

$$= (0)(5) - \frac{S}{40} = -\frac{S}{40}$$

(c)
$$\frac{dS}{dt} = -\frac{S}{40}$$

$$\int \frac{1}{S} dS = -\frac{1}{40} \int dt$$

$$\ln |S| = -\frac{1}{40}t + C_1$$

$$|S| = e^{-1/40t + C_1}$$

$$|S| = e^{C_1} \cdot e^{-1/40t}$$

$$S = \pm e^{C_1} \cdot e^{-1/40t}$$

$$S = Ce^{-t/40}$$

When $t = 0$, $S(0) = (2\text{lbs/gal})(200\text{gal}) = 400\text{lbs}$, so $400 = Ce^0$, or $C = 400$. So, $S(t) = 400e^{-t/40}$.

57. (a) The rate value is changing $=$ (rate balance increases due to interest)–(rate money is withdrawn).

$$\frac{dV}{dt} = rV - W$$

$$\int \frac{1}{rV - W} dV = \int dt$$

$$\frac{1}{r} \ln |rV - W| = t + C_1$$

$$\ln |rV - W| = rt + C_2$$

where $C_2 = rC_1$

$$|rV - W| = e^{rt + C_2}$$

$$|rV - W| = e^{C_2} \cdot e^{rt}$$

$$rV - W = \pm e^{C_2} \cdot e^{rt}$$

$$rV - W = Ce^{rt}$$

$$rV = Ce^{rt} + W$$

$$V(t) = \frac{C}{r}e^{rt} + \frac{W}{r}$$

When $t = 0$, $V(0) = S$, so

$$S = \frac{C}{r}e^0 + \frac{2}{r}$$

$$S = \frac{C + W}{r}$$

$$Sr - W = C$$

and

$$V(t) = \frac{Sr - W}{r}e^{rt} + \frac{W}{r} = \left(S - \frac{W}{r}\right)e^{rt} + \frac{W}{r}$$

(b)
$$V(10) = \left(500{,}000 - \frac{50{,}000}{0.05}\right)e^{0.05(10)}$$

$$+ \frac{50{,}000}{0.05}$$

$$\approx \$175{,}639.35$$

(c) Need annual interest on $500{,}000 = W$
interest $= 500{,}000(0.05)$
$= 25{,}000$
So, \$25,000 can be withdrawn annually without changing the annual balance.

(d)
$$0 = \left(500{,}000 - \frac{80{,}000}{0.05}\right)e^{0.05t} + \frac{80{,}000}{0.05}$$

$$\frac{-1{,}600{,}000}{-1{,}100{,}000} = e^{0.05t}$$

$$\ln \frac{16}{11} = \ln e^{0.05t}$$

$$\ln \frac{16}{11} = 0.05t$$

$$\text{or } t = 20 \ln \frac{16}{11} \approx 7.49 \text{ years}$$

59.
$$\frac{dp}{dt} = k(1 - p)$$

where k is a constant of proportionality

$$\int \frac{dp}{1 - p} = \int k \, dt$$

$$-\ln |1 - p| = kt + C_1$$

$$\ln |1 - p| = -kt - C_1$$

$$|1 - p| = e^{-kt - C_1}$$

$$|1 - p| = e^{-kt} \cdot e^{-C_1}$$

$$1 - p = \pm e^{-C_1}e^{-kt}$$

$$1 - p = Ce^{-kt}$$

$$p(t) = 1 - Ce^{-kt}$$

When $t = 0$, $p(0) = 0$, so

$$0 = 1 - Ce^0, \quad \text{or } C = 1$$

and $p(t) = 1 - e^{-kt}$.

Further, when $t = 8$, $p(8) = 0.05$, so

$$0.05 = 1 - e^{-8k}$$

$$e^{-8k} = 0.95$$

$$-8k = \ln 0.95, \quad \text{or } k = -\frac{\ln 0.95}{8}$$

and $p(t) = 1 - e^{-\left(-\frac{\ln 0.95}{8}\right)t}$

$$= 1 - e^{\left(\frac{\ln 0.95}{8}\right)t} = 1 - e^{\ln(0.95)\frac{1}{8}t} = 1 - (0.95)^{\frac{t}{8}}$$

61. Let $O(t)$ be the amount of ozone in the room at time t.
Rate ozone changes
$= $ (amt. ozone/cubic ft.)(rate ozone removed)

$$\frac{dO}{dt} = \left(\frac{O}{2400}\right)(-400) = -\frac{O}{6}$$

$$\int \frac{1}{O} \, dO = -\frac{1}{6} \int dt$$

$$\ln |O| = -\frac{1}{6}t + C_1$$

$$|O| = e^{-t/6 + C_1}$$

$$|O| = e^{C_1} \cdot e^{-t/6}$$

$$) = \pm e^{C_1}e^{-t/6}$$

$$O(t) = Ce^{-t/6}$$

When $t = 0$, $O(0) = O_0$, the initial amount of ozone in the room and $O(t) = O_0 e^{-t/6}$

Need t when $O(t) = \dfrac{O_0}{2}$.

$$\dfrac{O_0}{2} O_0 e^{-t/6}$$

$$\ln \dfrac{1}{2} = -\dfrac{t}{6}, \text{ or}$$

$$-t = 6 \ln \dfrac{1}{2}$$

$$t = 6 \ln 2, \text{ or approx 4.16 minutes.}$$

63. (a)

$$\dfrac{dp}{dt} = k(D - S)$$

$$= k \left[(7 - p) - (1 + p) \right]$$

$$= k(6 - 2p)$$

$$\dfrac{1}{6 - 2p} dp = k \, dt$$

$$-\dfrac{1}{2} \ln |6 - 2p| = kt + C_1$$

$$\ln |6 - 2p| = -2kt - 2C_1$$

$$|6 - 2p| = e^{-2kt - 2C_1}$$

$$|6 - 2p| = e^{-2C_1} \cdot e^{-2kt}$$

$$6 - 2p = \pm e^{-2C_1} e^{-2kt}$$

$$6 - 2 = Ce^{-2kt}$$

$$p(t) = \dfrac{6 - Ce^{-2k}}{2} = 3 - \dfrac{Ce^{-2kt}}{2}$$

When $t = 0$, $p(0) = 6$, so

$$6 = 3 - \dfrac{Ce^0}{2},$$

or $C = -6$

So $p(t) = 3 + 3e^{-2kt}$

When $t = 4$, $p(4) = 4$, so

$$4 = 3 + 3e^{-2k(4)}$$

$$\dfrac{1}{3} = e^{-8k}$$

$$\ln \dfrac{1}{3} = -8k,$$

$$\text{or } k = \dfrac{\ln \frac{1}{3}}{-8} = \dfrac{-\ln \frac{1}{3}}{8} = \dfrac{\ln 3}{8}$$

and $p(t) = 3 + 3e^{-2\left(\frac{\ln 3}{8} \right)t}$

$$= 3 + 3e^{\frac{-\ln 3}{4}t}$$

(b) $\displaystyle \lim_{t \to \infty} 3 + 3e^{\frac{-\ln 3}{4}t} = 3$

and $D = S$ when $7 - p = 1 + p$

$$6 = 2p$$

$$3 = p$$

65. (a) $\dfrac{dD}{dt} = aI$ and $\dfrac{dI}{dt} = bI$

Solve the second equation first since it involves only two variables.

$$\dfrac{dI}{I} = b \, dt$$

$$\ln I = bt + C_1, \ I(t) = Ce^{bt}$$

where $C = e^{C_1}$. Since $I(0) = I_0 = C$

$$I(t) = I_0 e^{bt}$$

Substitute $I(t)$ in the other differential equation to get

$$\dfrac{dD}{dt} = aI_0 e^{bt}$$

$$D(t) = \dfrac{aI_0}{b} e^{bt} + C_2$$

$$D(0) = D_0 = \dfrac{aI_0}{b} + C_2$$

$$D(t) = D_0 + \dfrac{aI_0}{b} \left(e^{bt} - 1 \right)$$

(b) L'Hôpital's rule is necessary to evaluate

$$\lim_{t \to +\infty} \frac{D(t)}{I(t)} = \lim_{t \to +\infty} \frac{D_0 + \frac{aI_0}{b}\left(e^{bt} - 1\right)}{I_0 e^{bt}}$$

$$= \lim_{t \to +\infty} \frac{aI_0 e^{bt}}{I_0 b e^{bt}} = \frac{a}{b}$$

67. Let $P(t) =$ number of infected residents and $C =$ total number of susceptible residents. We need to maximize the rate at which residents become infected, or

$$\frac{dP}{dt} = kP(C - P)$$

So, $\dfrac{d^2P}{dt^2} = k\left[P\left(-\dfrac{dP}{dt}\right) + (C - P)\left(\dfrac{dP}{dt}\right)\right]$

$$= k(C - 2P)\frac{dP}{dt}$$

$\dfrac{d^2P}{dt^2} = 0$ when $0 = k(C - 2P)$,

(eliminating when $\dfrac{dP}{dt} = 0$)

or, $P = \dfrac{C}{2}$.

When $0 < P < \dfrac{C}{2}$, $\dfrac{d^2P}{dt^2} > 0$, so $\dfrac{dP}{dt}$ is increasing

$P > \dfrac{C}{2}$, $\dfrac{d^2P}{dt^2} < 0$, so $\dfrac{dP}{dt}$ is increasing

Therefore, $\dfrac{dP}{dt}$ is a maximum when $P = \dfrac{C}{2}$.

69.

$$\frac{dC}{dt} = R - kC$$

$$\int \frac{1}{R - kC}\, dC = \int dt$$

$$-\frac{1}{k}\ln|R - kC| = t + C_1$$

$$\ln|R - kC| = -kt - dC_1$$

$$|R - kC| = e^{-kt - kC_1}$$

$$|R - kC| = e^{-kC_1} \cdot e^{-kt}$$

$$R - kC = \pm e^{kC_1} e^{-kt}$$

$$R - kC = C_2 e^{-kt}$$

$$C(t) = \frac{R - C_2 e^{-kt}}{k}$$

Since $= C(0) = C_0$,

$$C_0 = \frac{R - C_2 e^0}{e}.$$

or $C_2 = R - kC_0$

and

$$C(t) = \frac{R - (R - kC_0)e^{-kt}}{k}$$

$$C(t) = \frac{R}{k} - \left(\frac{R}{k} - C_0\right)e^{-kt}$$

$$= \frac{R}{k} + \left(C_0 - \frac{R}{k}\right)e^{-kt}$$

6.3 Improper Integrals; Continuous Probability

1.

$$\int_1^\infty \frac{1}{x^3}\, dx$$

$$= \lim_{N \to \infty} \int_1^N x^{-3} dx$$

$$= \lim_{N \to \infty} -\frac{1}{2}\left(\frac{1}{x^2}\right)\Bigg|_1^N$$

$$= -\frac{1}{2}\lim_{N \to \infty}\left(\frac{1}{N^2} - \frac{1}{1}\right) = -\frac{1}{2}(0 - 1) = \frac{1}{2}$$

3.
$$\int_1^\infty \frac{1}{\sqrt{x}}\,dx = \lim_{N\to\infty} \int_1^N x^{-1/2}\,dx$$

$$= \lim_{N\to\infty} 2\left(x^{1/2}\right)\Big|_1^N$$

$$= 2\lim_{N\to\infty} \left(x^{1/2}\right)\Big|_1^N$$

$$= 2\left(\sqrt{N}-1\right) = \infty$$

So, the integral diverges.

5.
$$\int_3^\infty \frac{1}{2x-1}\,dx = \lim_{N\to\infty} \int_3^N \frac{1}{2x-1}\,dx$$

$$= \lim_{N\to\infty} \frac{1}{2}\ln|2x-1|\,\Big|_3^N$$

$$= \frac{1}{2}\lim_{N\to\infty} \ln|2x-1|\,\Big|_3^N$$

$$= \frac{1}{2}\lim_{N\to\infty} [\ln(2N-1) - \ln 7]$$

$$= \infty$$

So, the integral diverges.

7.
$$\int_3^\infty \frac{1}{(2x-1)^2}\,dx$$

$$= \lim_{N\to\infty} \int_3^N (2x-1)^{-2}\,dx$$

$$= \lim_{N\to\infty} \frac{1}{2}\left(-\frac{1}{2x-1}\right)\Big|_3^N$$

$$= \frac{1}{2}\lim_{N\to\infty}\left(-\frac{1}{2N-1} + \frac{1}{5}\right) = \frac{1}{2}\cdot\frac{1}{5} = \frac{1}{10}$$

9.
$$\int_0^\infty 5e^{-2x}\,dx$$

$$= \lim_{N\to\infty} 5\int_0^N e^{-2x}\,dx$$

$$= 5\lim_{N\to\infty} -\frac{1}{2}\left(e^{-2x}\right)\Big|_0^N$$

$$= -\frac{5}{2}\lim_{N\to\infty}\left(e^{-2N} - e^0\right)$$

$$= -\frac{5}{2}\cdot -1 = \frac{5}{2}$$

11.
$$\int_1^\infty \frac{x^2}{(x^3+2)^2}\,dx = \lim_{N\to\infty} \int_1^N \frac{x^2}{(x^3+2)^2}\,dx$$

Using substitution with $u = x^3 + 2$,

$$= \lim_{N\to\infty} \frac{1}{3}\int_3^{N^3+2} u^{-2}\,du$$

$$= \frac{1}{3}\lim_{N\to\infty}\left(-\frac{1}{u}\right)\Big|_3^{N^3+2}$$

$$= \frac{1}{3}\lim_{N\to\infty}\left(-\frac{1}{N^3+2} + \frac{1}{3}\right)$$

$$= \frac{1}{3}\cdot\frac{1}{3} = \frac{1}{9}$$

13.
$$\int_1^\infty \frac{x^2}{\sqrt{x^3+2}}\,dx = \lim_{N\to\infty} \int_1^N \frac{x^2}{(x^3+2)^{1/2}}\,dx$$

Using substitution with $u = x^3 + 2$,

$$= \lim_{N\to\infty} \frac{1}{3}\int_3^{N^3+2} u^{-1/2}\,du$$

$$= \frac{1}{3}\lim_{N\to\infty} 2\left(u^{1/2}\right)\Big|_3^{N^3+2}$$

$$= \frac{2}{3}\lim_{N\to\infty}\left(\sqrt{N^3+2} - \sqrt{3}\right) = \infty$$

So, the integral diverges.

15.
$$\int_1^\infty \frac{e^{-\sqrt{x}}}{\sqrt{x}}\,dx = \lim_{N\to\infty} \int_1^N \frac{e^{-\sqrt{x}}}{\sqrt{x}}\,dx$$

Using substitution with $u = -\sqrt{x}$,

$$= \lim_{N\to\infty} -2\int_{-1}^{-\sqrt{N}} e^u\,du = 2\int_{-\sqrt{N}}^{-1} e^u\,du$$

$$= 2\lim_{N\to\infty}\left(e^u\right)\Big|_{-\sqrt{N}}^{-1}$$

$$= 2\lim_{N\to\infty}\left(\frac{1}{e} - \frac{1}{e^{\sqrt{N}}}\right) = \frac{2}{e}$$

17.
$$\int_0^\infty 2xe^{-3x}\,dx = \lim_{N\to\infty} 2\int_0^N xe^{-3x}\,dx$$

Using integration by parts, with $u = x$ and $dV = e^{-3x}\,dx$,

$$= 2 \lim_{N \to \infty} \left[-\frac{x}{3} e^{-3x} \Big|_0^N - \int_0^N -\frac{1}{3} e^{-3x} \, dx \right]$$

$$= 2 \lim_{N \to \infty} \left[-\frac{x}{3} e^{-3x} \Big|_0^N + \frac{1}{3} \int_0^N e^{-3x} \, dx \right]$$

$$= 2 \lim_{N \to \infty} \left(-\frac{x}{3} e^{-3x} - \frac{1}{9} e^{-3x} \right) \Big|_0^N$$

$$= 2 \lim_{N \to \infty} \left[\left(-\frac{N}{3} e^{-3N} - \frac{1}{9} e^{-3N} \right) - \left(0 - \frac{1}{9} e^0 \right) \right]$$

$$= 2 \lim_{N \to \infty} \left(-\frac{N}{3} e^{-3N} - \frac{1}{9} e^{-3N} + \frac{1}{9} \right)$$

$$= 2 \cdot \frac{1}{9} = \frac{2}{9}$$

19.
$$\int_1^\infty \frac{\ln x}{x} \, dx = \lim_{N \to \infty} \int_1^N \frac{\ln x}{x} \, dx$$

Using substitution with $u = \ln x$,

$$= \lim_{N \to \infty} \int_0^{\ln N} u \, du = \lim_{N \to \infty} \left(\frac{u^2}{2} \right) \Big|_0^{\ln N}$$

$$= \frac{1}{2} \lim_{N \to \infty} \left(u^2 \right) \Big|_0^{\ln N}$$

$$= \frac{1}{2} \lim_{N \to \infty} \left[(\ln N)^2 - 0 \right] = \infty$$

So, the integral diverges.

21.
$$\int_2^\infty \frac{1}{x \ln x} \, dx = \lim_{N \to \infty} \int_2^N \left(\frac{1}{\ln x} \right) \frac{1}{x} \, dx$$

Using substitution with $u = \ln x$,

$$= \lim_{N \to \infty} \int_{\ln 2}^{\ln N} \frac{1}{u} \, du = \lim_{N \to \infty} (\ln | u |) \Big|_{\ln 2}^{\ln N}$$

$$= \lim_{N \to \infty} [\ln(\ln N) - \ln(\ln 2)] = \infty$$

So, the integral diverges.

23.
$$\int_0^\infty x^2 e^{-x} \, dx = \lim_{N \to \infty} \int_0^N x^2 e^{-x} \, dx$$

Using integration by parts with $u = x^2$ and $dV = e^{-x} \, dx$,

$$= \lim_{N \to \infty} \left[-x^2 e^{-x} \Big|_0^N - \int_0^N -2x e^{-x} \, dx \right]$$

$$= \lim_{N \to \infty} \left[-x^2 e^{-x} \Big|_0^N + 2 \int_0^N x e^{-x} \, dx \right]$$

Using integration by parts with $u = x$ and $dV = e^{-x} \, dx$,

$$= \lim_{N \to \infty} \Bigg[-x^2 e^{-x} \Big|_0^N$$

$$+ 2 \left(-x e^{-x} \Big|_0^N - \int_0^N -e^{-x} \, dx \right) \Bigg]$$

$$= \lim_{N \to \infty} \Bigg[-x^2 e^{-x}$$

$$+ 2 \left(-x e^{-x} \Big|_0^N + \int_0^N e^{-x} \, dx \right) \Bigg]$$

$$= \lim_{N \to \infty} \left[-x^2 e^{-x} - 2x e^{-x} - 2e^{-x} \right] \Big|_0^N$$

$$= \lim_{N \to \infty} \left[\left(-N^2 e^{-N} - 2N e^{-N} - 2e^{-N} \right) \right.$$

$$\left. - \left(0 - 0 - 2e^0 \right) \right] = 2$$

25. Since $f(x) \geq 0$ for all x, the first condition is met. Checking the second condition,

$$\int_{-\infty}^\infty f(x) \, dx = \int_0^\infty \frac{10}{(x + 10)^2} \, dx$$

$$= \lim_{N \to \infty} \int_0^N \frac{10}{(x + 10)^2} \, dx = 10 \lim_{N \to \infty} \int_0^N \frac{1}{(x + 10)^2} \, dx$$

Using substitution with $u = x + 10$ and $du = dx$,

$$= 10 \lim_{N \to \infty} \int_{10}^{N+10} \frac{1}{u^2} \, du$$

$$= 10 \lim_{N \to \infty} \left(-\frac{1}{u} \Big|_{10}^{N+10} \right)$$

$$= 10 \lim_{N \to \infty} \left(-\frac{1}{N + 10} + \frac{1}{10} \right) = 10 \left(0 + \frac{1}{10} \right) = 1$$

The third condition is also met, so f is a probability density function.

27. Since $f(x) \geq 0$ for all x, the first condition is met. Checking the second condition,

$$\int_{-\infty}^{\infty} f(x)\, dx = \int_{0}^{\infty} x e^{-x}\, dx$$

$$= \lim_{N \to \infty} \int_{0}^{N} x e^{-x}\, dx$$

Using integration by parts with $u = x$ and $dV = e^{-x}\, dx$,

$$= \lim_{N \to \infty} \left[-x e^{-x} \big|_{0}^{N} - \int_{0}^{N} 1 \cdot -e^{-x}\, dx \right]$$

$$= \lim_{N \to \infty} \left[-x e^{-x} \big|_{0}^{N} + \int_{0}^{N} e^{-x}\, dx \right]$$

$$= \lim_{N \to \infty} \left[\left(-x e^{-x} - e^{-x} \right) \big|_{0}^{N} \right]$$

$$= \lim_{N \to \infty} \left[\left(-N e^{-N} - e^{-N} \right) - (0 - 1) \right]$$

$$= (0 - 0) - (0 - 1) = 1$$

The third condition is also met, so f *is* a probability density function.

29. The first condition is not met. For example $f(-1) = \frac{3}{2}(-1)^2 + 2(-1) = -\frac{1}{2}$. Since it is not the case that $f(x) \geq 0$ for all x, f is *not* a probability density function.

31. (a) $P(2 \leq x \leq 5) = \int_{2}^{5} \frac{1}{3}\, dx$

$$= \frac{x}{3} \big|_{2}^{5} = 1$$

Note: $\int_{-\infty}^{\infty} f(x)\, dx = \int_{2}^{5} f(x)\, dx$ in this problem, so needn't even integrate to conclude that the probability is 1.

(b) $P(3 \leq x \leq 4) = \int_{3}^{4} \frac{1}{3}\, dx$

$$= \frac{x}{3} \big|_{3}^{4} = \frac{1}{3}$$

(c) $P(X \geq 4) = \int_{4}^{5} \frac{1}{3}\, dx$

$$= \frac{x}{3} \big|_{4}^{5} = \frac{1}{3}$$

Note: can also calculate as $1 - \int_{0}^{4} \frac{1}{3}\, dx$.

33. (a) $P(0 \leq x \leq 4) = \int_{0}^{4} \frac{1}{8}(4 - x)\, dx$

$$= \int_{0}^{4} \frac{1}{2} - \frac{1}{8}x\, dx = \left(\frac{x}{2} - \frac{x^2}{16} \right) \big|_{0}^{4}$$

$$= (2 - 1) - 0 = 1$$

Note: $\int_{-\infty}^{\infty} f(x)\, dx = \int_{0}^{4} f(x)\, dx$ in this problem, so needn't even integrate to conclude that the probability is 1.

(b) $P(2 \leq x \leq 3) = \int_{2}^{3} \frac{1}{8}(4 - x)\, dx$

$$= \left(\frac{x}{2} - \frac{x^2}{16} \right) \big|_{2}^{3} = \left(\frac{3}{2} - \frac{9}{16} \right) - \left(1 - \frac{1}{4} \right)$$

$$= \frac{3}{16}$$

(c) $P(X \geq 1) = \int_{1}^{4} \frac{1}{8}(4 - x)\, dx$

$$= \left(\frac{x}{2} - \frac{x^2}{16} \right) \big|_{1}^{4} = (2 - 1) - \left(\frac{1}{2} - \frac{1}{16} \right) = \frac{9}{16}$$

Note: can also calculate as $1 - \int_{0}^{1} \frac{1}{8}(4 - x)\, dx$.

35. (a) $P(1 \leq x < \infty) = \int_{1}^{\infty} \frac{3}{x^4}\, dx$

$$= 3 \lim_{N \to \infty} \int_{1}^{N} \frac{1}{x^4}\, dx = 3 \lim_{N \to \infty} \left(-\frac{1}{3x^3} \big|_{1}^{N} \right)$$

$$= 3 \lim_{N \to \infty} \left(-\frac{1}{3N^3} + \frac{1}{3} \right) = 3 \left(0 + \frac{1}{3} \right) = 1$$

Note: $\int_{-\infty}^{\infty} f(x)\, dx = \int_{1}^{\infty} \frac{3}{x^4}\, dx$ in this problem, So needn't even integrate to conclude that the probability is 1.

(b) $P(1 \leq x \leq 2) = \int_{1}^{2} \frac{3}{x^4}\, dx$

$$= 3 \left(-\frac{1}{3x^3} \big|_{1}^{2} \right) = 3 \left(-\frac{1}{24} + \frac{1}{3} \right) = \frac{7}{8}$$

(c) $P(X \geq 2) = 1 - \int_{1}^{2} \frac{3}{x^4}\, dx$

$$= 1 - \frac{7}{8} = \frac{1}{8}$$

37. (a) $P(X \geq 0) = \int_0^\infty 2xe^{-x^2}\, dx$

$$= \lim_{N \to \infty} \int_0^N 2xe^{-x^2}\, dx$$

Using substitution with $u = -x^2$ and $-du = 2x\, dx$,

$$= \lim_{N \to \infty} -\int_0^{-N^2} e^u\, du = \lim_{N \to \infty} \left(-e^u \big|_0^{-N^2} \right)$$

$$= \lim_{N \to \infty} \left(-e^{-N^2} + e^0 \right) = 0 + 1 = 1$$

Note: $\int_{-\infty}^\infty f(x)\, dx = \int_0^\infty f(x)\, dx$ in this problem, so needn't even integrate to conclude that the probability is 1.

(b) $P(1 \leq x \leq 2) = \int_1^2 2xe^{-x^2}\, dx$

$$= -e^u \big|_{-1}^{-4} = -e^{-4} + e^{-1} = \frac{1}{e} - \frac{1}{e^4}$$

(c) $P(X \leq 2) = \int_0^2 2xe^{-x^2}\, dx$

$$= -e^u \big|_0^{-4} = -e^{-4} + 1 = 1 - \frac{1}{e^4}$$

39.
$$E(X) = \int_{-\infty}^\infty xf(x)\, dx$$

$$= \int_2^5 x \cdot \frac{1}{3}\, dx = \frac{1}{3} \int_2^5 x\, dx$$

$$= \frac{1}{3} \left(\frac{x^2}{2} \right) \Big|_2^5$$

$$= \frac{1}{6}(25 - 4) = \frac{21}{6} = \frac{7}{2}$$

41. $E(X) = \int_{-\infty}^\infty xf(x)\, dx$

$$= \int_0^4 x \cdot \frac{1}{8}(4 - x)\, dx = \frac{1}{8} \int_0^4 (4x - x^2)\, dx$$

$$= \frac{1}{8} \left(2x^2 - \frac{x^3}{3} \right) \Big|_0^4$$

$$= \frac{1}{8} \left[\left(2(4)^2 - \frac{(4)^3}{3} \right) - 0 \right] = \frac{1}{8} \cdot \frac{32}{3} = \frac{4}{3}$$

43.
$$E(X) = \int_{-\infty}^\infty xf(x)\, dx$$

$$= \int_1^\infty x \cdot \frac{3}{x^4}\, dx$$

$$= \lim_{N \to \infty} 3 \int_1^N x^{-3}\, dx$$

$$= 3 \lim_{N \to \infty} \left(-\frac{1}{2x^2} \right) \Big|_1^N$$

$$= -\frac{3}{2} \lim_{N \to \infty} \left(\frac{1}{x^2} \right) \Big|_1^N$$

$$= -\frac{3}{2} \lim_{N \to \infty} \left(\frac{1}{N^2} 0\frac{1}{1} \right) = -\frac{3}{2} \cdot -1 = \frac{3}{2}$$

45.
$$PV = \int_0^\infty 2{,}400e^{-0.04t}\, dt$$

$$= \lim_{N \to \infty} 2{,}400 \int_0^N e^{-0.04t}\, dt$$

$$= 2{,}400 \lim_{N \to \infty} \left(-25e^{-0.04t} \right) \Big|_0^N$$

$$= -60{,}000 \lim_{N \to \infty} \left(e^{-0.04t} \right) \Big|_0^N$$

$$= -60{,}000 \lim_{N \to \infty} \left(e^{-0.04N} - e^0 \right)$$

$$= -60{,}000 \cdot -1 = \$60{,}000$$

47.
$$PV = \int_0^\infty (12{,}000 + 900t)e^{-0.05t}\, dt$$

$$= \lim_{N \to \infty} \int_0^N (12{,}000 + 900t)e^{-0.05t}\, dt$$

Using integration by parts with $u = 12{,}000 + 900t$ and $dV = e^{-0.05t}\, dt$

$$= \lim_{N \to \infty} \left[-20(12{,}000 + 900t)e^{-0.05t} \Big|_0^N \right.$$

$$\left. - \int_0^N -18{,}000e^{-0.05t} \, dt \right]$$

$$= \lim_{N \to \infty} \left[-20(12{,}000 + 900t)e^{-0.05t} \Big|_0^N \right.$$

$$\left. + 18{,}000 \int_0^N e^{-0.05t} \, dt \right]$$

$$= -20 \lim_{N \to \infty} \left[(12{,}000 + 900t) \, e^{-0.05t} \right.$$

$$\left. + 18{,}000e^{-0.05t} \right] \Big|_0^N$$

$$= -20 \lim_{N \to \infty} \left[(12{,}000 + 900N)e^{-0.05N} \right.$$

$$\left. + 18{,}000e^{-0.05N} \right) - \left(12{,}000e^0 + 18{,}000e^0 \right) \right]$$

$$= -20 \lim_{N \to \infty} \left[30{,}000e^{-0.05N} \right.$$

$$\left. + 900Ne^{-0.05N} - 30{,}000 \right]$$

$$= -20(-30{,}000) = \$600{,}000$$

49. Number of
patients
$$= \lim_{N \to \infty} \int_0^N 10e^{-(N-t)/20} \, dt$$

$$= \lim_{N \to \infty} 10e^{-N/20} \int_0^N e^{t/20} \, dt$$

$$= 10 \lim_{N \to \infty} e^{-N/20} \left(20e^{t/20} \right) \Big|_0^N$$

$$= 200 \lim_{N \to \infty} e^{-N/20} \left(e^{N/20} - e^0 \right)$$

$$= 200 \lim_{N \to \infty} \left(e^0 - e^{-N/20} \right)$$

$$= 200 \cdot 1 = 200 \text{ patients.}$$

51.   Amount of drug $= \lim\limits_{N \to \infty} \int_0^N 5e^{-(N-t)/10} \, dt$

$$= \lim_{N \to \infty} 5e^{-N/10} \int_0^N e^{t/10} \, dt$$

$$= 5 \lim_{N \to \infty} e^{-N/10} \left(10e^{t/10} \right) \Big|_0^N$$

$$= 50 \lim_{N \to \infty} e^{-N/10} \left(e^{N/10} - e^0 \right)$$

$$= 50 \lim_{N \to \infty} \left(e^0 - e^{-N/10} \right)$$

$$= 50 \cdot 1 = 50 \text{ units}$$

53. The uniform density function for x, in seconds is

$$f(x) = \begin{cases} \frac{1}{45} & \text{if } 0 \le x \le 45 \\ 0 & \text{otherwise} \end{cases}$$

(a)
$$P(0 \le X \le 15) = \int_5^{15} \frac{1}{45} \, dx = \frac{1}{45}(x) \Big|_0^{15}$$

$$= \frac{1}{45}(15 - 0) = \frac{1}{3}$$

(b)
$$P(5 \le X \le 10) = \int_5^{10} \frac{1}{45} \, dx = \frac{1}{45}(x) \Big|_5^{10}$$

$$= \frac{1}{45}(10 - 5) = \frac{1}{9}$$

(c)
$$E(X) = \int_{-\infty}^{\infty} x f(x) \, dx$$

$$= \int_0^{45} x \cdot \frac{1}{45} \, dx = \frac{1}{45} \left(\frac{x^2}{2} \right) \Big|_0^{45}$$

$$= \frac{1}{90}(x^2) \Big|_0^{45} = \frac{1}{90} \left[(45)^2 - 0 \right]$$

$$= \frac{45}{2} \text{ seconds}$$

55. (a)
$$P(X > 3) = \int_3^{\infty} \frac{1}{3} e^{-x/3} \, dx$$

$$= \lim_{N \to \infty} \frac{1}{3} \int_3^N e^{-x/3} \, dx$$

$$= \frac{1}{3} \lim_{N \to \infty} \left(-3e^{x/3} \right) \Big|_3^N$$

$$= -1 \lim_{N \to \infty} \left(e^{-N/3} - e^{-1} \right)$$

$$= -1 \left(\frac{-1}{3} \right) = \frac{1}{e} \approx 0.368$$

(b)
$$P(2 \le X \rbrack e5) = \int_2^5 \frac{1}{3} e^{-x/3}\, dx$$

$$= -1\left(e^{-x/3}\right)\Big|_1^5 = -1\left(e^{-5/3} - e^{-2/3}\right)$$

$$= \frac{1}{e^{2/3}} - \frac{1}{e^{5/3}} \approx 0.325$$

(c)
$$E(X) = \int_{-\infty}^{\infty} x f(x)\, dx$$

$$= \lim_{N \to \infty} \int_0^N x \cdot \frac{1}{3} e^{-x/3}\, dx$$

$$= \lim_{N \to \infty} \frac{1}{3} \int_0^N x^{-x/3}\, dx$$

Using integration by parts with $u = x$ and $dV = e^{-x/3}\, dx$.

$$= \frac{1}{3} \lim_{N \to \infty} \left[-3x d^{-x/3}\Big|_0^N - \int_0^N -3e^{-x/3}\, dx \right]$$

$$= \lim_{N \to \infty} \left[-xe^{-x/3}\Big|_0^N + \int_0^N -e^{-x/3}\, dx \right]$$

$$= \lim_{N \to \infty} \left[-xe^{-x/3} - 3e^{-x/3} \right]\Big|_0^N$$

$$= \lim_{N \to \infty} \left[\left(-Ne^{N/3} - 3e^{-N/3} \right) - \left(0 - 3e^0 \right) \right]$$

$$= 3 \text{ minutes.}$$

57. (a)
$$P(10) \le X \le 15) = \int_{10}^{15} 0.02 e^{-0.02x}\, dx$$

$$= 0.02 \left(\frac{1}{-0.02} e^{-0.02x} \right)\Big|_{1-}^{15}$$

$$= \left(-e^{-0.02x} \right)\Big|_{10}^{15} = -e^{-0.3} + e^{0.2}$$

$$= \frac{1}{e^{0.2}} - \frac{1}{e^{0.3}} \approx 0.078$$

(b)
$$P(X < 8) = \int_0^8 0.02 e^{0.02x}\, dx$$

$$= \left(-e^{0.02x} \right)\Big|_0^8 = -e^{-0.16} + e^0$$

$$= 1 - \frac{1}{e^{0.16}} \approx 0.148$$

(c)
$$P(X) > 12 = \int_{12}^{\infty} 0.02 e^{0.02x}\, dx$$

$$= \lim_{N \to \infty} 0.02 \int_{12}^N e^{0.02x}\, dx$$

$$= \lim_{N \to \infty} \left(-e^{0.02x} \right)\Big|_{12}^N$$

$$= \lim_{N \to \infty} \left(-e^{0.02N} + e^{-24} \right)$$

$$= \frac{1}{e^{0.24}} \approx 0.787$$

(d)
$$E(X) = \int_{-\infty}^{\infty} x f(x)\, dx$$

$$= \lim_{N \to \infty} \int_0^N x \cdot 0.02 e^{0.02x}\, dx$$

$$= \lim_{N \to \infty} (0.02) \int_0^N x e^{0.02x}\, dx$$

Using integration by parts with $u = x$ and $dV = e^{0.02x}\, dx$,

$$= 0.02 \lim_{N \to \infty} \left[-50x e^{0.02x}\Big|_0^N - \int_0^N -50 e^{0.02x}\, dx \right]$$

$$= \lim_{N \to \infty} \left[-x e^{0.02x}\Big|_0^N + \int_0^N -e^{0.02x}\, dx \right]$$

$$= \lim_{N \to \infty} \left[-x e^{0.02x} - 50 e^{0.02x} \right]\Big|_0^N$$

$$= \lim_{N \to \infty} \left[\left(-N e^{0.02N} - 50 e^{0.02N} \right) - \left(0 - 50 e^0 \right) \right]$$

$$= 50 \text{ months.}$$

59. (a)
$$E(X) = \int_{-\infty}^{\infty} x f(x)\, dx$$

$$= \int_0^{\infty} x \cdot k e^{-kx}\, dx = \lim_{N \to \infty} \int_0^N x e^{-kx}\, dx$$

Using integration by parts with $u = x$ and $dV = e^{-kx}\, dx$.

$$= k \lim_{N \to \infty} \left[\frac{-x}{k} e^{-kx} \Big|_0^N - \int_0^N -\frac{1}{k} e^{-kx} \, dx \right]$$

$$= \lim_{N \to \infty} \left[-xe^{-kx} \Big|_0^N + \int_0^N e^{-kx} \right] dx \right]$$

$$= \lim_{N \to \infty} \left[-xe^{-kx} - \frac{1}{k} e^{-kx} \right] \Big|_0^N$$

$$= \lim_{N \to \infty} \left[\left(-Ne^{-kN} - \frac{1}{k} e^{-kN} \right) \right.$$

$$\left. \left(0 - \frac{1}{k} e^0 \right) \right] = \frac{1}{k}$$

So, $\frac{1}{k} = 5$, or $k = \frac{1}{5}$.

(b)
$$P(X < 2) = \int_0^2 \frac{1}{5} e^{-x/5} \, dx$$

$$= \left(-e^{-x/5} \right) \Big|_0^2 = -e^{-2/5} + e^0$$

$$= 1 - \frac{1}{e^{2/5}} \approx 0.330$$

(c)
$$P(X > 7) = \lim_{N \to \infty} \int_7^N \frac{1}{5} e^{-x/5} \, dx$$

$$= \lim_{N \to \infty} \left(-e^{-x/5} \right) \Big|_7^N$$

$$= \lim_{N \to \infty} \left(-e^{-N/5} + e^{-7/5} \right)$$

$$= \frac{1}{e^{7/5}} \approx 0.247$$

61. (a)
$$P(0 \le X \le 5) = \int_0^5 0.2 e^{-0.2x} \, dx$$

$$= 0.2 \left(\frac{1}{-0.2} e^{-0.2x} \right) \Big|_0^5$$

$$= \left(-e^{-0.2x} \right) \Big|_0^5 = -e^{-1} + e^0$$

$$= 1 - \frac{1}{e} \approx 0.632$$

(b)
$$P(X > 6) = \lim_{N \to \infty} \int_6^N 0.2 e^{-0.2x} \, dx$$

$$= \lim_{N \to \infty} \left(-e^{-0.2x} \right) \Big|_6^N$$

$$= \lim_{N \to \infty} \left(-e^{-0.2N} + e^{-1.2} \right) = e^{-1.2} \approx 0.301$$

(c)
$$E(X) = \int_{-\infty}^\infty x f(x) \, dx$$

$$= \lim_{N \to \infty} \int_0^N x \left(0.2 e^{-0.2x} \right) dx$$

$$= \lim_{N \to \infty} 0.2 \int_0^N x e^{-0.2x} \, dx$$

Using integration by parts with $u = x$ and $dV = e^{-0.2x} \, dx$,

$$= \lim_{N \to \infty} \frac{1}{5} \left[-5xe^{-0.2x} \Big|_0^N - \int_0^N -5e^{-0.2x} \, dx \right]$$

$$= \lim_{N \to \infty} \left[-xe^{-0.2x} \Big|_0^N + \int_0^N e^{-0.2x} \, dx \right]$$

$$= \lim_{N \to \infty} \left[-xe^{-0.2x} - 5e^{-0.2x} \right] \Big|_0^N$$

$$= \lim_{N \to \infty} \left[\left(-N^{-0.2N} - 5e^{-0.2N} \right) - \left(0 - 5e^0 \right) \right]$$

$$= 5 \text{ minutes.}$$

63.
$$PV = \lim_{N \to \infty} \int_0^N 70{,}000 e^{-0.08t} \, dt$$

$$= \lim_{N \to \infty} 70{,}000 \int_0^N e^{-0.08t} \, dt$$

$$= 70{,}000 \lim_{N \to \infty} \left(-\frac{25}{2} e^{-0.08t} \right) \Big|_0^N$$

$$= -875{,}000 \lim_{N \to \infty} \left(e^{-0.08t} \right) \Big|_0^N$$

$$= -875{,}000 \lim_{N \to \infty} \left(e^{-0.08N} - e^0 \right) = \$875{,}000$$

65. (a)
$$P(X \ge 6) = \lim_{N \to \infty} \int_6^N 0.0866 e^{-0.0866t} \, dt$$

$$= \lim_{N \to \infty} 0.0866 \left(\frac{1}{-0.0866t} e^{-0.0866t} \right) \Big|_6^N$$

$$= \lim_{N \to \infty} \left(-e^{-0.0866t} \right) \Big|_6^N$$

$$= \lim_{N \to \infty} \left(e^{-0.0866t} + e^{0.5196} \right) = \frac{1}{e^{0.5196}}$$

$$\approx 0.595$$

(b) $P(X \ge 6) = \lim\limits_{N \to \infty} \int_6^N 0.135 e^{-0.135t} \, dt$

$$= \lim_{N \to \infty} 0.135 \left(\frac{1}{-0.135t} e^{-0.135t} \right) \Big|_6^N$$

$$= \lim_{N \to \infty} \left(e^{-0.135t} \right) \Big|_6^N$$

$$= \lim_{N \to \infty} \left(e^{-0.135N} + e^{-0.81} \right) = \frac{1}{e^{0.81}}$$

$$\approx 0.445$$

(c) Writing Exercise—Answers will vary.

67.
$$\lim_{N \to \infty} \int_0^N (A + Bt) e^{-rt} \, dt$$

$$= \lim_{N \to \infty} -\frac{A}{r} e^{-rt} + B \left(-\frac{t}{r} e^{-rt} + \frac{1}{r} \int_0^N e^{-rt} \, dt \right)$$

$$= \lim_{N \to \infty} \left(-\frac{A}{r} e^{-rt} - \frac{Bt}{r} e^{-rt} - \frac{B}{r^2} e^{-rt} \right) \Big|_0^N$$

$$= 0 - \left(-\frac{A}{r} e^0 - 0 - \frac{B}{r^2} e^0 \right) = \frac{A}{r} + \frac{B}{r^2}$$

69.
$$E(x) = \int_{-\infty}^{\infty} x f(x) \, dx = \int_0^{\infty} k x e^{kx} \, dx$$

$$= \lim_{N \to \infty} \int_0^N k x e^{-kx} \, dx$$

$$= \lim_{N \to \infty} \left(-x e^{-kx} \Big|_0^N + \int_0^N e^{-kx} \, dx \right)$$

$$= \lim_{N \to \infty} \left(-x e^{-kx} - \frac{1}{k} e^{-kx} \right) \Big|_0^N$$

$$= \lim_{N \to \infty} \left(-N e^{-kN} - \frac{1}{k} e^{-kN} + \frac{1}{k} \right) = \frac{1}{k}$$

6.4   Numerical Integration

1.   For $\int_1^2 x^2 \, dx$ with $n = 4$, $\Delta x = \dfrac{2-1}{4} = 0.25$, and $x_1 = 1$, $x_2 = 1.25$, $x_3 = 1.50$, $x_4 = 1.75$, $x_5 = 2$.

(a) By the trapezoidal rule, $\int_1^2 x^2 \, dx$

$$= \frac{\Delta x}{2} \left[f(x_1) + 2 f(x_2) + 2 f(x_3) + 2 f(x_4) + f(x_5) \right]$$

$$= \frac{0.25}{2} \left[1^2 + 2(1.25)^2 + 2(1.5)^2 + 2(1.75)^2 + 2^2 \right]$$

$$\approx 2.3438.$$

(b) By Simpson's rule, $\int_1^2 x^2 \, dx$

$$= \frac{\Delta x}{3} \left[f(x_1) + 4 f(x_2) + 2 f(x_3) + 4 f(x_4) + f(x_5) \right]$$

$$= \frac{0.25}{3} \left[1^2 + 4(1.25)^2 + 2(1.5)^2 + 4(1.75)^2 + 2^2 \right]$$

$$\approx 2.3333.$$

3.   For $\int_0^1 \dfrac{1}{1+x^2} \, dx$ with $n = 4$, $\Delta x = \dfrac{1-0}{4} = 0.25$, and $x_1 = 0$, $x_2 = 0.25$, $x_3 = 0.50$, $x_4 = 0.75$, $x_5 = 1$.

(a) By the trapezoidal rule, $\int_0^1 \dfrac{1}{1+x^2} \, dx$

$$= \frac{\Delta x}{2} \left[f(x_1) + 2 f(x_2) + 2 f(x_3) + 2 f(x_4) + f(x_5) \right]$$

$$= \frac{0.25}{2} \left[1 + \frac{2}{1 + (0.25)^2} + \frac{2}{1 + (0.5)^2} \right.$$

$$\left. + \frac{2}{1 + (0.75)^2} + \frac{1}{2} \right] \approx 0.7828.$$

(b) By Simpson's rule, $\int_0^1 \dfrac{1}{1+x^2} \, dx$

$$= \frac{\Delta x}{3} \left[f(x_1) + 4f(x_2) + 2f(x_3) + 4f(x_4) + f(x_5) \right]$$

$$= \frac{0.25}{3} \left[1 + \frac{4}{1+(0.25)^2} + \frac{2}{1+(0.5)^2} \right.$$

$$\left. + \frac{4}{1+(0.75)^2} + \frac{1}{2} \right] \approx 0.7854.$$

5. For $\int_{-1}^{0} \sqrt{1+x^2}\,dx$ with $n=4$, $\Delta x = \frac{0-(-1)}{4} = 0.25$, and $x_1 = -1$, $x_2 = -0.75$, $x_3 = -0.5$, $x_4 = -0.25$, $x_5 = 0$.

(a) By the trapezoidal rule, $\int_{1}^{2} \sqrt{1+x^2}\,dx$

$$= \frac{\Delta x}{2} \left[f(x_1) + 2f(x_2) + 2f(x_3) + 2f(x_4) + f(x_5) \right]$$

$$= \frac{0.25}{2} \left[\sqrt{1+(-1)^2} + 2\sqrt{1+(-0.75)^2} \right.$$

$$\left. + 2\sqrt{1+(-0.5)^2} + 2\sqrt{1+(-0.25)^2} + \sqrt{1+(0)^2} \right]$$

$$\approx 1.1515.$$

(b) By Simpson's rule, $\int_{1}^{2} \sqrt{1+x^2}\,dx$

$$= \frac{\Delta x}{3} \left[f(x_1) + 4f(x_2) + 2f(x_3) + 4f(x_4) + f(x_5) \right]$$

$$= \frac{0.25}{3} \left[\sqrt{1+(-1)^2} + 4\sqrt{1+(-0.75)^2} \right.$$

$$\left. + 2\sqrt{1+(-0.5)^2} + 4\sqrt{1+(-0.25)^2} + \sqrt{1+(0)^2} \right]$$

$$\approx 1.1478.$$

7. For $\int_{0}^{1} e^{-x^2}\,dx$ with $n=4$, $\Delta x = \frac{1-0}{4} = 0.25$, and $x_1 = 0$, $x_2 = 0.25$, $x_3 = 0.50$, $x_4 = 0.75$, $x_5 = 1$.

(a) By the trapezoidal rule, $\int_{1}^{2} e^{-x^2}\,dx$

$$= \frac{\Delta x}{2} \left[f(x_1) + 2f(x_2) + 2f(x_3) + 2f(x_4) + f(x_5) \right]$$

$$= \frac{0.25}{2} \left[1 + 2e^{-(0.25)^2} + 2e^{-(0.5)^2} + 2e^{-(0.75)^2} + e^{-1} \right]$$

$$\approx 0.7430.$$

(b) By Simpson's rule, $\int_{1}^{2} e^{-x^2}\,dx$

$$= \frac{\Delta x}{3} \left[f(x_1) + 4f(x_2) + 2f(x_3) + 4f(x_4) + f(x_5) \right]$$

$$= \frac{0.25}{3} \left[1 + 4e^{-(0.25)^2} + 2e^{-(0.5)^2} + 4e^{-(0.75)^2} + e^{-1} \right]$$

$$\approx 0.7469.$$

9. For $\int_{2}^{4} \frac{dx}{\ln x}$ with $n=6$, $\Delta x = \frac{4-2}{6} = \frac{1}{3}$ and $x_1 = 2$, $x_2 = \frac{7}{3}$, $x_3 = \frac{8}{3}$, $x_4 = \frac{10}{3}$, $x_6 = \frac{11}{3}$, $x_7 = 4$.

(a) By the trapezoidal rule, $\int_{2}^{4} \frac{dx}{\ln x}$

$$\approx \frac{\Delta x}{2}$$

$$\left[f(x_1) + 2f(x_2) + 2f(x_3) + 2f(x_4) + 2f(x_5) + 2f(x_6) + f(x_7) \right]$$

$$= \frac{\frac{1}{3}}{2} \left[\frac{1}{\ln 2} + \frac{2}{\ln^{7/3}} + \frac{2}{\ln^{8/3}} + \frac{2}{\ln 3} + \frac{2}{\ln^{10/3}} + \frac{2}{\ln^{11/3}} + \frac{1}{\ln 4} \right]$$

$$\approx 1.9308$$

(b) By Simpson's rule, $\int_{2}^{4} \frac{dx}{\ln x}$

$$\approx \frac{\Delta x}{3}$$

$$\left[f(x_1) + 4f(x_2) + 2f(x_3) + 4f(x_4) + 2f(x_5) + 4f(x_6) + f(x_7) \right]$$

$$= \frac{\frac{1}{3}}{3} \left[\frac{1}{\ln 2} + \frac{4}{\ln^{7/3}} + \frac{2}{\ln^{8/3}} + \frac{4}{\ln 3} + \frac{2}{\ln^{10/3}} + \frac{4}{\ln^{11/3}} + \frac{1}{\ln 4} \right]$$

$$\approx 1.9228$$

11. For $\int_{0}^{1} \sqrt[3]{1+x^2}\,dx$ with $n=4$, $\Delta x = \frac{1-0}{4} = 0.25$ and $x_1 = 0$, $x_2 = 0.25$, $x_3 = 0.05$, $x - 4 = 0.75$, $x_5 = 1$.

(a) By the trapezoidal rule, $\int_{0}^{1} \sqrt[3]{1+x^2}\,dx$

$$\approx \frac{\Delta x}{2}\left[f(x_1)+4f(x_2)+2f(x_3)+4f(x_4)+2f(x_5)\right]$$

$$= \frac{0.25}{2}\left[1+\sqrt[3]{1.0625}+2\sqrt[3]{1.25}+2\sqrt[3]{1.5625}+\sqrt[3]{2}\right]$$

$$\approx 1.0970$$

(b) By Simpson's rule, $\displaystyle\int_0^1 \sqrt[3]{1+x^2}\,dx$

$$\approx \frac{\Delta x}{3}\left[f(x_1)+4f(x_2)+2f(x_3)+4f(x_4)+f(x_5)\right]$$

$$= \frac{0.25}{3}\left[1+4\sqrt[3]{1.0625}+2\sqrt[3]{1.25}+4\sqrt[3]{1.5625}+\sqrt[3]{2}\right]$$

$$\approx 1.0948$$

13. For $\displaystyle\int_0^2 e^{-\sqrt{x}}\,dx$ with $n=8$, $\Delta x=\dfrac{2-0}{8}=0.25$ and $x_1=0$, $x_2=0.25$, $x_3=0.5$, $x_4=0.75$, $x_5=1$, $x_6=1.25$, $x_7=1.5$, $x_8=1.75$, $x_9=2$.

(a) By the trapezoidal rule, $\displaystyle\int_0^2 e^{-\sqrt{x}}\,dx$

$$\approx \frac{\Delta x}{2}\left[f(x_1)+2f(x_2)+2f(x_3)+2f(x_4)+2f(x_5)\right.$$

$$\left.+2f(x_6)+2f(x_7)+2f(x_8)+f(x_9)\right]$$

$$= \frac{0.25}{2}\left[1+2e^{-\sqrt{0.25}}+2e^{-\sqrt{0.5}}+2e^{-\sqrt{0.75}}+2e^{-1}\right.$$

$$\left.+2e^{-\sqrt{1.25}}+2e^{-\sqrt{1.5}}+2e^{-\sqrt{1.75}}+e^{-\sqrt{2}}\right]$$

$$\approx 0.8492$$

(b) By Simpson's rule, $\displaystyle\int_0^2 e^{-\sqrt{x}}\,dx$

$$\approx \frac{\Delta x}{3}\left[f(x_1)+4f(x_2)+2f(x_3)+4f(x_4)+2f(x_5)\right.$$

$$\left.+4f(x_6)+2f(x_7)+4f(x_8)+f(x_9)\right]$$

$$= \frac{0.25}{3}\left[1+4e^{-\sqrt{0.25}}+2e^{-\sqrt{0.5}}+4e^{-\sqrt{0.75}}+2e^{-1}\right.$$

$$\left.+4e^{-\sqrt{1.25}}+2e^{-\sqrt{1.5}}+4e^{-\sqrt{1.75}}+e^{-\sqrt{2}}\right]$$

$$\approx 0.8362$$

15. For $\displaystyle\int_1^2 \frac{1}{x^2}\,dx$ with $n=4$, $\Delta x=\dfrac{2-1}{4}=0.25$, and $x_1=1$, $x_2=1.25$, $x_3=1.50$, $x_4=1.75$, $x_5=2$.

(a) By the trapezoidal rule, $\displaystyle\int_1^2 \frac{1}{x^2}\,dx$

$$= \frac{\Delta x}{2}\left[f(x_1)+2f(x_2)+2f(x_3)+2f(x_4)+f(x_5)\right]$$

$$= \frac{0.25}{2}\left[1+\frac{2}{(1.25)^2}+\frac{2}{(1.5)^2}+\frac{2}{(1.75)^2}+\frac{1}{2^2}\right]$$

$$\approx 0.5090.$$

The error estimate is $|\,E_n\,|\le \dfrac{M(b-a)^3}{12n^2}$. For $n=4$, $a=1$, and $b=2$, $|\,E_4\,|\le \dfrac{M(2-1)^2}{12(4^2)}=\dfrac{M}{192}$, where M is the maximum value of $|\,f''(x)\,|$ on $1\le x\le 2$. Now $f(x)=x^{-2}$, $f'(x)=-2x^{-3}$, and $f''(x)=6x^{-4}$. For $1\le x\le 2$, $|\,f''(x)\,|=\dfrac{6}{x^4}\le\dfrac{6}{1^4}=6$. So, $|\,E_4\,|=\dfrac{6}{192}\approx 0.03125$.

(b) By Simpson's rule, $\displaystyle\int_1^2 \frac{1}{x^2}\,dx$

$$= \frac{\Delta x}{3}\left[f(x_1)+4f(x_2)+2f(x_3)+4f(x_4)+f(x_5)\right]$$

$$= \frac{0.25}{3}\left[1+\frac{4}{(1.25)^2}+\frac{2}{(1.5)^2}+\frac{4}{(1.75)^2}+\frac{1}{2^2}\right]$$

$$\approx 0.5004.$$

The error estimate is $|\,E_n\,|\le \dfrac{M(b-a)^5}{180n^4}$. For $n=4$, $a=1$, and $b=2$, $|\,E_4\,|\le \dfrac{M(2-1)^5}{180(4^4)}=\dfrac{M}{46{,}080}$ where M is the maximum value of $|\,f^{(4)}(x)\,|$ on $1\le x\le 2$. Now $f''(x)=6x^{-4}$, $f^{(3)}(x)=-24x^{-5}$, and $f^{(4)}(x)=120x^{-6}$. For $1\le x\le 2$, $|\,f^{(4)}(x)\,|=\dfrac{120}{x^6}\le\dfrac{120}{1^6}=120$. So, $|\,E_4\,|\le\dfrac{120}{46{,}080}\approx 0.0026$.

17. For $\displaystyle\int_1^3 \sqrt{x}\,dx$ with $n=10$, $\Delta x=\dfrac{3-1}{10}=0.2$, and $x_1=1$, $x_2=1.2$, $x_3=1.4$, $\ldots$, $x_{10}=2.8$, $x_{11}=3$.

(a) By the trapezoidal rule, $\int_1^3 \sqrt{x}\, dx$

$$= \frac{\Delta x}{2}\Big[f(x_1) + 2f(x_2) + 2f(x_3) + \cdots$$

$$+ 2f(x_{10}) + f(x_{11}) \Big]$$

$$= \frac{0.2}{2}\Big[1 + 2\sqrt{1.2} + 2\sqrt{1.4} + 2\sqrt{1.6} + 2\sqrt{1.8}$$

$$+ 2\sqrt{2}\, 2\sqrt{2.2} + 2\sqrt{2.4} + 2\sqrt{2.6} + 2\sqrt{2.8} + \sqrt{3} \Big]$$

$$\approx 2.7967.$$

The error estimate is $|E_n| \le \dfrac{M(b-a)^3}{12n^2}$.
For $n = 10$, $a = 1$, and $b = 3$, $|E_{10}| \le$
$\dfrac{M(3-1)^3}{12(10^2)} = \dfrac{8M}{1{,}200} = \dfrac{M}{150}$, where M
is the maximum value of $|f''(x)|$ on
$1 \le x \le 3$. Now, $f(x) = x^{1/2}$, $f'(x) = \dfrac{1}{2}x^{-1/2}$,
and $f''(x) = -\dfrac{1}{4}x^{-3/2}$. For $1 \le x \le 3$,
$|f''(x)| = \left| -\dfrac{1}{4}x^{-3/2} \right| \le \dfrac{1}{4}(1^{-3/2}) = \dfrac{1}{4}$. So,
$|E_{10}| = \dfrac{1}{150}\left(\dfrac{1}{4} \right) \approx 0.0017.$

(b) By Simpson's rule, $\int_1^3 \sqrt{x}\, dx$

$$= \frac{\Delta x}{3}\Big[f(x_1) + 4f(x_2) + 2f(x_3) + \cdots + 4f(x_{10})$$

$$+ f(x_{11}) \Big]$$

$$= \frac{0.2}{3}\Big[1 + 4\sqrt{1.2} + 2\sqrt{1.4} + 4\sqrt{1.6} + 2\sqrt{1.8} + 4\sqrt{2}$$

$$+ 2\sqrt{2.2} + 4\sqrt{2.4} + 2\sqrt{2.6} + 4\sqrt{2.8} + \sqrt{3} \Big]$$

$$\approx 2.7974.$$

The error estimate is $|E_n| \le \dfrac{M(b-a)^5}{180n^4}$.
For $n = 10$, $a = 1$, and $b = 3$, $|E_{10}| \le$
$\dfrac{M(3-1)^5}{180(10^4)} = \dfrac{32M}{180(10^4)}$, where M is the
maximum value of $|f^{(4)}(x)|$ on $1 \le x \le 3$.
Now $f''(x) = -\dfrac{1}{4}x^{-3/2}$, $f^{(3)}(x) = \dfrac{3}{8}x^{-5/2}$,

and $f^{(4)}(x) = -\dfrac{15}{16}x^{-7/2}$. For $1 \le x \le 3$,

$$|f^{(4)}(x)| = \left| -\frac{15}{16}x^{-7/2} \right| \le \frac{15}{16}(1^{-7/2}) = \frac{15}{16}.$$

So, $|E_{10}| = \dfrac{32}{180(10{,}000)}\left(\dfrac{15}{16} \right) \approx 0.0000167.$

19. For $\int_0^1 e^{x^2}\, dx$ with $n = 4$, $\Delta x = \dfrac{1-0}{4} = 0.25$, and
$x_1 = 0$, $x_2 = 0.25$, $x_3 = 0.50$, $x_4 = 0.75$, $x_5 = 1$.

(a) By the trapezoidal rule, $\int_1^2 e^{x^2}\, dx$

$$= \frac{\Delta x}{2}\Big[f(x_1) + 2f(x_2) + 2f(x_3) + 2f(x_4) + f(x_5) \Big]$$

$$= \frac{0.25}{2}\Big[1 + 2e^{(0.25)^2} + 2e^{(0.5)^2} + 2e^{(0.75)^2} + e^1 \Big] \approx 1.4907.$$

The error estimate is $|E_n| \le \dfrac{M(b-a)^3}{12n^2}$. For

$n = 4$, $a = 0$, and $b = 1$, $|E_4| \le \dfrac{M(1-0)^3}{12(4^2)} =$

$\dfrac{M}{192}$, where M is the maximum value of
$|f''(x)|$ on $0 \le x \le 1$. Now, $f(x) = e^{x^2}$,
$f'(x) = -2xe^{-x^2}$, and $f''(x) = (4x^2 + 2)\, e^{x^2}$.
For $0 \le x \le 1$, $|f''(x)| = \big[4\,(1^2) + 2 \big] e^{1^2} = 6e$.
So, $|E_4| = \dfrac{6e}{192} \approx 0.0849.$

(b) By Simpson's rule, $\int_1^2 e^{x^2}\, dx$

$$= \frac{\Delta x}{3}\Big[f(x_1) + 4f(x_2) + 2f(x_3) + 4f(x_4) + f(x_5) \Big]$$

$$= \frac{0.25}{3}\Big[1 + 4e^{(0.25)^2} + 2e^{(0.5)^2} + 4e^{(0.75)^2} + e^1 \Big]$$

$$\approx 1.4637.$$

The error estimate is $|E_n| \le \dfrac{M(b-a)^5}{180n^4}$.
For $n = 4$, $a = 0$, and $b = 1$, $|E_4| \le$
$\dfrac{M(1-0)^5}{180(4^4)} = \dfrac{M}{46{,}080}$, where M is
the maximum value of $|f^{(4)}(x)|$ on
$0 \le x \le 1$. Now, $f''(x) = (4x^2 + 2)\, e^{x^2}$,
$f^{(3)}(x) = (8x^3 + 12x)\, e^{x^2}$, and $f^{(4)}(x) =$

$\left(16x^4 + 48x^2 + 12\right) e^{x^2}$. For $0 \le x \le 1$,

$\mid f^{(4)}(x) \mid = \left[16\left(1^4\right) + 48\left(1^2\right) + 12\right] e^{1^2} = 76e$.

So, $\mid E_4 \mid \le \dfrac{76e}{46,080} \approx 0.0045$.

21. The integral to be approximated is $\displaystyle\int_1^3 \dfrac{1}{x}\, dx$. The derivatives of $f(x) = \dfrac{1}{x} = x^{-1}$ are $f'(x) = -x^{-2}$, $f''(x) = 2x^{-3}$, $f^{(3)}(x) = -6x^{-4}$, and $f^{(4)}(x) = 24x^{-5}$.

(a) For the trapezoidal rule, $\mid E_n \mid \le \dfrac{M(b-a)^3}{12n^2}$, where M is the maximum value of $\mid f''(x) \mid$ on $1 \le x \le 3$. Now $\mid f''(x) \mid = \dfrac{2}{x^3} \le \dfrac{2}{1^3} = 2$ on $1 \le x \le 3$. $\mid E_n \mid \le \dfrac{2(3-1)^3}{12n^2} = \dfrac{4}{3n^2}$, which is less than 0.00005 if $4 < 3(0.00005)n^2$ or $n > \sqrt{\dfrac{4}{3(0.00005)}} \approx 163.3$. So, 164 intervals should be used.

(b) For Simpson's rule, $\mid E_n \mid \le \dfrac{M(b-a)^5}{180n^4}$, where M is the maximum value of $\mid f^{(4)}(x) \mid$ on $1 \le x \le 3$. Now, $\mid f^{(4)}(x) \mid = \left|\dfrac{24}{x^5}\right| \le \dfrac{24}{1^5} = 24$ on $1 \le x \le 3$. $\mid E_n \mid \le \dfrac{24(3-1)^5}{180n^4} = \dfrac{768}{180n^4}$ which is less than 0.00005 if $768 < 180(0.00005)n^4$ or $n > \sqrt[4]{\dfrac{768}{180(0.00005)}} \approx 17.1$. So, 18 subintervals should be used.

23. The integral to be approximated is $\displaystyle\int_1^2 \dfrac{1}{\sqrt{x}}\, dx$. The derivatives of $f(x) = \dfrac{1}{\sqrt{x}} = x^{-1/2}$ are $f'(x) = -\dfrac{1}{2}x^{-3/2}$, $f''(x) = \dfrac{3}{4}x^{-5/2}$, $f^{(3)}(x) = -\dfrac{15}{8}x^{-7/2}$, and $f^{(4)}(x) = \dfrac{105}{16}x^{-9/2}$.

(a) For the trapezoidal rule, $\mid E_n \mid \le \dfrac{M(b-a)^3}{12n^2}$, where M is the maximum value of $\mid f''(x) \mid$

on $1 \le x \le 2$. Now $\mid f''(x) \mid = \dfrac{3}{4}x^{-5/2} \le \dfrac{3}{4}$ on $1 \le x \le 2$. $\mid E_n \mid \le \dfrac{3}{4}\dfrac{(2-1)^3}{12n^2} = \dfrac{1}{16n^2}$, which is less than 0.00005 if $1 < 16(0.00005)n^2$ or $n > \sqrt{\dfrac{1}{16(0.00005)}} \approx 35.4$. So, 36 intervals should be used.

(b) For Simpson's rule, $\mid E_n \mid \le \dfrac{M(b-a)^5}{180n^4}$, where M is the maximum value of $\mid f^{(4)}(x) \mid$ on $1 \le x \le 2$. Now $\mid f^{(4)}(x) \mid = \left|\dfrac{105}{16}x^{-9/2}\right| \le \dfrac{105}{16}$ on $1 \le x \le 2$. $\mid E_n \mid \le \dfrac{105(2-1)^5}{16(180)n^4} = \dfrac{7}{192n^4}$, which is less than 0.00005 if $7 < 192(0.00005)n^4$ or $n > \sqrt[4]{\dfrac{7}{192(0.00005)}} \approx 5.2$. So, 6 subintervals should be used.

25. The integral to be approximated is $\displaystyle\int_{1.2}^{2.4} e^x\, dx$.

(a) For the trapezoidal rule, $\mid E_n \mid \le \dfrac{M(b-a)^3}{12n^2}$, where M is the maximum value of $\mid f''(x) \mid$ on $1.2 \le x \le 2.4$. Now $\mid f''(x) \mid = \mid e^x \mid \le e^{2.4}$ on $1.2 \le x \le 2.4$. $\mid E_n \mid \le \dfrac{e^{2.4}(2.4-1.2)^3}{12n^2} = \dfrac{1.728e^{2.4}}{12n^2}$ which is less than 0.00005 if $1.728e^{2.4} < 12(0.00005)n^2$ or $n > \sqrt{\dfrac{1.728e^{2.4}}{12(0.00005)}} \approx 178.2$. So, 179 intervals should be used.

(b) For Simpson's rule, $\mid E_n \mid \le \dfrac{M(b-a)^5}{180n^4}$, where M is the maximum value of $\mid f^{(4)}(x) \mid$ on $1.2 \le x \le 2.4$. Now $\mid f^{(4)}(x) \mid = \mid e^x \mid \le e^{2.4}$ on $1.2 \le x \le 2.4$. $\mid E_n \mid \le \dfrac{e^{2.4}(2.4-1.2)^5}{180n^4}$ which is less than 0.00005 if $e^{2.4}(1.2)^5 < 180(0.00005)n^4$ or $n > \sqrt[4]{\dfrac{e^{2.4}(1.2)^5}{180(0.00005)}} \approx 7.4$. So, 8 subintervals should be used.

27. For $\int_0^1 \sqrt{1-x^2}\,dx$ with $n=8$, $\Delta x = \dfrac{1-0}{8} =$ 0.125, and $x_1 = 0$, $x_2 = 0.125$, $x_3 = 0.25,\ \ldots,$ $x_8 = 1.875$, $x_9 = 2$.

(a) By the trapezoidal rule, $\int_0^1 \sqrt{1-x^2}\,dx$

$$= \frac{\Delta x}{2}\big[f(x_1) + 2f(x_2) + 2f(x_3)$$

$$+ \cdots + 2f(x_8) + f(x_9)\big]$$

$$= 0.0625\Big[\sqrt{1-(0)^2} + 2\sqrt{1-(0.125)^2}$$

$$+ 2\sqrt{1-(0.25)^2} + 2\sqrt{1-(0.375)^2}$$

$$+ 2\sqrt{1-(0.5)^2} + 2\sqrt{1-(0.625)^2}$$

$$+ 2\sqrt{1-(0.75)^2} + 2\sqrt{1-(0.875)^2}$$

$$+ \sqrt{1-(1)^2}\Big] \approx 0.7725$$

$(0.7725)(4) = 3.090$ as an approximation of π.

(b) By Simpson's rule, $\int_0^1 \sqrt{1-x^2}\,dx$

$$= \frac{\Delta x}{3}\big[f(x_1) + 4f(x_2) + 2f(x_3) + 4f(x_4)$$

$$+ \cdots + 4f(x_8) + f(x_9)\big]$$

$$= \frac{1}{24}\Big[\sqrt{1-(0)^2} + 4\sqrt{1-(0.125)^2}$$

$$+ 2\sqrt{1-(0.25)^2} + 4\sqrt{1-(0.375)^2}$$

$$+ 2\sqrt{1-(0.5)^2} + 4\sqrt{1-(0.625)^2}$$

$$+ 2\sqrt{1-(0.75)^2} + 4\sqrt{1-(0.875)^2}$$

$$+ \sqrt{1-(1)^2}\Big] \approx 0.7803$$

$(0.7803)(4) = 3.121$ as an approximation of π.

29. For $\int_1^6 \dfrac{e^{-0.4x}}{x}\,dx$ with $n=10$, $\Delta x = \frac{6-1}{10} = 0.5$, and $x_1 = 1$, $x_2 = 1.5$, $x_3 = 2.0$, $x_4 = 2.5$, $x_5 = 3.0$, $x_6 = 3.5$, $x_7 = 4.0$, $x_8 = 4.5$, $x_9 = 5.0$, $x_{10} = 5.5$, $x_{11} = 6.0$.

By the trapezoidal rule, $\int_1^6 \dfrac{e^{-0.4x}}{x}\,dx$

$$= \frac{\Delta x}{2}\big[f(x_1) + 2f(x_2) + 2f(x_3) + 2f(x_4)$$

$$+ 2f(x_5) + 2f(x_6) + 2f(x_7) + 2f(x_8)$$

$$+ 2f(x_9) + 2f(x_{10}) + f(x_{11})\big]$$

$$= 0.25\Bigg[\left(\frac{e^{-0.4(1)}}{1}\right) + 2\left(\frac{e^{-0.4(1.5)}}{1.5}\right)$$

$$+ 2\left(\frac{e^{-0.4(2)}}{2}\right) + 2\left(\frac{e^{-0.4(2.5)}}{2.5}\right)$$

$$+ 2\left(\frac{e^{-0.4(3)}}{3}\right) + 2\left(\frac{e^{-0.4(3.5)}}{3.5}\right)$$

$$+ 2\left(\frac{e^{-0.4(4)}}{4}\right) + 2\left(\frac{e^{-0.4(4.5)}}{4.5}\right)$$

$$+ 2\left(\frac{e^{-0.4(5)}}{5}\right) + 2\left(\frac{e^{-0.4(5.5)}}{5.5}\right)$$

$$+ \left(\frac{e^{-0.4(6)}}{6}\right)\Bigg] \approx 0.6929$$

So, the estimate of the average value is

$$\frac{1}{6-1}(0.6929) = 0.1386$$

31. Volumn of $S = \pi \int_0^1 \left(\dfrac{x}{1+x}\right)^2 dx$

Using the trapezoidal rule with $n=7$, $\Delta x = \dfrac{1-0}{7}$ and $x_1 = 0$, $x_2 = \dfrac{1}{7}$, $x_3 = \dfrac{2}{7}$, $x_4 = \dfrac{3}{7}$, $x_5 = \dfrac{4}{7}$, $x_6 = \dfrac{5}{7}$, $x_7 = \dfrac{6}{7}$, $x_8 = 1$.

$$\int_0^1 \left(\frac{x}{1+x}\right)^2 dx \approx \frac{\Delta x}{2}\big[f(x_1) + 2f(x_2) + 2f(x_3) + 2f(x_4)$$

$$+ 2f(x_5) + 2f(x_6) + 2f(x_6) + f(x_8)\big]$$

$$= \frac{1}{7} \left[0 + 2\left(\frac{1}{8}\right)^2 + 2\left(\frac{2}{9}\right)^2 + 2\left(\frac{3}{10}\right)^2 + 2\left(\frac{4}{11}\right)^2 \right.$$

$$\left. + 2\left(\frac{5}{12}\right)^2 + 2\left(\frac{6}{13}\right)^2 + \left(\frac{1}{2}\right)^2 \right]$$

$$\approx 0.114124$$

So, the volume is
$$\approx \pi(0.114124) \approx 0.3585$$

33. $$FV = e^{rT} \int_0^T f(t)e^{-rt}dt$$

$$= e^{0.06(10)} \int_0^{10} \sqrt{t}e^{-0.06t}dt$$

$$= e^{0.6} \int_0^{10} \sqrt{t}e^{-0.06t}dt$$

Using the trapezoidel rule with $n = 5$, $\Delta t = \dfrac{10 - 0}{5}$
and $t_1 = 0$, $t_2 = 2$, $t_3 = 4$, $t_4 = 6$, $t_5 = 8$, $t_6 = 10$

$$\int_0^{10} \sqrt{t}e^{-0.06t}dt \approx \frac{\Delta t}{2} \left[f(t_1) + 2f(t_2) + 2f(t_3) \right.$$

$$\left. + 2f(t_4) + 2f(t_5) + f(t_6) \right]$$

$$= \frac{2}{2} \left[0 + 2\sqrt{2}e^{0.12} + 2\sqrt{4}e^{-0.24} + 2\sqrt{6}e^{-0.36} \right.$$

$$\left. + 2\sqrt{8}e^{-0.48} + \sqrt{10}e^{-0.6} \right]$$

$$\approx 14.308884$$

So, $FV \approx e^{0.6}(14.308884) \approx 26.07249$ or $26,072

35. $$P(T) = P_0 S(T) + \int_0^T R S(T - t)dt$$

$$= 3000e^{-0.01(8)} + \int_0^8 50\sqrt{t} \cdot e^{-0.01(8-t)}dt$$

$$= 3000e^{-0.08} + 50e^{-0.08} \int_0^8 \sqrt{t}e^{0.01t}dt$$

$$= 50e^{-0.08} \left[60 + \int_0^8 \sqrt{t}e^{0.01t}dt \right]$$

Using Simpson's rule with $n = 8$, $\Delta t = \dfrac{8 - 0}{8}$
and $t_1 = 0$, $t_2 = 1$, $t_3 = 2$, ..., $t_9 = 8$.

$$\int_0^8 \sqrt{t}e^{0.01t}dt \approx \frac{\Delta t}{3} \left[f(t_1) + 4f(t_2) + 2f(t_3) + 4f(t_4) \right.$$

$$\left. + 2f(t_5) + 4f(t_6) + 2f(t_7) + 4f(t_8) + f(f_9) \right]$$

$$= \frac{1}{3} \left[0 + 4e^{0.01} + 2\sqrt{2}e^{0.02} + 4\sqrt{3}e^{0.03} + 2\sqrt{4}e^{0.04} \right.$$

$$\left. + 4\sqrt{5}e^{0.05} + 2\sqrt{6}e^{0.06} + 4\sqrt{7}e^{0.07} + \sqrt{8}e^{0.08} \right]$$

$$\approx 15.749112$$

So, the number of people with the flu is
$$\approx 50e^{-0.08}[60 + 15.749112] \approx 3{,}496 \text{ people.}$$

37. Since distance is the integral of velocity, we need
to approximate $\displaystyle\int_2^3 V(t)\, dt$ using the trapezoidal
rule. Since the readings are every 5 minutes,
$\Delta t = 5$ minutes $= \frac{1}{2}$ hour.

$$\text{Distance} \approx \frac{\frac{1}{12}}{2}[45 + 2(48) + 2(37) + 2(39) + 2(55)$$

$$+ 2(60) + 2(60) + 2(55) + 2(50)$$

$$+ 2(67) + 2(58) + 2(45) + 49]$$

$$\approx 51.75 \text{ miles}$$

39. We need to approximate

$$FV = \int_a^b (\text{rate income enters})e^{r(b-t)}\, dt$$

Since the readings are every 2 months, $\Delta t = 2$,
$r = \dfrac{0.04}{12}$, $a = 0$, and $b = 12$.

Future value
$$\approx \frac{2}{3} \left[(437)e^{(0.04/12)(12-0)} + 4(357)e^{(0.04/12)(12-2)} \right.$$

$$+ 2(615)e^{(0.04/12)(12-4)} + 4(510)e^{(0.04/12)(12-6)}$$

$$+ 2(415)e^{(0.04/12)(12-8)} + 4(550)e^{(0.04/12)(12-10)}$$

$$\left. + (593)e^{(0.04/12)(12-12)} \right]$$

$$\approx \$5949.70$$

41. We need to approximate $\int_a^b f(x) - g(x)\,dx$ using the trapzoidal rule. Since readings are made every 5 feet, $\Delta t = 5$.

$$\text{Area} \approx \frac{5}{2}\,[2 + 2(5) + 2(7) + 2(8) + 2(8) + 2(5)$$
$$+2(6) + 2(4) + 2(3) + 0]$$
$$\approx 235 \text{ square feet}$$

43. We need to approximate
$$PS = p_0 q_0 - \int_0^{q_0} S(q)\,dq$$
using the trapezsoidal rule. Since data was collected in increments of 1 thousand units, $\Delta q = 1$;

$$\int_0^7 S(q)\,dq \approx \frac{1}{2}\,[1.21 + 2(3.19) + 2(3.97) + 2(5.31)$$
$$+2(6.72) + 2(8.16) + 2(9.54) + 11.03]$$
$$= 43.01$$

So, $PS \approx (11.03)(7) - 43.01 = 34.2$ or \$34,200.

45. We need to approximate $2\pi \int_0^{10} r \cdot D(r)\,dr$ using the trapezoidal rule. Since measurements were made every 2 miles, $\Delta r = 2$;

$$\int_0^{10} r D(r)\,dr = \frac{2}{2}[0 + 2(2)(2844) + 2(4)(2087)$$
$$+ 2(6)(1752) + 2(8)(1109) + (10)(879)]$$
$$= 75{,}630$$

So, the total population is $\approx 2\pi(75{,}630) \approx 475{,}197$ people.

47. We need to approximate $\int_0^1 [x - L(x)]\,dx$ using the trapezoidal rule, with $\Delta x = 0.125$.

$$\approx \frac{0.125}{2}\,[0 + 2(0.125 - 0.0063) + 2(0.25 - 0.0631)$$
$$+2(0.375 - 0.1418) + 2(0.5 - 0.2305)$$
$$+2(0.625 - 0.3342) + 2(0.75 - 0.4713)$$
$$+2(0.875 - 0.6758) + (1 - 1)] \approx 0.197125$$

$$GI = 2\int_0^1 [x - L(x)]\,dx$$
$$\approx 2(0.197125) \approx 0.394$$

Checkup for Chapter 6

1. **(a)** $\int \sqrt{2x}\,\ln x^2\,dx$

Let $u = \ln x^2$ and $dV = \sqrt{2}x^{1/2}\,dx$

$\quad = 2\ln x \qquad V = \dfrac{2\sqrt{2}}{3}x^{3/2}$

$du = \dfrac{2}{x}\,dx$

$$= \frac{4\sqrt{2}}{3}x^{3/2}\ln x - \int \frac{2\sqrt{2}}{3}x^{3/2}\cdot\frac{2}{x}\,dx$$
$$= \frac{4\sqrt{2}}{3}x^{3/2}\ln x - \frac{4\sqrt{2}}{3}\int x^{1/2}\,dx$$
$$= \frac{4\sqrt{2}}{3}x^{3/2}\ln x - \frac{8\sqrt{2}}{9}x^{3/2} + C$$
$$= \frac{4\sqrt{2}}{9}x^{3/2}\,[3\ln|x| - 2] + C$$

(b) $\int_0^1 xe^{0.2x}\,dx$

Let $u = x$ and $dV = e^{0.2x}\,dx$
$\qquad du = dx \qquad\qquad = 5e^{0.2x}$

$$= 5xe^{0.2x}\Big|_0^1 - \int_0^1 5e^{0.2x}\,dx$$
$$= \left(5xe^{0.2x} - 25e^{0.2x}\right)\Big|_0^1$$
$$= \left[5(1)e^{0.2(1)} - 25e^{0.2(1)}\right] - \left[0 - 25e^0\right]$$
$$= 25 - 20e^{0.2}$$

(c) $\int_{-4}^0 x\sqrt{1 - 2x}\,dx$

Let $u = x$ and $dV = (1 - 2x)^{1/2}\,dx$
$\qquad du = dx \qquad\qquad = -\dfrac{1}{2}\cdot\dfrac{2}{3}(1 - 2x)^{3/2}$

$$= -\frac{x}{3}(1-2x)^{3/2}\Big|_{-4}^{0} - \int_{-4}^{0} -\frac{1}{3}(1-2x)^{3/2}\, dx$$

$$= -\frac{x}{3}(1-2x)^{3/2}\Big|_{-4}^{0} + \frac{1}{3}\int_{-4}^{0}(1-2x)^{3/2}\, dx$$

$$= \left[-\frac{x}{3}(1-2x)^{3/2} - \frac{1}{15}(1-2x)^{5/2}\right]\Big|_{-4}^{0}$$

$$= \left[0 - \frac{1}{15}(1)\right] - \left[\frac{4}{3}(9)^{3/2} - \frac{1}{15}(9)^{5/2}\right] = -\frac{298}{15}$$

(d) $\displaystyle\int \frac{x-1}{e^x}\, dx = \int (x-1)e^{-x}\, dx$

Let $\quad u = x - 1 \quad$ and $\quad dV = e^{-x}\, dx$

$\qquad du = dx \qquad\qquad\qquad V = -e^{-x}$

$$= -(x-1)e^{-x} - \int -e^{-x}\, dx$$

$$= -(x-1)e^{-x} + \int e^{-x}\, dx$$

$$= -(x-1)e^{-x} - e^{-x} + C$$

$$= \left[(-x+1) - 1\right]e^{-x} + C$$

$$= -xe^{-x} + C$$

2. (a) $\displaystyle\int_1^{\infty} \frac{1}{x^{1.1}}\, dx = \lim_{N\to\infty} \int_1^N x^{-1.1}\, dx$

$$= \lim_{N\to\infty}\left(-10x^{-0.1}\right)\Big|_1^N$$

$$= \lim_{N\to\infty}\left[-10N^{-0.1} + 10(1)^{-0.1}\right]$$

$$= 0 + 10 = 10$$

(b) $\displaystyle\int_1^{\infty} xe^{-2x}\, dx = \lim_{N\to\infty}\int_1^N xe^{-2x}\, dx$

Let $\quad u = x \quad$ and $\quad dV = e^{-2x}$

$\qquad du = dx \qquad\qquad V = -\frac{1}{2}e^{-2x}$

$$= \lim_{N\to\infty}\left[-\frac{x}{2}e^{-2x}\Big|_1^N - \int_1^N -\frac{1}{2}e^{-2x}\, dx\right]$$

$$= \lim_{N\to\infty}\left[-\frac{x}{2}e^{-2x}\Big|_1^N + \frac{1}{2}\int_1^N e^{-2x}\, dx\right]$$

$$= \lim_{N\to\infty}\left[-\frac{x}{2}e^{-2x} - \frac{1}{4}e^{-2x}\right]\Big|_1^N$$

$$= \lim_{N\to\infty}\left[\left(-\frac{N}{2}e^{-2N} - \frac{1}{4}e^{-2N}\right)\right.$$

$$\left. - \left(-\frac{1}{2}e^{-2(1)} - \frac{1}{4}e^{-2(1)}\right)\right]$$

$$= 0 + \frac{1}{2}e^{-2} + \frac{1}{4}e^{-2} = \frac{3}{4}e^{-2}$$

(c) $\displaystyle\int_1^{\infty} \frac{x}{(x+1)^2}\, dx = \lim_{N\to\infty}\int_1^N x(x+1)^{-2}\, dx$

Let $\quad u = x \quad$ and $\quad dV = (x+1)^{-2}\, dx$

$\qquad du = dx \qquad\qquad V = -\dfrac{1}{(x+1)}$

$$= \lim_{N\to\infty}\left[-\frac{x}{x+1}\Big|_1^N - \int_1^N -\frac{1}{x+1}\, dx\right]$$

$$= \lim_{N\to\infty}\left[-\frac{x}{x+1}\Big|_1^N + \int_1^N \frac{1}{x+1}\, dx\right]$$

$$= \lim_{N\to\infty}\left[-\frac{x}{x+1} + \ln|x+1|\right]\Big|_1^N$$

$$= \lim_{N\to\infty}\left[\left(-\frac{N}{N+1} + \ln(N+1)\right) - \left(-\frac{1}{2} + \ln 2\right)\right]$$

Since $\displaystyle\lim_{N\to\infty} -\frac{N}{N+1} = \lim_{N\to\infty} -\frac{1}{1} = -1$, and

$\displaystyle\lim_{N\to\infty} \ln(N+1) = \infty,$

$$= \lim_{N\to\infty}\left[-\frac{N}{N+1} + \ln(N+1) + \frac{1}{2} - \ln 2\right] = \infty$$

so, the integral diverges.

(d) $\displaystyle\int_{-\infty}^{\infty} xe^{-x^2}\, dx$

$$= \lim_{M\to\infty}\int_M^0 xe^{-x^2}\, dx + \lim_{N\to\infty}\int_0^N xe^{-x^2}\, dx$$

Using substitution with $u = -x^2$ and $-\frac{1}{2} du = x\, dx$,

$$= \lim_{M \to -\infty} -\frac{1}{2} \int_{-M^2}^{0} e^u\, du + \lim_{N \to \infty} -\frac{1}{2} \int_{0}^{-N^2} e^u\, du$$

$$= -\frac{1}{2} \lim_{M \to -\infty} \int_{-M^2}^{0} e^u\, du + \frac{1}{2} \lim_{N \to \infty} \int_{N^2}^{0} e^u\, du$$

$$= -\frac{1}{2} \lim_{M \to -\infty} \left(e^u \Big|_{-M^2}^{0} \right) + \frac{1}{2} \lim_{N \to \infty} \left(e^u \Big|_{N^2}^{0} \right)$$

$$= -\frac{1}{2} \lim_{M \to -\infty} \left(e^0 - e^{-M^2} \right) + \frac{1}{2} \lim_{N \to \infty} \left(e^0 - e^{-N^2} \right)$$

$$= \frac{1}{2}(1 - 0) + \frac{1}{2}(1 - 0 (= 0$$

3. **(a)** $\displaystyle \int \left(\ln \sqrt{3x} \right)^2 dx$

$$= \int \ln(3x)^{1/2} \cdot \ln(3x)^{1/2}\, dx$$

$$= \int \frac{1}{2} \ln(3x) \cdot \frac{1}{2} \ln(3x)\, dx$$

$$= \frac{1}{4} \int (\ln 3x)^2\, dx$$

which most resembles $\displaystyle \int (\ln u)^n\, du$ (formula #27). Let $u = 3x$; then $du = 3\, dx$ or $\frac{1}{3} du = dx$,

$$= \frac{1}{4} \int (\ln u)^2 \cdot \frac{1}{3}\, du = \frac{1}{12} \int (\ln u)^2\, du$$

$$= \frac{1}{12} \left[u(\ln u)^2 - 2 \int \ln u\, du \right]$$

Using formula #23,

$$= \frac{1}{12} \left[u(\ln u)^2 - 2(u \ln |u| - u) \right] + C$$

$$= \frac{1}{12} \left[3x(\ln 3x)^2 - 2(3x) \ln |3x| + 3x \right] + C$$

$$= \frac{x}{4}(\ln 3x)^2 - \frac{x}{2} \ln 3x + \frac{x}{4} + C$$

$$= \frac{x}{4} \left[(\ln |3x|)^2 - 2 \ln |3x| + 2 \right] + C$$

(b) $\displaystyle \int \frac{dx}{x\sqrt{4 + x^2}}$ is of the form $\displaystyle \int \frac{du}{u\sqrt{a^2 + u^2}}$ (formula #11). Let $x = u$, $dx = du$, and $a = 2$,

$$= -\frac{1}{2} \ln \left| \frac{\sqrt{4 + x^2} + 2}{x} \right| + C$$

(c) $\displaystyle \int \frac{dx}{x^2\sqrt{x^2 - 9}}$ is of the form $\displaystyle \int \frac{du}{u^2\sqrt{u^2 - a^2}}$ (formula #21). Let $x = u$, $dx = du$, and $a = 3$,

$$= \frac{\sqrt{x^2 - 9}}{9x} + C$$

(d) $\displaystyle \int \frac{dx}{3x^2 - 4x}$ can be written as $\displaystyle \int \frac{dx}{x(-4 + 3x)}$ so it is of the form $\displaystyle \int \frac{du}{u(a + bu)}$ (formula #6). Let $x = u$, $dx = du$, $a = -4$, and $b = 3$,

$$= -\frac{1}{4} \ln \left| \frac{x}{3x - 4} \right| + C$$

4. **(a)**
$$\frac{dy}{dx} = \frac{-2}{x^2 y}$$

$$\int y\, dy = \int -\frac{2}{x^2}\, dx$$

$$\int y\, dy = -2 \int x^{-2}\, dx$$

$$\frac{y^2}{2} = -2 \left(-\frac{1}{x} \right) + C$$

$$y^2 = \frac{4}{x} + 2C$$

Since $y = 1$ when $x = -1$,

$$(1)^2 = \frac{4}{-1} + 2C, \quad \text{or} \quad C = \frac{5}{2}$$

So, $y^2 = \dfrac{4}{x} + 5$, or $y = \sqrt{\dfrac{4}{x} + 5}$.

(b)
$$\frac{dy}{dx} = \frac{xy}{x^2 + 1}$$

$$\int \frac{1}{y}\, dy = \int \frac{x}{x^2 + 1}\, dx$$

Using substitution with $u = x^2 + 1$,

$$\int \frac{1}{y}\,dy = \frac{1}{2}\int \frac{1}{u}\,du$$

$$\ln|y| = \ln|u| + C_1$$

$$\ln|y| = \frac{1}{2}\ln|x^2 + 1| + C_1$$

$$\ln\left|\frac{y}{\sqrt{x^2+1}}\right| = C_1$$

$$\left|\frac{y}{\sqrt{x^2+1}}\right| = e^{C_1}$$

$$y = \pm e^{C_1}\sqrt{x^2+1}$$

$$y = C\sqrt{x^2+1}$$

Since $y = -3$ when $x = 0$, $C = -3$. So,
$y = -3\sqrt{x^2+1}$.

(c) $\dfrac{dy}{dx} = xe^{y-x} = xe^y e^{-x}$

$$\int e^{-y}\,dy = \int xe^{-x}\,dx$$

Using integration by parts, with $u = x$ and
$dV = e^{-x}\,dx$,

$$\int e^{-y}\,dy = -xe^{-x} - \int -e^{-x}\,dx$$

$$-e^{-y} = -xe^{-x} = e^{-x} + C$$

$$-e^{-y} = -(x+1)e^{-x} + C$$

$$e^{-y} = (x+1)e^{-x} + C$$

$$\ln e^{-y} = \ln\left[(x+1)e^{-x} + C\right]$$

$$-y = \ln\left[(x+1)e^{-x} + C\right]$$

$$y = -\ln\left[(x+1)e^{-x} + C\right]$$

Since $y = 0$ when $x = 0$,
$0 = -\ln\left[(0+1)e^0 + C\right]$, or $C = 0$. So,

$$y = \ln\left[(x+1)e^{-x}\right]$$

$$= \left[\ln(x+1) + \ln e^{-x}\right]$$

$$= -\ln(x+1) - (-x)$$

$$= -\ln(x+1) + x$$

5.

$$\frac{dA}{dt} = 0.05A$$

$$\int \frac{1}{A}\,dA = 0.05\,dt$$

$$\ln|A| = 0.05t + C_1$$

$$e^{\ln|A|} = e^{0.05t + C_1}$$

$$|A| = e^{C_1} \cdot e^{0.05t}$$

$$A = \pm e^{C_1} \cdot e^{0.05t}$$

$$A(t) = Ce^{0.05t}$$

Since $A = 10{,}000$ when $t = 0$, $C = 10{,}000$. So
$A(t) = 10{,}000e^{0.05t}$. When $t = 10$,

$$A(10) = 10{,}000e^{0.05(10)}$$

$$\approx \$16{,}487.21$$

6.

$$PV = \int_0^\infty (50 + 3t)e^{-0.06t}\,dt$$

$$\lim_{N\to\infty} \int_0^N (50 + 3t)e^{-0.06t}\,dt$$

Using integration by parts with $u = 50 + 3t$ and
$dV = e^{-0.06t}\,dt$,

$$= \lim_{N\to\infty}\left[(50 + 3t) - \frac{50}{3}e^{-0.06t}\Big|_0^N\right.$$

$$\left. - \int_0^N -\frac{50}{3}e^{-0.06t}3\,dt\right]$$

$$= \lim_{N\to\infty}\left[-\frac{50}{3}(50 + 3t)e^{-0.06t}\Big|_0^N + 50\int_0^N e^{-0.06t}\,dt\right]$$

$$= \lim_{N\to\infty} -\frac{50}{3}\left[(50 + 3t)e^{-0.06t} + 50e^{-0.06t}\right]\Big|_0^N$$

$$= -\frac{50}{3}\lim_{N\to\infty}\left[50e^{-0.06t} + 3te^{-0.06t} + 50e^{-0.06t}\right]\Big|_0^N$$

$$= -\frac{50}{3}\lim_{N\to\infty}\left(100e^{-0.06t} + 3te^{-0.06t}\right)\Big|_0^N$$

$$= -\frac{50}{3}\lim_{N\to\infty}\left[\left(100e^{-0.06N} + 3Ne^{-0.06N}\right) - \left(100e^0 + 0\right)\right]$$

$$= -\frac{50}{3} \cdot -100 = \frac{5{,}000}{3} \approx 1{,}666.6667 \text{ thousand,}$$

or approximately $\$1{,}666{,}666.67$

7. Since x is measured in months, we need

(a)

$$P(X > 12) = \int_{12}^{\infty} 0.03 e^{-0.03x}\, dx$$

$$= \lim_{N \to \infty} 0.03 \int_{12}^{N} e^{-0.03x}\, dx$$

$$= \lim_{N \to \infty} 0.03 \cdot \frac{1}{-0.03} e^{-0.03x} \Big|_{12}^{N}$$

$$= \lim_{N \to \infty} \left(e^{-0.03x} \right) \Big|_{12}^{N}$$

$$= \lim_{N \to \infty} \left[-e^{-0.03N} + e^{-0.03(12)} \right]$$

$$= e^{-0.36} \approx 0.6977$$

(b)

$$P(3 \le X \le 6) = \int_{3}^{6} 0.03 e^{-0.03x}\, dx$$

$$= \left(-e^{-0.03x} \right) \Big|_{3}^{6} = -e^{-0.18} + e^{-0.09}$$

$$\approx 0.07866$$

(c)

$$E(X) = \int_{-\infty}^{\infty} x f(x)\, dx$$

$$= \lim_{N \to \infty} 0.03 \int_{0}^{N} x e^{-0.03x}\, dx$$

Using integration by parts with $u = x$ and $dV = e^{-0.03x} dx$.

$$= \lim_{N \to \infty} 0.03 \left[\frac{x}{-0.03} e^{-0.03x} \Big|_{0}^{N} \right.$$

$$\left. - \int_{0}^{N} \frac{1}{-0.03} e^{-0.03x}\, dx \right]$$

$$= \lim_{N \to \infty} \left[-x e^{-0.03x} \Big|_{0}^{N} + \int_{0}^{N} e^{-0.03x}\, dx \right]$$

$$= \lim_{N \to \infty} \left[-x e^{-0.03x} - \frac{1}{0.03} e^{-0.03x} \right] \Big|_{0}^{N}$$

$$= \lim_{N \to \infty} \left[\left(-N e^{-0.03N} - \frac{1}{0.03} e^{-0.03N} \right) \right.$$

$$\left. - \left(0 - \frac{1}{0.03} e^{0} \right) \right]$$

$$= \frac{100}{3} \approx 33.3 \text{ months}$$

8. Amount of drug $= \displaystyle\lim_{N \to \infty} \int_{0}^{N} 0.7 e^{-0.2(N-t)}\, dt$

$$= \lim_{N \to \infty} 0.7 e^{-0.2N} \int_{0}^{N} e^{0.2t}\, dt$$

$$= \lim_{N \to \infty} 0.7 e^{-0.2N} \left(5 e^{0.2t} \right) \Big|_{0}^{N}$$

$$= 3.5 \lim_{N \to \infty} \left[e^{-0.2N} \left(e^{0.2N} - e^{0} \right) \right]$$

$$= 3.5 \lim_{N \to \infty} \left(e^{0} - e^{-0.2N} \right)$$

$$= 3.5 \cdot 1 = 3.5 \text{ mg}$$

9. (a)

$$\frac{dm}{dt} = kmt$$

$$\int \frac{1}{m}\, dm = \int kt\, dt$$

$$\ln |m| = \frac{kt^2}{2} + C_1$$

$$e^{\ln |m|} = e^{kt^2/2 + C_1}$$

$$|m| = e^{C_1} e^{kt^2/2}$$

$$m = \pm e^{C_1} e^{kt^2/2}$$

$$m(t) = C e^{kt^2/2}$$

When $t = 0$, $m(0)m_0$, the initial mass of the protein and $m(t) = m_0 e^{kt^2/2}$. Since the half-life is 12 hours,

$$\frac{m_0}{2} = m_0 e^{k(12)^2/2}$$

$$\frac{1}{2} = e^{72k}$$

$$\ln \frac{1}{2} = 72k,$$

$$\text{or } k = \frac{\ln 0.5}{72}$$

$$\text{So, } m(t) = m_0 e^{\ln 0.5 t^2/144}$$

$$= m_0 e^{-\frac{\ln 2}{144}t^2}$$

(b)
$$m(9) = m_0 e^{\frac{\ln 2}{144}(9)^2}$$

$$= m_0(0.6771)$$

So, approximately 67.7% of the original mass remains.

10. To approximate $\displaystyle\int_3^4 \frac{\sqrt{25 - x^2}}{x}\, dx$ using the

trapezoidal rule with $n = 8$, $\Delta x = \dfrac{4 - 3}{8} = 0.125$,

$$\approx \frac{0.125}{2}\left[\left(\frac{\sqrt{25 - (3)^2}}{3}\right) + \left(\frac{\sqrt{25 - (3.125)^2}}{3.125}\right)\right.$$

$$+ 2\left(\frac{\sqrt{25 - (3.25)^2}}{3.25}\right) + 2\left(\frac{\sqrt{25 - (3.375)^2}}{3.375}\right)$$

$$+ 2\left(\frac{\sqrt{25 - (3.5)^2}}{3.5}\right) + 2\left(\frac{\sqrt{25 - (3.625)^2}}{3.625}\right)$$

$$+ 2\left(\frac{\sqrt{25 - (3.75)^2}}{3.75}\right) + 2\left(\frac{\sqrt{25 - (3.875)^2}}{3.875}\right)$$

$$+ \left(\frac{\sqrt{25 - (4)^2}}{4}\right) \approx 1.027552$$

Using formula #17 with $x = u$, $dx = du$, and $a = 5$,

$$= \left[\sqrt{25 - x^2} - 5 \ln \left|\frac{5 + \sqrt{25 - x^2}}{x}\right|\right]\Bigg|_3^4$$

$$= \left[\sqrt{25 - 4^2} - 5 \ln \left|\frac{5 + \sqrt{25 - 4^2}}{4}\right|\right]$$

$$= -\left[\sqrt{25 - 3^2} - 5 \ln \left|\frac{5 + \sqrt{25 - 3^2}}{3}\right|\right]$$

$$= (3 - 5 \ln 2) - (4 - 5 \ln 3)$$

$$= -1 - \ln 2^5 + \ln 3^5$$

$$= -1 + \ln \left(\frac{3}{2}\right)^5 = -1 + 5 \ln \left(\frac{3}{2}\right) \approx 1.027326$$

Review Problems

1.
$$\int t e^{1-t}\, dt$$

Let $\quad u = t \quad$ and $\quad dV = e^{1-t}\, dt$
$$du = dt \qquad\qquad V = -e^{1-t}$$

$$= -t e^{1-t} - \int -e^{1-t}\, dt$$

$$= -t e^{1-t} + \int e^{1-t}\, dt$$

$$= -t e^{1-t} - e^{1-t} + C$$

$$= -e^{1-t}(t + 1) + C$$

3.
$$\int x(2x + 3)^{1/2}\, dx$$

Let $\quad u = x \quad$ and $\quad dV = (2x + 3)^{1/2}$
$$du = dx$$

Using substitution with $u = 2x + 3$,

$$V = \frac{1}{2}\left[\frac{2}{3}(2x + 3)^{3/2}\right]$$

$$= \frac{1}{3}(2x + 3)^{3/2}$$

So, $\displaystyle\int x(2x + 3)^{1/2}\, dx$

$$= \frac{x}{3}(2x+3)^{3/2} - \int \frac{1}{3}(2x+3)^{3/2}\, dx$$

Using substitution with $u = 2x + 3$,

$$= \frac{x}{3}(2x+3)^{3/2} - \frac{1}{3}\left(\frac{1}{2}\right)\left(\frac{2}{5}\right)(2x+3)^{5/2} + C$$

$$= \frac{x}{3}(2x+3)^{3/2} - \frac{1}{15}(2x+3)^{5/2} + C$$

5.
$$\int_1^4 \frac{\ln \sqrt{S}}{\sqrt{S}}\, dS = \int_1^4 S^{-1/2} \ln S^{1/2}\, dS$$

Let $u = \ln S^{1/2}$ and $dV = S^{-1/2}\, dS$

$$= \frac{1}{2}\ln S \qquad V = 2S^{1/2}$$

$$du = \frac{1}{2S}\, dS$$

$$= S^{1/2}\ln S \Big|_1^4 - \int_1^4 2S^{1/2} \cdot \frac{1}{2S}\, dS$$

$$= S^{1/2}\ln S \Big|_1^4 - \int_1^4 S^{-1/2}\, dS$$

$$= \left(S^{1/2}\ln S - 2S^{1/2}\right)\Big|_1^4$$

$$= \left[\sqrt{4}\ln 4 - 2\sqrt{4}\right] - [1\ln 1 - 2(1)]$$

$$= 2\ln 4 - 2 = 2\ln(2)^2 - 2 = 4\ln 2 - 2$$

7.
$$\int_{-2}^1 (2x+1)(x+3)^{3/2}\, dx$$

Let $u = 2x + 1$ and $dV = (x+3)^{3/2}\, dx$

$$du = 2\, dx \qquad V = \frac{2}{5}(x+3)^{5/2}$$

$$= \frac{2}{5}(2x+1)(x+3)^{5/2}\Big|_{-2}^1 - \int_{-2}^1 \frac{2}{5}(x+3)^{5/2} \cdot 2\, dx$$

$$= \left[\frac{2}{5}(2x+1)(x+3)^{5/2}\right.$$

$$\left. - \left(\frac{4}{5}\right)\left(\frac{2}{7}\right)(x+3)^{7/2}\right]\Big|_{-2}^1$$

$$= \left[\frac{2}{5}(2(1)+1)(1+3)^{5/2} - \frac{8}{35}(1+3)^{7/2}\right]$$

$$- \left[\frac{2}{5}(2(-2)+1)(-2+3)^{5/2} - \frac{8}{35}(-2+3)^{7/2}\right]$$

$$= \frac{74}{7}$$

9.
$$\int x^3 \left(3x^2+2\right)^{1/2}\, dx = \int x^2 \cdot x \left(3x^2+2\right)^{1/2}\, dx$$

Let $u = x^2$ and $dV = x\left(3x^2+2\right)^{1/2}\, dx$

$$du = 2x\, dx$$

Using substitution with $u = 3x^2 + 2$,

$$V = \left(\frac{1}{6}\right)\left(\frac{2}{3}\right)\left(3x^2+2\right)^{3/2}$$

$$V = \frac{1}{9}\left(3x^2+2\right)^{3/2}$$

So, $\displaystyle \int x^2 \cdot x(3x^2+2)^{1/2}\, dx$

$$= \frac{x^2}{9}\left(3x^2+2\right)^{3/2} - \int \frac{1}{9}\left(3x^2+2\right)^{3/2} 2x\, dx$$

$$= \frac{x^2}{9}\left(3x^2+2\right)^{3/2} - \frac{2}{9}\int \left(3x^2+2\right)^{3/2} x\, dx$$

$$= \frac{x^2}{9}\left(3x^2+2\right)^{3/2}$$

$$- \left(\frac{2}{9}\right)\left(\frac{1}{6}\right)\left(\frac{2}{5}\right)\left(3x^2+2\right)^{5/2} + C$$

$$= \frac{x^2}{9}\left(3x^2+2\right)^{3/2} - \frac{2}{135}\left(3x^2+2\right)^{5/2} + C$$

11.
$$\int \frac{5\, dx}{8 - 2x^2} = \int \frac{5\, dx}{2(4 - x^2)} = \frac{5}{2}\int \frac{dx}{4 - x^2}$$

which is of the form $\displaystyle \int \frac{du}{a^2 - u^2}$ (formula #16). Let $x = u, dx = du$, and $a = 2$,

$$= \frac{5}{2}\left[\frac{1}{2(2)}\ln\left|\frac{2+x}{2-x}\right| + C\right]$$

$$= \frac{5}{8}\ln\left|\frac{2+x}{2-x}\right| + C$$

13.
$$\int w^2 e^{-w/3} dw = \int w^2 e^{-\frac{1}{3}w} dw$$

which is of the form $\int u^n e^{au}\, du$ (formula #26). Let
$w = u,\, dw = du,$ and $a = -\dfrac{1}{3}$,

$$= \frac{1}{-\frac{1}{3}} w^2 e^{-w/3} - \frac{2}{-\frac{1}{3}} \int w e^{-w/3}\, dw$$

$$= -3w^2 e^{-w/3} + 6 \int w e^{-w/3}\, dw$$

Using formula #22,

$$= -3w^2 e^{-w/3} + 6 \left[\frac{1}{(-\frac{1}{3})^2} \left(-\frac{1}{3}w - 1 \right) e^{-w/3} \right] + C$$

$$= -3w^2 e^{-w/3} + 54 \left(-\frac{1}{3}w - 1 \right) e^{-w/3} + C$$

$$= -3w^2 e^{-w/3} - 18w e^{-w/3} - 54 e^{-w/3} + C$$

15.
$$\int (\ln 2x)^3\, dx = \frac{1}{2} \int (\ln 2x)^3 \cdot 2\, dx$$

which is of the form $\int (\ln u)^n\, du$ (formula #27). Let
$u = 2x,\, du = 2\, dx,$ and $n = 3$,

$$= \frac{1}{2} \left[2x(\ln 2x)^3 - 3 \int (\ln 2x)^2 2\, dx \right]$$

$$= x(\ln 2x)^3 - \frac{3}{2} \left[2x(\ln 2x)^2 - 2 \int (\ln 2x)2\, dx \right]$$

$$= x(\ln 2x)^3 - 3x(\ln 2x)^2 + 3\,[2x \ln | 2x | - 2x] + C$$

$$= x(\ln 2x)^3 - 3x(\ln 2x)^2 + 6x \ln 2x - 6x + C$$

$$= x \left[(\ln 2x)^3 - 3(\ln 2x)^2 + 6(\ln 2x) - 6 \right] + C$$

17.
$$\int_0^\infty \frac{1}{\sqrt[3]{1 + 2x}}\, dx$$

Using substitution with $u = 1 + 2x$,

$$= \lim_{N \to \infty} \int_0^N (1 + 2x)^{-1/3}\, dx$$

$$= \lim_{N \to \infty} \frac{3}{4}(1 + 2x)^{2/3} \Big|_0^N = \infty.$$

So, the interval diverges.

19.
$$\int_0^\infty \frac{3t}{t^2 + 1}\, dx$$

Using substitution with $u = t^2 + 1$,

$$= 3 \lim_{N \to \infty} \int_0^N \frac{3t}{t^2 + 1}\, dx$$

$$= 3 \lim_{N \to \infty} \frac{1}{2} \ln(t^2 + 1) \Big|_0^N = \infty.$$

So, the interval diverges.

21.
$$\int_0^\infty x e^{-2x}\, dx$$

Using integration by parts with $u = x$ and
$dV = e^{-2x}\, dx$,

$$= \lim_{N \to \infty} \int_0^N x e^{-2x}\, dx$$

$$= \lim_{N \to \infty} \left[\left(-\frac{1}{2} x e^{-2x} \right) \Big|_0^N + \frac{1}{2} \int_0^N e^{-2x}\, dx \right]$$

$$= \lim_{N \to \infty} \left(-\frac{1}{2} x e^{-2x} - \frac{1}{4} e^{-2x} \right) \Big|_0^N = \frac{1}{4}$$

23.
$$\int_0^\infty x^2 e^{-2x}\, dx = \lim_{N \to \infty} \int_0^N x^2 e^{-2x}\, dx$$

Using integration by parts with $u = x^2$ and
$dV = e^{-2x}\, dx$,

$$= -\lim_{N \to \infty} \frac{1}{2} x^2 e^{-2x} \Big|_0^N + \lim_{N \to \infty} \int_0^N x e^{-2x}\, dx$$

$$= -\lim_{N \to \infty} \frac{1}{2} x^2 e^{-2x} \Big|_0^N - \lim_{N \to \infty} \frac{1}{2} x e^{-2x} \Big|_0^N$$

$$\quad - \lim_{N \to \infty} \frac{1}{4} x e^{-2x} \Big|_0^N = \frac{1}{4}$$

25.
$$\int_1^\infty \frac{\ln x}{\sqrt{x}}\, dx = \lim_{N \to \infty} \int_1^N x^{-1/2} \ln x\, dx$$

Using integration by parts with $u = \ln x$ and
$dV = x^{-1/2}\, dx$,

$$= \lim_{N \to \infty} \left[2x^{1/2} \ln x \Big|_1^N - \int_1^N 2x^{1/2} \cdot \frac{1}{x} \, dx \right]$$

$$= \lim_{N \to \infty} \left[2x^{1/2} \ln x \Big|_1^N - 2 \int_1^N x^{-1/2} \, dx \right]$$

$$= \lim_{N \to \infty} 2 \left[x^{1/2} \ln x - 2x^{1/2} \right] \Big|_1^N$$

$$= 2 \lim_{N \to \infty} \left[\left(N^{1/2} \ln N - 2N^{1/2} \right) - (\ln 1 - 2) \right]$$

$= \infty$, so the integral diverges.

27.
$$\frac{dy}{dx} = x^3 - 3x^2 + 5,$$

$$y = \int (x^3 - 3x^2 + 5) \, dx$$

$$= \frac{x^4}{4} - x^3 + 5x + C.$$

29. Separate the variables of

$$\frac{dy}{dx} = k(80 - y)$$

and integrate to get

$$\int \frac{1}{80 - y} \, dy = \int k \, dx,$$

$$- \ln | 80 - y | = kx + C_1,$$

$$| 80 - y | = e^{-kx - C_1} = e^{-C_1} e^{-kx},$$

$$80 - y = Ce^{-kx}, \text{ or } y = 80 - Ce^{-kx}$$

$$\text{where } C = \pm e^{-C_1}$$

31.
$$\frac{dy}{dx} = 5x^4 - 3x^2 - 2,$$

$$y = \int (5x^4 - 3x^2 - 2) \, dx = x^5 - x^3 - 2x + C.$$

Since $y = 4$ when $x = 1$, $4 = 1 - 1 - 2 + C$, or
$C = 6$.
So,

$$y = x^5 - x^3 - 2x + 6$$

33.
$$\frac{dy}{dx} = \frac{xy}{\sqrt{1 - x^2}}$$

$$\frac{dy}{y} = \frac{x \, dx}{\sqrt{1 - x^2}}$$

Using substitution with $u = 1 - x^2$,

$$\ln | y | = -\sqrt{1 - x^2} + C$$

Since $y = 2$ when $x = 0$, $C = 1 + \ln 2$ and

$$\ln | y | = -\sqrt{1 - x^2} + 1 + \ln 2$$

$$\ln \left| \frac{y}{2} \right| = 1 - \sqrt{1 - x^2}$$

$$y = 2e^{1 - \sqrt{1 - x^2}}$$

35. (a)
$$P(1 \le X \le 4) = \int_1^4 f(x) \, dx$$

$$= \int_1^4 \frac{1}{3} \, dx = \frac{x}{3} \Big|_1^4 = 1.$$

(b)
$$P(2 \le X \le 3) = \int_2^3 f(x) \, dx$$

$$= \int_2^3 \frac{1}{3} \, dx = \frac{x}{3} \Big|_2^3 = \frac{1}{3}.$$

(c)
$$P(X \le 2) = \int_{-\infty}^2 f(x) \, dx$$

$$= \int_1^2 \frac{1}{3} \, dx = \frac{x}{3} \Big|_1^2 = \frac{1}{3}.$$

37. (a)
$$P(X \ge 0) = \int_0^\infty f(x) \, dx$$

$$= \lim_{N \to \infty} \int_0^N -.2e^{-0.2x} \, dx$$

$$= \lim_{N \to \infty} \left(-e^{-0.2x} \right) \Big|_0^N$$

$$= \lim_{N \to \infty} \left(-e^{-0.2N} + 1 \right) = 1.$$

(b)
$$P(1 \le X \le 4) = \int_1^4 f(x)\, dx$$

$$= \int_1^4 0.2e^{-0.2x}\, dx$$

$$= -e^{-0.2x}\Big|_1^4$$

$$= -e^{-0.8} + e^{-0.2} \approx 0.3694.$$

(c)
$$P(X \ge 5) = \int_5^\infty f(x)\, dx$$

$$= \lim_{N\to\infty} \int_5^N 0.2e^{-0.2x}\, dx$$

$$= -\lim_{N\to\infty} e^{-0.2x}\Big|_5^N$$

$$= \lim_{N\to\infty}\left[-e^{-0.2N} + e^{-1}\right] \approx 0.3679.$$

39. The rate of change of the value is

$$\frac{dV}{dt} = k(V - 5{,}000),$$

Separate the variables and integrate to get

$$\int \frac{1}{V - 5{,}000}\, dV = \int k\, dt$$

$$\ln(V - 5{,}000) = kt + C_1,$$

$$V - 5{,}000 = e^{kt+C_1} = e^{C_1}e^{kt},$$

or
$V(t) = 5{,}000 + Ce^{kt}$
where $C = e^{C_1}$ and the absolute values can be dropped since $V - 5{,}000 > 0$.
Since the machine was originally worth \$40,000,
$40{,}000 = V(0) = 5{,}000 + C$
or $C = 35{,}000$. So,
$V(t) = 5{,}000 + 35{,}000e^{kt}$.
Since the machine was worth \$30,000 after 4 years,
$39{,}000 = V(4) = 5{,}000 + 35{,}000e^{4k}$,
$35{,}000e^{4k} = 25{,}000$ or

$$e^{4k} = \frac{25{,}000}{35{,}000} = \frac{5}{7}.$$

The value of the machine after 8 years is

$$V(8) = 5{,}000 + 35{,}000e^{8k}$$

$$= 5{,}000 + 35{,}000(e^{4k})^2$$

$$= 5{,}000 + 35{,}000\left(\frac{5}{7}\right)^2 \approx \$22{,}857.14$$

41. Let $Q(t)$ denote the number of pounds of salt in the tank after t minutes.
Then $\dfrac{dQ}{dt}$ is the rate of change of salt with respect to time (measured in pounds per minute).

$$\frac{dQ}{dt} = (\text{rate at which salt enters})$$

$$- (\text{rate at which salt leaves})$$

$$= \frac{\text{pounds entering}}{\text{gallon}}\; \frac{\text{gallons entering}}{\text{minute}}$$

$$- \frac{\text{pounds leaving}}{\text{gallon}}\; \frac{\text{gallons leaving}}{\text{minute}}.$$

Now, $\dfrac{\text{gallons leaving}}{\text{gallon}}$

$$= \frac{\text{pounds of salt in the tank}}{\text{gallons of brine in the tank}}$$

$$= \frac{Q}{200}.$$

So, $\dfrac{dQ}{dt} = -\dfrac{Q}{200}(4) = -\dfrac{Q}{50}$.
Separate the variables and integrate to get

$$\int \frac{1}{Q}\, dQ = -\int \frac{1}{50}\, dt,$$

$$\ln|Q| = -\frac{t}{50} + C_1,$$

$$Q = e^{C_1}e^{-t/50} = Ce^{-t/50},$$

where $C = e^{C_1}$. Since there are initially 600 pounds of salt in the tank (3 pounds of salt per gallon times 200 gallons), $600 = Q(0) = C$. So,
$Q(t) = 600e^{-t/50}$
The amount of salt in the tank after 100 minutes is
$Q(100) = 600e^{-2} = 81.2012$ pounds.

43. Let $Q(t)$ denote the amount (in million of dollars) of new currency in circulation at time t. Then $\dfrac{dQ}{dt}$ is

$$f'(x) = (x)\left(e^{1/x} \cdot \frac{-1}{x^2}\right) + \left(e^{1/x}\right)(1)$$

$$= e^{1/x}\left(-\frac{1}{x} + 1\right)$$

$$f''(x) = \left(e^{1/x}\right)\left(\frac{1}{x^2}\right)$$

$$+ \left(-\frac{1}{x} + 1\right)\left(e^{1/x} \cdot \frac{1}{x^2}\right)$$

$$= \frac{1}{x^2}d^{1/x}\left[1 + -\left(-\frac{1}{x} + 1\right)\right]$$

$$= \frac{1}{x^3}e^{1/x}$$

Since $f''(x)$ is always positive and decreasing on $1 \le x \le 2$ $M = |f''(1)| = e$.

$$|E_8| \le \frac{e}{768} \approx 0.003539$$

(b) By Simpson's rule,

$$\int_1^2 xe^{1/x}\, dx$$

$$= \frac{\Delta x}{3}\left[f(x_1) + 4f(x_2) + 2f(x_3) + 4f(x_4)\right.$$

$$+ \cdots + 4f(x_8) + f(x_9)\Big]$$

$$= \frac{1}{24}\Big[(1)e^1 + 4(1.125)e^{1/1.125}$$

$$+ 2(1.25)e^{1/125} + 4(1.275)e^{1/1.375}$$

$$+ 2(1.5)e^{1/1.5} + 4(1.625)e^{1/1.625}$$

$$+ 2(1.75)e^{1/1.75} + 4(1.875)e^{1/1.875}$$

$$+ (2)e^{1/2}\Big] \approx 2.94834$$

For the error estimate,

$$|E_8| \le \frac{M(2-1)^5}{180(8)^4} = \frac{M}{737,280}$$

where M is the maximum value of $|f^{(4)}(x)|$ on $1 \le x \le 2$.

$$f^{(3)}(x) = \left(\frac{1}{x^3}\right)\left(e^{1/x} \cdot -\frac{1}{x^2}\right) + \left(e^{1/x}\right)\left(-\frac{3}{x^4}\right)$$

$$= e^{1/x}\left(-\frac{1}{x^5} - \frac{3}{x^4}\right)$$

$$f^{(4)} = \left(e^{1/x}\right)\left(\frac{5}{x^6} + \frac{12}{x^5}\right)$$

$$+ \left(-\frac{1}{x^5} - \frac{3}{x^4}\right)\left(e^{1/x} \cdot -\frac{1}{x^2}\right)$$

$$= e^{1/x}\left(\frac{5 + 12x}{x^6}\right) + e^{1/x}\left(\frac{1 + 3x}{x^7}\right)$$

$$= \frac{1}{x^7}e^{1/x}\left[x(5 + 12x) + (1 + 3x)\right]$$

$$= \frac{1}{x^7}e^{1/x}\left(12x^2 + 8x + 1\right)$$

Since $|f^{(4)}(x)|$ is always positive and decreasing on $1 \le x \le 2$, $M = |f^{(4)}(1)| = 21e$.

$$|E_8| \le \frac{21e}{737,280} \approx 0.000077.$$

65. (a)

$$|E_n| \le \frac{M(b-a)^3}{12n^2} < 0.00005$$

$$\frac{M(1-0.5)^3}{12n^2} < 0.00005$$

$$n^2 > \frac{0.125M}{12(0.00005)}$$

$$n^2 > 208,33333M$$

$$f(x) = e^{1-1x}$$

$$f'(x) = -1.13^{-1.1x}$$

$$f''(x) = 1.21e^{-1.1x}$$

Since $f''(x)$ is always decreasing for $0.5 \le x \le 1$ but greater than zero. The maximum value of $|f''(x)| = 1.21e^{1.1(0.5)} = 1.21e^{-0.55} \approx 0.69811$. So

$$n^2 > 145.439$$

$$n > 12.0598, \quad \text{or} \quad n = 13.$$

(b)

$$|E_n| \le \frac{M(b-a)^5}{180n^4} < 0.00005$$

$$\frac{M(1-0.5)^5}{180n^4} < 0.00005$$

$$n^4 > \frac{0.03125M}{180(0.00005)}$$

$$n^4 > 3/4722M$$

$$f^{(3)}(x) = -1.331e^{-1.1x}$$

$$f^{(4)}(x) = -1.4641e^{-1.1x}$$

which again is always decreasing for $0.5 \le x \le 1$ and greater than zero. So the maximum value of $|f^{(4)}(x)| = 1.4641e^{-1.1(0.5)} \approx 0.8447$.

So, $\qquad n^4 > (3.4722)(0.8447) \approx 2.9330$

$$n > 1.30867, \quad \text{or} \quad n = 2.$$

67. $\displaystyle\int_0^{24} qp(q)\,dq$

$$\approx \frac{\Delta q}{3}[f(0) + 4f(4) + 2f(8) + 4f(12)$$
$$+ 2(f)(16) + 4f(20) + f(24)]$$

$$= \frac{4}{3}[0_4(4)(42.9) + 2(8)(31.32) + 4(12)(19,83)$$

$$+ 2(16)(13.87) + 4(20)(10.58) + (24)(7.25)]$$

$$\approx 4804.8 \text{ thousand, or } \$4,804,800$$

69. To use the graphing utility to find where the curves intersect, and then find the area region bounded by the curves,

Press [y=] and input $-x \wedge 3 - 2x^2 + 5x - 2$

for $y_1 =$ and input $x \ln(x)$ for $y_2 = .$

Use window dimensions $[-4, 3]0.5$ by $[-0.8, 0.4]0.1$

Press [graph].

Use trace and zoom to find the points of intersection or use the intersect function under the calc menu to find that $(0.406, -0.37)$ and $(1, 0)$ are the two points of intersection.

To find the area bounded by the curves, we must find

$$\int_{0.406}^1 \left(-x^3 - 2x^2 + 5x - 2 - x \ln x\right)\,dx$$

Use the $\displaystyle\int f(x)\,dx$ function under the calc menu (making sure that y_1 is shown in the upper left corner) with $x = 0.406$ as the lower limit and $x = 1$ as the upper limit to find that

$$\int_{0.406}^1 \left(-x^3 - 2x^2 + 5x - 2\right)\,dx = .03465167.$$

Repeat this process with y_2 activated to find that

$$\int_{0.406}^1 x \ln x\,dx \approx -.1344992.$$

The area is $0.03465167 - (-0.1344992) \approx 0.1692$. Alternatively, you can use fn Int function under the math menu:

$$\text{fn Int}(y_1 - y_2, x, 0.406, 1)$$

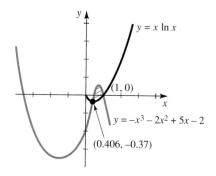

71. To use numeric integration feature to evaluate the integral,

Press [y=] and input $\dfrac{2}{(9 - x^2)}$ for $y_1 = .$

Use window dimensions $[-5, 5]1$ by $[-5, 5]1$.

Press [graph].

Use the $\displaystyle\int f(x)\,dx$ function under the calc menu with $x = -1$ as the lower limit and $x = 1$ as the upper limit to find $\displaystyle\int_{-1}^1 \frac{2}{9 - x^2}\,dx \approx 0.4621$.

73. To use numeric integration feature to compute the integral,

Press $\boxed{\text{y=}}$ and enter $\left(\dfrac{1}{\sqrt{\pi}}\right) * e^{\wedge(-x^2)}$ for $y_1 = .$

Use window dimensions $[-50, 50]20$ by $[-3, 3]1.$

Press $\boxed{\text{graph}}$.

Use the $\displaystyle\int f(x)\,dx$ function under the calc menu with $x = 0$ as the lower limit and $x = 1$ as the upper limit to find

$$\int_0^1 \frac{1}{\sqrt{\pi}} e^{-x^2}\,dx = 0.4214$$

Repeat this process with $x = 10$ as the upper limit to find

$$\int_0^{10} \frac{1}{\sqrt{\pi}} e^{-x^2}\,dx = 0.5$$

Repeat this process with $x = 50$ as the upper limit to find

$$\int_0^{50} \frac{1}{\sqrt{\pi}} e^{-x^2}\,dx = 0.5$$

The improper integral $\displaystyle\int_0^{\infty} \frac{1}{\sqrt{\pi}} e^{-x^2}$ appears to converge to 0.5.

75.
$$\frac{dS}{dt} = \frac{aS}{b + cS + S^2}$$

$$\int \frac{S^2 + cS + b}{aS}\,dS = \int dt$$

$$\int \left(\frac{1}{a}S + \frac{c}{a} + \frac{b}{a}\frac{1}{S}\right) dS = \int dt$$

$$\frac{1}{2a}S^2 + \frac{c}{a}S + \frac{b}{a}\ln S = t + c$$

35. $f(x, y) = Ax^a y^b$.

$$f(2x, 2y) = A(2x)^a(2y)^b = A(2)^a x^a(2)^b y^b$$
$$= (2^{a+b})Ax^a y^b.$$

$x \geq 0$, $y \geq 0$, and $A > 0$.

(a) If $a + b > 1$, $2^{a+b} > 2$ and f more than doubles.

(b) If $a + b < 1$, $2^{a+b} < 2$ and f increases but does not double.

(c) If $a + b = 1$, $2^{a+b} = 2$ and f doubles (exactly).

37. Let R denote the manufacturer's revenue. Then
$R = $ (revenue from domestic sales) + (revenue from sales abroad)

$$R(x, y) = x\left(60 - \frac{x}{5} + \frac{y}{20}\right) + y\left(50 - \frac{y}{10} + \frac{x}{20}\right)$$

$$= 60x + 50y - \frac{x^2}{5} - \frac{y^2}{10} + \frac{xy}{10}.$$

39. (a) $S(15.83, 87.11)$

$$= 0.0072(15.83 \wedge 0.425)(87.11 \wedge 0.725)$$

Input into home screen to find $S(15.83, 87.11)$
≈ 0.5938
To sketch several additional level curves of $S(W, H)$, we will use the list feature of the calculator.
In general, $0.0072W^{0.425}H^{0.725} = S$

$$H^{0.725} = \frac{S}{0.0072}W^{-0.425}$$

$$H = \left(\frac{S}{0.0072}W^{-0.425}\right)^{1/0.725}$$

We will use $S = 0.3$, 0.5938, and 1.5.
Press $\boxed{y=}$.
Input $((L_1/0.0072) * x \wedge (-0.425)) \wedge$ $(1/0.725)$ for $y_1 =$.
From the home screen, input $\{0.3, 0.5938, 1.5\}$
$\boxed{\text{STO}\rightarrow}$ $\boxed{\text{2nd}}$ L_1.
Use window dimensions [0, 400]50 by [0, 150]25.
Press $\boxed{\text{graph}}$.
Different combinations of height and weight that result in the same surface area.

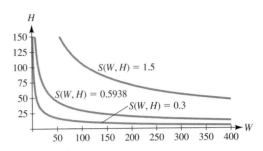

(b) $0.648 = 0.0072(18.37)^{0.425}H^{0.725}$,
$H^{0.725} = 26.121$, $H = 90.05$ cm.

(c) Let W_0, H_0 be Jenny's weight and height at birth. Then,

$$S(W_0, H_0) = 0.0072W_0^{0.425}H_0^{0.725}$$

When $W = 6W_0$ and $H = 2H_0$,

$$S(6W_0, 2H_0) = 0.0072(6W_0)^{0.425}(2H_0)^{0.725}$$

$$= 0.0072(6)^{0.425}W_0^{0.425}(2)^{0.725}H_0^{0.725}$$

$$\approx 3.53966S(W_0, H_0)$$

The % change in surface area is:

$$100\frac{3.53966S(W_0, H_0) - S(W_0, H_0)}{S(W_0, H_0)}$$

$$= 100\frac{2.53966S(W_0, H_0)}{S(W_0, H_0)} \approx 253.97\% \text{ increase.}$$

(d) Writing Exercise—Answers will vary.

41. (a) $Q(10, 20) = 30 + 40 = 70$ units

(b) $3x + 2y = 70$
or $y = -\frac{3}{2}x + 35$

(c)

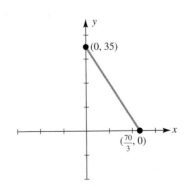

(d) $70 = 3 \cdot (12) + 2(20 + \Delta y)$

$$2\Delta y = 70 - 36 - 40$$

$$\Delta y = -\frac{6}{2} = -3, \text{ or decrease}$$

unskilled labor by 3 workers.

43. $U(25, 8) = (25 + 1)(8 + 2) = 260$

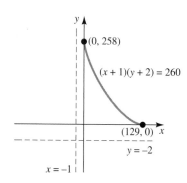

45. (a) $V(3,875, 1.675, 0.004)$

$$= \frac{9.3(3, 875)}{1.675}\left[(0.0075)^2 - (0.004)^2\right]$$

$$\approx 0.866 \text{cm/sec}$$

(b) For the fixed values of L and R,

$$V(P, r,) = \frac{9.3P}{1.675}\left[(0.0075)^2 - r^2\right]$$

$$= 5.55P(0.0000563 - r^2)$$

To sketch several level curves of V, set $V(P, r) = C$ for several values of C and solve for P. We will use the list feature of the calculator with $C = 100, 200$ and 300. Setting $V(P, r) = C$

$$5.55(0.0000563 - r^2) = C$$

In general,

$$P = \frac{0.1802C}{0.0000563 - r^2}$$

Press $\boxed{y=}$.
Input $(0.1802L_1)/(0.0000563 - x^2)$ for $y_1 =$.
From the home screen, enter
$\{100, 200, 300\}$ $\boxed{\text{STO}\rightarrow}$ $\boxed{\text{2nd}}$ L_1.
Use z-standard function under the zoom menu for the standard window dimensions.
Press $\boxed{\text{graph}}$.
Note that there are vertical asymptotes when $r = \pm\sqrt{0.0000563}$ but that the graph is defined in between these asymptotes as well.

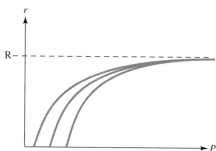

The curves represent different combinations of pressure and distance from the axis that result in the same speed.

47. (a) To sketch graphs of several level curves, for simplicity's sake, we will choose $a = b = 1$. We use the list feature of the calculator to sketch level curves for $T(P, V) = C$ for $C = -100, 0, 100$.
In general,

$$0.0122\left(P + \frac{1}{V^2}\right)(V - 1) - 273.15 = C$$

and $P = \dfrac{C + 273.15}{0.0122(V - 1)} - \dfrac{1}{V^2}$.
Press $\boxed{y=}$.
Input $(L_1 + 273.15)/(0.0122(x - 1)) - \left(\frac{1}{x^2}\right)$ for $y_1 =$.
From the home screen, enter $\{-100, 0, 100\}$
$\boxed{\text{Sto}\rightarrow}$ $\boxed{\text{2nd}}$ L_1.
Use window dimensions $[0, 35000]5,000$ by $[0, 2.9]0.3$.
Press $\boxed{\text{graph}}$.

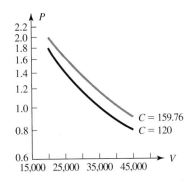

(b) To find $T(1.13, 31.275 \times 10^3)$,
From the home screen, enter $0.0122(1.13 + (6.49 \times 10^6)/31,275^2)(31,275 - 56.2) - 273.15 \approx 159.76$.
Thus, the temperature is $159.76°C$.

49. (a) $B_m(90, 190, 22) = 66.47 + 13.75(90) + 5.00(190) - 6.77(22) = 2,105.03$ kilo calories.

(b) $B_f(61, 170, 27) = 655.10 + 9.60(61) + 1.85(170) - 4.68(27) = 1,428.84$ kilo calories.

(c) $B_m(85, 193, A) = 66.47 + 13.75(85) + 5.00(193) - 6.77A$

$$2,018 = 2,200.22 - 6.77A$$
$$A \approx 26.9 \text{ years old.}$$

(d) $B_f(67, 173, A) = 655.10 + 9.60(67) + 1.85(173) - 4.68A$

$$1,504 = 1,618.35 - 4.68A$$
$$A \approx 24.4 \text{ years old.}$$

51. $M(A, n, i) = \dfrac{A_i}{1 - (1 + i)^{-12n}}$

(a) $M\left(250000, 15, \dfrac{0.052}{12}\right) = \dfrac{250,000\left(\dfrac{0.052}{12}\right)}{1 - \left(1 + \dfrac{0.052}{12}\right)^{-12(15)}}$

$\approx \$2,003.13$
The total amount paid is
$(2003.13)(12)(15) = \$360,563.40$
Since the original loan is for $250000, the interest paid is $360,563.4 - 250,000 = \$110,563.40$

(b) $M\left(250000, 30, \dfrac{0.056}{12}\right) = \dfrac{250,000\left(\dfrac{0.056}{12}\right)}{1 - \left(1 + \dfrac{0.056}{12}\right)^{-12(30)}}$

$\approx \$1,435.20$
The total amount paid is
$(1435.20)(12)(30) = \$516,672$
Since the original loan is for $250000, the interest paid is $516,672 - 250,000 = \$266,672$

53. $P(2, 0.53, 23) = 0.075(2)(0.53)(273.15 + 23)$
≈ 23.54 atmospheres.

55. $Q(K, L) = A\left[\propto K^{-\beta} + (1 - \propto)L^{-\beta}\right]^{-1/\beta}$
$Q(sK, sL) = A\left[\propto (sK)^{-\beta} + (1 - \propto)(sL)^{-\beta}\right]^{-1/\beta}$
$= A\left[\propto s^{-\beta}K^{-\beta} + (1 - \propto)s^{-\beta}L^{-\beta}\right]^{-1/\beta}$
$= A(s^{-\beta})^{-1/\beta}\left[\propto K^{-\beta} + (1 - \propto)L^{-\beta}\right]^{-1/\beta}$
$= sA\left[\propto K^{-\beta} + (1 - \propto)L^{-\beta}\right]^{-1/\beta}$
$= sQ(K, L)$

7.2 Partial Derivatives

1.
$$f(x, y) = 7x - 3y + 4$$
$$f_x = 7 \quad f_y = -3$$

3.
$$f(x, y) = 4x^3 - 3x^2y + 5x$$
$$f_x = 12x^2 - 6xy + 5$$
$$f_y = -3x^2$$

5. $f(x, y) = 2xy^5 + 3x^2y + x^2$
$$f_x = 2y^5 + 6xy + 2x$$
$$f_y = 2x(5y^4) + 3x^2 = 10xy^4 + 3x^2$$

7. $z = (3x + 2y)^5$
$$\frac{\partial z}{\partial x} = 5(3x + 2y)^4\frac{\partial}{\partial x}(3x + 2y)$$
$$= 15(3x + 2y)^4$$
$$\frac{\partial z}{\partial y} = 5(3x + 2y)^4\frac{\partial}{\partial y}(3x + 2y)$$
$$= 10(3x + 2y)^4$$

9.
$$f(s, t) = \frac{3t}{2s} = \frac{3}{2}s^{-1}t$$

$$f_s = \frac{3}{2}(-1)s^{-2}t = -\frac{3t}{2s^2}$$

$$f_t = \frac{3}{2}s^{-1} = \frac{3}{2s}$$

11.
$$z = xe^{xy}$$

$$\frac{\partial z}{\partial x} = x(ye^{xy}) + e^{xy}(1)$$

$$= (xy + 1)e^{xy}$$

$$\frac{\partial z}{\partial y} = x(e^{xy})(x) = x^2e^{xy}$$

13.
$$f(x, y) = \frac{e^{2-x}}{y^2} = e^{2-x}y^{-2}$$

$$f_x = -e^{2-x}y^{-2} = -\frac{e^{2-x}}{y^2}$$

$$f_y = e^{2-x}(-2y^{-3}) = -\frac{2e^{2-x}}{y^3}$$

15.
$$f(x, y) = \frac{2x + 3y}{y - x}$$

$$f_x = \frac{(y - x)(2) - (2x + 3y)(-1)}{(y - x)^2}$$

$$= \frac{5y}{(y - x)^2}$$

$$f_y = \frac{(y - x)(3) - (2x + 3y)(1)}{(y - x)^2}$$

$$= -\frac{5x}{(y - x)^2}$$

17.
$$z = u \ln v$$

$$\frac{\partial z}{\partial u} = (1) \ln v = \ln v$$

$$\frac{\partial z}{\partial v} = u\left(\frac{1}{v}\right) = \frac{u}{v}$$

19.
$$f(x, y) = \frac{\ln(x + 2y)}{y^2}$$

$$f_x = \frac{(y^2)[1/(x + 2y)] - \ln(x + 2y)(0)}{y^4}$$

$$= \frac{1}{y^2(x + 2y)}$$

$$f_y = \frac{(y^2)[2/(x + 2y)] - \ln(x + 2y)(2y)}{y^4}$$

$$= \frac{(y)(2) - (x + 2y)\ln(x + 2y)(2)}{(x + 2y)y^3}$$

$$= \frac{2[y - (x + 2y)\ln(x + 2y)]}{y^3(x + 2y)}$$

21.
$$f(x, y) = x^2 + 3y$$
$$f_x(x, y) = 2x \quad f_x(1, -1) = 2(1) = 2$$
$$f_y(x, y) = 3 \quad f_y(1, -1) = 3$$

23.
$$f(x, y) = \frac{y}{2x + y} = y(2x + y)^{-1}$$

$$f_x(x, y) = -y(2x + y)^{-2}(2) = -\frac{2y}{(2x + y)^2}$$

$$f_x(0, -1) = -\frac{2(-1)}{(2(0) + -1)^2} = 2$$

$$f_y(x, y) = \frac{(2x + y)(1) - (y)(1)}{(2x + y)^2} = \frac{2x}{(2x + y)^2}$$

$$f_y(0, -1) = \frac{2(0)}{(2(0) + {}^-1)^2} = 0$$

25.
$$f(x, y) = 3x^2 - 7xy + 5y^3 - 3(x + y) - 1$$
$$f_x = 6x - 7y - 3$$
$$f_y = -7x + 15y^2 - 3$$
$$f_x(-2, 1) = -12 - 7 - 3 = -22$$
$$f_y(-2, 1) = 14 + 15 - 3 = 26$$

27.
$$f(x, y) = xe^{-2y} + ye^{-x} + xy^2$$
$$f_x = e^{-2y} - ye^{-x} + y^2$$
$$f_y = -2xe^{-2y} + e^{-x} + 2xy$$
$$f_x(0, 0) = 1 - 0 + 0 = 1$$
$$f_y(0, 0) = 0 + 1 + 0 = 1$$

29. $f(x, y) = 5x^4 y^3 + 2xy$

$$f_x = 5(4x^3)y^3 + 2y = 20x^3 y^3 + 2y$$

$$f_y = 5x^4(3y^2) + 2x = 15x^4 y^2 + 2x$$

$$f_{xx} = \frac{\partial}{\partial x}(f_x)$$

$$= 20(3x^2)y^3 + 0 = 60x^2 y^3$$

$$f_{yy} = \frac{\partial}{\partial y}(f_y) = 15x^4(2y) + 0 = 30x^4 y$$

$$f_{xy} = \frac{\partial}{\partial y}(f_x)$$

$$= 20x^3(3y^2) + 2(1) = 60x^3 y^2 + 2$$

$$f_{yx} = \frac{\partial}{\partial x}(f_y)$$

$$= 15(4x^3)y^2 + 2(1) = 60x^3 y^2 + 2 = f_{xy}$$

31. $f(x, y) = e^{x^2 y}$

$$f_x = 2xye^{x^2 y} \text{ and } f_y = x^2 e^{x^2 y}$$

$$f_{xx} = \frac{\partial}{\partial x}(f_x)$$

$$= 2xy(e^{x^2 y})(2xy) + e^{x^2 y}(2y)$$

$$= 2y(2x^2 y + 1)e^{x^2 y}$$

$$f_{yy} = \frac{\partial}{\partial y}(f_y)$$

$$= x^2(e^{x^2 y})(x^2) = x^4 e^{x^2 y}$$

$$f_{xy} = \frac{\partial}{\partial y}(f_x)$$

$$= 2xy(e^{x^2 y})(x^2) + e^{x^2 y}(2x)$$

$$= 2x(x^2 y + 1)e^{x^2 y}$$

$$f_{yx} = \frac{\partial}{\partial x}(f_y)$$

$$= x^2(e^{x^2 y})(2xy) + e^{x^2 y}(2x)$$

$$= 2x(x^2 y + 1)e^{x^2 y} = f_{xy}$$

33. $f(s, t) = \sqrt{s^2 + t^2} = (s^2 + t^2)^{1/2}$

$$f_s = \frac{1}{2}(s^2 + t^2)^{-1/2}(2s) = s(s^2 + t^2)^{-1/2}$$

$$f_t = \frac{1}{2}(s^2 + t^2)^{-1/2}(2t) = t(s^2 + t^2)^{-1/2}$$

$$f_{ss} = s\left[-\frac{1}{2}(s^2 + t^2)^{-3/2}(2s)\right]$$

$$+ (s^2 + t^2)^{-1/2}(1)$$

$$= \frac{-s^2}{(s^2 + t^2)^{3/2}} + \frac{1}{(s^2 + t^2)^{1/2}}\frac{(s^2 + t^2)}{(s^2 + t^2)}$$

$$= \frac{t^2}{(s^2 + t^2)^{3/2}}$$

$$f_{tt} = t\left[-\frac{1}{2}(s^2 + t^2)^{-3/2}(2t)\right]$$

$$+ (s^2 + t^2)^{-1/2}(1)$$

$$= \frac{s^2}{(s^2 + t^2)^{3/2}}$$

$$f_{st} = \frac{\partial}{\partial t}(f_s) = s\left[-\frac{1}{2}(s^2 + t^2)^{-3/2}(2t)\right]$$

$$= \frac{-st}{(s^2 + t^2)^{3/2}}$$

$$f_{ts} = \frac{\partial}{\partial s}(f_t) = t\left[-\frac{1}{2}(s^2 + t^2)^{-3/2}(2s)\right]$$

$$= \frac{-st}{(s^2 + t^2)^{3/2}} = f_{st}$$

35. $D_1(p_1, p_2) = 500 - 6p_1 + 5p_2$
$D_2(p_1, p_2) = 200 + 2p_1 - 5p_2$

$$\frac{\partial D_1}{\partial p_2} = 5 \text{ and } \frac{\partial D}{\partial p_1} = 2$$

Since both partial derivatives are positive for all p_1 and p_2, the commodities are substitute commodities.

37. $D_1(p_1, p_2) = 3,000 + \dfrac{400}{p_1 + 3} + 50p_2$

$$D_1(p_1, p_2) = 2,000 - 100p_1 + \dfrac{500}{p_2 + 4}$$

$$\frac{\partial D_1}{\partial p_2} = 50 \text{ and } \frac{\partial D_2}{\partial p_1} = -100$$

Since the partial derivaties are opposite in sign for all p_1 and p_2, the commodities are neither substitute nor complementary.

39.
$$D_1(p_1, p_2) = \frac{7p_2}{1 + p_1^2}$$

$$D_2(p_1, p_2) = \frac{p_1}{1 + p_2^2}$$

$$\frac{\partial D_1}{\partial p_2} = \frac{7}{1 + p_1^2} > 0 \text{ and } \frac{\partial D_2}{\partial p_1} = \frac{1}{1 + p_2^2}$$
Since both partial derivatives are positive for all p_1 and p_2, the commodities are substitute commdities.

41. $z = x^2 - y^2$

$$\frac{\partial z}{\partial x} = 2x \text{ and } \frac{\partial^2 z}{\partial x^2} = 2$$

$$\frac{\partial z}{\partial y} = -2y \text{ and } \frac{\partial^2 z}{\partial y^2} = -2$$

Since $\dfrac{\partial^2 z}{\partial x^2} + \dfrac{\partial^2 z}{\partial y^2} = 0$ the function satisfies Laplace's equation.

43.
$$z = xe^y - ye^x$$

$$\frac{\partial z}{\partial x} = e^y - ye^x \text{ and } \frac{\partial^2 z}{\partial x^2} = -ye^x$$

$$\frac{\partial z}{\partial y} = xe^y - e^x \text{ and } \frac{\partial^2 z}{\partial y^2} = xe^y$$

Since $\dfrac{\partial^2 z}{\partial x^2} + \dfrac{\partial^2 z}{\partial y^2} = -ye^x + xe^y \neq 0$ the function does not satisfy Laplace's equation.

45. The partial derivative

$$Q_K = \frac{\partial Q}{\partial K} = 30K^{-1/2}L^{1/3}$$

$$= \frac{30L^{1/3}}{K^{1/2}}$$

is the rate of change of the output with respect to the capital investment. This is an approximation to the additional number of units that will be produced each week if the capital investment is increased from K to $K + 1$ while the size of the labor force is not changed. In particular, if the capital investment K

is increased from 900 (thousand) to 901 (thousand) and the size of the labor force is $L = 1,000$, the resulting change in output is

$$\Delta Q = Q_K(900, 1000)$$

$$= \frac{30(1,000)^{1/3}}{(900)^{1/2}}$$

$$= \frac{30(10)}{30} = 10, \text{ or}$$

daily output will increase by 10 units.

47. $Q(K, L) = 150[0.4k^{-1/2} + 0.6L^{-1/2}]^{-2}$

(a) $Q_K = -300[0.4k^{-1/2} + 0.6L^{-1/2}]^{-3}(-0.2k^{-3/2})$
$$= 60k^{-3/2}[0.4k^{-1/2} + 0.6L^{-1/2}]^{-3}$$
$$Q_L = -300[0.4k^{-1/2} + 0.6L^{-1/2}]^{-3}(-0.3k^{-3/2})$$
$$= 90L^{-3/2}[0.4k^{-1/2} + 0.6L^{-1/2}]^{-3}$$

(b) $Q_k(5041, 4900)$
$$= 60(5041)^{-3/2}[0.4(5041)^{-1/2} + 0.6(4900)^{-1/2}]^{-3}$$
$$= \frac{60}{(\sqrt{5041})^3}\left[\frac{0.4}{\sqrt{5041}} + \frac{0.6}{\sqrt{4900}}\right]^{-3}$$
$$\approx 58.48$$
$$Q_L(5041, 4900)$$
$$= 90(4900)^{-3/2}[0.4(5041)^{-1/2} + 0.6(4900)^{-1/2}]^{-3}$$
$$= \frac{90}{(\sqrt{4900})^3}\left[\frac{0.4}{\sqrt{5041}} + \frac{0.6}{\sqrt{4900}}\right]^{-3}$$
$$\approx 91.54$$

(c) additional labor employment

49. $F(L, r) = \dfrac{kL}{r^4}$

(a) $F(3.17, 0.085) = 60,727.24\,k$

$$\frac{\partial F}{\partial r} = \frac{k}{r^4} = 19,156.86\,k$$

$$\frac{\partial F}{\partial r} = -\frac{4kL}{r^5} = -2,857,752.58\,k$$

So, $f_x = 0$ when $0 = 3(x^2 - 2y + 3)$, or $0 = x^2 - 2y + 3$.

$$f_y = 2y - 6x + 5$$

So, $f_y = 0$ when $0 = 2y - 6x + 5$. Solving this system of equations by adding,

$$0 = x^2 - 6x + 8$$
$$= (x - 2)(x - 4)$$
$$\text{So, } x = 2, 4.$$

When $x = 2$, $0 = (2)^2 - 2y + 3$, or $y = \dfrac{7}{2}$.

When $x = 4$, $0 = (4)^2 - 2y + 3$, or $y = \dfrac{19}{2}$.

So, the critical points are $\left(2, \dfrac{7}{2}\right)$ and $\left(4, \dfrac{19}{2}\right)$.

$$f_{xx} = 6x, \ f_{yy} = 2, \ f_{xy} = -6$$

For the point $\left(2, \dfrac{7}{2}\right)$,

$$D = 6(2)(2) - (-6)^2 < 0$$

So, $\left(2, \dfrac{7}{2}\right)$ is a saddle point.

For the point $\left(4, \dfrac{19}{2}\right)$,

$$D = 6(4)(2) - (-6)^2 > 0$$

and $f_{xx} > 0$, so $\left(4, \dfrac{19}{2}\right)$ is a relative minimum.

11.
$$f(x, y) = xy^2 - 6x^2 - 3y^2$$
$$f_x = y^2 - 12x$$

So, $f_x = 0$ when $y^2 - 12x = 0$, or $x = \dfrac{y^2}{12}$

$$f_y = 2xy - 6y$$

So, $f_y = 0$ when

$$2xy - 6y = 0$$
$$2\left(\dfrac{y^2}{12}\right)y - 6y = 0$$
$$\dfrac{1}{6}y^3 - 6y = 0$$
$$y^3 - 36y = 0$$
$$y(y + 6)(y - 6) = 0$$

or $y = 0$, $y = -6$, $y = 6$
When $y = 0$, $x = 0$; $y = -6$, $x = 3$; $y = 6$, $x = 3$.
So the critical points are $(0, 0)$, $(3, -6)$ and $(3, 6)$.
Now,

$$f_{xx} = -12, \ f_{yy} = 2x - 6, \ f_{xy} = 2y$$

For the point $(0, 0)$,

$$D = (-12)(-6) - 0^2 > 0$$

Since $f_{xx} < 0$, the point $(0, 0)$ is a relative maximum.
For the point $(3, -6)$,

$$D = (-12)(0) - [2(-6)]^2 < 0$$

So, the point $(3, -6)$ is a saddle point.
For the point $(3, 6)$,

$$D = (-12)(0) - [2(6)]^2 < 0$$

So, the point $(3, 6)$ is a saddle point.

13. $f(x, y) = (x^2 + 2y^2)e^{1-x^2-y^2}$

$$f_x = (x^2 + 2y^2)(-2xe^{1-x^2-y^2}) + (e^{1-x^2-y^2})(2x)$$
$$= -2xe^{1-x^2-y^2}(x^2 + 2y^2 - 1)$$

So, $f_x = 0$ when $x = 0$ or $x^2 + 2y^2 - 1 = 0$

$$f_y = (x^2 + 2y^2)(-2ye^{1-x^2-y^2}) + (e^{1-x^2-y^2})(4y)$$
$$= -2ye^{1-x^2-y^2}(x^2 + 2y^2 - 2)$$

So, $f_y = 0$ when $y = 0$, or $x^2 + 2y^2 - 2 = 0$.
There are no solutions to the system of equations $x^2 + 2y^2 - 1 = 0$ and $x^2 + 2y^2 - 2 = 0$. Further, when $x = 0$, $f_y = 0$ when $0 = -2ye^{1-y^2}(2y^2 - 2)$, or $y = 0, -1, 1$. When $y = 0$, $f_x = 0$ when

$0 = -2xe^{1-x^2}(x^2 - 1)$ or, $x = 0, -1, 1$. So, the critical points are $(-1, 0)$, $(0, 0)$, $(1, 0)$, $(0, -1)$ and $(0, 1)$.

Rewriting f_x as

$$f_x = -2e^{1-x^2-y^2}(x^3 + 2xy^2 - x)$$

$$f_{xx} = -2\left[e^{1-x^2-y^2}(3x^2 + 2y^2 - 1)\right.$$

$$\left. +(x^3 + 2xy^2 - x)(-2xe^{1-x^2-y^2})\right]$$

$$f_{yy} = -2\left[e^{1-x^2-y^2}(x^2 + 6y^2 - 2)\right.$$

$$\left. +(x^2y + 2y^3 - 2y)(-2ye^{1-x^2-y^2})\right]$$

$$f_{xy} = -2\left[e^{1-x^2-y^2}(4xy)\right.$$

$$\left. +(x^3 + 2xy^2 - x)(-2ye^{1-x^2-y^2})\right]$$

For the point $(-1, 0)$,

$$D = (-4)(2) - 0 < 0$$

So, $(-1, 0)$ is a saddle point.

For the point $(0, 0)$,

$$D = (2e)(4e) - 0 > 0$$

and $f_{xx} > 0$, so $(0, 0)$ is a relative minimum.

For the point $(1, 0)$,

$$D - (-4)(2) - 0 < 0$$

So, $(1, 0)$ is a saddle point.

For the point $(0, -1)$,

$$D = (-2)(-8) - 0 > 0$$

and $f_{xx} < 0$, so $(0, -1)$ is a relative maximum.

For the point $(0, 1)$,

$$D = (-2)(-8) - 0 > 0$$

and $f_{xx} < 0$, so $(0, 1)$ is a relative maximum.

15. $f(x, y) = x^3 - 4xy + y^3$

$$f_x = 3x^2 - 4y$$

So, $f_x = 0$ when $0 = 3x^2 - 4y$, or $y = \dfrac{3x^2}{4}$.

$$f_y = -4x + 3y^2$$

So, $f_y = 0$ when $0 = -4x + 3y^2$

$$= -4x + 3\left(\frac{3x^2}{4}\right)^2$$

$$= \frac{27}{16}x^4 - 4x$$

$$= 4x\left(\frac{27}{64}x^3 - 1\right) = 0,$$

or $x = 0, \dfrac{4}{3}$.

When $x = 0$, $f_x = 0$ when $y = 0$.

When $x = \dfrac{4}{3}$, $f_x = 0$ when $0 = 3\left(\dfrac{4}{3}\right)^2 - 4y$,

or $y = \dfrac{4}{3}$.

So the critical points are $(0, 0)$ and $\left(\dfrac{4}{3}, \dfrac{4}{3}\right)$.

$$f_{xx} = 6x, \quad f_{yy} = 6y, \quad f_{xy} = -4$$

For the point $(0, 0)$,

$$D = 6(0)6(0) - (-4)^2 < 0$$

So, $(0, 0)$ is a saddle point.

For the point $\left(\dfrac{4}{3}, \dfrac{4}{3}\right)$,

$$D = 6\left(\frac{4}{3}\right)6\left(\frac{4}{3}\right) - (-4)^2 > 0$$

and $f_{xx} > 0$, so $\left(\dfrac{4}{3}, \dfrac{4}{3}\right)$ is a relative minimum.

17.
$$f(x, y) = 4xy - 2x^4 - y^2 + 4x - 2y$$
$$f_x = 4y - 8x^3 + 4$$

So, $f_x = 0$ when
$$4y - 8x^3 + 4 = 0$$
$$f_y = 4x - 2y - 2$$

So, $f_y = 0$ when
$$4x - 2y - 2 = 0, \text{ or } y = 2x - 1$$

Substituting above,
$$4y - 8x^3 + 4 = 0$$
$$4(2x - 1) - 8x^3 + 4 = 0$$
$$-8x^3 + 8x = 0$$
$$-8x(x + 1)(x - 1) = 0$$

or $x = 0, x = -1, x = 1$
When $x = 0$, $y = -1$; when $x = -1$, $y = -3$;
when $x = 1$, $y = 1$.
So, the critical points are $(0, -1)$, $(-1, -3)$ and $(1, 1)$.
Now,
$$f_{xx} = -24x^2 \quad f_{yy} = -2 \quad f_{xy} = 4$$

For the point $(0, -1)$,
$$D = (0)(-2) - [4]^2 < 0$$

So, the point $(0, -1)$ is a saddle point.
For the point $(-1, -3)$,
$$D = (-24)(-2) - [4]^2 > 0$$

Since $f_{xx} < 0$, the point $(-1, -3)$ is a relative maximum.
For the point $(1, 1)$,
$$D = (-24)(-2) - [4]^2 > 0$$

Since $f_{xx} < 0$, the point $(1, 1)$ is a relative maximum.

19.
$$f(x, y) = \frac{1}{x^2 + y^2 + 3x - 2y + 1}$$
$$f_x = \frac{-(2x + 3)}{(x^2 + y^2 + 3x - 2y + 1)^2}$$

So, $f_x = 0$ when $x = -\frac{3}{2}$.

$$f_y = \frac{-(2y - 2)}{(x^2 + y^2 + 3x - 2y + 1)^2}$$

So, $f_y = 0$ when $y = 1$. The only critical point is $\left(-\frac{3}{2}, 1\right)$.

$$f_{xx} = \frac{1}{(x^2 + y^2 + 3x - 2y + 1)^4}$$
$$\left((x^2 + y^2 + 3x - 2y + 1)^2(-2)\right.$$
$$\left. + (2x + 3) [2(x^2 + y^2 + 3x - 2y + 1)(2x + 3)]\right)$$

$$f_{yy} = \frac{1}{(x^2 + y^2 + 3x - 2y + 1)^4}$$
$$\left((x^2 + y^2 + 3x - 2y + 1)^2(-2) + (2y - 2)\right.$$
$$\left. + [2(x^2 + y^2 + 3x - 2y + 1)(2y - 2)]\right)$$

$$f_{xy} = \frac{1}{(x^2 + y^2 + 3x - 2y + 1)^4}$$
$$\left(0 + (2x + 3)\right.$$
$$\left. [2(x^2 + y^2 + 3x - 2y + 1)(2y - 2)]\right)$$

For the point $\left(-\frac{3}{2}, 1\right)$,
$$D = (-4)(-4) - 0 > 0$$

and $f_{xx} < 0$, so $\left(-\frac{3}{2}, 1\right)$ is a relative maximum.

21.
$$f(x, y) = x \ln\left(\frac{y^2}{x}\right) + 3x - xy^2$$
$$= x(\ln y^2 - \ln x) + 3x - xy^2$$
$$= x \ln y^2 - x \ln x + 3x - xy^2$$
$$f_x = \ln y^2 - \left[x\left(\frac{1}{x}\right) + \ln x(1)\right] + 3 - y^2$$
$$= \ln y^2 - \ln x + 2 - y^2$$

So, $f_x = 0$ when $0 = 2 \ln y - \ln x + 2 - y^3$
$$f_y = 2x\left(\frac{1}{y}\right) - 2xy = \frac{2x(1 - y^2)}{y}$$

So, $f_y = 0$ when $x = 0$, $y = -1$, 1. We must reject $x = 0$, since f is undefined when $x = 0$.
When $y = -1$, $f_x = 0$ when

$$0 = \ln 1 - \ln x + 2 - 1$$
$$0 = 1 - \ln x$$
$$\ln x = 1, \text{ or } x = e.$$

When $y = 1$, $f_x = 0$ when
$0 = \ln 1 - \ln x + 2 - 1$, or $x = e$.
So, the critical points are $(e, -1)$ and $(e, 1)$.

$$f_{xx} = -\frac{1}{x}, \ f_{yy} = -\frac{2x}{y^2} - 2x, \ f_{xy} = \frac{2}{y} - 2y$$

For the point $(e, -1)$,

$$D = \left(\frac{-1}{e}\right)(-4e) - 0 > 0$$

and $f_{xx} < 0$, so $(e, -1)$ is a relative maximum.
For the point $(e, 1)$,

$$D = \left(-\frac{1}{e}\right)(-4e) - 0 > 0$$

and $f_{xx} < 0$, so $(e, 1)$ is a relative maximum.

23. Profit = (profit from sales Duncan shirts)
    + (profit from sales James shirts)

$$P(x, y) = (x - 2)(40 - 50x + 40y)$$
$$\qquad + (y - 2)(20 + 60x - 70y)$$
$$P_x = (x - 2)(-50) + (40 - 50x + 40y)(1)$$
$$\qquad + (y - 2)(60) + 0$$
$$= 20(-5x + 5y + 1)$$

So, $P_x = 0$ when $0 = 20(-5x + 5y + 1)$, or $-5x + 5y + 1 = 0$.

$$P_y = (x - 2)(40) + 0 + (y - 2)(-70)$$
$$\qquad + (20 + 60x - 70y)(1)$$
$$= 20(5x - 7y + 4)$$

So, $P_y = 0$ when $0 = 20(5x - 7y + 4)$, or $0 = 5x - 7y + 4$.
Solving this system of equations by adding,

$$0 = -2y + 5, \text{ or } y = \frac{5}{2} = 2.5$$

When $y = 2.5$, $P_x = 0$ when $0 = -5x + 5(2.5) + 1$,
or $x = 2.7$
So the critical point is $(2.7, 2.5)$

$$P_{xx} = -100, \ P_{yy} = -140, \ P_{xy} = 100$$
$$D = (-100)(-140) - (100)^2 > 0$$

and $P_{xx} < 0$
So, profit is maximized when Duncan shirts sell for $2.70 and James shirts sell for $2.50.

25. Let l, w, h be the dimensions of the box
Cost = (area) (cost per area)
Cost bottom = $(lw)(3)$
Cost top = $(lw)(5)$
Cost 4 sides = $2(lh)(1) + 2(wh)(1)$
$C = 8lw + 2lh + 2wh$
Since volume must be 32,
$32 = lwh$, or $h = \dfrac{32}{lw}$

$$C(l, w) = 8lw + 2l\left(\frac{32}{lw}\right) + 2w\left(\frac{32}{lw}\right)$$
$$= 8lw + \frac{64}{w} + \frac{64}{l}$$
$$C_l = 8w - \frac{64}{l^2}$$

So, $C_l = 0$ when $0 = 8w - \dfrac{64}{l^2}$.

$$C_w = 8l - \frac{64}{w^2}$$

So, $C_w = 0$ when $0 = 8l - \dfrac{64}{w^2}$.
Solving each equation for w^2,

$$8w = \frac{64}{l^2}$$
$$w = \frac{8}{l^2}, \ w^2 = \frac{64}{l^4}$$
$$8l = \frac{64}{w^2}$$
$$w^2 = \frac{8}{l}$$

So, $\frac{64}{l^4} = \frac{8}{l}$, $64l = 8l^4$

$$8l(l^3 - 8) = 0, \text{ or } l = 2.$$

When $l = 2$, $w = \dfrac{8}{(2)^2} = 2$.

So, $(2, 2)$ is the critical point.

$$C_{ll} = \frac{128}{l^3}, \ C_{ww} = \frac{128}{w^3}, \ C_{lw} = 8$$

$$D = (32)(32) - (8)^2 > 0 \text{ and } C_{ll} > 0$$

When $l = 2$ and $w = 2$, $h = \dfrac{32}{(2)(2)}$.

So, cost is minimized when the dimensions of the box are 2 ft × 2 ft × 8 ft.

27. Profit = revenue − cost

$$P(x, y) = [x(100 - x) + y(100 - y)]$$
$$ - [x^2 + xy + y^2]$$
$$ = -2x^2 - 2y^2 + 100x + 100y - xy$$
$$P_x = 4x + 100 - y$$

So, $P_x = 0$ when $0 = -4x + 100 - y$.

$$P_y = -4y + 100 - x$$

So, $P_y = 0$ when $0 = -4y + 100 - x$.
Solving this system of equations by multiplying the first equation by −4 and adding to second,

$$0 = 15x - 300, \text{ or } x = 20.$$

When $x = 20$, $P_x = 0$ when $0 = -4(20) + 100 - y$, or $y = 20$. So, the critical point is $(20, 20)$.

$$P_{xx} = -4; \ P_{yy} = -4; \ P_{xy} = -1$$

$$D = (-4)(-4) - (-1)^2 > 0 \text{ and } P_{xx} < 0$$

So, profit is maximized when 20 gallons of each are produced.

29. $f(x, y) = C + xye^{1-x^2-y^2}$

$$f_x = y\left[x(-2xe^{1-x^2-y^2}) + e^{1-x^2-y^2}(1)\right]$$
$$ = ye^{1-x^2-y^2}(-2x^2 + 1)$$

So, $f_x = 0$ when $y = 0$, or $x = \dfrac{\sqrt{2}}{2}$ (rejecting the negative solution).

$$f_y = x\left[y(-2ye^{1-x^2-y^2}) + e^{1-x^2-y^2}(1)\right]$$
$$ = xe^{1-x^2-y^2}(-2y^2 + 1)$$

When $y = 0$, $f_y = 0$ when $x = 0$.

When $x = -\dfrac{\sqrt{2}}{2}$, $f_y = 0$ when $y = \dfrac{\sqrt{2}}{2}$.

When $x = \dfrac{\sqrt{2}}{2}$, $f_y = 0$ when $y = \dfrac{\sqrt{2}}{2}$.

Again rejecting the negative solutions, the critical points are $(0, 0)$ and $\left(\dfrac{\sqrt{2}}{2}, \dfrac{\sqrt{2}}{2}\right)$. Rewriting f_x as

$$f_x = e^{1-x^2-y^2}(-2x^2y + y)$$
$$f_{xx} = (e^{1-x^2-y^2})(-4xy)$$
$$\phantom{f_{xx} =} + (-2x^2y + y)(-2xe^{1-x^2-y^2})$$

Similarly,

$$f_{yy} = (e^{1-x^2-y^2})(-4xy)$$
$$\phantom{f_{yy} =} + (-2xy^2 + x)(-2ye^{1-x^2-y^2})$$
$$f_{xy} = (e^{1-x^2-y^2})(-2x^2 + 1)$$
$$\phantom{f_{xy} =} + (-2x^2y + y)(-2ye^{1-x^2-y^2})$$

For the point $(0, 0)$,

$$D = (0)(0) - (e)^2 < 0$$

So, the point $(0, 0)$ does not correspond to the maximum.

For the point $\left(\dfrac{\sqrt{2}}{2}, \dfrac{\sqrt{2}}{2}\right)$,

$$D = (-2)(-2) - 0 > 0 \text{ and } f_{xx} < 0$$

So, $\dfrac{\sqrt{2}}{2}$ units of each stimuli maximizes performance.

31. $V_0 = xyz$, so $z = \dfrac{V_0}{xy}$ and

$$E(x, y) = \frac{k^2}{8m}\left(\frac{1}{x^2} + \frac{1}{y^2} + \frac{x^2y^2}{V_0}\right)$$

$$E_x = \frac{k^2}{8m}\left(-\frac{2}{x^3} + \frac{2xy^2}{V_0^2}\right)$$

So, $E_x = 0$ when $0 = -\dfrac{2}{x^3} + \dfrac{2xy^2}{V_0^2}$,

$$\text{or } x^2 = \frac{V_0}{y}.$$

$$E_y = \frac{k^2}{8m}\left(-\frac{2}{y^3} + \frac{2x^2y}{V_0^2}\right)$$

So, $E_y = 0$ when $0 = -\dfrac{2}{y^3} + \dfrac{2x^2y}{V_0^2}$,

$$\text{or } x^2 = \frac{V_0^2}{y^4}$$

$$\text{and } \frac{V_0}{y} = \frac{V_0^2}{y^4}, \text{ or } y = V_0^{1/3}.$$

When $y = V_0^{1/3}$, $x = \sqrt{\dfrac{V_0}{V_0^{1/3}}} = V_0^{1/3}$

and $z = \dfrac{V_0}{V_0^{1/3}V_0^{1/3}} = V_0^{1/3}.$

$$E_{xx} = \frac{k^2}{8m}\left(\frac{6}{x^4} + \frac{2y^2}{V_0^2}\right)$$

$$E_{yy} = \frac{k^2}{8m}\left(\frac{6}{y^4} + \frac{2x^2}{V_0^2}\right)$$

$$E_{xy} = \frac{k^2}{8m}\left(\frac{4xy}{V_0^2}\right)$$

$$D = \left(\frac{k^2}{mV_0^{4/3}}\right)\left(\frac{k^2}{mV_0^{4/3}}\right) - \left(\frac{k^2}{2mV_0^{4/3}}\right)^2 > 0$$

and $E_{xx} > 0$, so the ground state energy is maximized when $x = y = z = V_0^{1/3}$.

33.   profit = (profit from domestic market)
                  + profit from foreign market)

$$P(x, y) = x\left(60 - \frac{x}{5} + \frac{y}{20}\right) + y\left(50 - \frac{y}{10} + \frac{x}{20}\right)$$

$$= 50x - \frac{x^2}{5} + \frac{xy}{10} + 40y - \frac{y^2}{10}$$

$$P_x = 50 - \frac{2}{5}x + \frac{y}{10}$$

So, $P_x = 0$ when $0 = 50 - \dfrac{2}{5}x + \dfrac{y}{10} =$
$500 - 4x + y.$

$$P_y = \frac{x}{10} + 40 - \frac{y}{5}$$

So $P_y = 0$ when $0 = \dfrac{x}{10} + 40 - \dfrac{y}{5} = x + 400 - 2y$
Solving this system by multiplying the first equation by two and adding to the second,

$$0 = 1400 - 7x, \text{ or } x = 200.$$

When $x = 200$, $P_y = 0$ when
$0 = 200 + 400 - 2y$, or $y = 300.$

$$P_{xx} = -\frac{2}{5},\ P_{yy} = -\frac{1}{5},\ P_{xy} = \frac{1}{10}$$

$$D = \left(-\frac{2}{5}\right)\left(-\frac{1}{5}\right) - \left(\frac{1}{10}\right)^2 > 0$$

and $P_{xx} < 0$

So, profit is maximized when 200 machines are supplied to the domestic market and 300 are supplied to the foreign market.

35. The square of the distance from $S(a, b)$ to each point is:

$$(a + 5)^2 + (b - 0)^2 = a^2 + 10a + 25 + b^2$$
$$(a - 1)^2 + (b - 7)^2 = a^2 - 2a + b^2 - 14b + 50$$
$$(a - 9)^2 + (b - 0)^2 = a^2 - 18a + 81 + b^2$$
$$(a - 0)^2 + (b + 8)^2 = a^2 + b^2 + 16b + 64$$

So, the sum of the distances is

$$f(a, b) = 4a^2 - 10a + 4b^2 + 2b + 220$$

$$f_a = 8a - 10, \text{ so } f_a = 0 \text{ when } a = \frac{5}{4}$$

$$f_b = 8b + 2, \text{ so } f_b = 0 \text{ when } b = -\frac{1}{4}$$

$$f_{aa} = 8, f_{bb} = 8, f_{ab} = 0 \text{ so,}$$
$$D = (8)(8) - 0 > 0 \text{ and } f_{aa} > 0$$

The sum is minimized at $\left(\frac{5}{4}, -\frac{1}{4}\right)$.

37. Since $p + q + r = 1, r = 1 - p - q$ and

$$P(p, q) = 2pq + 2p(1 - p - q) + 2(1 - p - q)q$$
$$= 2p - 2p^2 - 2pq + 2q - 2q^2$$
$$P_p = 2 - 4p - 2q$$

So, $p_p = 0$ when $0 = 2 - 4p - 2q$, or $0 = 1 - 2p - q$.

$$P_q = -2p + 2 - 4q$$

So, $P_q = 0$ when $0 = -2p + 2 - 4q$, or $0 = -p + 1 - 2q$.
Solving this system of equations by multiplying the first equation by negative two and adding to the second,

$$0 = -1 + 3p, \text{ or } p = \frac{1}{3}.$$

When $p = \frac{1}{3}$, $P_q = 0$ when $0 = -\frac{1}{3} + 1 - 2q$, or $q = \frac{1}{3}$.

$$P_{pp} = -4, P_{qq} = -4, P_{pq} = -2$$

$$D = (-4)(-4) - (-2)^2 > 0 \text{ and } P_{pp} < 0$$

So, so P is maximized when $p = \frac{1}{3}, q = \frac{1}{3}$, and $r = \frac{1}{3}$. The maximum is

$$P = 2\left(\frac{1}{3}\right)\left(\frac{1}{3}\right) + 2\left(\frac{1}{3}\right)\left(\frac{1}{3}\right) + 2\left(\frac{1}{3}\right)\left(\frac{1}{3}\right) = \frac{2}{3}$$

39. (a) The problem is to minimize the total time $T(x, y)$, where

$$T = \frac{\sqrt{(1.2)^2 + x^2}}{2} + \frac{\sqrt{(2.5)^2 + y^2}}{4}$$
$$+ \frac{4.3 - (x + y)}{6}$$

$$\frac{\partial T}{\partial x} = \frac{1}{2}\left[\frac{1}{2}\frac{2x}{\sqrt{(1.2)^2 + x^2}}\right] - \frac{1}{6}$$

$$\frac{\partial T}{\partial y} = \frac{1}{4}\left[\frac{1}{2}\frac{2y}{\sqrt{(2.5)^2 + y^2}}\right] - \frac{1}{6}$$

$$\frac{\partial T}{\partial x} = \frac{\partial T}{\partial y} = 0 \text{ when}$$

$$\frac{1}{2}\frac{x}{\sqrt{(1.2)^2 + x^2}} = \frac{1}{6} \text{ and } \frac{1}{4}\frac{y}{\sqrt{(2.5)^2 + y^2}} = \frac{1}{6}$$

which leads to $x = 0.424$ and $y = 2.236$.
In addition to his path, the "boundary" cases must also be considered. That is, a path where Tom moves directly to the river (perpendicular to the river), then Tom swims directly across the river (perpendicular to the river), and Mary runs to the finish. The second boundary path is along the diagonal connection S and F.
Case 1

$$x = 0, y = 0$$
$$\text{Time} = \frac{1.2}{2} + \frac{2.5}{4} + \frac{4.3}{6} \approx 1.942$$

Case 2

$$x = 0.424, y = 2.236$$
$$\text{Time} = \frac{1.273}{2} + \frac{3.354}{4} + \frac{1.64}{6} = 1.748$$

Case 3

$$x = 1.395, y = 2.905$$
$$\text{Time} = \frac{1.84}{2} + \frac{3.833}{4} + \frac{0}{6} = 1.878$$

The minimum time is when $x = 0.424$ miles and $y = 2.236$ miles.

(b) For the second team, the time is

$$T = \frac{\sqrt{(1.2)^2 + x^2}}{1.7} + \frac{\sqrt{(2.5)^2 + y^2}}{3.5} + \frac{4.3 - (x + y)}{6.3}$$

$$\frac{\partial T}{\partial x} = \frac{1}{1.7} \left[\frac{x}{\sqrt{(1.2)^2 + x^2}} \right] - \frac{1}{6.3}$$

$$\frac{\partial T}{\partial y} = \frac{1}{3.5} \left[\frac{y}{\sqrt{(2.5)^2 + y^2}} \right] - \frac{1}{6.3}$$

We must find when $\dfrac{\partial T}{\partial x} = \dfrac{\partial T}{\partial y} = 0$

Press $\boxed{y=}$.

Input $\dfrac{\partial T}{\partial x}$ for $y_1 =$.

Use window dimensions $[0, 2]0.5$ by $[-1, 2]0.5$.

Press $\boxed{\text{graph}}$.

Use the zero function under the calc menu to find $x \approx 0.3363$.

Repeat process for $\dfrac{\partial T}{\partial y}$ to find $y \approx 1.6704$.

Repeating the case scenarios as in part (a)

Case	x	y	Time
1	0	0	2.103
2	0.3363	1.6704	1.9562
3	1.395	2.905	2.177

Tom, Dick, and Mary will win by 0.208 hours (12.5 minutes)

(c) Writing Exercise—Answers will vary.

41. The goal is to maximize the livable space subject to a constraint on the surface area. Let s be the length along the floor, at each end, where a 6 foot tall person cannot stand. Then, the livable space is

$$L = 6(x - 2s)y$$

From similar triangles,

$$\frac{s}{6} = \frac{\dfrac{x}{2}}{\dfrac{\sqrt{3}}{2}x}$$

$$\text{or, } s = \frac{6}{\sqrt{3}} \text{ and}$$

$$L = 6\left(x - \frac{12}{\sqrt{3}}\right)y = 6xy - \frac{72}{\sqrt{3}}y$$

Since the surface area must be 500, the constraint is

$$500 = 2xy + 2\left(\frac{\sqrt{3}}{4}x^2\right)$$

and $\qquad g(x) = 2xy + \dfrac{\sqrt{3}}{2}x^2$

$$L_x = 6y; L_y = 6x - \frac{72}{\sqrt{3}}$$

$$g_x = 2y + \sqrt{3}x; g_y = 2x$$

So, the three Lagrange equations are

$$6y = (2y + \sqrt{3}x)\lambda$$

$$6x - \frac{72}{\sqrt{3}} = 2x\lambda$$

$$2xy + \frac{\sqrt{3}}{2}x^2 = 500$$

Solving the second equation for λ and substituting into the first equation gives

$$6y = (2y + \sqrt{3}x)\left(3 - \frac{36}{\sqrt{3}x}\right)$$

$$6y = 6y + 3\sqrt{3}x - \frac{72y}{\sqrt{3}x} - 36$$

$$\frac{72}{\sqrt{3}x}y = 3\sqrt{3}x - 36$$

$$y = \frac{1}{8}x^2 - \frac{\sqrt{3}}{2}x$$

Substituting into the third equation gives

$$2x\left(\frac{1}{8}x^2 - \frac{\sqrt{3}}{2}x\right) + \frac{\sqrt{3}}{2}x^2 = 500$$

$$\frac{1}{4}x^3 - \sqrt{3}x^2 + \frac{\sqrt{3}}{2}x^2 = 500$$

$$x^3 - 4\sqrt{3}x^2 + 2\sqrt{3}x^2 = 2,000$$

$$x^3 - 2\sqrt{3}x^2 - 2,000 = 0$$

For our exponential model, $y = Ae^{mx}$. Since $\ln A = b$,

$$A = e^b = e^{3.003} \approx 20.15$$

So, the exponential function that best fits the data is $y = 20.15e^{-0.202x}$.

17. (a) Let x be the number of catalogs requested and y the number of applications received (both in units of 1,000). The given points (x, y) are plotted on the accompanying graph.

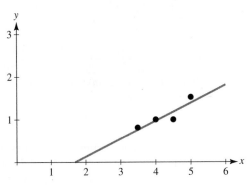

(b)

x	y	xy	x^2
4.5	1.0	4.5	20.25
3.5	0.8	2.8	12.25
4.0	1.0	4.0	16.00
5.0	1.5	7.5	25.00

$\sum x = 17.0$ $\sum y = 4.3$ $\sum xy = 18.8$ $\sum x^2 = 73.50$

Using the formulas with $n = 4$,
$$m = \frac{4(18.8) - 17(4.3)}{4(73.5) - (17)^2} \approx 0.42 \text{ and}$$
$$b = \frac{73.5(4.3) - 17(18.8)}{4(73.5) - (17)^2} \approx -0.71$$
So, the equation of the least-squares line is $y = 0.42x - 0.71$.

(c) If 4,800 catalogs are requested by December 1, $x = 4.8$ and $y = 0.42(4.8) - 0.71 = 1.306$, which means that approximately 1,306 completed applications will be received by March 1.

19. (a)

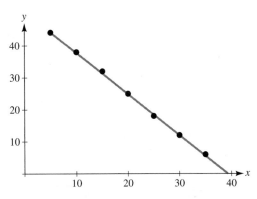

(b)

x	y	xy	x^2
5	44	220	25
10	38	380	100
15	32	480	225
20	25	500	400
25	18	450	625
30	12	360	900
35	6	210	1,225

$\sum x = 140$ $\sum y = 175$ $\sum xy = 2{,}600$ $\sum x^2 = 3{,}500$

Using the formulas with $n = 7$,
$$m = \frac{7(2{,}600) - (140)(175)}{7(3{,}500) - (140)^2} = \frac{-6{,}300}{4{,}900}$$
$$\approx -1.29 \text{ and}$$

$$b = \frac{(3{,}500)(175) - (140)(2{,}600)}{7(3{,}500) - (140)^2}$$
$$= \frac{248{,}500}{4{,}900} \approx 50.71.$$ So, the equation of the least-squares line is $y = -1.29x + 50.71$

(c) If 4,000 units are produced, $x = 40$ and

$$y = -1.29(40) + 50.71 = -0.89$$

Since this predicted price is negative, all 4,000 units cannot be sold at any price.

21. (a) Let x denote the number of hours after the polls open and y the corresponding percentage of registered voters that have already cast their ballots. Then

x	2	4	6	8	10
y	12	19	24	30	37

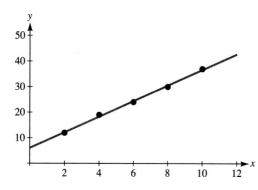

(b)

x	y	xy	x^2
2	12	24	4
4	19	76	16
6	24	144	36
8	30	240	64
10	37	370	100

$\sum x = 30$ $\sum y = 122$ $\sum xy = 854$ $\sum x^2 = 220$

Using the formulas with $n = 5$,

$$m = \frac{5(854) - (30)(122)}{5(220) - (30)^2} = \frac{610}{200} = 3.05 \text{ and}$$

$$b = \frac{(220)(122) - (30)(854)}{5(220) - (30)^2} = \frac{1,220}{200} = 6.10$$

So, the equation of the least-squares line is $y = 3.05x + 6.10$

(c) When the polls close at 8:00 p.m., $x = 12$ and so $y = 3.05(12) + 6.1 = 42.7$, which means that approximately 42.7% of the registered voters can be expected to vote.

23. (a) Let x denote the number of decades after 1950 and y the corresponding population (in millions). Then,

x	0	1	2	3	4	5
y	150.7	179.3	203.2	226.5	248.7	291.4

Since $y = Ae^{mx}$,

$$\ln y = \ln A + \ln e^{mx}$$
$$\ln y = mx + \ln A$$

We can find the least-squares line, $Y = Mx + b$, using $Y = \ln y$. Then, use $M = m$ and $b = \ln A$.

x	$y = \ln y$	xy	x^2
0	5.02	0	0
1	5.19	5.19	1
2	5.31	10.62	4
3	5.42	16.26	9
4	5.52	22.08	16
5	5.67	28.35	25

$\sum x = 15$ $\sum y = 32.13$ $\sum xy = 82.5$ $\sum x^2 = 55$

Using the formulas with $n = 6$,

$$m = \frac{6(82.5) - (15)(32.13)}{6(55) - (15)^2} = \frac{13.05}{105} \approx 0.124$$

and

$$b = \frac{(55)(32.13) - (15)(82.5)}{6(55) - (15)^2} = \frac{529.65}{105}$$

≈ 5.044. For our exponential model, $P = Ae^{mx}$. Since $\ln A = b$,

$$A = e^b = e^{5.044} \approx 155.089$$

So, the exponential function that best fits the data is $P = 155.089e^{0.124x}$. So, the population is growing approximately 12.4% per decade.

(b) In the year 2005, $x = 5.5$ and $P = 155.089e^{0.124(5.5)} \approx 306.74$ million. In the year 2010, $x = 6$ and $P = 155.089e^{0.124(6)} \approx 326.36$ million.

25. (a) Since $V(t) = Ae^{rt}$,

$$\ln V = \ln A + \ln e^{rt}$$
$$\ln V = rt + \ln A$$

We can find the least-squares line using $y = \ln V$. Then use $m = r$, $x = t$, and $b = \ln A$.

x	$y = \ln V$	xy	x^2
1	4.04	4.04	1
2	4.09	8.18	4
3	4.13	12.39	9
4	4.17	16.68	16
5	4.13	20.65	25
6	4.17	25.02	36
7	4.25	29.75	49
8	4.32	34.56	64

| 9 | 4.37 | 39.33 | 81 |
| 10 | 4.44 | 44.40 | 100 |

$$\sum x = 55 \quad \sum y = 42.11 \quad \sum xy = 235.0 \quad \sum x^2 = 385$$

Using the formulas with $n = 10$,

$$m = \frac{10(235.0) - (55)(42.11)}{10(385) - (55)^2} = \frac{33.95}{825}$$

≈ 0.041 and

$$b = \frac{(385)(42.11) - (55)(235.0)}{10(385) - (55)^2} = \frac{3{,}287.35}{825}$$

≈ 3.985. For our exponential model, $V(t) = Ae^{rt}$. Since $\ln A = b$,

$$A = e^b = e^{3.985} \approx 53.785$$

So, the exponential function that best fits the data is $V(t) = 53.785e^{0.041t}$. Her account is growing at a rate of approximately 4.1% per year.

(b) When $t = 20$, $V(20) \approx 53.785e^{0.041(20)} \approx$ 122.1 thousand, or \$122,100.

(c) To find t when $V(t) \approx 300$ thousand,

$$300 = 53.785e^{0.041t}$$

$$5.5778 = e^{0.041t}$$

$$\ln 5.5778 = 0.041t, \text{ or}$$

$$t \approx \frac{\ln 5.5778}{0.041} \approx 42 \text{ years}$$

(d) Using the two points named by Frank,

$$57 = Ae^{r(1)}$$

$$68 = Ae^{r(10)}$$

Solving the first for A and substituting in the second gives

$$68 = (57e^{-r})e^{10r}$$

$$1.19298 = e^{9r}$$

$$\ln 1.19298 = 9r$$

or $r \approx \dfrac{\ln 1.19298}{9} \approx 0.0196$ and $A = 57e^{-0.0196}$ ≈ 55.89. Frank's function fits the first and last data point, but may not be a good fit with the other data points. Frank's function would be less usable to predict other values.

27. (a)

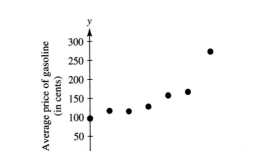

(b)

x	y	xy	x^2
0	95	0	0
3	114	342	9
6	111	666	36
9	123	1,107	81
12	151	1,812	144
15	159	2,385	225
18	259	4,662	324
$\sum x$	$\sum y$	$\sum xy$	$\sum x^2$
$= 63$	$= 1{,}012$	$= 10{,}974$	$= 819$

Using the formulas with $n = 7$,

$$m = \frac{7(10{,}974) - 63(1{,}012)}{7(819) - (63)^2} = \frac{13{,}062}{1{,}764} \approx 7.40$$

$$b = \frac{819(1{,}012) - 63(10{,}974)}{7(819) - (63)^2} = \frac{137{,}466}{1{,}764} \approx 77.9$$

So, the equation of the least squares line is $y = 7.4x + 77.9$.
No, ths line is not a good fit.

(c) In the year 2010, when $x = 22$, the prediction is $7.4(22) + 77.9 = 240.7$, or approx. \$2.41.

29. (a) Let t denote the number of years after 1996 and y the corresponding GDP in billions of yuan. Then,

t	0	1	2	3	4	5
y	6,788	7,446	7,835	8,191	8,940	9,593

t	y	ty	t^2
0	6,788	0	0
1	7,446	7,446	1
2	7,835	15,670	4
3	8,191	24,573	9
4	8,940	35,760	16
5	9,593	47,965	25
$\sum t$	$\sum y$	$\sum ty$	$\sum t^2$
$= 15$	$= 48,793$	$= 131,414$	$= 55$

Using the formulas with $n = 6$,

$$m = \frac{6(131,414) - (15)(48,793)}{6(55) - (15)^2} = \frac{56,589}{105}$$

$$\approx 538.9 \text{ and } b = \frac{(55)(48,793) - (15)(131,414)}{6(55) - (15)^2}$$

$$= \frac{712,405}{105} \approx 6,784.8. \text{ So, the equation of}$$
the least-squares line is $y = 538.9x + 6,784.8$

(b) In the year 2008, when $x = 12$, the prediction
is $538.9(12) + 6,784.8 = 13,251.6$, or approx.
13,252 billion yuan.

(b)

x	y	xy	x^2
0	99	0	0
4	6,360	25,440	16
8	36,064	288,512	64
12	79,477	953,724	144
16	61,109	977,744	256
20	42,156	843,120	400
24	37,726	905,424	576
$\sum x$	$\sum y$	$\sum xy$	$\sum x^2$
$= 84$	$= 262,991$	$= 3,993,964$	$= 1,456$

Using the formulas with $n = 7$,

$$m = \frac{7(3,993,964) - 84(262,991)}{7(1,456) - (84)^2}$$

$$= \frac{5,866,504}{3,136} \approx 1,871$$

$$b = \frac{1,456(262,991) - 84(3,993,964)}{7(1,456) - (84)^2}$$

$$= \frac{47,421,920}{3,136} \approx 15,122.$$

So, the equation of the least squares line is
$y = 1,871x + 15,122$.

(c) In the year 2008, when $x = 28$, the prediction is
$1,871(28) + 15,122 \approx 67,510$ cases.

(d) Writing Exercise—Answers will vary.

33. (a)

ln W	4.054	4.693	5.297	5.704	5.873	6.040	6.284	6.611
ln C	1.668	2.617	3.645	4.358	4.649	4.905	5.276	5.766

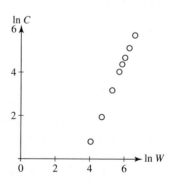

31. (a)

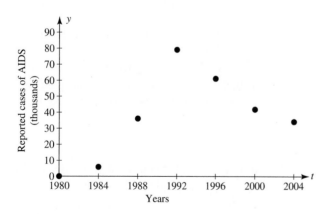

(b)

x	y	xy	x^2
4.054	1.668	6.762	16.435
4.693	2.617	12.282	22.024
5.297	3.645	19.308	28.058
5.704	4.358	24.858	32.536
5.873	4.649	27.304	34.492
6.040	4.905	29.626	36.482
6.284	5.276	33.154	39.489
6.611	5.766	38.119	43.705
$\sum x$ $= 44.556$	$\sum y$ $= 32.884$	$\sum xy$ $= 191.413$	$\sum x^2$ $= 253.221$

Using the formulas with $n = 8$,

$$m = \frac{8(191.413) - (44.556)(32.884)}{8(253.221) - (44.556)^2}$$

$$\approx \frac{66.124}{40.531} \approx 1.631 \text{ and}$$

$$b = \frac{(253.221)(32.884) - (44.556)(191.413)}{8(253.221) - (44.556)^2}$$

$$= \frac{-201.68}{40.531} \approx -4.976. \text{ So, the equation of the}$$
least-squares line is $y = 1.631x - 4.976$

(c)

$$\ln C = 1.631 \ln W - 4.976$$

$$e^{\ln C} = e^{1.631 \ln W - 4.976}$$

$$C = e^{\ln W^{1.631}} e^{-4.976}$$

$$C = e^{-4.976} W^{1.631}$$

$$C(W) = 0.00690 W^{1.631}$$

7.5 Constrained Optimization: The Method of Lagrange Multipliers

1.

$$f(x, y) = xy$$
$$g(x, y) = x + y$$
$$f_x = y; \; f_y = x; \; g_x = 1; \; g_y = 1$$

The three Lagrange equations are:

$$y = \lambda; \; x = \lambda; \; x + y = 1$$

From the first two equations, $x = y$ which, when substituted into the third equation gives

$$2x = 1, \text{ or } x = \frac{1}{2}.$$

Since $x = y$, the corresponding value for y is $y = \frac{1}{2}$. So, the constrained maximum is

$$f\left(\frac{1}{2}, \frac{1}{2}\right) = \frac{1}{4}.$$

3.

$$f(x, y) = x^2 + y^2$$
$$g(x, y) = xy$$
$$f_x = 2x; \; f_y = 2y; \; g_x = y; \; g_y = x$$

The three Lagrange equations are:

$$2x = \lambda y; \; 2y = \lambda x; \; xy = 1$$

Multiply the first equation by y and the second by x to get $2xy = \lambda y^2$ and $2xy = \lambda x^2$. Set the two expressions for $2xy$ equal to each other to get $\lambda y^2 = \lambda x^2$, $y^2 = x^2$, or $x = \pm y$. (Note that another solution of the equation $\lambda y^2 = \lambda x^2$ is $\lambda = 0$, which implies that $x = 0$ and $y = 0$, which is not consistent with the third equation.)
If $y = x$, the third equation becomes $x^2 = 1$, which implies that $x = \pm 1$ and $y = \pm 1$.
If $y = -x$, the third equation becomes $-x^2 = 1$, which has no solutions. So, the two points at which the constrained extrema can occur are $(1, 1)$ and $(-1, -1)$.
Since $f(1, 1) = 2$ and $f(-1, -1) = 2$, the constrained minimum is 2.

5.

$$f(x, y) = x^2 - y^2$$
$$g(x, y) = x^2 + y^2$$
$$f_x = 2x; \; f_y = -2y; \; g_x = 2x; \; g_y = 2y$$

The three Lagrange equations are:

$$2x = 2\lambda x; \; -2y = 2\lambda y; \; x^2 + y^2 = 4$$

From the first equation, either $\lambda = 1$ or $x = 0$. If $x = 0$, the third equation becomes $y^2 = 4$ or $y = \pm 2$.
From the second equation, either $\lambda = -1$ or $y = 0$. If $y = 0$, the third equation becomes $x^2 = 4$ or $x = \pm 2$.

If neither $x = 0$ nor $y = 0$, the first equation implies $\lambda = 1$ while the second equation implies $\lambda = -1$, which is impossible.

So, the only points at which the constrained extrema can occur are $(0, -2)$, $(0, 2)$, $(-2, 0)$, and $(2, 0)$. Now, $f(0, -2) = -4$, $f(0, 2) = -4$, $f(-2, 0) = 4$, and $f(2, 0) = 4$. So, the constrained minimum is -4.

7.
$$f(x, y) = x^2 - y^2 - 2y$$
$$g(x, y) = x^2 + y^2$$
$$f_x = 2x; \ f_y = -2y - 2; \ g_x = 2x; \ g_y = 2y$$

The three Lagrange equations are:

$$2x = 2\lambda x; \ -2y - 2 = 2\lambda y; \ x^2 + y^2 = 1$$

From the first equation, either $\lambda = 1$ or $x = 0$. If $\lambda = 1$, the second equation becomes $2y - 2 = 2y$, $4y = -2$, or $y = -\frac{1}{2}$. From the third equation,

$$x^2 + \left(-\frac{1}{2}\right)^2 = 1, \text{ or } x = \pm\frac{\sqrt{3}}{2}.$$

If $x = 0$, the third equation becomes $0^2 + y^2 = 1$ or $y = \pm 1$. So, the only points at which the constrained

extrema can occur are $\left(-\frac{\sqrt{3}}{2}, -\frac{1}{2}\right)$, $\left(\frac{\sqrt{3}}{2}, -\frac{1}{2}\right)$,

$(0, -1)$, and $(0, 1)$. Now, $f\left(\frac{\sqrt{3}}{2}, -\frac{1}{2}\right)$

$$= f\left(-\frac{\sqrt{3}}{2}, -\frac{1}{2}\right) = \frac{3}{2}, \ f(0, -1) = 1, \text{ and}$$

$f(0, 1) = -3$. So, the constrained maximum is $\frac{3}{2}$ and the constrained minimum is -3.

9.
$$f(x, y) = 2x^2 + 4y^2 - 3xy - 2x - 23y + 3$$
$$g(x, y) = x + y - 15 = 0$$
$$f_x = 4x - 3y - 2$$
$$f_y = 8y - 3x - 23$$
$$g_x = g_y = 1$$

The three Lagrange equations are:

$$4x - 3y - 2 = \lambda$$
$$-3x + 8y - 23 = \lambda$$
$$x + y = 15$$

The first two lead to $7x - 11y = -21$.
Substitute $y = 15 - x$ to obtain $18x = 144$ or $x = 8$ and $y = 7$.
The constrained minimum is $f(8, 7) = -18$.

11.
$$f(x, y) = e^{xy}$$
$$g(x, y) = x^2 + y^2 - 4 = 0$$
$$f_x = ye^{xy}, \text{ and } f_y = xe^{xy}$$
$$g_x = 2x \text{ and } g_y = 2y$$

The three Lagrange equations are:

$$ye^{xy} = 2\lambda x$$
$$xe^{xy} = 2\lambda y$$
$$x^2 + y^2 - 4 = 0$$

Dividing the first two leads to $\frac{y}{x} = \frac{x}{y}$, or $x^2 = y^2$.

Substitute in $x^2 + y^2 = 4$ to obtain $x = \pm\sqrt{2}$ and $y = \pm\sqrt{2}$.
Now, $f(\sqrt{2}, -\sqrt{2}) = f(-\sqrt{2}, \sqrt{2}) = e^{-2}$ and $f(\sqrt{2}, \sqrt{2}) = f(-\sqrt{2}, -\sqrt{2}) = e^2$. So, the constrained maximum is e^2 and the constrained minimum is e^{-2}.

13.
$$f(x, y, z) = xyz$$
$$g(x, y, z) = x + 2y + 3z - 24 = 0$$
$$f_x = yz, \ f_y = xz, \text{ and } f_z = xy$$
$$g_x = 1, \ g_y = 2, \text{ and } g_z = 3$$

The three Lagrange equations are:

$$yz = \lambda; \ xz = 2\lambda; \ xy = 3\lambda$$

Dividing the first two leads to $y = \frac{x}{2}$, dividing the first by the third leads to $z = \frac{x}{3}$.
Substitute in $x + 2y + 3z = 24$ to obtain $x = 8$, $y = 4$, and $z = \frac{8}{3}$.

$$\lambda = \frac{\alpha x^{\alpha-1}y^\beta}{a} = \frac{\alpha y^\beta}{ax^{1-\alpha}}$$

$$= \left(\frac{\alpha}{a}\right)\left(\frac{k\beta}{b}\right)^\beta\left(\frac{\alpha}{k\alpha}\right)^{1-\alpha}$$

$$= \left(\frac{\alpha}{a}\right)\left(\frac{k\beta}{b}\right)^\beta\left(\frac{\alpha}{k\alpha}\right)^\beta$$

$$= \left(\frac{\alpha}{a}\right)\left(\frac{k\beta a}{bk\alpha}\right)^\beta = \frac{\alpha\beta^\beta a^{\beta-1}}{\alpha^\beta b^\beta}$$

$$= \frac{\alpha^{\beta-1}\beta^\beta}{\alpha^{\beta-1}b^\beta} = \left(\frac{\alpha}{a}\right)^\alpha\left(\frac{\beta}{b}\right)^\beta$$

45. Let $Q(x, y)$ be the production level curve subject to $px + qy = k$. The three Lagrange equations then are $Q_x = \lambda p$, $Q_y = \lambda q$, and $px + qy = k$. From the first two equations $\dfrac{Q_x}{p} = \dfrac{Q_y}{q}$.

47. Need to find extrema of
$Q(K, L) = 55[0.6K^{-1/4} + 0.4L^{-1/4}]^{-4}$
subject to $g(K, L) = 2K + 5L - 150 = 0$.

$$Q_K = -220\left[0.6K^{-1/4} + 0.4L^{-1/4}\right]^{-5}\left(-0.15K^{-5/4}\right)$$

$$Q_L = -220\left[0.6K^{-1/4} + 0.4L^{-1/4}\right]^{-5}\left(-0.1L^{-5/4}\right)$$

$$g_K = 2 \quad g_L = 5$$

The three Lagrange equations are

$$-220\left(0.6K^{-1/4} + 0.4L^{-1/4}\right)^{-5}\left(-0.15K^{-5/4} = 2\right)\lambda$$

$$-220\left(0.6K^{-1/4} + 0.4L^{-1/4}\right)^{-5}\left(-0.1L^{-5/4}\right) = 5\lambda$$

$$2K + 5L - 150 = 0$$

Solving the first two equations for λ gives

$$\frac{33K^{-5/4}\left(0.6K^{1/4} + 0.4L^{-1/4}\right)^{-5}}{2} = \lambda$$

$$\frac{22L^{-5/4}\left(0.6K^{1/4} + 0.4L^{-1/4}\right)^{-5}}{5} = \lambda$$

Setting these equal,

$$\frac{33K^{-5/4}\left(0.6K^{1/4} + 0.4L^{-1/4}\right)^{-5}}{2}$$
$$= \frac{22L^{-5/4}\left(0.6K^{1/4} + 0.4L^{-1/4}\right)^{-5}}{5}$$

$$\frac{33K^{-5/4}}{2} = \frac{22L^{-5/4}}{5}$$

$$165L^{5/4} = 44K^{-5/4}$$

$$L = \left(\frac{44K^{4/5}}{165}\right)^{4/5} = \left(\frac{44}{165}\right)^{4/5}K$$

Using the third equation,

$$2K + 5\left(\frac{44}{165}\right)^{4/5}K - 150 = 0$$

$$K \approx 40.14$$

$$L \approx \left(\frac{44}{165}\right)^{4/5}K \approx 13.89$$

$$Q(40.14, 13.89) = 55\left[0.6(40.14)^{-1/4} + 0.4(13.89)^{-1/4}\right]^{-4}$$

$$\approx 1395.4$$

49. $Q(K, L) = A[\alpha K^{-\beta} + (1-\alpha)L^{-\beta}]^{-1/\beta}$
Since the constraint is $c_1K + c_2L = B$, $g(K, L) = c_1K + c_2L$.

$$Q_K = -\frac{A}{\beta}[\alpha K^{-\beta} + (1-\alpha)L^{-\beta}]^{-1/\beta-1}(-\alpha\beta K^{\beta-1})$$
$$= A\alpha K^{\beta-1}[\alpha K^{-\beta} + (1-\alpha)L^{-\beta}]^{-1/\beta-1}$$

$$Q_L = -\frac{A}{\beta}[\alpha K^{-\beta} + (1-\alpha)L^{-\beta}]^{-1/\beta-1}(-\beta(1-\alpha)L^{-\beta-1})$$
$$= A(1-\alpha)L^{-\beta-1}[\alpha K^{-\beta} + (1-\alpha)L^{-\beta}]^{-1/\beta-1}$$

$$g_K = c; \ g_L = c_2$$

The three Lagrange equations are:

$$A\alpha K^{-\beta-1}[\alpha K^{-\beta} + (1-\alpha)L^{-\beta}]^{-1/\beta-1} = c_1\lambda$$

$$A(1-\alpha)L^{-\beta-1}[\alpha K^{-\beta} + (1-\alpha)L^{-\beta}]^{-1/\beta-1} = c_2\lambda$$

Solving both for λ and equating gives

$$\frac{A\alpha K^{-\beta-1}[\alpha K^{-\beta} + (1-\alpha)L^{-\beta}]^{-1/\beta-1}}{c_1}$$

$$= \frac{A(1-\alpha)L^{-\beta-1}[\alpha K^{-\beta} + (1-\alpha)L^{-\beta}]^{-1/\beta-1}}{c_2}$$

$$\frac{\alpha K^{-\beta-1}}{c_1} = \frac{(1-\alpha)L^{-\beta-1}}{c_2}$$

$$\left(\frac{K}{L}\right)^{-\beta-1} = \frac{c_1}{c_2}\left(\frac{1-\alpha}{\alpha}\right)$$

51. Need to find extrema of $f(x, y) = x - y$ subject to $g(x, y) = x^5 + x - z - y = 0$.

$$f_x = 1 \quad f_y = -1 \quad g_x = 5x^4 + 1 \quad g_y = -1$$

The three Lagrange equations are:

$$1 = \lambda(5x^4 + 1)$$
$$-1 = \lambda(-1)$$
$$x^5 + x - z - y = 0$$

From the second equation, $\lambda = 1$.
Then, from the first equation,

$$1 = 5x^4 + 1$$
$$5x^4 = 0$$
$$x = 0$$

Finally, from the third equation,

$$-2 - y = 0$$
$$y = -2$$

Therefore, a possible extremum occurs at the point $(0, -2)$. However, $f(1, 0) = 1$ and $f(-1, -4) = 3$, which shows $f(0, -2) = 2$ is not a local maximum or minimum point.
Press [y=].
Input $x \wedge 5 + x - 2$ for $y_1 =$ and input $x - L_1$ for $y_2 =$.
From the home screen, input $\{2, 1, 0, -1\}$ [sto→] [2nd] L_1.
Use window dimensions $[-4, 4]1$ by $[-4, 4]1$.
Press [Graph].
From the graphs that the point $(0, -2)$ is an inflection point.

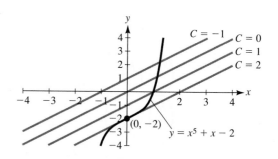

53. The goal is to maximize $P(K, L)$ subject to the constraint $C(K, L) = A$, so $g(K, L) = C(K, L)$. The three Lagrange equations are

$$\frac{\partial P}{\partial K} = \lambda\frac{\partial C}{\partial K}, \quad \frac{\partial P}{\partial L} = \lambda\frac{\partial C}{\partial L}, \quad C(K, L) = A$$

Divide the first two equations to eliminate λ and

$$\frac{\dfrac{\partial P}{\partial K}}{\dfrac{\partial P}{\partial L}} = \frac{\dfrac{\partial C}{\partial K}}{\dfrac{\partial C}{\partial L}} \quad \text{or} \quad \frac{\dfrac{\partial P}{\partial K}}{\dfrac{\partial C}{\partial K}} = \frac{\dfrac{\partial P}{\partial L}}{\dfrac{\partial C}{\partial L}}$$

55. $F(x, y) = xe^{xy^2} + \frac{y}{x} + x\ln(x + y)$

(a)
$$0 = (x)\left[e^{xy^2}(x \cdot 2y\frac{dy}{dx} + y^2 \cdot 1)\right] + (e^{xy^2})(1)$$

$$+ \frac{x\dfrac{dy}{dx} - y \cdot 1}{x^2} + (x)\left[\frac{1}{x + y}\left(1 + \frac{dy}{dx}\right)\right]$$

$$+ \ln(x + y) \cdot 1$$

$$0 = 2x^2ye^{xy^2}\frac{dy}{dx} + xy^2e^{xy^2} + e^{xy^2} + \frac{1}{x}\frac{dy}{dx}$$

$$- \frac{y}{x^2} + \frac{x}{x + y} + \frac{x}{x + y}\frac{dy}{dx} + \ln(x + y)$$

$$\frac{y}{x^2} - \frac{x}{x + y} - xy^2e^{xy^2} - e^{xy^2} + \ln(x + y)$$

$$= \left(2x^2ye^{xy^2} + \frac{1}{x} + \frac{x}{x + y}\right)\frac{dy}{dx}$$

$$\frac{dy}{dx} = \frac{-xy^2 e^{xy^2} - e^{xy^2} + \dfrac{y}{x^2} - \dfrac{x}{x+y} - \ln(x+y)}{2x^2 y e^{xy^2} + \dfrac{1}{x} + \dfrac{x}{x+y}}$$

$$= -\frac{xy^2 e^{xy^2} + e^{xy^2} - \dfrac{y}{x^2} + \dfrac{x}{x+y} + \ln(x+y)}{2x^2 y e^{xy^2} + \dfrac{1}{x} + \dfrac{x}{x+y}}$$

(b)
$$F_x = xy^2 e^{xy^2} + e^{xy^2} - \frac{y}{x^2}$$
$$+ \frac{x}{x+y} + \ln(x+y)$$

$$F_y = 2x^2 y e^{xy^2} + \frac{1}{x} + \frac{x}{x+y}$$

$$\frac{dy}{dx} = -\frac{F_x}{F_y}$$

$$= -\frac{xy^2 e^{xy^2} + e^{xy^2} - \dfrac{y}{x^2} + \dfrac{x}{x+y} + \ln(x+y)}{2x^2 y e^{xy^2} + \dfrac{1}{x} + \dfrac{x}{x+y}}$$

57. Minimize $f(x, y) = \ln(x + 2y)$ subject to $xy + y = 5$.

$$f(x, y) = \ln(x + 2y) \qquad g(x, y) = xy + y - 5 = 0$$

$$f_x = \frac{1}{x + 2y} \qquad f_y = \frac{2}{x + 2y}$$

$$g_x = y \qquad g_y = x + 1$$

The three Lagrange equations are:

$$\frac{1}{x + 2y} = \lambda y$$

$$\frac{2}{x + 2y} = \lambda(x + 1)$$

$$xy + y = 5$$

From the first equation, $\lambda = \dfrac{1}{y(x + 2y)}$.

From the second equation, $\lambda = \dfrac{2}{(x + 1)(x + 2y)}$.

Equating these two gives $(x + 1)(x + 2y)$
$= 2y(x + 2y)$ or $y = \dfrac{(x + 1)}{2}$.

Substituting $y = \dfrac{1}{2}(x + 1)$ into the third equation,

$$\frac{1}{2}x(x + 1) + \frac{1}{2}(x + 1) = 5$$

$$x(x + 1) + (x + 1) = 10$$

$$(x + 1)[x + 1] = 10$$

$$(x + 1)^2 = 10$$

This gives $x \approx -4.1623$, $x \approx 2.1623$. This leads to the points $(-4.1623, -1.5811)$ and $(2.1623, 1.5811)$. We cannot use $(-4.1623, -1.5811)$ since this point leads $f(x, y)$ to be undefined.
Find $f(2.1623, 1.5811) = \ln[2.1623 + 2(1.5811)]$
≈ 1.6724.

59.
$$f(x, y) = xe^{x^2 - y} \text{ and}$$
$$g(x, y) = x^2 + 2y^2 - 1 = 0$$

$$f_x = e^{x^2 - y} + (x)(e^{x^2 - y})(2x)$$

$$f_y = xe^{x^2 - y}(-1) = -xe^{x^2 - y}$$

$$f_x = (2x^2 + 1)(e^{x^2 - y})$$

$$g_x = 2x \qquad g_y = 4y$$

The three Lagrange equations are:

$$(2x^2 + 1)(e^{x^2 - y}) = \lambda(2x)$$

$$-xe^{x^2 - y} = \lambda(4y)$$

$$x^2 + 2y^2 = 1$$

From the first equation, $\lambda = \dfrac{(2x^2 + 1)(e^{x^2 - y})}{2x}$.

From the second equation, $\lambda = \dfrac{-xe^{x^2 - y}}{4y}$.

Equating these and simplifying,

$$8x^2y + 4y = -2x^2$$

$$2x^2(1 + 4y) = -4y$$

$$x^2 = -\frac{2y}{4y + 1}$$

Substituting this into the third equation,

$$-\frac{2y}{4y + 1} + 2y^2 = 1$$

$$-2y + 2y^2(4y + 1) = 4y + 1$$

$$8y^3 + 2y^2 - 6y - 1 = 0$$

To solve, press $\boxed{y=}$ and
input $8x \wedge 3 + 2x^2 - 6x - 1$ for $y_1 =$ (remember
we are actually solving for y).
Use window dimensions $[-4, 4]1$ by $[-4, 4]1$.
Press $\boxed{\text{Graph}}$.
Use the zero function under the calc menu to find
that $y \approx -0.9184$, $y \approx -0.1636$, and $y \approx 0.832$.
We reject $y \approx -0.9184$ and $y \approx 0.832$ since these
would result in x being undefined. If $y = -0.1636$,
then $x = \pm 0.9729$.
The two points for consideration are $(0.9729,$
$-0.1636)$ and $(-0.9729, -0.1636)$.
Press $\boxed{y=}$.
Input $xe \wedge (x^2 - L_1)$ for $y_1 =$.
From the home screen, input $\{-0.1636\}\boxed{\text{sto}\rightarrow}\boxed{\text{2nd}}\ L_1$.
Press $\boxed{\text{Graph}}$.
Use the value function under the calc menu to find
$f(0.9729, -0.1636) \approx 2.952$ and
$f(-0.9729, -0.1636) \approx -2.952$
The maximum point is $(0.9729, -0.1636)$.

7.6   Double Integrals

1.

$$\int_0^1 \int_1^2 x^2 y\, dx dy$$

$$= \int_0^1 \left[\int_1^2 x^2 y\, dx \right] dy$$

$$= \int_0^1 \left[\frac{x^3}{3} y \Big|_1^2 \right] dy$$

$$= \int_0^1 \left[\frac{8}{3}y - \frac{1}{3}y \right] dy$$

$$= \frac{7}{6}y^2 \Big|_0^1 = \frac{7}{6}$$

3.

$$\int_0^{\ln 2} \int_{-1}^0 2xe^y\, dx dy$$

$$= \int_0^{\ln 2} \left[\int_{-1}^0 2xe^y\, dx \right] dy$$

$$= \int_0^{\ln 2} \left[x^2 e^y \Big|_{-1}^0 \right] dy$$

$$= \int_0^{\ln 2} \left[-e^y \right]\, dy = -e^y \Big|_0^{\ln 2} = -1.$$

5.

$$\int_1^3 \int_0^1 \frac{2xy}{x^2 + 1}\, dx dy$$

$$= \int_1^3 \left[\int_0^1 \frac{2xy}{x^2 + 1}\, dx \right] dy$$

$$= \int_1^3 \left[y \ln(x^2 + 1) \Big|_0^1 \right] dy$$

$$= \int_1^3 y \ln 2\, dy = \ln 2 \left(\frac{1}{2} \right) y^2 \Big|_1^3 = 4 \ln 2$$

7.

$$\int_0^4 \int_{-1}^1 x^2 y\, dx dy$$

$$= \int_0^4 \left[\int_{-1}^1 x^2 y\, dx \right] dx$$

$$= \int_0^4 \left[\frac{y^2}{2}x^2 \Big|_{-1}^1 \right] dx = 0$$

9.
$$\int_2^3 \int_1^2 \frac{x+y}{xy}\, dy\, dx$$

$$= \int_2^3 \int_1^2 \left[\frac{1}{y} + \frac{1}{x}\right] dy\, dx$$

$$= \int_2^3 \left[\ln(y) + \frac{y}{x}\right]\Big|_1^2 dx$$

$$= (x \ln 2 + \ln x)\Big|_2^3 = \ln 2 + \ln \frac{3}{2} = \ln 3$$

11.
$$\int_0^4 \int_0^{\sqrt{x}} x^2 y\, dy\, dx = \int_0^4 \left[\int_0^{\sqrt{x}} x^2 y\, dy\right] dx$$

$$= \int_0^4 \left[\frac{x^2 y^2}{z}\right]\Big|_0^{\sqrt{x}} dx = \int_0^4 \frac{x^3}{2}\, dx$$

$$= \frac{x^4}{8}\Big|_0^4 = 32$$

13.
$$\int_0^1 \int_{y-1}^{1-y} (2x + y)\, dx\, dy$$

$$= \int_0^1 \left[\int_{y-1}^{1-y} (2x + y)\, dx\right] dy$$

$$= \int_0^1 \left[(x^2 + xy)\Big|_{y-1}^{1-y}\right] dy$$

$$= \int_0^1 \Big[[(1-y)^2 + (1-y)y]$$

$$\qquad -[(y-1)^2 + (y-1)y]\Big]\, dy$$

$$= \int_0^1 2y - 2y^2\, dy = y^2 - \frac{2y^3}{3}\Big|_0^1 = \frac{1}{3}$$

15.
$$\int_0^1 \int_0^4 \sqrt{xy}\, dy\, dx = \int_0^1 \left[\int_0^4 x^{\frac{1}{2}} y^{\frac{1}{2}}\, dy\right] dx$$

$$= \int_0^1 \left[\frac{2x^{\frac{1}{2}} y^{\frac{3}{2}}}{3}\right]\Big|_0^4 dx = \int_0^1 \frac{16x^{\frac{1}{2}}}{3}\, dx$$

$$= \frac{32x^{\frac{3}{2}}}{9}\Big|_0^1 = \frac{32}{9}$$

17.
$$\int_1^e \int_0^{\ln x} xy\, dy\, dx = \int_1^e \left[\int_0^{\ln x} xy\, dy\right] dx$$

$$= \int_1^e \left[\frac{xy^2}{2}\Big|_0^{\ln x}\right] dx = \int_1^e \frac{x(\ln x)^2}{2}\, dx$$

Using integration by parts with

$$u = (\ln x)^2 \quad \text{and} \quad dV = \frac{x}{2}\, dx$$

$$= \frac{x^2}{4}(\ln x)^2\Big|_1^e - \int_1^e \frac{x}{2} \ln x\, dx$$

$$= \frac{e^2}{4} - \int_1^e \frac{x}{2} \ln x\, dx$$

Using integration by parts again, with

$$u = \ln x \quad \text{and} \quad dV = \frac{x}{2}\, dx$$

$$= \frac{e^2}{4} - \left[\frac{x^2}{4} \ln x\Big|_1^e - \int_1^e \frac{x}{4}\, dx\right]$$

$$= \frac{e^2}{4} - \left[\left(\frac{x^2}{4} \ln x - \frac{x^2}{8}\right)\Big|_1^e\right]$$

$$= \frac{e^2}{4} - \left[\left(\frac{e^2}{4} - \frac{e^2}{8}\right) - \left(0 - \frac{1}{8}\right)\right] = \frac{e^2 - 1}{8}$$

19. Solving $x^2 = 3x$ yields $x = 0$ and $x = 3$. Similarly, after solving each equation for x, $\sqrt{y} = \frac{y}{3}$ when $y = 0$ and $y = 9$. So, R can be described in terms of vertical cross sections by $0 \le x \le 3$ and $x^2 \le y \le 3x$ and in terms of horizontal cross sections by $0 \le y \le 9$ and $\frac{y}{3} \le x \le \sqrt{y}$.

21. The given points form a rectangle. So, R can be described in terms of vertical cross sections by $-1 \le x \le 2$ and $1 \le y \le 2$ and in terms of horizontal cross sections by $1 \le y \le 2$ and $-1 \le x \le 2$.

23. Solving $\ln x = 0$ yields $x = 1$, with the second boundary given as $x = e$. Similarly, solving $y = \ln x$ for x yields $x = e^y$, with the second boundary given as $y = 0$. So, R can be described in terms of vertical cross sections by $1 \le x \le e$ and $0 \le y \le \ln x$ and in terms of horizontal cross sections by $0 \le y \le 1$ and $e^y \le x \le e$.

25.

$$\iint_R 3xy^2 \, dA = \int_{-1}^0 \int_{-1}^2 3xy^2 \, dxdy$$

$$= \int_{-1}^0 \left[\int_{-1}^2 3xy^2 \, dx \right] dy = \int_{-1}^0 \left[\frac{3x^2y^2}{2} \Big|_{-1}^2 \right] dy$$

$$= \int_{-1}^0 \frac{9y^2}{2} \, dy = \frac{3y^3}{2} \Big|_{-1}^0 = \frac{3}{2}$$

Note: problem can be equivalently worked as

$$\int_{-1}^2 \int_{-1}^0 3xy^2 \, dydx.$$

27. Since the line joining the points $(0, 0)$ and $(1, 1)$ is $y = x$,

$$\iint_R xe^y \, dA = \int_0^1 \int_0^x xe^y \, dydx$$

$$= \int_0^1 \left[\int_0^x xe^y \, dy \right] dx = \int_0^1 \left[xe^y \Big|_0^x \right] dx$$

$$= \int_0^1 (xe^x - x) \, dx = \int_0^1 xe^x \, dx - \int_0^1 x \, dx$$

$$= \int_0^1 xe^x \, dx - \frac{x^2}{2} \Big|_0^1 = \int_0^1 xe^x \, dx - \frac{1}{2}$$

Using integration by parts with

$$u = x \quad \text{and} \quad dV = e^x \, dx$$

$$= xe^x \Big|_0^1 - \int_0^1 e^x \, dx - \frac{1}{2}$$

$$= (xe^x - e^x) \Big|_0^1 - \frac{1}{2} = \frac{1}{2}$$

Note: problem can be equivalently worked as $\int_0^1 \int_0^y xe^y \, dxdy$.

29. Solving $x^2 = 2x$ yields $x = 0$ and $x = 2$, so

$$\iint_R (2y - x) \, dA = \int_0^2 \int_{x^2}^{2x} (2y - x) \, dydx$$

$$= \int_0^2 \left[\int_{x^2}^{2x} (2y - x) \, dy \right] dx$$

$$= \int_0^2 \left[(y^2 - xy) \Big|_{x^2}^{2x} \right] dx$$

$$= \int_0^2 \left[[(2x)^2 - x(2x)] - [(x^2)^2 - x(x^2)] \right] dx$$

$$= \int_0^2 (2x^2 - x^4 + x^3) \, dx$$

$$= \left(\frac{2x^3}{3} - \frac{x^5}{5} + \frac{x^4}{4} \right) \Big|_0^2 = \frac{44}{15}$$

Note: problem can be equivalently worked as

$$\int_0^4 \int_{\sqrt{y}}^{\frac{y}{2}} (2y - x) \, dxdy.$$

31. The line joining the points $(-1, 0)$ and $(0, 1)$ is $y = x + 1$, or $x = y - 1$. Similarly, the line joining the points $(0, 1)$ and $(1, 0)$ is $y = 1 - x$, or $x = 1 - y$. So,

$$\iint_R (2x + 1) \, dA = \int_0^1 \int_{y-1}^{1-y} (2x + 1) \, dxdy$$

$$= \int_0^1 \left[\int_{y-1}^{1-y} (2x + 1) \, dx \right] dy$$

$$= \int_0^1 \left[(x^2 + x) \Big|_{y-1}^{1-y} \right] dy$$

$$= \int_0^1 \left[[(1 - y)^2 + (1 - y)] \right.$$

$$\left. -[(y - 1)^2 + (y - 1)] \right] dy$$

$$= \int_0^1 (2 - 2y) \, dy = (2y - y^2) \Big|_0^1 = 1$$

33. After solving each equation for x, $2y = -y$ when $y = 0$, with the other boundary given as $y = 2$. So,

$$\iint_R \frac{1}{y^2 + 1} \, dA = \int_0^2 \int_{-y}^{2y} \frac{1}{y^2 + 1} \, dxdy$$

$$= \int_0^2 \left[\int_{-y}^{2y} \frac{1}{y^2 + 1} \, dx \right] dy = \int_0^2 \left[\frac{x}{y^2 + 1} \Big|_{-y}^{2y} \right] dy$$

$$= \int_0^2 \left[\left[\frac{2y}{y^2+1} - \frac{-y}{y^2+1} \right] \right] dy = \int_0^2 \frac{3y}{y^2+1}\, dy$$

$$= 3\int_0^2 \frac{y}{y^2+1}\, dy$$

Using substitution with $u = y^2 + 1$,

$$= 3\int_1^5 \frac{1}{u} \cdot \frac{1}{2}\, du = \frac{3}{2}\int_1^5 \frac{1}{u}\, du$$

$$= \frac{3}{2}\left(\ln|u|\Big|_1^5 \right) = \frac{3}{2}(\ln 5 - \ln 1) = \frac{3\ln 5}{2}$$

35. After solving each equation for x, $y^{\frac{1}{3}} = y$ when $y = 0$ and $y = 1$. So,

$$\iint_R 12x^2 e^{y^2}\, dA = \int_0^1 \int_y^{y^{\frac{1}{3}}} 12x^2 e^{y^2}\, dx\, dy$$

$$= \int_0^1 \left[\int_y^{y^{\frac{1}{3}}} 12x^2 e^{y^2}\, dx \right] dy$$

$$= \int_0^1 \left[4x^3 e^{y^2}\Big|_y^{y^{\frac{1}{3}}} \right] dy$$

$$= \int_0^1 (4ye^{y^2} - 4y^3 e^{y^2})\, dy$$

$$= 4\int_0^1 ye^{y^2}\, dy - 4\int_0^1 y^2(ye^{y^2})\, dy$$

Using substitution for the first integral with $u = y^2$, and using integration by parts for the second integral with

$$u = y^2 \quad \text{and} \quad dV = ye^{y^2}\, dy$$

(where solving for V requires substitution as well)

$$= 4\int_0^1 \frac{e^4}{2}\, du - 4\left[\frac{y^2}{2} e^{y^2}\Big|_0^1 - \int_0^1 ye^{y^2}\, dy \right]$$

$$= 4\left(\frac{1}{2}e^{y^2}\Big|_0^1 \right) - 4\left[\left(\frac{y^2}{2}e^{y^2}\Big|_0^1 \right) - \frac{1}{2}e^{y^2}\Big|_0^1 \right]$$

$$= 2\left(e^{y^2} - y^2 e^{y^2} + e^{y^2} \right)\Big|_0^1$$

$$= 2\left(2e^{y^2} - y^2 e^{y^2} \right)\Big|_0^1 = 2(e-2)$$

37. The region for $\displaystyle\int_0^2 \int_0^{4-x^2} f(x, y)\, dy\, dx$ is bounded above by $y = 4 - x^2$ and below by $y = 0$. It is bounded on the left by $x = 0$ and on the right by $x = 2$. So, the region is:

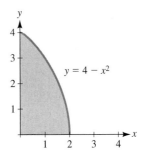

Reversing the integration yields

$$\int_0^4 \int_0^{\sqrt{4-y}} f(x, y)\, dx\, dy.$$

39. The region for $\displaystyle\int_0^1 \int_{x^3}^{\sqrt{x}} f(x, y)\, dy\, dx$ is bounded above by $y = \sqrt{x}$ and below by $y = x^3$. It is bounded on the left by $x = 0$ and on the right by $x = 1$. So, the region is:

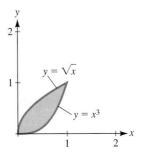

Reversing the integration yields

$$\int_0^1 \int_{y^2}^{y^{\frac{1}{3}}} f(x, y)\, dx\, dy.$$

41. The region for $\int_1^{e^2} \int_{\ln x}^2 f(x, y)\, dydx$ is bounded above by $y = 2$ and below by $y = \ln x$. It is bounded on the left by $x = 1$ and on the right by $x = e^2$. So, the region is:

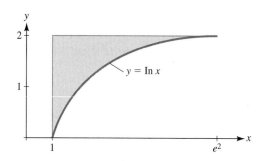

Reversing the integration yields

$$\int_0^2 \int_1^{e^y} f(x, y)\, dxdy.$$

43. The region for $\int_{-1}^1 \int_{x^2+1}^2 f(x, y)\, dydx$ is bounded above by $y = 2$ and below by $y = x^2 + 1$. It is bounded on the left by $x = -1$ and on the right by $x = 1$. So, the region is:

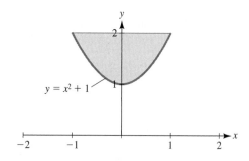

Reversing the integration yields

$$\int_1^2 \int_{-\sqrt{y-1}}^{\sqrt{y-1}} f(x, y)\, dxdy.$$

45. The line joining the points $(-4, 0)$ and $(2, 6)$ is $y = x + 4$, which the bottom boundary being $y = 0$. So, the area of R is

$$\int_{-4}^2 \int_0^{x+4} (1)\, dydx = \int_{-4}^2 \left[\int_0^{x+4} 1\, dy \right] dx$$

$$= \int_{-4}^2 \left[y \big|_0^{x+4} \right] dx = \int_{-4}^2 (x + 4)\, dx$$

$$= \left(\frac{x^2}{2} + 4x \right) \bigg|_{-4}^2 = 18$$

47. Solving $\frac{1}{2}x^2 = 2x$ yields $x = 0$ and $x = 4$. So, the area of R is

$$\int_0^4 \int_{\frac{x^2}{2}}^{2x} (1)\, dydx = \int_0^4 \left[\int_{\frac{x^2}{2}}^{2x} 1\, dy \right] dx$$

$$= \int_0^4 \left[y \big|_{\frac{x^2}{2}}^{2x} \right] dx = \int_0^4 \left(2x - \frac{x^2}{2} \right) dx$$

$$= \left(x^2 - \frac{x^3}{6} \right) \bigg|_0^4 = \frac{16}{3}$$

49. Solving $x^2 - 4x + 3 = 0$ yields $x = 1$ and $x = 3$. So, the area of R is

$$\int_1^3 \int_0^{x^2-4x+3} (1)\, dydx$$

$$= \int_1^3 \left[\int_{x^2-4x+3}^0 1\, dy \right] dx$$

$$= \int_1^3 \left[y \big|_{x^2-4x+3}^0 \right] dx$$

$$= \int_1^3 (-x^2 + 4x - 3)\, dx$$

$$= \left(-\frac{x^3}{3} + 2x^2 - 3x \right) \bigg|_1^3 = \frac{4}{3}$$

51. Solving $\ln x = 0$ yields $x = 1$, with the other boundary given as $x = e$. So, the area of R is

$$\int_1^e \int_0^{\ln x} (1)\, dydx = \int_1^e \left[\int_0^{\ln x} 1\, dy \right] dx$$

$$= \int_1^e \left[y \big|_0^{\ln x} \right] dx = \int_1^e \ln x\, dx$$

Using integration by parts with

$$u = \ln x \quad \text{and} \quad dV = dx$$

$$= x \ln x \big|_1^e - \int_1^e 1 \, dx$$

$$= (x \ln x - x) \big|_1^e = 1$$

53. After solving each equation for x, $\sqrt{4 - y} = \dfrac{y}{3}$ when $y = -12$ and $y = 3$. However, the region is also bounded by $y = 0$, making the limits $y = 0$ and $y = 3$. So, the area of R is

$$\int_0^3 \int_{\frac{y}{3}}^{\sqrt{4-y}} (1) \, dx dy = \int_0^3 \left[\int_{\frac{y}{3}}^{\sqrt{4-y}} 1 \, dy \right] dx$$

$$= \int_0^3 \left[x \big|_{\frac{y}{3}}^{\sqrt{4-y}} \right] dy = \int_0^3 \left(\sqrt{4-y} - \frac{4}{3} \right) dy$$

$$= \int_0^3 \sqrt{4-y} \, dy - \int_0^3 \frac{y}{3} \, dy$$

$$= \int_0^3 \sqrt{4-y} \, dy - \frac{y^2}{6} \Big|_0^3 = \int_0^3 \sqrt{4-y} \, dy - \frac{3}{2}$$

Using substitution with $u = 4 - y$,

$$= \int_4^1 u^{\frac{1}{2}} - du - \frac{3}{2} = -\int_4^1 u^{\frac{1}{2}} \, du - \frac{3}{2}$$

$$= \int_1^4 u^{\frac{1}{2}} du - \frac{3}{2} = \frac{2}{3} u^{\frac{3}{2}} \Big|_1^4 - \frac{3}{2} = \frac{19}{6}$$

55.
$$V = \int_0^1 \int_0^2 (6 - 2x - 2y) \, dy dx$$

$$= \int_0^1 \left[\int_0^2 (6 - 2x - 2y) \, dy \right] dx$$

$$= \int_0^1 \left[(6y - 2xy - y^2) \big|_0^2 \right] dx$$

$$= \int_0^1 (8 - 4x) \, dx$$

$$= (8x - 2x^2) \Big|_0^1 = 6$$

Note: problem can be equivalently worked as $\int_0^2 \int_0^1 (6 - 2x - 2y) \, dx dy$.

57.
$$V = \int_1^2 \int_1^3 \frac{1}{xy} \, dy dx$$

$$= \int_1^2 \left[\int_1^3 \frac{1}{x} \cdot \frac{1}{y} \, dy \right] dx$$

$$= \int_1^2 \left[\frac{1}{x} \ln |y| \, \Big|_1^3 \right] dx = \int_1^2 \frac{1}{x} \ln 3 \, dx$$

$$= \left[\ln 3 \ln |x| \right]_1^2 = (\ln 3)(\ln 2)$$

Note: problem can be equivalently worked as $\int_1^3 \int_1^2 \frac{1}{xy} \, dx dy$.

59.
$$V = \int_0^1 \int_0^2 xe^{-y} \, dy dx$$

$$= \int_0^1 \left[\int_0^2 xe^{-y} \, dy \right] dx$$

$$= \int_0^1 \left[-xe^{-y} \, \Big|_0^2 \right] dx = \int_0^1 (-xe^{-2} + x) \, dx$$

$$= \int_0^1 (1 - e^{-2}) x \, dx = (1 - e^{-2}) \frac{x^2}{2} \Big|_0^1$$

$$= \frac{e^2 - 1}{2e^2} = \frac{1}{2} \left(1 - \frac{1}{e^2} \right)$$

61. After solving both equations for x, $y = 2 - y$ when $y = 1$, with the other boundary given as $y = 0$. So,

$$V = \int_0^1 \int_y^{2-y} (2x + y) \, dx dy$$

$$= \int_0^1 \left[\int_y^{2-y} (2x + y) \, dx \right] dy$$

$$= \int_0^1 \left[(x^2 + xy) \, \Big|_y^{2-y} \right] dy$$

$$= \int_0^1 \left[\left[(2 - y)^2 + (2 - y)y \right] - \left[(y)^2 + (y)y \right] \right] dy$$

$$= \int_0^1 (4 - 2y - 2y^2) \, dy$$

$$= \left(4y - y^2 - \frac{2y^3}{3} \right) \Big|_0^1 = \frac{7}{3}$$

63. Solving $8 - x^2 = x^2$ yields $x = -2$ and $x = 2$. So,

$$V = \int_{-2}^{2} \int_{x^2}^{8-x^2} (x+1) \, dydx$$

$$= \int_{-2}^{2} \left[\int_{x^2}^{8-x^2} (x+1) \, dy \right] dx$$

$$= \int_{-2}^{2} \left[(x+1)y \Big|_{x^2}^{8-x^2} \right] dx$$

$$= \int_{-2}^{2} \left[(x+1)(8-x^2) - (x+1)(x^2) \right] dx$$

$$= \int_{-2}^{2} (8 + 8x - 2x^2 - 2x^3) \, dx$$

$$= \left(8x + 4x^2 - \frac{2x^3}{3} - \frac{x^4}{2} \right) \Big|_{-2}^{2} = \frac{64}{3}$$

65. The area of the rectangular region is 15.

$$f_{av} = \frac{1}{15} \int_{-2}^{3} \int_{-1}^{2} xy(x - 2y) \, dydx$$

$$= \frac{1}{15} \int_{-2}^{3} \left(\frac{x^2 y^2}{2} - \frac{2xy^3}{3} \right) \Big|_{-1}^{2} dx$$

$$= \frac{1}{15} \int_{-2}^{3} \left(2x^2 - \frac{16x}{3} - \frac{x^2}{2} - \frac{2x}{3} \right) dx$$

$$= \frac{1}{15} \int_{-2}^{3} (1.5x^2 - 6x) dx$$

$$= \frac{1}{15} \left(\frac{x^3}{2} - 3x^2 \right) \Big|_{-2}^{3} = \frac{1}{6}$$

$$\approx 0.1667$$

67. The area of the rectangular region is 2.

$$f_{av} = \frac{1}{2} \int_{0}^{2} \int_{0}^{1} xye^{x^2 y} \, dxdy$$

Using substitution with $u = x^2 y$,

$$= \frac{1}{2} \int_{0}^{2} \left[\int_{0}^{y} e^{u} \cdot \frac{1}{2} \, du \right] dy$$

$$= \frac{1}{4} \int_{0}^{2} \left(e^{u} \Big|_{0}^{y} \right) dy$$

$$= \frac{1}{4} \int_{0}^{2} (e^{y} - 1) \, dy$$

$$= \frac{1}{4} (e^{y} - y) \Big|_{0}^{2} = \frac{1}{4} (e^2 - 3) \approx 1.0973$$

69. The area of the rectangular region is $\frac{3}{2}$. The line joining the points $(0, 0)$ and $(3, 1)$ is $y = \frac{x}{3}$.

$$f_{av} = \frac{1}{\frac{3}{2}} \int_{0}^{3} \int_{\frac{x}{3}}^{1} 6xy \, dydx$$

$$= \frac{2}{3} \int_{0}^{3} \left[3xy^2 \Big|_{\frac{x}{3}}^{1} \right] dx$$

$$= \frac{2}{3} \int_{0}^{3} \left(3x - \frac{x^3}{3} \right) dx$$

$$= \frac{2}{3} \left(\frac{3x^2}{2} - \frac{x^4}{12} \right) \Big|_{0}^{3} = \frac{9}{2}$$

Note: problem can be equivalently worked as $\int_{0}^{1} \int_{0}^{3y} 6xy \, dxdy$.

71. The area of the given region is

$$\int_{-2}^{2} 4 - x^2 \, dx = \left(4x - \frac{x^3}{3} \right) \Big|_{-2}^{2} = \frac{32}{3}$$

$$f_{av} = \frac{32}{3} \int_{-2}^{2} \int_{0}^{4-x^2} x \, dydx$$

$$= \frac{32}{3} \int_{-2}^{2} (xy) \Big|_{0}^{4-x^2} \, dx = \frac{1}{16} \int_{-2}^{2} (4x - x^3) \, dx$$

$$= \frac{32}{3} \left(2x^2 - \frac{x^4}{4} \right) \Big|_{-2}^{2} = 0$$

73. $$\int_{1}^{3} \int_{2}^{5} \frac{\ln xy}{y} \, dydx = \int_{1}^{3} \int_{2}^{5} \ln xy \cdot \frac{1}{y} \, dydx$$

Using substitution with $u = \ln xy$,

$$= \int_1^3 \left[\int_{\ln 2x}^{\ln 5x} u\, du \right] dx = \int_1^3 \left(\frac{u^2}{2} \right) \Big|_{\ln 2x}^{\ln 5x} dx$$

$$= \frac{1}{2} \int_1^3 (\ln^2 5x - \ln^2 2x)\, dx$$

$$= \frac{1}{2} \int_1^3 (\ln 5x + \ln 2x)(\ln 5x - \ln 2x)\, dx$$

$$= \frac{1}{2} \int_1^3 (\ln 10x^2) \left(\ln \frac{5}{2} \right) dx$$

$$= \frac{\ln 2.5}{2} \int_1^3 \ln 10x^2\, dx$$

Using integration by parts with

$$u = \ln 10x^2 \qquad \text{and} \qquad dV = dx$$

$$du = \frac{2}{x}\, dx \qquad\qquad V = x$$

$$= \frac{\ln 2.5}{2} \left[x \ln 10x^2 \Big|_1^3 - \int_1^3 x \cdot \frac{2}{x} dx \right]$$

$$= \frac{\ln 2.5}{2} \left[x \ln 10x^2 - 2x \right]_1^3$$

$$= \frac{\ln 2.5}{2} [(3 \ln 90 - 6) - (\ln 10 - 2)] \approx 3.297$$

75. $$\int_0^1 \int_0^1 x^3 e^{x^2 y}\, dy\, dx = \int_0^1 \int_0^1 x e^{x^2 y} x^2\, dy\, dx$$

Using substitution with $u = x^2 y$,

$$= \int_0^1 \int_0^{x^2} x e^u\, du\, dx = \int_0^1 \left[x \left(e^u \Big|_0^{x^2} \right) \right] dx$$

$$= \int_0^1 (x e^{x^2} - x e^0)\, dx = \int_0^1 x e^{x^2}\, dx - \int_0^1 x\, dx$$

Using substitution with $u = x^2$,

$$= \frac{1}{2} \int_0^1 e^u\, du - \int_0^1 x\, dx$$

$$= \frac{1}{2} \left(e^u \Big|_0^1 \right) - \frac{x^2}{2} \Big|_0^1$$

$$= \frac{1}{2}(e^1 - e^0) - \left(\frac{1}{2} - 0 \right)$$

$$= \frac{1}{2} e - 1 = \frac{e-2}{2}$$

77. $$Q_{av} = \frac{1}{35} \int_0^7 \int_0^5 (2x^3 + 3x^2 y + y^3)\, dx\, dy$$

$$= \frac{1}{35} \int_0^7 (0.5x^4 + x^3 y + xy^3) \Big|_0^5 dy$$

$$= \frac{1}{7} ((0.5)(125y) + (0.5)(25y^2) + 0.25y^4) \Big|_0^7$$

$$= \frac{943}{4} = 235.75$$

79. $$P(xy) = \int_{70}^{89} \int_{100}^{125} [(x - 30)(70 + 5x - 4y)$$

$$+ (y - 40)(80 - 6x + 7y)]\, dx\, dy$$

$$= \int_{70}^{89} \int_{100}^{125} [5x^2 + 7y^2 + 160x$$

$$- 10xy - 80y - 5{,}300]\, dx\, dy$$

$$= \int_{70}^{89} [1.6667x^3 + 7xy^2 + 80x^2$$

$$- 5x^2 y - 80xy - 5{,}300x] \Big|_{100}^{125} dy$$

$$= \int_{70}^{89} [1{,}909{,}218.75 + 175y^2 - 30{,}125y]\, dy$$

$$= [1{,}906{,}041.67y + 58.33y^3 - 15{,}062.5y^2] \Big|_{70}^{89}$$

$$= 1.1826(10^7)$$

The area is $(125 - 100)(89 - 70) = 475$.

The average profit is $\dfrac{1.1826(10^7)}{475} = 24{,}896.8$ or $2,489,800$.

81. $$E(x, y) = \frac{90}{5{,}280} (2x + y^2) \text{ miles}$$

$$E_{av} = \frac{0.01705}{12} \int_0^3 \int_0^4 (2x + y^2)\, dx\, dy$$

$$= 0.00142 \int_0^3 (16 + 4y^2)\, dy$$

$$= 0.00142(16y + 1.333y^3) \Big|_0^3 = 630 \text{ ft.}$$

83. $\text{Value} = \int_{-1}^{1} \int_{-1}^{1} (300 + x + y)e^{-0.01x} \, dx \, dy$

$= \int_{-1}^{1} \int_{-1}^{1} [(300 + y)e^{-0.01x} + xe^{--0.01x}] \, dx \, dy$

$= \int_{-1}^{1} \left[\dfrac{(300 + y)}{-0.01}e^{-0.01x} \atop -100xe^{-0.01x} - 10,000e^{-0.01x} \right] \Bigg|_{x=-1}^{x=1} dy$

$= \int_{-1}^{1} \left[\begin{array}{l} 39,900e^{0.01} - 40,100e^{-0.01} \\ +(100e^{0.01} - 100e^{-0.01})y \end{array} \right] dy$

$= 79,800e^{0.01} - 80,200e^{-0.01} = 1,200.007$

or roughly 1.2 million dollars.

85. (a) $f(x, y) = 2,500e^{-0.01x - 0.02y}$

First, the triangular regions should be divided into two sections, using the y-axis as the dividing line. Then, the left region is bounded above by $y = x + 3$ and below by $y = -2$. The values of x are from $x = -5$ to $x = 0$. Similarly, the right region is bounded above by $y = -x + 3$ and below by $y = -2$. The values of x are from $x = 0$ to $x = 5$. So, the total population is

$2,500 \int_{-5}^{0} \int_{-2}^{x+3} e^{-0.01x - 0.02y} \, dy \, dx$

$\quad + 2,500 \int_{0}^{5} \int_{-2}^{-x+3} e^{-0.01x - 0.02y} \, dy \, dx$

$= 2,500 \int_{-5}^{0} \left[\dfrac{1}{-0.02} e^{-0.01x - 0.02y} \Big|_{-2}^{x+3} \right] dx$

$\quad + 2,500 \int_{0}^{5} \left[\dfrac{1}{-0.02} e^{-0.01x - 0.02y} \Big|_{-2}^{-x+3} \right] dx$

$= -125,000 \int_{-5}^{0} \left[e^{-0.01x - 0.02(x+3)} \right.$

$\qquad\qquad \left. - e^{-0.01x - 0.02(-2)} \right] dx$

$\quad - 125,000 \int_{0}^{5} \left[e^{-0.01x - 0.02(-x+3)} \right.$

$\qquad\qquad \left. - e^{-0.01x - 0.02(-2)} \right] dx$

$= -125,000 \left[\int_{-5}^{0} e^{-0.03x - 0.06} \, dx \right.$

$\qquad\qquad - \int_{-5}^{0} e^{-0.01x + 0.04} \, dx$

$\qquad\qquad + \int_{0}^{5} e^{0.01x - 0.06}$

$\qquad\qquad \left. - \int_{0}^{5} e^{-0.01x + 0.04} \, dx \right]$

$= -125,000 \left[\dfrac{1}{-0.03} \left(e^{-0.03x - 0.06} \Big|_{-5}^{0} \right) \right.$

$\qquad\qquad + \dfrac{1}{0.01} \left(e^{-0.01x + 0.04} \Big|_{-5}^{0} \right)$

$\qquad\qquad + \dfrac{1}{0.01} \left(e^{0.01x - 0.06} \Big|_{0}^{5} \right)$

$\qquad\qquad \left. + \dfrac{1}{0.01} \left(e^{-0.01x + 0.04} \Big|_{0}^{5} \right) \right]$

$= -125,000 \left[-\dfrac{1}{0.03} \left(e^{-0.06} - e^{0.09} \right) \right.$

$\qquad\qquad + \dfrac{1}{0.01} \left(e^{0.04} - e^{0.09} \right)$

$\qquad\qquad + \dfrac{1}{0.01} \left(e^{-0.01} - e^{-0.06} \right)$

$\qquad\qquad \left. + \dfrac{1}{0.01} \left(e^{-0.01} - e^{0.04} \right) \right]$

$\approx -125,000[5.080325 - 5.336351$

$\qquad\qquad + 4.828530 - 5.076094]$

$\approx 62,949 \text{ people}$

(b) The area of the original triangle is $\frac{1}{2}bh = \frac{1}{2}(10)(5) = 25$. So, the average population density is $\frac{1}{25}(62,949)$, or approx. 2,518 people per square unit.

(c) Writing Exercise—Answers will vary.

87. (a) $S_{av} = \dfrac{0.0072}{(142)(76.8)} \int_{3.2}^{80} \int_{38}^{180} W^{0.425} H^{0.725} \, dH \, dW$

$$= \frac{0.0072}{(142)(76.8)} \int_{3.2}^{80} W^{0.425} \left(\int_{38}^{180} H^{0.725} \, dH \right) dW$$

$$= \frac{0.0072}{(142)(76.8)} \int_{3.2}^{80} W^{0.425} \left(\frac{H^{1.725}}{1.725} \Big|_{38}^{180} \right) dW$$

$$\approx \frac{0.0072}{(142)(76.8)} \int_{3.2}^{80} W^{0.425}(4195.71) \, dW$$

$$\approx 0.00277 \int_{3.2}^{80} W^{0.425} \, dW$$

$$0.00277 \left(\frac{W^{1.425}}{1.425} \Big|_{3.2}^{80} \right)$$

$$\approx 0.00277(357.802) \approx 0.991 \text{ sq meters}$$

(b) No. It could only be interpreted as the person's average surface area from birth until his/her adult weight and height was first reached.

89. Solving $4 - x^2 = 0$ yields $x = -2$ and $x = 2$. So,

$$V = \int_{-2}^{2} \int_{0}^{4-x^2} (20 - x^2 - y^2) dy \, dx$$

$$= \int_{-2}^{2} \left[\left(20y - x^2 y - \frac{y^3}{3} \right)_{0}^{4-x^2} \right] dx$$

$$= \int_{-2}^{2} \left[20(4 - x^2) - x^2(4 - x^2) - \frac{(4 - x^2)^3}{3} \right] dx$$

$$= \int_{-2}^{2} \left[80 - 20x^2 - 4x^2 + x^4 - \frac{64 - 48x^2 + 12x^4 - x^6}{3} \right] dx$$

$$= \int_{-2}^{2} \left[\frac{176}{3} - 8x^2 - 3x^4 + \frac{x^6}{3} \right] dx$$

$$= \left[\frac{176}{3}x - \frac{8}{3}x^3 - \frac{3}{5}x^5 + \frac{1}{21}x^7 \right]_{-2}^{2}$$

$$= \left[\left(\frac{352}{3} - \frac{64}{3} - \frac{96}{5} + \frac{128}{21} \right) - \left(-\frac{352}{3} + \frac{64}{3} + \frac{96}{5} - \frac{128}{21} \right) \right]$$

$$= \frac{17408}{105} \approx 165.79 \ m^3$$

91. $$E = \int_{-2}^{2} \int_{-2}^{2} \left(1 - \frac{1}{9} \left(x^2 + y^2 \right) \right) dy dx$$

$$= \int_{-2}^{2} \left[y - \frac{1}{9} \left(x^2 y + \frac{y^3}{3} \right) \right] \Big|_{y=-2}^{y=2} dx$$

$$= \left(4x - \frac{4x^3}{27} - \frac{16x}{27} \right) \Big|_{x=-2}^{x=2}$$

$$= 2 \left(8 - \frac{64}{27} \right) = \frac{304}{27}$$

93. $$\int_{0}^{2} \int_{0}^{3} x^2 e^{-xy} \, dy \, dx$$

$$= \int_{0}^{2} x^2 \left[-\frac{1}{x} e^{-xy} \Big|_{0}^{3} \right] dx = \int_{0}^{2} -x \left[e^{-3x} - 1 \right] dx$$

$$= \int_{0}^{2} x \, dx - \int_{0}^{2} x e^{-3x} \, dx$$

Using integration by parts for the second integral, with $u = x$ and $dV = e^{-3x} \, dx$ gives

$$\frac{x^2}{2} \Big|_{0}^{2} - \left[-\frac{1}{3} x e^{-3x} \Big|_{0}^{2} + \frac{1}{3} \int_{0}^{2} e^{-3x} \, dx \right]$$

$$= 2 - \left[-\frac{1}{3} x e^{-3x} - \frac{1}{9} e^{-3x} \Big|_{0}^{2} \right]$$

$$= 2 - \left[\left(-\frac{2}{3} e^{-6} - \frac{1}{9} e^{-6} \right) - \left(0 - \frac{1}{9} \right) \right]$$

$$= 2 - \left(-\frac{7}{9} e^{-6} + \frac{1}{9} \right) = \frac{7}{9} e^{-6} + \frac{17}{9}$$

Checkup for Chapter 7

1. (a) $f(x, y) = x^3 + 2xy^2 - 3y^4$
The domain is the set of all real pairs (x, y).

$$f_x = 3x^2 + 2y^2; \ f_y = 4xy - 12y^3;$$
$$f_{xx} = 6x; \ f_{yx} = 4y$$

(b) $f(x, y) = \dfrac{2x + y}{x - y}$
The domain is the set of all real pairs (x, y) such that $x - y \neq 0$, or $y \neq x$.

$$f_x = \frac{(x-y)(2)-(2x+y)(1)}{(x-y)^2} = -\frac{3y}{(x-y)^2}$$

$$f_y = \frac{(x-y)(1)-(2x+y)(-1)}{(x-y)^2} = \frac{3x}{(x-y)^2}$$

$$f_{xx} = (-3y)-2(x-y)^{-3}(1) = \frac{6y}{(x-y)^3}$$

$$f_{yx} = \frac{(x-y)^2(3)-(3x)2(x-y)(1)}{(x-y)^4}$$

$$= -\frac{3(x+y)}{(x-y)^3}$$

(c) $f(x,y) = e^{2x-y} + \ln(y^2-2x)$
The domain of e^{2x-y} is the set of all real pairs (x,y), but the domain of $\ln(y^2-2x)$ is the set of all real pairs such that $y^2-2x > 0$, or $y^2 > 2x$.

$$f_x = 2e^{2x-y} - \frac{2}{y^2-2x}$$

$$f_y = -e^{2x-y} + \frac{2y}{y^2-2x}$$

$$f_{xx} = 4e^{2x-y} + 2(y^2-2x)^{-2}(-2)$$

$$= 4e^{2x-y} - \frac{4}{(y^2-2x)^2}$$

$$f_{yx} = -2e^{2x-y} - 2y(y^2-2x)^{-2}(-2)$$

$$= -2e^{2x-y} + \frac{4y}{(y^2-2x)^2}$$

2. **(a)** $f(x,y) = x^2+y^2$
Level curves are of the form $x^2+y^2 = C$, which are circles having the origin as their center and radius $\sqrt{C}$, and also the single point $(0,0)$, when $C = 0$.

(b) $f(x,y) = x+y^2$
Level curves are of the form $x+y^2 = C$, which are parabolas having a horizontal axis, opening to the left, and a vertex on the x-axis.

3. **(a)** $f(x,y) = 4x^3+y^3-6x^2-6y^2+5$

$$f_x = 12x^2-12x = 12x(x-1)$$

$$f_x = 0 \text{ when } x = 0, 1$$

$$f_y = 3y^2-12y = 3y(y-4)$$

$$f_y = 0 \text{ when } y = 0, 4$$

So, the critical points are $(0,0)$, $(0,4)$, $(1,0)$, and $(1,4)$.

$$f_{xx} = 24x-12; \quad f_{yy} = 6y-12; \quad f_{xy} = 0$$

For the point $(0,0)$,

$$D = [24(0)-12][6(0)-12]-0 > 0$$

$$\text{and } f_{xx} < 0$$

So, $(0,0)$ is a relative maximum.
For the point $(0,4)$,

$$D = [24(0)-12][6(4)-12]-0 < 0$$

So, $(0,4)$ is a saddle point.
For the point $(1,0)$,

$$D = [24(1)-12][6(0)-12]-0 < 0$$

So, $(1,0)$ is a saddle point.
For the point $(1,4)$,

$$D = [24(1)-12][6(4)-12]-0 > 0$$

$$\text{and } f_{xx} > 0$$

So, $(1,4)$ is a relative minimum.

(b) $f(x,y) = x^2-4xy+3y^2+2x-4y$

$$f_x = 2x-4y+2$$

$$f_x = 0 \text{ when } 2x-4y = -2$$

$$f_y = -4x+6y-4$$

$$f_y = 0 \text{ when } -4x+6y = 4$$

Solving this system of equations, by multiplying the first by two and adding to the second, gives $y = 0$, and $x = -1$. So, the only critical point is $(-1,0)$.

$$f_{xx} = 2; \quad f_{yy} = 6; \quad f_{xy} = -4$$

$$D = (2)(6)-(-4)^2 < 0$$

So, $(-1,0)$ is a saddle point.

(c) $f(x, y) = xy - \dfrac{1}{y} - \dfrac{1}{x}$

$f_x = y + \dfrac{1}{x^2}$

$f_x = 0$ when $y = -\dfrac{1}{x^2}$, or $y^2 = \dfrac{1}{x^4}$

$f_y = y + \dfrac{1}{x^2}$

$f_y = 0$ when $0 = x + \dfrac{1}{y^2}$

$0 = x + x^4$

$0 = x(x^3 + 1)$

or, $x = -1$ (rejecting $x = 0$ since f undefined for $x = 0$) and $y = -1$. So, the only critical point is $(-1, -1)$.

$f_{xx} = -\dfrac{2}{x^3}; \ f_{yy} = -\dfrac{2}{y^3}; \ f_{xy} = 1$

$D = \left[-\dfrac{2}{(-1)^3} \right] \left[-\dfrac{2}{(-1)^3} \right] - (1)^2 > 0$

and $f_{xx} > 0$

So, $(-1, -1)$ is a relative minimum.

4. (a) $f(x, y) = x^2 + y^2$
$g(x, y) = x + 2y$

$f_x = 2x; \ f_y = 2y; \ g_x = 1; \ g_y = 2$

The three Lagrange equations are

$2x = \lambda; \ 2y = 2\lambda; \ x + 2y = 4$

Equating λ from the first two equations gives

$2x = y$

Substituting in the third equation gives $x = \dfrac{4}{5}$.

Then, $y = \dfrac{8}{5}$ and the minimum value of the function is $f\left(\dfrac{4}{5}, \dfrac{8}{5} \right) = \dfrac{16}{5}$.

(b) $f(x, y) = xy^2$
$g(x, y) = 2x^2 + y^2$

$f_x = y^2; \ f_y = 2xy; \ g_x = 4x; \ g_y = 2y$

The three Lagrange equations are

$y^2 = 4\lambda x; \ 2xy = 2\lambda y$

$2x^2 + y^2 = 6$

Solving the first two equations for λ and equating gives $y^2 = 4x^2$.
Substituting into the third equation gives $x = -1, 1$. When $x = -1$, $y = -2$ or 2. When $x = 1$, $y = -2$ or 2. So, the critical points are $(-1, -2)$, $(-1, 2)$, $(1, -2)$, and $(1, 2)$.

$f(-1, -2) = f(-1, 2) = -4$ and
$f(1, -2) = f(1, 2) = 4$

So, the maximum value of f is 4, and the minimum value of f is -4.

5. (a) $\displaystyle\int_{-1}^{3} \int_{0}^{2} x^3 y \, dx \, dy$

$= \displaystyle\int_{-1}^{3} \left(\dfrac{x^4 y}{4} \bigg|_0^2 \right) dy = \int_{-1}^{3} 4y \, dy = (2y^2)\bigg|_{-1}^{3}$

$= 16$

(b) $\displaystyle\int_{0}^{2} \int_{-1}^{1} x^2 e^{xy} \, dx \, dy$

$= \displaystyle\int_{-1}^{1} \int_{0}^{2} x^2 e^{xy} \, dy \, dx$

$= \displaystyle\int_{-1}^{1} \int_{0}^{2} x e^{xy} x \, dy \, dx$

Using substitution with $u = xy$,

$= \displaystyle\int_{-1}^{1} x \int_{0}^{2x} e^u \, du \, dx$

$= \displaystyle\int_{-1}^{1} x \left(e^u \bigg|_0^{2x} \right) dx$

$= \displaystyle\int_{-1}^{1} x(e^{2x} - e^0) \, dx$

$= \displaystyle\int_{-1}^{1} (xe^{2x} - x) \, dx$

$= \displaystyle\int_{-1}^{1} xe^{2x} \, dx - \int_{-1}^{1} x \, dx$

Using integration by parts with

$$u = x \quad \text{and} \quad dV = e^{2x}\, dx$$

$$du = dx \qquad V = \frac{1}{2}e^{2x}$$

$$= \frac{x}{2}e^{2x}\Big|_{-1}^{1} - \int_{-1}^{1} \frac{1}{2}e^{2x}\, dx - \int_{-1}^{1} x\, dx$$

$$= \left(\frac{x}{2}e^{2x} - \frac{1}{4}e^{2x} - \frac{x^2}{2}\right)\Big|_{-1}^{1}$$

$$= \left(\frac{1}{2}e^2 - \frac{1}{4}e^2 - \frac{1}{2}\right)$$

$$\quad - \left(-\frac{1}{2}e^{-2} - \frac{1}{4}e^{-2} - \frac{1}{2}\right)$$

$$= \frac{1}{4}e^2 + \frac{3}{4}e^{-2} = \frac{1}{4}(e^2 + 3e^{-2})$$

$$= \frac{1}{4}\left(e^2 + \frac{3}{e^2}\right) = \frac{1}{4}\left(\frac{e^4 + 3}{e^2}\right)$$

$$= \frac{e^4 + 3}{4e^2}$$

(c)
$$\int_{1}^{2}\int_{1}^{y} \frac{y}{x}\, dx\, dy = \int_{1}^{2} y\left(\int_{1}^{y} \frac{1}{x}\, dx\right) dy$$

$$= \int_{1}^{2} y\left(\ln|x|\,\Big|_{1}^{y}\right) dy = \int_{1}^{2} y \ln y\, dy$$

Using integration by parts with

$$u = \ln y \quad \text{and} \quad dV = y\, dy$$

$$= \frac{y^2}{2}\ln y\Big|_{1}^{2} - \int_{1}^{2} \frac{y}{2}\, dy$$

$$= \left(\frac{y^2}{2}\ln y - \frac{y^2}{4}\right)\Big|_{1}^{2} = (2\ln 2 - 1) - \left(0 - \frac{1}{4}\right)$$

$$= 2\ln 2 - \frac{3}{4}$$

(d)
$$\int_{0}^{2}\int_{0}^{2-x} xe^{-y}\, dy\, dx = \int_{0}^{2}(x - e^{-y})\Big|_{0}^{2-x}\, dx$$

$$= \int_{0}^{2} -xe^{x-2} + x\, dx$$

Using integration by parts with

$$u = -x \text{ and } dV = e^{x-2}\, dx$$

$$= -xe^{x-2}\Big|_{0}^{2} - \int_{0}^{2} -e^{x-2}\, dx + \int_{0}^{2} x\, dx$$

$$= -xe^{x-2}\Big|_{0}^{2} + \int_{0}^{2} e^{x-2}\, dx + \int_{0}^{2} x\, dx$$

$$= \left(-xe^{x-2} + e^{x-2} + \frac{x^2}{2}\right)\Big|_{0}^{2}$$

$$= (-2e^0 + e^0 + 2) - (0 + e^{-2} + 0)$$

$$= 1 - \frac{1}{e^2} = \frac{e^2 - 1}{e^2}$$

6. $Q(K, L) = 120K^{3/4}L^{1/4}$

$$Q_K = \frac{90L^{1/4}}{K^{1/4}};\ Q_L = \frac{30K^{3/4}}{L^{3/4}}$$

When $K = 1{,}296$ thousand dollars and $L = 20{,}736$ worker-hours,

$$Q_K = 180 \quad \text{and} \quad Q_L = 3.75$$

7. $U(x, y) = \ln(x^2\sqrt{y});\ g(x, y) = 20x + 50y$

$$U_x = \frac{1}{x^2\sqrt{y}} \cdot 2x\sqrt{y} = \frac{2}{x}$$

$$U_y = \frac{1}{x^2\sqrt{y}} \cdot \frac{1}{2}x^2 y^{-1/2} = \frac{1}{2y}$$

$$g_x = 20;\ g_y = 50$$

The three Lagrange equations are

$$\frac{2}{x} = 20\lambda;\ \frac{1}{2y} = 50\lambda;$$

$$20x + 50y = 500$$

Solving the first two equations for λ and equating gives $x = 10y$. Substituting in the third equation gives $y = 2$, from which follows that $x = 20$. So, Everett should buy 20 DVDs and 2 video games.

8. $E = 0.05(xy - 2x^2 - y^2 + 95x + 20y)$

$$E_x = 0.05(y - 4x + 95)$$

$$E_x = 0 \text{ when } 4x - y = 95$$

$$E_y = 0.05(x - 2y + 20)$$

$$E_y = 0 \text{ when } -x + 2y = 20$$

Solving the system of equations by multiplying the first by two and adding to the second gives $x = 30$ units of A, so $y = 25$ units of B.
Since the combined dosage is less than 60 units, there will not be a risk of side effects. Further, this is an equivalent dosage of $E(30, 25) = 83.75$ units, it will be effective.

9. The area of the rectangular region is 2.

$$T_{AV} = \frac{1}{2} \int_0^1 \int_0^2 10ye^{-xy}\, dx\, dy$$

Using substitution with $u = -xy$ and $-du = y\, dy$,

$$= \frac{1}{2} \int_0^1 \left[-10e^u \Big|_0^{-2y} \right] dx$$

$$= -5 \int_0^1 (e^{-2y} - 1)\, dy$$

$$= -5 \left(-\frac{1}{2}e^{-2y} - y \right) \Big|_0^1$$

$$= -5 \left[\left(-\frac{1}{2}e^{-2} - 1 \right) - \left(\frac{1}{2}e^0 - 0 \right) \right]$$

$$= -5 \left(-\frac{1}{2}e^{-2} - 1 + \frac{1}{2} \right) = -5 \left(-\frac{1}{2}e^{-2} - \frac{1}{2} \right)$$

$$= \frac{5}{2}(e^{-2} + 1)\ °C$$

10. Let x denote the year of operation and y the corresponding profit, in millions of dollars.

(a)

(b)

x	y	xy	x^2
1	1.03	1.03	1
2	1.52	3.04	4
3	2.03	6.09	9
4	2.41	9.64	16
5	2.84	14.20	25

$\sum x = 15 \quad \sum y = 9.83 \quad \sum xy = 34.00 \quad \sum x^2 = 55$

Using the formulas with $n = 5$,

$$m = \frac{5(34) - (15)(9.83)}{5(55) - (15)^2} = \frac{22.55}{50} \approx 0.451$$

$$b = \frac{(55)(9.83) - (15)(34)}{5(55) - (15)^2} = \frac{30.65}{50} \approx 0.613$$

So, the equation of the least squares line is $y = 0.451x + 0.613$.

(c) When $x = 6$, $y = 0.451(6) + 0.613 = 3.319$ so the prediction is \$3,319,000.

Review Problems

1. $f(x, y) = 2x^3y + 3xy^2 + \frac{y}{x}$

$$f_x = 6x^2y + 3y^2 - \frac{y}{x^2}$$

$$f_y = 2x^3 + 6xy + \frac{1}{x}$$

3. $f(x, y) = \sqrt{x}(x - y^2) = x^{3/2} - x^{1/2}y^2$

$$f_x = \frac{3}{2}x^{1/2} - \frac{1}{2}x^{-1/2}y^2$$

$$= \frac{3}{2}\sqrt{x} - \frac{y^2}{2\sqrt{x}} = \frac{3x - y^2}{2\sqrt{x}}$$

$$f_y = -2x^{1/2}y = -2y\sqrt{x}$$

5. $f(x, y) = \sqrt{\frac{x}{y}} + \sqrt{\frac{y}{x}} = x^{1/2}y^{-1/2} + x^{-1/2}y^{1/2}$

$$f_x = \frac{1}{2}x^{-1/2}y^{-1/2} - \frac{1}{2}x^{-3/2}y^{1/2}$$

$$= \frac{1}{2\sqrt{xy}} - \frac{\sqrt{y}}{2x^{3/2}}$$

$$f_y = -\frac{1}{2}x^{1/2}y^{-3/2} + \frac{1}{2}x^{-1/2}y^{-1/2}$$

$$= -\frac{\sqrt{x}}{2y^{3/2}} + \frac{1}{2\sqrt{xy}}$$

7. $f(x, y) = \frac{x^3 - xy}{x+y}$

$$f_x = \frac{(x+y)(3x^2 - y) - (x^3 - xy)(1)}{(x+y)^2}$$

$$= \frac{2x^3 + 3x^2 y - y^2}{(x+y)^2}$$

$$f_y = \frac{(x+y)(-x) - (x^3 - xy)(1)}{(x+y)^2}$$

$$= \frac{-x^3 - x^2}{(x+y)^2} = \frac{-x^2(x+1)}{(x+y)^2}$$

9. $f(x, y) = \frac{x^2 - y^2}{2x+y}$

$$f_x = \frac{(2x+y)(2x) - (x^2 - y^2)(2)}{(2x+y)^2}$$

$$= \frac{2x^2 + 2xy + 2y^2}{(2x+y)^2} = \frac{2(x^2 + xy + y^2)}{(2x+y)^2}$$

$$f_y = \frac{(2x+y)(-2y) - (x^2 - y^2)(1)}{(2x+y)^2}$$

$$= \frac{-x^2 - 4xy - y^2}{(2x+y)^2}$$

11. $f(x, y) = e^{x^2 + y^2}$

$$f_x = 2xe^{x^2 + y^2}$$

$$f_{xx} = (2x)(2xe^{x^2 + y^2}) + (e^{x^2 + y^2})(2)$$

$$= 2e^{x^2 + y^2}(2x^2 + 1)$$

$$f_y = 2ye^{x^2 + y^2}$$

$$f_{yy} = (2y)(2ye^{x^2 + y^2}) + (e^{x^2 + y^2})(2)$$

$$= 2e^{x^2 + y^2}(2y^2 + 1)$$

$$f_{xy} = f_{yx} = 4xye^{x^2 + y^2}$$

13. $f(x, y) = x \ln y$

$$f_x = \ln y \quad f_y = \frac{x}{y}$$

$$f_{xx} = 0 \quad f_{yy} = -\frac{x}{y^2}$$

$$f_{xx} = 0$$

$$f_{xy} = f_{yx} = \frac{1}{y}$$

15. (a) When $f = 2$, the level curve $x^2 - y = 2$ is a parabola, with vertical axis, opening up, and having the vertex $(0, -2)$.
When $f = -2$, the level curve $x^2 - y = -2$ is a parabola, with vertical axis, opening up, and having the vertex $(0, 2)$.

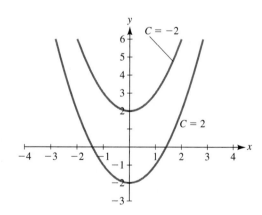

(b) When $f = 0$, the level curve is $6x + 2y = 0$, or $y = -3x$, which is a line through the origin with slope -3. When $f = 1$, the level curve is $6x + 2y = 1$, or $y = -3x + \frac{1}{2}$, which is the same line translated up $\frac{1}{2}$ a unit. When $f = 2$, the level curve is $6x + 2y = 2$, or $y = -3x + 1$, which is the same line translated up one unit.

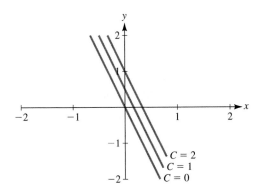

C = 2
C = 1
C = 0

17. $f(x, y) = (x + y)(2x + y - 6)$

$$f_x = (x + y)(2) + (2x + y - 6)(1)$$
$$= 4x + 3y - 6$$
$$f_y = (x + y)(1) + (2x + y - 6)(1)$$
$$= 3x + 2y - 6$$

To find the critical points, set $f_x = 0$ and $f_y = 0$ and solve the system of equations.

$$4x + 3y - 6 = 0$$
$$3x + 2y - 6 = 0$$

Multiply the first equation by 2 and the second equation by -3. Then, add the two resulting equations

$$8x + 6y - 12 = 0$$
$$\underline{-9x - 6y + 18 = 0}$$
$$-x + 6 = 0$$
$$x = 6$$

When $x = 6$,

$$4(6) + 3y - 6 = 0$$
$$y = -6$$

So, the only critical point is $(6, -6)$.

$$f_{xx} = 4 \ f_{yy} = 2 \ f_{xy} = 3$$
$$D = (4)(2) - (3)^2 < 0$$

So, the point $(6, -6)$ is a saddle point.

19. $f(x, y) = x^3 + y^3 + 3x^2 - 3y^2$

$f_x = 3x^2 + 6x \ f_y = 3y^2 - 6y$

$f_x = 0$ when $3x(x + 2) = 0$, $x = 0$ and $x = -2$

$f_y = 0$ when $3y(y - 2) = 0$, $y = 0$ and $y = 2$

So, the critical points are $(0, 0)$, $(0, 2)$, $(-2, 0)$ and $(-2, 2)$.

$$f_{xx} = 6x + 6 \ f_{yy} = 6y - 6 \ f_{xy} = 0$$

For the point $(0, 0)$,

$$D = (6)(-6) - 0 < 0$$

So it is a saddle point.
For the point $(0, 2)$,

$$D = (6)(6) - 0 > 0$$

Since $f_{xx} > 0$, it is a relative minimum.
For the point $(-2, 0)$,

$$D = (-6)(-6) - 0 > 0$$

Since $f_{xx} < 0$, it is a relative maximum.
For the point $(-2, 2)$,

$$D = (-6)(6) - 0 > 0$$

So it is a saddle point.

21. $$f(x, y) = x^2 + y^3 + 6xy - 7x - 6y$$
$$f_x = 2x + 6y - 7$$
$$f_y = 3y^2 + 6x - 6$$

To find the critical points, set $f_x = 0$ and $f_y = 0$.
So, $2x + 6y - 7 = 0$ and $3y^2 + 6x - 6 = 0$,
or $2x + 6y - 7 = 0$ and $2x + y^2 - 2 = 0$.
Subtracting the two equations gives $y^2 - 6y + 5 = 0$,
$(y - 1)(y - 5) = 0$, or $y = 1$ and $y = 5$.
When $y = 1$, the first equation gives $x = \dfrac{1}{2}$ and when
$y = 5$, the first equation gives $x = -\dfrac{23}{2}$.

So, the critical points of f are $\left(\dfrac{1}{2}, 1\right)$, $\left(-\dfrac{23}{2}, 5\right)$.

Since $f_{xx} = 2$, $f_{yy} = 6y$, and $f_{xy} = 6$,

$$D = f_{xx}f_{yy} - (f_{xy})^2 = (2)(6y) - 36 = 12(y - 3)$$

For the point $\left(\dfrac{1}{2}, 1\right)$,

$$D = 12(-2) = -24 < 0$$

and f has a saddle point at $\left(\dfrac{1}{2}, 1\right)$.

For the point $\left(-\dfrac{23}{2}, 5\right)$,

$$D = 12(2) = 24 > 0$$

$$\text{and } f_{xx} > 0$$

So, f has a relative minimum at $\left(-\dfrac{23}{2}, 5\right)$.

23. $f(x, y) = xe^{2x^2+5xy+2y^2}$

$$f_x = (x)\left[e^{2x^2+5xy+2y^2}(4x+5y)\right]$$

$$+ (e^{2x^2+5xy+2y^2})(1)$$

$$= e^{2x^2+5xy+2y^2}\left[x(4x+5y)+1\right]$$

$$= e^{2x^2+5xy+2y^2}(4x^2+5xy+1)$$

$$f_x = 0 \text{ when } 4x^2+5xy+1 = 0$$

$$f_y = x\left[e^{2x^2+5xy+2y^2}(5x+4y)\right]$$

$$f_y = 0 \text{ when } x(5x+4y)e^{2x^2+5xy+2y^2} = 0$$

So, $f_y = 0$ when $x = 0$ and when $5x + 4y = 0$, or

$$x = -\frac{4}{5}y$$

When $x = 0$, substituting into $f_x = 0$ yields no solution.

When $x = -\dfrac{4}{5}y$, $f_x = 0$ when

$$0 = 4\left(-\frac{4}{5}y\right)^2 + 5\left(-\frac{4}{5}y\right)(y) + 1$$

$$\text{or, } y = \pm\frac{5}{6}$$

When $y = \dfrac{5}{6}$, $x = -\dfrac{4}{5}\left(\dfrac{5}{6}\right) = -\dfrac{2}{3}$

When $y = -\dfrac{5}{6}$, $x = -\dfrac{4}{5}\left(-\dfrac{5}{6}\right) = \dfrac{2}{3}$

So, the critical points are $\left(-\dfrac{2}{3}, \dfrac{5}{6}\right)$ and $\left(\dfrac{2}{3}, -\dfrac{5}{6}\right)$.

$$f_{xx} = (e^{2x^2+5xy+2y^2})(8x+5y)$$

$$+ (4x^2+5xy+1)[e^{2x^2+5xy+2y^2}(4x+5y)]$$

$$f_{yy} = x[(e^{2x^2+5xy+2y^2})(4)$$

$$+ (5x+4y)e^{2x^2+5xy+2y^2}(5x+4y)]$$

$$f_{xy} = (e^{2x^2+5xy+2y^2})(5x)$$

$$+ (4x^2+5xy+1)e^{2x^2+5xy+2y^2}(5x+4y)$$

For the point $\left(-\dfrac{2}{3}, \dfrac{5}{6}\right)$,

$$D \approx (-0.7076)(-2.0218) - (-1.6174)^2 < 0$$

So, $\left(-\dfrac{2}{3}, \dfrac{5}{6}\right)$ is a saddle point.

For the point $\left(\dfrac{2}{3}, -\dfrac{5}{6}\right)$,

$$D \approx (0.7076)(2.0218) - (1.6174)^2 < 0$$

So, $\left(\dfrac{2}{3}, -\dfrac{5}{6}\right)$ is also a saddle point.

25. $f(x, y) = x^2 + 2y^2 + 2x + 3; x^2 + y^2 = 4$
Since the constraint is $x^2 + y^2 = 4$,
$g(x, y) = x^2 + y^2$.

$$f_x = 2x + 2 \quad f_y = 4y$$

$$g_x = 2x \quad\quad g_y = 2y$$

The three Lagrange equations are

$$2x + 2 = 2x\lambda$$

$$4y = 2y\lambda$$

$$x^2 + y^2 = 4$$

From the second equation, $\lambda = 2$, or $y = 0$.
Substituting $\lambda = 2$ in the first equation gives
$2x + 2 = 4x$, or $x = 1$. Using the third equation,
$y = -\sqrt{3}$ or $y = \sqrt{3}$.
Substituting $y = 0$ into the third equation gives
$x = -2$ or $x = 2$. So, the critical points are $(2, 0)$,
$(-2, 0)$, $(1, -\sqrt{3})$ and $(1, \sqrt{3})$.
Testing all points in the original function yields:

$$f(2, 0) = 11 \quad\quad f(-2, 0) = 3$$

$$f(1, -\sqrt{3}) = 12 \quad f(1, \sqrt{3}) = 12$$

So, the maximum value is 12, and it occurs at the points $(1, -\sqrt{3})$ and $(1, \sqrt{3})$. The minimum value is 3 and it occurs at $(-2, 0)$.

27. $f(x, y) = x + 2y, \ 4x^2 + y^2 = 68$
Since the constraint is $4x^2 + y^2 = 68$, $g(x, y) = 4x^2 + y^2$.

$$f_x = 1 \ f_y = 2 \ g_x = 8x \ g_y = 2y$$

The three Lagrange equations are

$$1 = 8x\lambda \ \ 2 = 2y\lambda, \ \ 4x^2 + y^2 = 68$$

Solving the first two equations for λ and equating gives $y = 8x$. Substituting in the third equation gives $68x^2 = 68$, or $x = -1$ and $x = 1$. It follows that $y = -8$ and $y = 8$. So, the critical points are $(-1, -8)$ and $(1, 8)$. Testing these points in the original function gives

$$f(-1, -8) = -17$$
$$f(1, 8) = 17$$

So, the maximum value is 17 and it occurs at $(1, 0)$. The minimum value is -17 and it occurs at $(-1, -8)$.

29. $Q = 40K^{1/3}L^{1/2}$
The marginal product of capital is

$$\frac{\partial Q}{\partial K} = \frac{40}{3}K^{-2/3}L^{1/2} = \frac{40L^{1/2}}{3K^{2/3}}$$

which is approximately the change ΔQ in output due to one (thousand dollar) unit increase in capital. When $K = 125$ (thousand) and $L = 900$,

$$\Delta Q \approx \frac{\partial Q}{\partial K} = \frac{40(900)^{1/2}}{3(125)^{2/3}} = 16 \text{ units}$$

31.
$$Q(x, y) = 60x^{1/3}y^{2/3}$$

For any value of x, the slope of the level curve $Q = k$ is an approximation of the change in unskilled labor y that should be made to offset a one-unit increase in skilled labor x so that the level of output will remain constant. So,

$\Delta Q =$ change in unskilled labor

$$\approx \frac{dQ}{dx} = -\frac{Q_x}{Q_y}$$

$$= -\frac{20x^{-2/3}y^{2/3}}{40x^{1/3}y^{-1/3}} = -\frac{y}{2x}$$

When $x = 10$ and $y = 40$,

$$\Delta Q \approx \frac{dQ}{dx} = -\frac{40}{2(10)} = -2$$

That is, the level of unskilled labor should be decreased by approximately 2 workers.

33. The goal is to maximize the area of a rectangle

$$A(l, w) = lw$$

subject to the comstraint $2l + 2w = k$, where k is some positive constant. So, $g(l, w) = 2l + 2w$.

$$A_l = w; \ A_w = l; \ g_l = 2; \ g_w = 2$$

The three Lagrange equations are

$$w = 2\lambda; \ l = 2\lambda; \ 2l + 2w = k$$

Solving the first two for λ and equating gives $\dfrac{w}{2} = \dfrac{l}{2}$, or $w = l$. So, the rectangle having the greatest area is a square.

35. From problem 18, the profit function is

$$P(x, y) = \frac{50y}{y + 2} + \frac{20x}{x + 5} - x - y$$

The constraint is $x + y = 11$ thousand dollars, so $g(x, y) = x + y$.

$$P_x = \frac{100}{(x + 5)^2} - 1; \ P_y = \frac{100}{(y + 2)^2} - 1;$$

$g_x = 1; g_y = 1$
The three Lagrange equations are

$$\frac{100}{(x + 5)^2} - 1 = \lambda$$

$$\frac{100}{(y + 2)^2} - 1 = \lambda$$

$$x + y = 11$$

From the first two equations,

$$(x + 5)^2 = (y + 2)^2$$

or $y = x + 3$ (rejecting the negative solution).
Substituting into the third equation gives $x = 4$, and
the corresponding value of y is 7.
So, to maximize profit, \$4,000 should be spent
on development and \$7,000 should be spent on
promotion.

37.
$$f(x, y) = \frac{12}{x} + \frac{18}{y} + xy$$

Suppose y is fixed (say at $y = 1$), then f is very large
when x is quite small.
f is also large when x is large, with smaller values
of f occurring between these extremes. The same
reasoning applies to y when x is fixed.

$$f_x = -\frac{12}{x^2} + y; \ f_y = -\frac{18}{y^2} + x$$

To find the critical points, set $f_x = 0$ and $f_y = 0$.
Then $y = \frac{12}{x^2}$ and $x = \frac{18}{y^2}$. Substituting leads to

$$y = \frac{12}{x^2} = \frac{12}{\left(\frac{18}{y^2}\right)^2} = \frac{12y^4}{18^2}$$

or $y = 0$ (which is not in the domain of the function)
and $12y^3 = 18^2$, $y^3 = 27$, $y = 3$. The corresponding
value for $x = \frac{18}{3^2} = 2$. So, the critical point of f is
$(2, 3)$.

$$f_{xx} = \frac{24}{x^3}; \ f_{yy} = \frac{36}{y^3}; f_{xy} = 1$$

For the point $(2, 3)$,
$$D = \frac{(24)(36)}{(2^3)(3^3)} - 1 > 0 \text{ and } f_{xx}(2, 3) > 0, \text{ so } f \text{ the}$$
minimum is $f(2, 3) = 18$.

39.
$$\int_0^1 \int_0^2 e^{-x-y} \, dy dx$$

$$= \int_0^1 \int_0^2 e^{-x} e^{-y} \, dy dx$$

$$= \int_0^1 (-e^{-x} e^{-y}) \Big|_0^2 \, dx$$

$$= \int_0^1 (-e^{-x} e^{-2} + e^{-x}) \, dx$$

$$= (1 - e^{-2}) \int_0^1 e^{-x} \, dx$$

$$= (1 - e^{-2})(-e^{-x}) \Big|_0^1$$

$$= (1 - e^{-2})(-e^{-1} + 1) = 0.5466$$

41.
$$\int_0^1 \int_{-1}^1 xe^{2y} \, dy dx$$

$$= \int_0^1 \left(\frac{1}{2}\right) xe^{2y} \Big|_{-1}^1 \, dx$$

$$= \int_0^1 \left(\frac{xe^2}{2} - \frac{xe^{-2}}{2}\right) \, dx$$

$$= \frac{e^2 - e^{-2}}{2} \int_0^1 x \, dx$$

$$= \frac{e^2 - e^{-2}}{4} \approx 1.8134$$

43.
$$I = \int_1^e \int_1^e (\ln x + \ln y) \, dy dx$$

$$= \int_1^e [y(\ln x) + (y \ln y - y)] \Big|_1^e \, dx$$

$$= \int_1^e [(e - 1) \ln x + 1] \, dx$$

$$= [(e - 1)(x \ln x - x) + x] \Big|_1^e = 3.4366$$

45.

$$\int_1^2 \int_0^x e^{\frac{y}{x}} \, dy \, dx = \int_1^2 \int_0^x e^{\frac{1}{x}y} \, dy \, dx$$

$$= \int_1^2 xe^{\frac{y}{x}} \Big|_0^x \, dx = \int_1^2 xe - x \, dx$$

$$= \int_1^2 (e-1)x \, dx = (e-1)\frac{x^2}{2}\Big|_1^2$$

$$= (e-1)\left(2 - \frac{1}{2}\right) = \frac{3}{2}(e-1)$$

47.

$$\int\int_R (x+2y)dA$$

$$= \int_0^1 \int_{-2}^2 (x+2y) \, dy dx$$

$$= \int_0^1 (xy + y^2)\Big|_{-2}^2 \, dx$$

$$= \int_0^1 4x \, dx = 2x^2\Big|_0^1 = 2$$

49.

$$V = \int_1^2 \int_2^3 xe^{-y} \, dy dx$$

$$= \int_1^2 (-xe^{-y})\Big|_2^3 \, dx$$

$$= \int_1^2 (x)(e^{-2} - e^{-3}) \, dx$$

$$= (e^{-2} - e^{-3})\frac{3}{2} = 0.1283$$

51. The sum of the three numbers is $x + y + z = 20$, so $z = 20 - x - y$. Their product is

$$P = xyz = xy(20 - x - y) = 20xy - x^2y - xy^2$$

$$P_x = 20y - 2xy - y^2$$

$$P_x = 0 \text{ when } y(20 - 2x - y) = 0$$

$$P_y = 20x - x^2 - 2xy$$

$$P_y = 0 \text{ when } x(20 - x - 2y) = 0$$

Since the numbers must be positive, reject the solution $x = 0$ or $y = 0$. Solving the system of equations by multiplying the first by -2 and adding to the second gives $x = \dfrac{20}{3}$. When $x = \dfrac{20}{3}$, $20 - \dfrac{20}{3} - 2y = 0$,

or $y = \dfrac{20}{3}$. Then, $z = 20 - \dfrac{20}{3} - \dfrac{20}{3} = \dfrac{20}{3}$. So, the

product is maximized when $x = y = z = \dfrac{20}{3}$.

53. Using the hint in the problem, let D denote the square of the distance from the origin to the surface. Then,

$$D = x^2 + y^2 + z^2$$

Since $y^2 - z^2 = 10$, $y^2 = 10 + z^2$ and

$$D = x^2 + 10 + 2z^2$$
$$D_x = 2x, \text{ so } D_x = 0 \text{ when } x = 0$$
$$D_z = 4z, \text{ so } D_z = 0 \text{ when } z = 0$$

When $z = 0$, $y^2 = 10$ or $y = \pm\sqrt{10}$.
So, the critical points are $(0, -\sqrt{10}, 0)$ and $(0, \sqrt{10}, 0)$.

$$D_{xx} = 2, \quad D_{zz} = 4, \quad D_{xz} = 0$$

For the point $(0, -\sqrt{10}, 0)$,

$$D = (2)(4) - 0 > 0$$
$$\text{and } D_{xx} > 0$$

So, $(0, -\sqrt{10}, 0)$ is a relative minimum.
For the point $(0, \sqrt{10}, 0)$,

$$D > 0 \text{ and } D_{xx} > 0$$

So, it is also a relative minimum. The square of the distance, using either point, is

$$D = 0 + 10 + 0 = 10$$

So, the minimum distance $= \sqrt{10}$.

55. (a) Let x denote the monthly advertising expenditure and y the corresponding sales (both measured in units of $1,000). Then

x	3	4	7	9	10
y	78	86	138	145	156

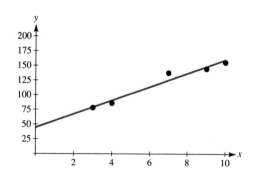

(b)

x	y	xy	x^2
3	78	234	9
4	86	344	16
7	138	966	49
9	145	1,305	81
10	156	1,560	100
$\sum x$	$\sum y$	$\sum xy$	$\sum x^2$
$= 33$	$= 603$	$= 4,409$	$= 255$

Using the formulas with $n = 5$,

$$m = \frac{5(4,409) - 33(603)}{5(255) - (33)^2} = 11.54$$

$$b = \frac{255(603) - 33(4,409)}{5(255) - (33)^2} = 44.45$$

So, the equation of the least-squares line is

$$y = 11.54x + 44.45$$

(c) $y = 11.54(5) + 44.45 = 102.15$ thousand, or
$102,150.

57.
$$Q(x, y) = 200 + 10x^2 - 20y$$
$$x(t) = 18 + 0.02t$$
$$y(t) = 21 + 0.4\sqrt{t}$$

$$\frac{dQ}{dt} = \frac{\partial Q}{\partial x}\frac{dx}{dt} + \frac{\partial Q}{\partial y} \cdot \frac{dy}{dt}$$

$$= (20x)(0.02) + (-20)\left(\frac{0.2}{\sqrt{t}}\right)$$

When $t = 9$, $x(9) = 18.18$ and

$$\frac{dQ}{dt} = 20(18.18)(0.02) + (-20)\left(\frac{0.2}{\sqrt{9}}\right)$$

$$\approx 5.94$$

So, demand is decreasing at a rate of approx. 6 quarts per month.

59.
$$p(x, y) = \frac{1}{4}x^{1/3}y^{1/2}$$
$$x = 129 - \sqrt{8t}$$
$$y = 15.60 + 0.2t$$
$$Q = \frac{4184}{p}$$

$$\frac{dQ}{dt} = \frac{dQ}{dp} \cdot \frac{dp}{dt}$$
$$\text{where } \frac{dp}{dt} = \frac{\partial p}{\partial x} \cdot \frac{dx}{dt} + \frac{\partial p}{\partial y} \cdot \frac{dy}{dt}$$

$$\frac{dQ}{dt} =$$

$$-\frac{4184}{p^2}\left[\left(\frac{1}{12}x^{2/3}y^{1/2}\right)\left(-\frac{\sqrt{8}}{2\sqrt{t}}\right) + \left(\frac{1}{8}x^{1/3}y^{1/2}\right)(0.2)\right]$$

When $t = 2$, $x = 125$, $y = 16$ and $p(125, 16) = 5$ so

$$\frac{dQ}{dt} = -\frac{4184}{(5)^2}\left[\left(\frac{1}{12} \cdot \frac{1}{25} \cdot 4\right)\left(-\frac{\sqrt{8}}{2\sqrt{2}}\right)\right.$$

$$\left. + \left(\frac{1}{8} \cdot 5 \cdot \frac{1}{4}\right)(0.2)\right]$$

$$\approx -3.00$$

or demand is decreasing at a rate of 3 pies per week.

61. $Q(E, T) = 125E^{2/3}T^{1/2}$

$$\frac{dQ}{dt} = \frac{\partial Q}{\partial E} \cdot \frac{dE}{dt} + \frac{\partial Q}{\partial T} \cdot \frac{dT}{dt}$$

$$= \left(\frac{250}{3}E^{-1/3}T^{1/2}\right)\left(\frac{1}{11}\right)$$

$$+ \left(\frac{125}{2}E^{2/3}T^{-1/2}\right)(-0.21)$$

$$= \left[\frac{250}{3}(151)^{-1/3}(10)^{1/2}\right]\left(\frac{1}{11}\right)$$

$$+ \left[\frac{125}{2}(151)^{2/3}(10)^{-1/2}\right](-0.21)$$

$$\approx -113.19$$

or decreasing at a rate of 113 units per day.

63. $N(r, s) = 40e^{-r/2}e^{-s/3}$

$$\text{Pollution} = \int_2^3 \int_1^2 40e^{-r/2}e^{-s/3}ds\ dr$$

$$= \int_2^3 \left(40e^{-r/2} \cdot -3e^{s/3}\Big|_1^2\right) dr$$

$$= -120 \int_2^3 \left[e^{-r/2}\left(e^{-2/3} - e^{-1/3}\right)\right] dr$$

$$= -120 \left(e^{-2/3} - e^{-1/3}\right) \int_2^3 e^{-r/2}dr$$

$$= -120 \left(e^{-2/3} - e^{1/3}\right)\left[-2e^{-r/2}\Big|_2^3\right]$$

$$= 240 \left(e^{2/3} - e^{-1/3}\right)\left(e^{-3/2} - e^{-1}\right)$$

$$\approx 7.056 \text{ units}$$

65. With $Q = x^a y^b$, $Q_x = ax^{a-1}y^b$ and $Q_y = bx^a y^{b-1}$.

$$xQ_x + yQ_y = x(ax^{a-1}y^b) + y(bx^a y^{b-1})$$

$$= (a+b)x^a y^b = (a+b)Q$$

If $b = 1 - a$, then $xQ_x + yQ_y = (a+b)Q = Q$.

Notes

Notes

Notes

Notes

Notes

Notes

Notes

Notes

Notes

Notes

Notes

Notes